AN INTRODUCTION TO PSYCHOLOGICAL STATISTICS

AN INTRODUCTION TO PSYCHOLOGICAL STATISTICS

PHILIP H. DuBois

PROFESSOR OF PSYCHOLOGY
WASHINGTON UNIVERSITY

HARPER & ROW, PUBLISHERS

New York, Evanston, and London

To Margo, Dick, and Lynne

AN INTRODUCTION TO PSYCHOLOGICAL STATISTICS

COPYRIGHT © 1965 BY PHILIP H. DuBois

LIBRARY OF CONGRESS CATALOG CARD NUMBER: 65-10164

CONTENTS

PREFACE

This text has been written on the premise that, for students of the behavioral sciences, the first course in statistics should be definitely within the subject-matter field. Accordingly, it emphasizes quantitative thinking in psychology and education, areas from which materials for examples and exercises have been drawn.

An attempt has been made to reduce "symbol shock," often a difficulty for the beginner in psychological and educational statistics. One of the advantages of starting with categorical data is that the introduction of unfamiliar symbols and processes can be gradual. However, by the time the book has been studied throughout, the student's acquaintance with statistical symbols and concepts should be sufficient for reading the major portion of contemporary psychological research.

The order selected for the presentation of certain major topics owes much to the thinking of S. S. Stevens, as expressed in "Mathematics, Measurement, and Psychophysics," in the *Handbook of Experimental Psychology*. After an overall view of statistics in experimental and professional psychology, there are two chapters involving description by counting or enumeration, then a chapter on methods based on ranking, followed by six chapters involving summing and averaging of continuous measures. These six chapters include a systematic presentation of linear correlation.

The two chapters on distribution functions are mathematical, but are presented at a simple and somewhat intuitive level. Much of the difficult mathematics in advanced statistics has to do with probability curves. Consequently, discussion centers on the logic of the functions, together with some of their applications. The separation of the chapters on inference and on simple analysis of variance from the chapters on probability is merely for clarity of presentation.

In a one-semester course, the instructor may find it convenient to omit one or more of the final topics: test construction, matrix algebra, factor analysis, and distribution-free statistics. Just as the chapter on the analysis of variance can be considered as preliminary orientation to an advanced course in experimental design, so these final chapters aim to give an introduction to advanced work in psychometrics, factor theory, and other specialized topics.

While no familiarity with mathematics beyond elementary algebra is assumed, an attempt has been made to emphasize the mathematical reasonableness of common descriptive statistics, both as a basis for the prediction of behavior in individual instances and as a means of generalization in more broadly oriented studies. Although the emphasis is on the logic of statistical procedures, attention has been given to the presentation of efficient methods of computation, both by hand and by desk calculator, with some reference to electronic computers.

In an era in which most psychologists are applied psychologists working with patients in clinics and hospitals, students in educational institutions, clients in counseling organizations, employees in business and industry, and officers and men in the military services, an emphasis in the elementary course on the statistics applicable to individual differences seems to be appropriate. However, it is believed that statistical methods useful in solving psychological problems of general scientific interest have not been neglected.

Considerable thought has been given to the matter of statistical symbols. A survey of the symbols used in statistical texts written by psychologists and educators showed wide variation in usage, with authors frequently introducing notation of their own. For the concepts for which notation is relatively uniform established usage has been followed. In other cases what seems to be the best current practice has been followed. In special instances minor innovations have been introduced.

I am indebted to various authors and publishers for permission to reproduce certain tables, for which due acknowledgement is made in each specific instance. I am especially indebted to the late Sir Ronald A. Fisher, F.R.S., and to Dr. Frank Yates, F.R.S., Rothamsted, also to Messrs. Oliver and Boyd, Ltd., Edinburgh, for permission to reprint Tables III, IV, V and VI from their book *Statistical Tables for Biological, Agricultural and Medical Research.* I am also indebted to Professor E. S. Pearson and the *Biometrika* Trustees for permission to reproduce portions of W. F. Sheppard's *New Tables of the Probability Integral*, which appeared in Volume 2 of *Biometrika*.

Table Z was prepared at the Washington University Computing Facilities, supported in part by National Science Foundation Grant No. G–22296.

For helpful suggestions in the preparation of this text, I am grateful both to Dr. Gardner Murphy, long-time psychology editor for Harper & Row, and to the incoming editor, Dr. Wayne H. Holtzman. For detailed and exceedingly useful comments I am particularly indebted to Dr. Clarke W. Crannell of Miami University, Oxford, Ohio, Dr. Walter L. Deemer of the U.S. Air Force, Washington, D.C., and Dr. Robert W. Heath of Educational Testing Service, Berkeley, California. Others whose comments are much appreciated include Miss Lolafaye Coyne and Dr. Riley K. Gardner of the Menninger Foundation, Topeka; Dr. Robert I. Watson of Northwestern University, Evanston; Dr. G. Douglas Mayo, LTJG A. A. Longo, and Mr. David S. Thomas of CNATECHTRA, Naval Air Station, Memphis; Dr. Marilyn K. Rigby of St. Louis University; Dr. Winton H. Manning of Texas Christian University, Fort Worth; Dr. David K. Trites of the Civil Aeromedical Research Institute, Oklahoma City; Dr. Kenneth S. Teel of the Autonetics Division, North American Aviation Corporation; Dr. E. Muriel J. Wright of San Fernando Valley State College, Northridge, California; Dr. Daniel S. Lordahl of the University of Miami, Coral Gables; and Mr. Edward V. Hackett of Memphis State University, Memphis. Colleagues at Washington University have been very helpful with their suggestions, particularly Dr. James M. Vanderplas, Dr. Richard H. Willis, Dr. Norman L. Corah and Mr. King M. Wientge. Numerous useful comments have been made by students who have used the material in class, especially Mrs. Virginia Proctor, Miss Charlan Nemeth, and Mr. J. Philip Miller. To all of these individuals I express my sincere appreciation for their helpfulness. Responsibility for errors and ambiguities remaining in the text belongs of course, to the author. For typing the entire manuscript and assistance with many of the details of its preparation I am grateful to Miss Madeline Coran.

Washington University
St. Louis

PHILIP H. DuBois

AN INTRODUCTION TO PSYCHOLOGICAL STATISTICS

STATISTICS IN EXPERIMENTAL AND APPLIED PSYCHOLOGY

1

AIMS OF PSYCHOLOGICAL STATISTICS

Science is built upon planned, systematic observations. Collected with reference to definite hypotheses, observations are quantified and used in the development of principles and laws. Information obtained in some scientific investigations has a high degree of precision so that relationships can be stated more or less exactly. Psychology, however, requires the use of statistical methods, developed to deal with data that involve considerable unexplained variation, but which are often capable of yielding important generalizations. With statistical methods, imperfect relationships can be described, and the dependability of a set of observations can be estimated.

In psychology, statistical methods have six important objectives:

1. The refinement of measures[1] used to describe in numerical terms defined aspects of the behavior of individuals;
2. The description of characteristics of individuals and of groups in terms of these measures;

---

[1] Since values obtained from these measures vary from person to person they are called *variables* or *variates*.

3. The description of relationships among these variables;
4. The generalization of findings within specific samples of individuals to wider populations;
5. The prediction of the behavior of individuals under specified conditions; and
6. The estimation of the consistency or reliability of information.

Both generalization and prediction are based upon descriptive statistics. After a specific sample (representative of cases not yet studied) has been precisely described, it often becomes possible to formulate widely applicable principles and to forecast aspects of the behavior of individuals not yet observed. The term *descriptive statistics* refers to procedures for simplifying quantitative information so that the structure or form of the data becomes easier to perceive. Methods are either graphical or numerical.

DESCRIPTIVE STATISTICS: GRAPHICAL METHODS

A useful graphical technique is the preparation of a "pie chart" to show numbers or relative proportions in several categories. (Example 1.1.)

EXAMPLE 1.1

PREPARATION OF A PIE CHART

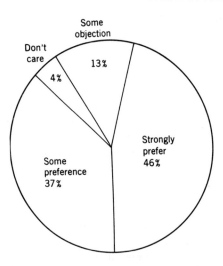

FIG. 1.1. PREFERENCES OF 70 INDUSTRIAL TRAINEES FOR PROGRAMMED INSTRUCTION

Hughes and McNamara (5) used programmed instruction for 70 students in an introductory course in data processing. At the termination of the course, the students were asked: "In future company courses you may take, would you like to see the programmed instruction method used in place of the regular classroom method?" Responses to the question are shown in the table.

RESPONSE	f	PERCENTAGE	DEGREES (CIRCLE = 360°)
Strongly prefer	32	46	165
Some preference	26	37	134
Don't care	3	4	15
Some objection	9	13	46
Strongly object	0	0	0
TOTAL	70	100	360

Entries in the percentage column were found by multiplying each frequency (f) by 100 and dividing by the total number of cases (N). Entries in the column headed "Degrees" were found by multiplying f by 360 and dividing by N. In constructing the pie chart, shown as Fig. 1.1, each sector is bounded by radii of the circle, separated by the number of degrees appropriate to the frequency and corresponding percentage.

With continuous data such as those representing scores on a psychological or educational test, a histogram or frequency polygon may be constructed to show characteristics of the distribution. Such characteristics may include the location of the central point in terms of a corresponding score; how much the scores vary from the central point; and whether the scores are symmetrically distributed about the central point or whether the distribution is lopsided or skewed. (Examples 1.2 and 1.3.)

EXAMPLE 1.2

PREPARATION OF A HISTOGRAM

Purpose. A histogram or column diagram is a convenient format to show the shape of a distribution.

Method. Generally, the vertical axis (the y axis, or ordinate) shows the frequencies, and the horizontal axis (the x axis, or abscissa) shows the values, with the higher values toward the right.

In each step or category a horizontal line is drawn at the vertical point representing the frequency. These lines are then connected with vertical lines, which sometimes are extended down to the x axis.

If the area of the entire surface is taken as 1.000, the area of each column is proportional to the frequency within the step.

Data Represented. A symmetrical distribution of scores of 1016 high school seniors on a reading test is given below and is depicted graphically as Fig. 1.2A. A step interval of 3 is used; that is, all scores of 3, 4, or 5 are tabulated on the

NUMBER OF CASES

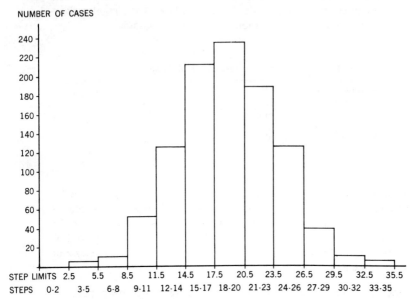

FIG. 1.2A. HISTOGRAM SHOWING SCORES OF 1016 HIGH SCHOOL SENIORS ON A READING COMPREHENSION TEST

lowest step; all scores of 6, 7, or 8 on the second step; all scores of 9, 10, and 11 on the next step; and so on. The frequency and the proportion in each category are given in the accompanying table.

STEP	FREQUENCY	PROPORTION
33–35	3	.003
30–32	14	.014
27–29	38	.037
24–26	129	.127
21–23	191	.188
18–20	233	.229
15–17	215	.212
12–14	128	.126
9–11	52	.051
6–8	10	.010
3–5	3	.003
	$N = 1016$	

A Second Histogram. Data for Fig. 1.2B are from Jones (6). This distribution of Air Force pilots having various numbers of reportable accidents in an 8-year period is highly asymmetrical, or skewed, since there were far fewer accidents than pilots and the vast majority had no accidents at all. (Most of these accidents involved damage only to aircraft or to other property.)

NUMBER OF PILOTS

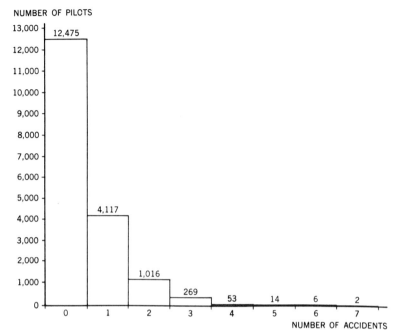

NUMBER OF ACCIDENTS

FIG. 1.2B. DISTRIBUTION IN HISTOGRAM FORM OF ACCIDENTS OF 17,952 U.S. AIR FORCE PILOTS DURING AN 8-YEAR PERIOD

On the histogram, numbers of pilots are represented on the y axis and number of accidents on the x axis. In addition, the precise number of pilots within each accident category is indicated in the column.

EXAMPLE 1.3

PREPARATION OF A FREQUENCY POLYGON

Purpose. Like the histogram, the frequency polygon in Fig. 1.3 shows the shape of a distribution. The data here are the scores of 1016 high school seniors on the reading test used also in Example 1.2.

Method. Instead of a line at the top of each column to represent the frequency in each step, a point is placed at the midpoint of the step. The vertical position of the point represents the frequency. The several points are then connected directly with straight lines to form the frequency polygon. The last line of the polygon on either side ends at the midpoint of the zero-frequency class adjacent.

Both end points of the frequency polygon are thus on the base line, and the area under the polygon is equal to the area under the corresponding histogram. As with the histogram, area is used as a representation of frequency.

Smoothing the Polygon. Sometimes, to visualize the distribution as it would be if the effect of sampling errors were reduced, the curve is "smoothed". One

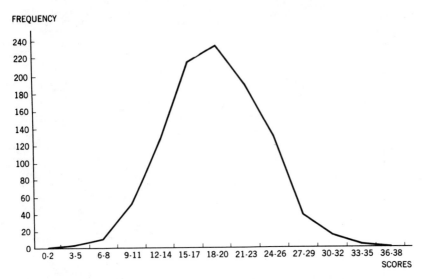

FREQUENCY

FIG. 1.3. FREQUENCY POLYGON SHOWING SCORES OF 1,016 HIGH SCHOOL SENIORS ON A READING COMPREHENSION TEST
(Data the same as in Figure 1.2A.)

method involves plotting, not the obtained frequency in each step, but the average (called the "moving average") of three frequencies, those of the preceding step, the step itself, and the following step.

Charts involving two sets of measurements for the same group of individuals enable one to see whether the association between the variables is marked or slight. When the association is definite, a chart can indicate whether the relationship is better expressed mathematically as a straight line or as some sort of a curve. (Examples 1.4, 1.5, 1.6.)

EXAMPLE 1.4

TWO VARIABLES NO RELATIONSHIP

1st Class ("Cours supérieur")	4.9 words
2nd Class	4.8 words
3rd Class	4.9 words
4th Class ("Cours élémentaire")	4.6 words

FIG. 1.4. AVERAGE NUMBER OF WORDS REPRODUCED PRECISELY AFTER A SINGLE REPETITION OF A SERIES OF SEVEN WORDS

Source of Data. In a study published 10 years before his first intelligence scale, Binet (1) was apparently surprised to find no relationship between class standing and memory span for digits. Subjects were 32 children between the ages of 7 and 12 years in each of 4 classes.

Method. His negative findings are presented in graphic form in Fig. 1.4. The length of each bar is proportional to the obtained average.

EXAMPLE 1.5

TWO VARIABLES WITH MARKED RELATIONSHIP

Source of Data. In a pioneer study in applied psychology, Thurstone (12) found a definite relationship between scores on a rhythm test and later success in telegraphy, measured in terms of receiving speed.

TABLE 1.1. TWO-WAY FREQUENCY DIAGRAM

RECEIVING SPEED, WORDS PER MINUTE	ERRORS ON RHYTHM TEST									TOTAL
	32–35	28–31	24–27	20–23	16–19	12–15	8–11	4–7	0–3	
12 or more	0	0	1	1	1	1	1	2	7	14
10–11	1	1	1	1	0	7	0	0	2	13
8–9	0	0	1	0	2	3	1	1	1	9
6–7	0	1	3	0	4	3	1	4	0	16
4–5	1	1	2	3	3	2	2	0	0	14
2–3	0	1	0	4	3	0	2	0	0	10
0–1	1	3	0	1	2	0	0	0	0	7
TOTAL	3	7	8	10	15	16	7	7	10	($N = 83$)

Two-Way Frequency Diagram. Findings are presented in Table 1.1. On the vertical axis, or ordinate, desirable values (fast receiving speed) are toward the top of the distribution and undesirable values are toward the bottom. On the horizontal axis, or abscissa, desirable scores (freedom from errors) are toward the right.

It will be noted that there are relatively few cases in the upper left-hand corner of the diagram or in the lower right-hand corner. Instead, there is definite concentration of cases along the line that might be drawn from the lower left-hand corner to the upper right-hand corner. This indicates a tendency for low receiving speed to be associated with errors on the rhythm test, and vice-versa.

Dichotomized Diagrams. Three charts representing the same data are also presented as Figs. 1.5A, 1.5B, and 1.5C.

In Fig. 1.5A, the percentage with 15 or fewer errors on the rhythm test has been plotted for the seven groups according to receiving speed. It will be noted that the higher the receiving speed, the greater the percentage having 15 or fewer errors. The particular dividing point is arbitrary. However, it divides the total group of 83 into two approximately equal subgroups, which means that the average percentage is not far from 50 percent.

RECEIVING SPEED, WORDS PER MINUTE	f	f WITH 15 ERRORS OR LESS	
12 or more	14	11	79%
10–11	13	9	69%
8–9	9	6	67%
6–7	16	8	50%
4–5	14	4	29%
2–3	10	2	20%
0–1	7	0	0%

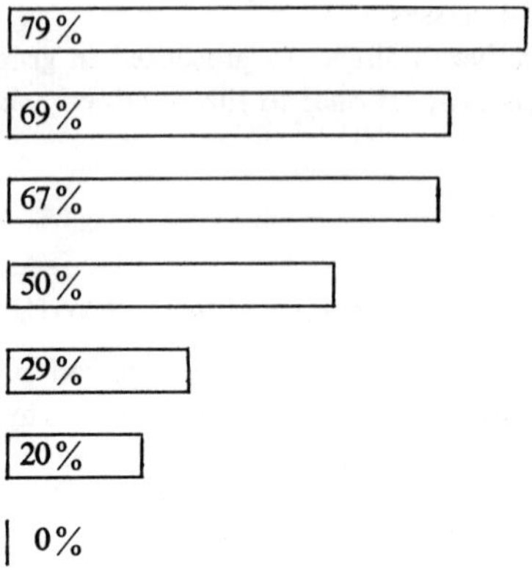

FIG. 1.5A. PERCENTAGE AT EACH RECEIVING SPEED WITH 15 ERRORS OR LESS ON PREDICTIVE TEST

For each category of receiving speed, the frequency of cases with 15 errors or less is found by combining appropriate cells in Table 1.1.

In Fig. 1.5B the same basic information is presented as an "Expectancy Chart." The group has been divided into three categories according to standing on the rhythm test, and differential expectancy of attaining 8 words per minute receiving speed has been plotted.

ERRORS ON RHYTHM TEST	f	f WITH 8 OR MORE WORDS PER MINUTE	
0–11	24	15	63%
12–23	41	16	39%
24–35	18	5	28%

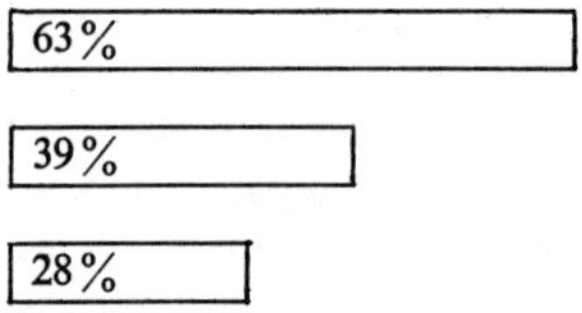

FIG. 1.5B PERCENT ATTAINING RECEIVING SPEED OF 8 WORDS PER MINUTE OR BETTER FOR THREE GROUPS ON RHYTHM TEST

From Table 1.1 it can be seen that of the 24 individuals who had fewer than 21 errors on the rhythm test, 15 had receiving speeds of 8 or more words per minute (15/24 = .625). Accordingly, the graph indicates that 63 percent of those with 0 to 11 errors attained a receiving speed of 8 or more words a minute. The other percentages are determined similarly.

When the standard is changed to 6 words per minute, as in Fig. 1.5C, the general picture is practically the same.

ERRORS ON RHYTHM TEST	f	f WITH 6 OR MORE WORDS PER MINUTE	
0–11	24	20	83%
12–23	41	23	56%
24–35	18	9	50%

FIG. 1.5C. PERCENT ATTAINING RECEIVING SPEED OF 6 WORDS PER MINUTE OR BETTER FOR THREE GROUPS ON RHYTHM TEST

EXAMPLE 1.6

CURVILINEAR RELATIONSHIP BETWEEN TWO VARIABLES

Nature of Data. Two instances of curvilinear relationship between two variables are shown graphically in Fig. 1.6. The upper curve (single line) shows the relationship between age and the mean sum of "scaled scores" on six verbal tests of the Wechsler adult intelligence scale (15). The lower curve (double line) shows the relationship between age and mean sum of "scaled scores" on five Wechsler

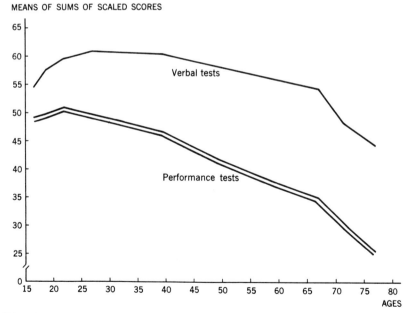

FIG. 1.6. SCALED SCORES CORRESPONDING TO VERBAL I.Q. OF 100 AND PERFORMANCE I.Q. OF 100 AT DIFFERENT AGE LEVELS

performance tests. (On the 11 subtests, obtained scores are converted to "scaled scores" to make them comparable from test to test. Methods of scaling are treated in later chapters.) Information for both is abstracted from Wechsler's manual (15). Values are plotted at the midpoints of the age groupings. Data as reported by Wechsler are given in the following table.

AGE	VERBAL	PERFORMANCE
16–17	54.6	48.8
18–19	57.3	49.4
20–24	59.5	50.6
25–34	60.8	49.5
35–44	60.2	46.1
45–54	58.0	41.1
55–64	55.8	37.1
65–69	54.0[a]	34.5[a]
70–74	48.0[a]	29.5[a]
75–	44.0[a]	25.0[a]

[a] Data taken from tables of norms.

Interpretation. By definition, mean performance at any age results in an I.Q. of 100. It is to be noted that for both verbal and performance material, the score required for a I.Q. of 100 rises and then declines. With verbal material, the decline begins in the thirties or forties, but with performance material, it appears that the decline begins in the twenties. It is to be noted, however, that the successive age groups involve different individuals. Had the same persons been followed through their life span, findings might have been greatly altered.

A time dimension is included in many charts. In reports of psychological research, the horizontal axis is frequently used to show units of time, such as trials in learning studies, and the vertical axis to show units of proficiency. (Example 1.7.)

EXAMPLE 1.7

LEARNING CURVE WITH TIME DIMENSION

In graphically exhibiting the progress of learning, it is customary to plot a measure of attainment, such as seconds required for each trial on the vertical or *y* axis, and the time dimension, often in terms of trials, on the horizontal or *x* axis.

Data abstracted from Bunch *et al.* (2) are plotted in Fig. 1.7. Average time scores in seconds for the first ten trials and for certain subsequent trials are listed in the table below.

Sometimes graphical methods become fairly complicated, as when an attempt is made to portray three dimensions in two-dimensional space. (Example 1.8.) Graphs and charts, however, lose their point if they are not

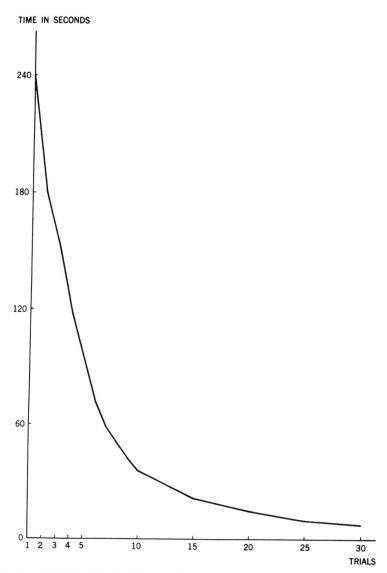

TIME IN SECONDS

FIG. 1.7. AVERAGE TIME SCORES AT SUCCESSIVE STAGES OF LEARNING IN
TERMS OF TRIALS

of direct assistance in understanding the data they represent. Sometimes
simple charts show that laborious computations are unnecessary, or reveal
unanticipated trends requiring more complete investigation. When research results are reported to an audience not technically trained, a graph
may make clear an otherwise unintelligible finding.

TABLE 1.2. DATA FOR FIG. 1.7

TRIAL	TIME IN SECONDS
1	240
2	180
3	153
4	118
5	93
6	72
7	58
8	50
9	43
10	35
15	21
20	15
25	10
30	8

EXAMPLE 1.8

RELATIONSHIP AMONG THREE VARIABLES

In the three-variable diagram of Fig. 1.8, data for which come from a chart prepared by the Office of the Surgeon, AAF Training Command (8), aptitude rating is represented on the axis extending toward the left and previous flying experience on the axis extending toward the right. In the vertical dimension is represented the proportion in each cell eliminated for flying deficiency. The number of cases in each cell is given at the top of each vertical column. The height of each column is proportional to the percentage.

Previous flying experience is coded as follows:

A.   Pilot's license.
B.   Student pilot certificate with solo privileges.
C.   Student pilot certificate.
D.   Experience as passenger in plane, no formal instruction.
E.   No experience in air.

The aptitude ratings, or stanines, are single-digit scores based on psychological tests and ranging from 1 (low) to 9 (high). To point up the relationship, aptitude ratings have been consolidated into three groups: low, average, and high.

It is clear from the chart that as aptitude rating and previous flying experience increase, elimination rate decreases. To some extent, previous experience can compensate for low aptitude, and high aptitude can compensate for lack of experience.

DESCRIPTIVE STATISTICS: NUMERICAL METHODS

Numerical operations in descriptive statistics have much the same primary aim as graphic methods. Their purpose is to simplify information so that form and trends implicit in the data become apparent. In addition, summarization of sets of observations provides the bases for the generalizations and predictions which are the end result of all statistical work.

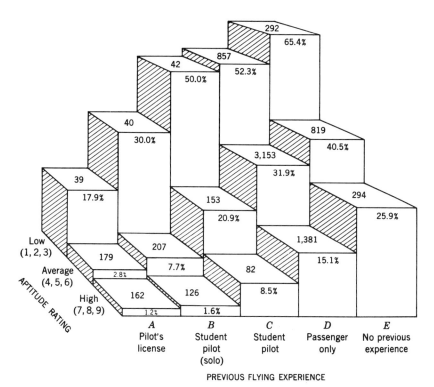

FIG. 1.8. REPRESENTATION OF THREE VARIABLE RELATIONSHIP SHOWING
PERCENTAGES OF AVIATION CADETS ELIMINATED BY CATEGORIES ACCORDING
TO PREVIOUS FLYING EXPERIENCE AND ACCORDING TO PILOT APTITUDE RATING
$N = 7826$, OF WHOM 30.2 PERCENT WERE ELIMINATED FOR FLYING DEFICIENCY

There are five main results in descriptive statistics of numerical operations
with continuous data. These are:

1. Measures of central tendency;
2. Measures of variability;
3. Transformations of variables;
4. Measures reflecting the shapes of distributions; and
5. Measures of relationships.

The first four apply to single variables, that is, to the numbers representing one kind of observation on a group of cases such as scores of
individuals on a reading test. Measures of relationship apply to data
involving two or more variables. In addition to these five classes of
statistical measures, there are various techniques designed to determine the
fundamental structure underlying a large number of variables, so that a few
variables will provide the description originally requiring many measures.

MEASURES OF CENTRAL TENDENCY

A measure of central tendency provides a single number that represents a whole series of numbers. An example is the familiar "average," which in statistics is called the *arithmetic mean* to distinguish it from various other averages known to mathematics. The arithmetic mean is simply the sum of all the values in a series divided by the number of cases. The procedure of computing a mean yields a single value, which can often be taken as a summary of all the numbers in the series. The mean or some other measure of central tendency is employed in most psychological studies using statistical methods.

MEASURES OF VARIABILITY

Measures of variability are designed to describe the spread or scatter of numbers. In one set of observations, all the numbers may be fairly close together; in another, they may vary considerably one from another. When the variability of a series of numbers is expressed in a form technically known as the *variance* (which will be defined later), it may often be analyzed into component parts. Thus, in the development of a psychological test, an estimate is made of how much of the variance of the total score is reliable or consistent, and how much is inconsistent or "error variance." When the proportion of error variance is low, the test yields consistent results, either from one administration to another or from part to part of the test. In somewhat similar fashion, the total variance of a variable can often be divided into two parts: the portion that is predictable from one or more sources, and the portion that remains unpredictable. The predictable portion, in turn, may be subdivided so as to indicate the relative importance of the several predictors or "sources of the variance."

TRANSFORMATIONS OF VARIABLES

A third function of descriptive statistics is transformation of a series of numbers to a new scale. In one type of transformation both the central tendency and the variability of the new series have assigned values. In this way results on different psychological tests can be made comparable. The scores that a person obtains on half a dozen tests have little meaning in their original form. The obtained or raw score is often the number of questions answered correctly. Such a score is merely a function of the number and difficulty of the items making up the test. When, however, the obtained scores are interpreted by means of *norms*, which are transformations of the scores, standing of the same individual on several variables may be readily compared.

DESCRIPTION OF DISTRIBUTIONS

Another use of statistical measures is to describe the shapes of distributions. The shape can be readily assessed in a general way from a graph, but measures exist that help to describe more precisely whether a distribution is flat or peaked, as well as the degree to which it departs from symmetry.

MEASUREMENT OF RELATIONSHIP

A fifth use of descriptive statistics is to measure the degree of relationship between variables. In physical sciences such as physics and astronomy, it is often possible to state the relationship between two variables as a relatively exact equation, with negligible error. In psychology, an equation expressing the relationship between two variables can often be established, but typically the association is partial. Stating the same fact in different language, the description of the relationship between pairs of psychological variables is imprecise because various conditions influencing their relationship remain unknown. Methods to describe partial relationships between pairs of variables and between combinations of variables are useful both in formulating general psychological principles and in forecasting behavior of individuals.

STATISTICS APPLIED TO GENERALIZATION

The determination of the degree to which the results of descriptive statistics are likely to apply universally or to a large population is another function of statistics.

Statistics such as measures of central tendency, variability, and relationship can be actually computed only for specific samples of individuals. Within the limitations of the methods employed in observing, recording, and computing, these statistics are exact. However, from these statistics we wish to infer as much as possible about the unobserved situation in the population which the sample represents. The unknown and unknowable values in the population corresponding to the statistics in the sample are designated as *parameters*. Although unknowable, parameters can be estimated. The degree of precision in the estimates can also be assessed. Hence it is often possible to reach fairly dependable conclusions about the population.

The degree to which estimates of parameters actually correspond to the situation in the population depends primarily on how well the sample represents the population. This, in turn, depends chiefly on two factors: the methods used in selecting the sample and the sample size. Obviously, the more successful the precautions have been in making the sample truly representative of the entire population, the closer the statistics will approximate parameters. Again, within any valid method of selecting a representative sample, the greater the number of cases, the closer the statistics will represent the parameter values. A third consideration is the particular statistic used. Some statistical measures are unbiased and, without correction, can be taken as representative of parameters. Others are biased and must be corrected. Often the correction is for sample size, and becomes of less consequence as sample size increases.

STATISTICS OF PREDICTION

Statistical prediction, or forecasting, like statistical inference, is based upon the description of a relationship observed within a sample. After the inductive process of making a psychological generalization comes the deductive process of applying it to an individual who was not measured as part of the original group.

One of the simplest types of forecasting involves two steps. The first step is to establish the differential expectancy of an event for several categories of individuals. The second is to determine to which of these categories a particular individual belongs. In this way the determination of the category or class to which the individual belongs reveals the likelihood of the event.

More elaborate mathematically, but much the same logically, is the procedure that involves finding the degree of relationship between two variables, followed by the establishment of an equation for forecasting purposes. Suppose, for example, that in a representative sample of high school students a substantial relationship has been discovered between scores on a scholastic aptitude test and grades in English composition. If we have the scholastic aptitude score of a student who has not yet taken the course in English composition, we can make a reasonable prediction of his grade in the course. Furthermore, we can estimate with considerable exactness the amount of error in a set of such predictions for a number of individuals, always provided the sample studied is truly representative of the population about whom predictions are to be made.

The logic used in applied psychology, including making diagnoses in clinical work, selecting candidates for admission to schools, and hiring employees, is the logic of prediction. Relationships are observed in specific samples. Knowledge of these relationships, taken as generalizations, is used in forecasting the behavior of individuals. In educational institutions and in the armed services, selection procedures are often based directly on carefully developed prediction equations. In clinical work with abnormal patients and in educational and vocational counseling, procedures are sometimes less formal because criteria are less exact, but sound psychological practice always demands that relationships within a representative sample be ascertained before predictions are made for individuals.

SYSTEMS OF DESCRIPTIVE STATISTICS

There are three main systems of statistical description by numerical methods: counting, ranking, and averaging. Although the systems are based upon different principles and employ different arithmetical operations, all are useful with psychological data. With some information, such as time and error measures in laboratory experiments and scores on educational and psychological tests, the statistical procedures of all three systems are customarily applied. For other data, counting and ranking are appropriate, but averaging is not. For the simplest type of information, the basic operation is counting, or enumeration.

COUNTING

A fundamental type of description used in psychology is the so-called *nominal scale*[2], which is not a scale in the ordinary sense of the word but simply two or more classes in the same general domain. Sex (male or female), race (Caucasian, Mongoloid, or Negro), and eye color (brown, blue, green, gray, or hazel) are examples of nominal scales. In using a nominal scale, the classes or categories are defined so that each individual is placed in one and only one class in the series of classes. After individuals are so classified, counts are made of the number in each of the categories, and arithmetical operations based on these counts are performed. Such operations are described in Chapters 2 and 3.

RANKING

A second type of quantification commonly used in psychology is the *ordinal scale*, which comprises cases or categories placed in order, as from high to low, with regard to a characteristic. Assigning numbers to runners in the order in which they finish a race, lining up a squad of recruits according to height, and arranging a set of colored papers according to gray value are examples of the use of rudimentary ordinal scales. If no ties are permitted, each pair of cases is, in effect, judged as to which member possesses the characteristic to the greater degree. If ties are involved, the judgment of equality of the attribute in two or more cases is permitted. This is, of course, the type of judgment required for the simpler nominal scale. Formal ordinal scales have been used for the measurement of the magnitude of stars and the hardness of metals.

While order within a series is sometimes used in psychological research, the ranking system is also useful with data originally obtained in the form of scores. From time to time there has been debate as to whether psychological measures yield scores in meaningful units or whether relative order within some defined group is the extent to which significant information can be extracted. Complete agreement has not been reached on this point. It is common practice, however, to treat test scores both as rankable information and as having meaningful units. Also, information in the form of ranks is often summarized through conventional arithmetical

---

[2] An informative discussion of types of scales and of statistical measures applicable to them is given by Stevens (10).

operations, including addition. Statistical methods based on ranking are discussed in Chapter 4.

SUMMING AND AVERAGING

When we can measure in units (as contrasted with merely counting or arranging in order), descriptive statistics based on sums and averages are clearly appropriate. There are two types of information to which summation methods apply directly: *interval scales* and *ratio scales.* The difference between them is that a ratio scale starts at a true and known zero, whereas an interval scale starts at some arbitrary point. Among physical measures, temperature is commonly measured on interval scales; weight, length, and duration of time on ratio scales.

Scores on psychological and educational tests do not constitute ratio scales because an obtained score of zero seldom if ever indicates that the individual possesses none of the trait being measured. Such scores are, however, often treated as though they were from interval scales.

Basic descriptive statistics in the summation system are discussed in Chapters 5 through 9.

STATISTICAL NOTATION AND FORMULAS

Although theoretical statistics is a highly developed branch of mathematics rooted in probability theory, elementary statistics as used by the typical research or applied psychologist requires chiefly algebra as a mathematical background. A few new symbols and operations extend arithmetic and algebra into an important tool of psychological research and practice.

Many of the concepts are stated as formulas, the most common of which are ways of indicating in precise notation the operations or steps used in treating data so as to arrive at a statistic.

FIVE VARIETIES OF STATISTICAL SYMBOLS

Statistical formulas include five distinct varieties of symbols as follows:

1. Symbols indicating statistical concepts or end products of statistical operations, such as N for the total number of cases (a product of counting) and M for the mean (a product of averaging). After computation, end products of this sort become "statistical constants" because they have unique values for a set of data, and often enter as constants into formulas for further analyses.

2. "Operators," or symbols indicating one or more arithmetical operations, such as a line, (————), for division, or the summation sign,[3] Σ, for indicating that a series of numbers is to be added. Most of the

---

[3] Although the Greek capital letter sigma is used as the summation sign, it is generally read "sum of" rather than "sigma."

symbols used in elementary algebra to indicate basic arithmetical operations, such as addition, subtraction, multiplication, division, raising to a power, and extracting a root, are used in statistics.

3. Symbols, such as X and Y, to indicate variables. These symbols, somewhat like their algebraic counterparts, represent the different arithmetical values in series of numbers. Thus X may be used to represent the reading test scores of 100 eighth grade boys. In the main, the last letters of the alphabet are used for variables. In this text, however, Z is never used as an original variable, thus reducing possible confusion with z, which is used for variables that have been transformed in a certain manner.

4. Symbols, such as cardinal numbers and letters early in the alphabet, indicating constants. As stated above, any of the symbols for end products of statistical operations, such as N or M, may also appear in formulas as constants.

5. Symbols, including subscripts and superscripts, to make precise that which is denoted by other symbols. For example, the subscript x in the expression M_x indicates that reference is made to the mean of variable X. Variables may be numbered, in which case M_1 may refer to the mean of variable 1 and M_2 to the mean of variable 2. On the other hand, the values of a single variable may be numbered to correspond to cases so that X_1 represents the first observation or score for the first individual, X_2 the second observation or score for the second individual, and so on. Symbols of functions involving two or more variables are also appropriately distinguished with two or more subscripts.

A bar over the letter indicating a variable is often used to indicate the mean. Thus $\bar{X}$ is an alternate way of indicating M_x.

Another use for this type of symbol is to show the limits of summation by writing one of the limits below the summation sign and the other above it. Thus

$$\sum_{i=1}^{i=N} X$$

or, more briefly,

$$\sum_{1}^{N} X_i$$

indicates the operation of summing variable X from the first instance, X_1, through the Nth case, X_N. In cases of double or triple summation, as when sums are summed, the order of summing is shown. The summation sign closest to the variable indicates the first summation; the next closest, the second; and so on.

For instance

$$\sum_{1}^{j} \sum_{1}^{n} X$$

indicates that jn values of X (that is, j sets of n cases each) have been summed. First, each set of n values is summed from the first case through the nth case. Then these j sums are added together from the first sum through the jth sum. In mathematical statistics the limits and conditions of summation are generally carefully indicated; in psychological statistics they are written out when needed for clarity.

Another symbol included in this fifth category is the tilde ($\sim$), written above a symbol for a variable to show that the value is predicted rather than obtained. Thus ($\tilde{X}$) represents a predicted rather than an obtained score in variable X. If a variable has been modified in some way, as by adding or subtracting a constant from the original values, it is sometimes identified with a prime ('). Thus X' is some sort of modification of X. Primes may also be used to distinguish among values of statistical constants under specified conditions.

Roman letters are preferred for statistics and Greek letters for corresponding parameters, as M for the mean in the sample and μ for the population mean. Knowledge of the convention is essential in reading advanced statistics. In this text, commonly recognized statistical symbols are used whether or not they are in accordance with this convention. Accordingly, Greek letters are used for certain descriptive statistics. When needed for clarity, a circumflex accent ($\wedge$) indicates a parameter.

In print it is conventional to substitute italic letters for Roman, thus better distinguishing symbols from text.

UNDERSTANDING A FORMULA

Not all the implications in a formula can be grasped at a glance, even by one with long experience in statistics. Writers of statistical texts and articles vary widely in their use of notation. Another difficulty is that a formula may indicate, in what is essentially a kind of shorthand, a complex series of numerical operations.

The first step in understanding any formula is to be sure that the meaning of each symbol is clear. The second step is to perceive how the symbols are put together to convey the meaning the writer intended. The sequence of operations usually becomes clear if the formula is carefully studied. Operations within parentheses are performed before operations on the quantity enclosed by the parentheses, and operations within a summation sign are done before operations outside the summation sign. Thus,

$$\sqrt{\frac{\sum_{i=1}^{i=N}(X_i - \overline{X})^2}{N-1}} \quad \text{or} \quad \sqrt{\frac{\sum(X - M_x)^2}{N-1}}$$

indicates the following steps:

1. From each value of X, the mean of all the X's is to be subtracted;
2. Each of the values of $(X - M_x)$ is to be squared;
3. The sum of all the values of $(X - M_x)^2$ is to be obtained;
4. This sum is to be divided by $N - 1$;
5. The square root of the quotient is then to be obtained.

As in conventional algebra, there is some flexibility in the order of operations. A constant multiplier (or divisor) within parentheses, or a summation sign, may be placed outside, thus indicating a different sequence of operations without change in the final result. Accordingly, if a is a constant, $\sum aX = a\sum X$.

A constant within a root sign may be brought outside, but only if its power in the expression as a whole is maintained. Thus, in the preceding example,

$$\sqrt{\frac{\Sigma(X - M_x)^2}{N - 1}} = \frac{1}{\sqrt{N - 1}} \sqrt{\Sigma(X - M_x)^2}$$

When studied carefully, it will be found that a statistical formula is generally an economical way of stating operations and relationships that would be cumbersome to describe in words.

THE FIVE CLASSES OF STATISTICAL FORMULAS

Of interest in psychology are five classes of statistical formulas:

1. Formulas defining the concepts of descriptive statistics;
2. Formulas setting forth economical computing routines;
3. Formulas for using descriptive statistics for making estimates of various kinds;
4. Formulas of mathematical functions serving as hypotheses; and
5. Measures of the discrepancy between a hypothesis and corresponding empirical findings.

FORMULAS AS DEFINITIONS

For each descriptive statistic, the basic formula constitutes an operational definition, that is, a schedule of the operations or steps used in treating original data so as to arrive at the statistic. The nature of measures of central tendency and variability is usually apparent directly from the formulas, which need no derivation. Statistics reflecting the relationship between pairs of ordered variables may involve fitting a line by the mathematical principle of least squares,[4] while some may involve assumptions

---

[4] A generally accepted mathematical convention, which states that the fit of a line representing a joint function of two variables is best when the sum of the squares of the errors in fitting is as small as possible.

regarding the underlying nature of one or more variables. In such cases the formula still constitutes an operational definition, but the essential nature of the measure becomes clear only by considering the assumptions involved and by following through the steps of the derivation.

COMPUTING FORMULAS

Formulas that define statistical concepts logically are not necessarily the most efficient for actual computation. For example, the basic formula for the variance calls for the sum of the squares of numbers that are ordinarily decimal fractions. Since computations with such decimal fractions are generally awkward, computing formulas have been devised which yield more or less identical results but which are based on sums of original scores and their squares.

Computing machines, from the desk calculator to the giant electronic computer, can handle numerical information more or less automatically. To utilize them to best advantage in statistical work, it is often necessary to rewrite formulas so as to take advantage of the economies inherent in their mode of operation. A computing formula is simply an algebraic variation of a basic formula developed so as to indicate precisely the arithmetical steps required by some particular method to arrive at the statistic concerned. Often it permits analyses of data in a fraction of the time that otherwise would be required.

FORMULAS FOR MAKING ESTIMATES

Formulas used in making estimates fall into three main categories:

1. Formulas useful in estimating parameters from statistics computed from particular samples;
2. Formulas for estimating what the statistic would be under changed circumstances; and
3. Equations of best fitting functions (straight lines or curves) for making predictions in individual cases.

MATHEMATICAL FUNCTIONS

The fourth class of formulas comprises two types of mathematical functions serving as hypotheses. These are functions representing the theoretical distribution of cases along a continuous scale, or of observations within a series of categories, and functions representing the shape of a line of relationship between two variables.

Mathematical statistics provides a number of formulas for generating various types of theoretical frequency curves. These curves show how large masses of data would be distributed if a stated hypothesis were operating and if all deviations from this hypothesis resulted purely from chance. Most frequently, formulas yielding distribution functions are used in practical situations in the form of tables. The use of these functions in table form provides a convenient way of determining how unusual a particular event would be under a stated hypothesis.

In psychology, the equation for a straight line is frequently used for representing the relationship between two variables. However, any mathematical function representing the relationship between two sets of observations for the same group of cases can be used as a hypothesis. When the function is established, it may be used for making predictions in individual instances.

MEASURES OF DISCREPANCY BETWEEN FACTS AND THEORY

In an experimental investigation, when we compute a measure of the relationship between two variables, or of the difference in some statistic computed in two groups, or of the difference between an obtained and a theoretical distribution, some degree of relationship or of difference is almost always found. The question is whether the observed relationship or difference exists in the population, or whether it could have arisen in the sample merely by chance. If it can be assumed that the sample fairly represents the population, it can be determined whether the obtained trend is great enough to indicate a real trend in the population. This is the function of the fifth class of formulas.

Often it is formally hypothesized that there is no relationship in the population or that the difference is zero. Even though no relationship or difference is found in the particular sample or in other samples, this hypothesis logically can never be proved. However, if empirical findings are compared to the probability function of such findings, that is, with the distribution expected purely by chance, we may either accept the hypothesis of no relationship as possible, pending further evidence, or regard the hypothesis of no relationship as disproved, at a stated level of certainty.

STATISTICS IN EXPERIMENTAL PSYCHOLOGY

Of objects known to exist, the human nervous system is undoubtedly the most intricate, both in structure and in function. Not only is it elaborately responsive to external events of the moment, but its behavior is greatly influenced by results of preceding events and their interrelationships. It is hardly surprising that a mathematical representation of psychological processes such as sensing, perceiving, thinking, and learning must include provision for error or uncertainty.

In the development of all the sciences, naturalistic observation and the formulation of broad general principles have preceded the use of measurement and the statement of relationships in mathematical terms. However, as a science matures, the use of mathematics permits greater precision in stating principles and in the prediction of future events.

The development of psychological statistics is definitely related to the attempts of psychologists to define and measure pertinent variables, and to describe and understand complex phenomena. In some investigations, the effect of extraneous variables can be eliminated by careful selection and training of subjects, by the use of control groups, and by the isolation of observers and subjects from events that might introduce error into the results. In other studies, experimental controls can be replaced to some degree by statistical controls; that is, by the statistical removal from the variables directly concerned the variance associated with one or more disturbing variables. This is accomplished by modifying the variables of direct interest so that they become uncorrelated with the extraneous variables.

The literature of experimental psychology is largely unreadable without knowledge of measures of central tendency, variability, and relationship, and of methods of using a series of observations within a sample as a basis for inferring widely applicable generalizations. Laboratory psychology requires considerable statistical sophistication on the part of the investigator in order to evaluate pertinent research and to communicate research findings to others.

STATISTICS IN PROFESSIONAL PSYCHOLOGY

Personnel, counseling, and clinical psychologists depend upon statistical studies for the fundamental information on which their practice is based. In working with individuals, statistical concepts form the basis for interpretation of test results.

First, consider the case of a personnel psychologist. He may be concerned with selection or classification of employees, or with their training, morale, or efficiency. In any event, his work will involve studies in which quantitative records are made of the behavior in which he is interested. His observations are reduced to numerical form and are then studied in order to arrive at conclusions as to the relative value of different methods of selection, classification, or training. He seeks to establish general principles which apply to cases beyond those actually observed. Statistical methods not only reveal the form of his data, but also afford an indication as to how well they are likely to represent situations not yet observed.

The applied psychologist who deals with individuals also bases his work upon research involving statistical methods. For example, the raw score obtained on a test has little, if any, intrinsic significance. In order to interpret the score, it must be related to the typical performance of individuals similar to the person who has been tested, as well as to the variation to be expected among such individuals.

When a relationship has been established between psychological measurements, we can forecast the behavior of individuals in terms of probabilities. Probabilities seldom, if ever, become certainties because the number of pertinent variables is generally large and some usually remain unmeasured. As additional relevant information is collected, the known probabilities about a future event will often change. For certainty, the actual event must be awaited, but the known probabilities are often sufficient basis for action. Thus, when a very dull child is enrolled in school, it is not necessary to subject him to failure in the regular curriculum before assigning him to studies that can reasonably be expected to be within his capacities.

SOURCES OF PSYCHOLOGICAL STATISTICS

Although statistics is often regarded as a branch of mathematics, it must not be supposed that psychologists have been mere borrowers from the warehouses of the mathematicians. A goodly proportion of the techniques of psychological statistics were invented by psychologists as means of solving psychological problems. Some of these techniques have been incorporated into the body of mathematical statistics; in other cases application has been restricted to psychology and allied fields.

The idea of the median is attributed to Gustav Fechner (1801–1887). In the history of psychology, Fechner is best known as one of the founders of psychophysics, concerned with relationships between external stimulation and resultant sensation.

In connection with his studies of the inheritance of individual differences, Sir Francis Galton (1822–1911) developed the concept of correlation between two variables. Karl Pearson, his student, expanded on his discovery by the derivation of the product-moment formula for correlation, and numerous refinements and extensions of correlation theory and practice were made by Pearson and his followers.

Charles Spearman (1863–1945), professor of psychology at University College, London, made a number of important contributions to psychological statistics. He worked out methods of correlating ranked data. He developed the concept of test reliability, and published a formula for estimating the reliability of a test when lengthened. He showed how to estimate what correlations would be obtained if the variables were freed of error variance.

Spearman formulated the problem of explaining the intercorrelations of a group of observed variables in terms of a smaller number of underlying variables. His methods laid the foundations of factor analysis, which attempts to reduce the number of psychological variables. Further development of factor analysis was also largely the work of psychologists, especially L. L. Thurstone (1887–1955).

In developing his scale for measuring intelligence, Alfred Binet (1857–1911) used the basic concepts of item analysis, including item difficulty and the correlation of an item with a criterion. Later these concepts became formalized in the work of numerous psychologists working with test data.

Especially influential were the psychologists trained by James McKeen Cattell (1860–1944) and E. L. Thorndike (1874–1949) at Columbia; also the group centered at the University of Chicago, who were trained by Thurstone and who in 1935 founded *Psychometrika*,[5] a journal "devoted to the development of psychology as a quantitative rational science."

The percentile method of scaling variables was developed by Galton. Standard scores in various forms seem to be the work of Truman L. Kelley (1884–1961), William A. McCall (born 1891), and Clark Hull (1884–1952), the last named being better known for his work on hypnosis and on learning.

For a number of years, psychological statistics has been greatly influenced by the work of Sir Ronald A. Fisher (1890–1962) whose work was first applied in agriculture. His notable contributions have included the discovery of important theoretical distributions, knowledge of which permits better inference as to generalizations valid in populations represented by observed samples.

While psychologists have drawn freely on the mathematicians for distribution functions and on other applied fields for various specialized techniques, the field of psychological statistics has a claim to considerable autonomy. It has been largely developed by psychologists who, in connection with their research and practice, have felt the need for quantifying observations, for determining their underlying structure, and for using the resulting generalizations both for formulation of principles and for prediction of behavior in individual instances.

SUMMARY

Both in psychological research and in psychological practice, statistics is an important tool. Within samples, statistical methods permit the description of relationships between variables that are imperfectly measured. On the basis of information obtained from samples, generalizations applicable to unobserved populations can often be developed. In professional psychology, statistical procedures are used in the interpretation of test results and in predicting the attainments of individuals.

Graphical and numerical methods are used in describing samples. The three numerical systems of description are based on counting, ranking, and averaging. Numerical operations are conveniently summarized as formulas which indicate how a given statistic is obtained.

---

[5] The number of statistical journals to be seen in any university library is large. Among the journals that have published articles of particular interest in psychological statistics are *The British Journal of Statistical Psychology*, *Educational and Psychological Measurement*, *The Journal of Educational Psychology*, *The Journal of Educational Research*, and *The Psychological Bulletin*.

EXERCISES

1. On the initiative scale of a self-description inventory, Ghiselli (4) reports mean scores for four occupational levels as follows:

OCCUPATIONAL LEVEL	MEAN
Top management	33.4
Middle management	30.7
Lower management	29.8
Line workers	28.3

Show these results as a bar graph.

2. Lawton and Goldman (7) queried 66 cancer scientists about their opinion of cigarette smoking as a cause of lung cancer. Opinions were as follows:

OPINION	*f*
Is a cause	13
Probably a cause	42
Evidence equivocal	8
Probably not a cause	3

Present these results as a pie chart.

3. By the use of pie charts, compare age grouping of the population of the United States in 1940 with the age grouping in 1960. Source of data: *Health, Education and Welfare Indicators* (14).

AGE GROUP	POPULATION (IN MILLIONS) 1940	1960
65 and over	9.0	16.6
45–64	26.2	36.1
20–44	51.6	58.2
5–19	34.7	48.8
Under 5	10.6	20.3

4. Physician interest scores of 670 university students whose occupational careers were known over a period of 20 years have been reported by Strong and Tucker (11). The distribution of scores for 108 who became physicians and for 562 who did not are:

PHYSICIAN INTEREST RATING	STUDENTS BECOMING PHYSICIANS	STUDENTS NOT BECOMING PHYSICIANS
A	70	63
B+	14	56
B	10	73
B−	9	73
C	5	297

Summarize the results in an appropriate chart.

5. Prepare a chart to show prevalence of impaired hearing according to age and sex, using the following data from Weiss (16):

AGE IN YEARS	DEAFNESS CASES[a] PER 1000 POPULATION	
	MALE	FEMALE
Under 5	0.49	0.43
5–14	2.95	2.26
15–24	3.51	2.93
25–34	4.76	4.99
35–44	9.70	9.28
45–54	14.93	15.45
55–64	29.27	26.43
65–74	73.64	54.68
75 or over	175.08	135.95

[a] Equivalent to an average hearing loss of 47 decibels or more at 1024 and 2048 cycles per second.

6. The following data are frequencies of aptitude scores (stanines) of pilot trainees who either graduated or were eliminated for flying deficiency or for fear or at own request in an Air Force class (3). Construct a chart to show these results graphically.

STANINE	NUMBER GRADUATED	NUMBER ELIMINATED
9	119	15
8	41	11
7	99	24
6	135	68
5 or below	20	28

7. In a study of SAS pilots, Trankell (13) reported dismissals as follows for four categories of judged suitability for employment:

CATEGORY	TOTAL EMPLOYED	SUBSEQUENTLY DISMISSED
Particularly suitable	49	0
Suitable	218	8
Doubtful	59	4
Unsuitable	37	17

In each category, plot dismissals as a percentage of those employed.

8. In a study of the effect of practice on an autokinetic illusion, Rethlingshafer and Sherrer (9) report the following means scores for successive sessions for two groups tested under different social conditions:

SESSION	MEAN NUMBER OF LETTERS REPORTED	
	GROUP 1	GROUP 2
1	8.1	5.4
2	11.6	7.2
3	10.0	8.2

Present these results graphically.

REFERENCES

1. BINET, A., AND HENRI, V., "La Mémoire des Mots," *L'Année Psychologique*, 1894, **1**, 1–23.
2. BUNCH, M. E., FRERICHS, J. B., AND LICKLIDER, J. R., "An experimental study of maze learning ability after varying periods of wakefulness," *J. Comp. Psychol.*, 1938, **26**, 499–514.
3. DUBOIS, P. H. (ED.), *The Classification Program*. Report No. 2, AAF Aviation Psychology Program Research Reports. Washington, D.C.: U.S. Government Printing Office, 1947. xiv + 394.
4. GHISELLI, EDWIN E., "Traits differentiating management personnel," *Personnel Psychol.*, 1959, **12**, 535–544.
5. HUGHES, J. L., AND MCNAMARA, W. J., "A comparative study of programmed and conventional instruction in industry," *J. Appl. Psychol.*, 1961, **45**, 225–231.
6. JONES, EDWARD R., *A Study of Accident Proneness*, Unpublished Ph.D. dissertation. St. Louis: Washington University, 1954.
7. LAWTON, M. POWELL, AND GOLDMAN, ALFRED E., "Cigarette smoking and attitude toward the etiology of lung cancer," *J. Soc. Psychol.*, 1961, **54**, 235–248.
8. Office of the Surgeon, unpublished chart. Fort Worth: Headquarters, AAF Flying Training Command, 1943.
9. RETHLINGSHAFER, DOROTHY, AND SHERRER, THOMAS I., "Supplementary report: effect of practice on an illusion," *J. Exper. Psychol.*, 1961, **62**, 95–96.
10. STEVENS, S. S ., "Mathematics, measurement, and psychophysics," in Stevens, S. S., (ed.), *Handbook of Experimental Psychology*. New York: John Wiley & Sons, Inc., 1951.
11. STRONG, EDWARD K., JR., AND TUCKER, ANTHONY C., "The use of vocational interest scales in planning a medical career," *Psychol. Monogr.*, 1952, **66**, 1–61.
12. THURSTONE, L. L., "Mental tests for prospective telegraphers; a study of the diagnostic value of mental tests for predicting ability to learn telegraphy," *J. Appl. Psychol.*, 1919, **3**, 110–117.
13. TRANKELL, A., "The psychologist as an instrument of prediction," *J. Appl. Psychol.*, 1959, **43**, 170–175.
14. United States Department of Health, Education and Welfare. *Health, Education and Welfare Indicators*, 1961.
15. WECHSLER, DAVID, *Manual for the Wechsler Adult Intelligence Scale*. New York: The Psychological Corporation, 1955. vi + 110.
16. WEISS, ALFRED D., "Sensory Functions," in Birren, James E., (ed.), *Handbook of Aging and the Individual*. Chicago; University of Chicago Press, 1959.

DESCRIPTION
BY COUNTING

2

THE NATURE OF CATEGORICAL DATA

Assignment to categories and enumerating or counting within them is the basis of a system of descriptive statistics.

As noted in Chapter 1, the term *nominal scale* is sometimes applied to the simplest form of statistical description; that is, sorting the members of a group into two or more subgroups. Classification of individuals into categories carries no implication that one category is in any way superior to another, or that the categories can be placed in any logical order. Rather it implies that each of the subgroups has internal unity and that each can be mutually distinguished by descriptive terms or names.

The number of nominal scales or sets of coordinate categories that can be used to describe the same group of individuals is unlimited. After a group has been classified with regard to eye color, the same group can be classified again as to hair color, race, political affiliation, religious belief, occupation, or with respect to any other set of categories that may be appropriate. Preferably, categories should be logically consistent, mutually exclusive, and exhaustive.

Terminology referring to this type of classification is by no means uniform. In some statistics texts, categorical information is called census, or nonvariate, or enumeration, or discrete data, while the statistical measures employed are sometimes denoted as the statistics of attributes. All these terms refer to the same area of statistical description.

Ordinarily, information defining the categories cannot be given meaningful numerical values. This is in contrast to measuring height in inches or centimeters and weight in pounds or kilograms. With nominal data an appropriate number of classes or categories is established, individuals are assigned to the categories, and counts are made of the individuals so assigned. The establishment of a series of mutually exclusive groupings carries the implication of description in a definable area rather than of measurement along a dimension involving a single characteristic, such as time or distance. For example, in an investigation of the inheritance of eye color we may find that four categories are sufficient: brown eyes, blue eyes, hazel eyes, and gray-green eyes. Although these attributes are certainly in a single area, it is likely that more than a single dimension is involved. In this case it is impossible to assign a fixed and meaningful order to the four classes. Nevertheless, after individuals have been assigned to categories, statistics can be computed to summarize group characteristics. Such statistics can then be applied to making inferences about the population from which the sample has been drawn.

STATISTICS APPLICABLE TO CATEGORICAL DATA

Statistics that are applicable to nominal or categorical data include:

1. N, the total number of cases in a given sample;
2. f, the frequency or number of cases in a category or subcategory;
3. p, the proportion of cases within any category (which may also be expressed as a percentage);
4. M_0, the mode, or category with the greatest frequency;
5. C, the contingency coefficient, used to measure association between two categorical variables;
6. χ^2, used in the chi-square test to determine whether the distribution of frequencies within the categories is in accordance with some hypothesis.

BUILDING A NOMINAL SCALE

In all sciences a first step is the development of a classification system for the objects or processes studied. The biologist, for example, divides the plant and animal kingdoms into a hierarchy of categories from the phylum down through class, order, family, and genus to the species. At each level an indefinite number of coordinate categories are possible, constituting one or more nominal scales. However, the totality of categories cannot be considered a single nominal scale because a hierarchy implies order.

In psychology the chief use of sets of categories comes when people can be classified by descriptive types. Type-like categories are often useful before precise measurement is possible.

PRINCIPLES IN ESTABLISHING NOMINAL SCALES

There are five principles in establishing a nominal scale:

1. All categories or classes must lie within a single area. Division must be on the basis of a single principle, such as pathology, or behavior symptoms, or pigmentation.
2. Categories must be coordinate. Categories from higher and lower levels (for example, genus and species) are not to be mixed in the same scale.
3. Categories must be mutually exclusive.
4. Categories must be clearly defined so that there is a minimum of difficulty in making assignments to them. The definition must cover all cases properly belonging to the class and must exclude all others.
5. There should be a sufficient number of classifications so that each observed case can be definitely assigned to a category. A miscellaneous category is generally undesirable, since its use means that a part of the group have not been assigned places on the scale.

Nominal scales developed according to these principles are important research tools. They provide the framework for the collection of data which, when treated statistically, may yield valid generalizations and lead to useful applications of results.

BASIC STATISTICAL OPERATIONS WITH NOMINAL SCALES

After a nominal scale has been constructed, the first operation is to make decisions as to which individuals are to be classified in each of the categories. As each case is studied, the class to which the individual belongs must be determined. The act of judgment required is whether or not the individual being classified possesses or does not possess the attribute that defines the category. In the simplest cases, this may lead merely to rosters of persons in different groups.

For statistical purposes it is necessary to make counts or tallies representing individuals.

After the data have been tallied, the frequency (denoted as f) is found for each of the n categories. The sum of all the frequencies is N, the total number of cases. In statistical notation it can be stated that

$$\Sigma f = N \tag{2.1}$$

or, more precisely,

$$\sum_{i=1}^{n} f_i = N \tag{2.1a}$$

Certain other operations with nominal data are correspondingly simple. The mode is the most popular class, that is, the category with the greatest frequency. With types of measurements in which the observations can be arranged in order, from the cases showing the highest degree of the characteristic down to the cases showing the lowest degree, the mode becomes a "measure of central tendency." In such cases it sometimes shows, in a rather crude fashion, the location of the middle of the distribution.

PERCENTAGES AND PROPORTIONS

In order to obtain a measure of the relative popularity of the categories in a nominal scale, the percentage of the total sample that falls in each group can be found. This is accomplished merely by dividing each f by N and multiplying by 100 (or, of course, multiplying f by 100 and dividing the product by N). In notation:

$$\text{percent } f = \frac{f}{N} \times 100 = \frac{100f}{N} \tag{2.2}$$

For any given sample, percentages should, of course, add up to 100 percent (with the likelihood of a small divergence from precisely 100 percent because of rounding). By means of percentages, those distributions from samples that have different total N may be readily compared. If the categories are identical, the percentages falling into the different categories may be directly observed.

Proportions (which are designated as p) have the same intent as percentages. However, since there is no multiplication by 100, proportions for a total sample add up to 1.00. In notation:

$$p = \frac{f}{N} \tag{2.3}$$

A special case of the use of proportions is one in which only two categories are in the nominal scale, such as male and female or citizen and alien. In this case the proportion in one of the two categories is denoted as p and the proportion in the other as q. Then, $p + q = 1.00$.

Example 2.1 illustrates the use of a nominal scale. It shows the making of tallies as individuals are assigned to categories, counting the frequencies to determine the f and N, and converting f to percentages and proportions.

EXAMPLE 2.1

USE OF A NOMINAL SCALE

Source of Data. Each student in elementary psychology was asked to report the color of his mother's eyes, using the following four categories: brown, blue, gray-green (various shades of off-blue), or hazel (various shades of off-brown).

Tallying the Results. After a nominal scale for the description of individuals has been constructed, the next operation is to determine which individuals may be properly classified in each of the categories. As each case is studied, the class best describing the individual in the area covered by the scale must be determined. As the individual is compared with each of the possible classes, the judgment is "like" or "not like." Since there is no implication of a hierarchy in a nominal scale, no judgments of "greater than" or "less than" are involved.

When information is tallied by hand, it is convenient to make tallies in groups of five, thus facilitating later counting. In making the fifth tally in any group, we strike through the first four, showing that the group of five is complete. An alternate method is to make little boxes with the first four tallies, and to cross the box for the fifth. Thus, $| = 1$; $\llcorner = 2$; $\sqsubset = 3$; $\square = 4$; and $\boxtimes = 5$. Both methods are shown here and in Example 4.1.

Counting. The number of cases in each category is the frequency (denoted as f).

Determination of N. The sum of the frequencies is, naturally enough, N, or total number of cases used in the investigation.

Computation of Percentages and Proportions. To compute percentages for the several categories, f is merely divided by N, pointing off the results so that the quotient is, in effect, multiplied by 100. Computation of proportions is exactly the same, except that there is no multiplication of the quotient by 100. In either case, any appropriate number of decimal places may be retained.

With a calculating machine, multiplication is generally easier than division. The reciprocal of N, $1/N$, is set into the keyboard. To effect division, this figure is then multiplied by the several frequencies, f.

Frequencies are both positive and integral. Percentages and proportions are positive but not necessarily integral.

Listed in the table below are 149 individuals assigned places on a scale of eye color.

CATEGORY	TALLIES	FREQUENCY (f)	PERCENTAGE ($\%$)	PROPORTION (p)
Brown		60	40	.403
Blue		42	28	.282
Gray-Green		26	17	.174
Hazel		21	14	.141
TOTAL		149	99	1.000

Note: Modal class = brown; $1/N$ (reciprocal of N) = $1/149$ = .00671.

The alternate system of writing tallies for the same data would be as follows:

CATEGORY	TALLIES	FREQUENCY (f)
Brown	☑ ☑ ☑ ☑ ☑ ☑ ☑ ☑ ☑ ☑ ☑ ☑	60
Blue	☑ ☑ ☑ ☑ ☑ ☑ ☑ ☑ ☑	42
Gray-Green	☑ ☑ ☑ ☑ ☑ ǀ	26
Hazel	☑ ☑ ☑ ☑ ǀ	21

In summing percentages and proportions, there is often "rounding" error in the final digit resulting from the cumulative effect of adding a series of numbers of which all have been rounded off to the nearest digit. In the example, there is an error of 1 percent in the sum of the percentages, but the proportions happen to sum to 1.000 precisely.

A Note on the Degrees of Freedom. If N is unknown or has no limit (as is often the case when information is being tabulated), the concept of the "degrees of freedom" has no particular pertinency. However, in advanced work with data arranged in categories, as will be explained later, knowledge of the degrees of freedom (or df) is often essential.

If n is the number of categories in a nominal scale, then, when N is fixed, $(n - 1)$ is the number of degrees of freedom.

In the present example, when N is fixed, $df = 3$. The fact that information on three groups plus information on the total sample leads directly to complete information on all four groups is a simple instance of the concept of df.

MEASURING RELATIONSHIP WITH THE CONTINGENCY COEFFICIENT

The degree to which two nominal scales vary together can be assessed with the contingency coefficient, denoted as C. It increases as individuals in certain categories on one nominal scale are more likely to appear in certain categories on a second nominal scale. If the distribution on one scale has no relationship to the distribution on the second scale, $C = .00$. If the contingency coefficient is not zero, it is positive. Negative values are impossible.

Actually, the use of C is in no way restricted to unordered data. It is applicable to finding the relationship between any two sets of observations that have been grouped into categories. However, when both sets of categories have order, or are measured in units, types of correlation to be described in later chapter are generally more useful than contingency. Accordingly, the C coefficient is used chiefly when one of the variables or both are in unordered or nominal categories.

Data of Example 2.2, reflecting the status of patients one year after discharge from a mental hospital, illustrate C. The three categories of a simple nominal scale for psychiatric diagnosis are: "schizophrenia," the "affective psychoses" (manic depressive insanity and involutional melancholia), and "psychoneuroses." The two categories for status are "unimproved" and "improved." These latter two categories may reasonably be considered as constituting a simple scale involving ordered data, since improvement is better than lack of improvement. However, whether these categories are regarded as ordinal or merely as descriptive without evaluation, the procedure is identical.

EXAMPLE 2.2

COMPUTATION OF C THE CONTINGENCY COEFFICIENT

Source of Data. Status of 417 mental patients one year after discharge from a mental hospital, as reported by Pascal *et al.* (5).

Analytic Formulation. C is computed from a two-way frequency diagram in which each case is classified in one of the categories of a first scale and also in one of the categories of a second scale.

Categories need not be ordered. There may be any number of rows and columns corresponding to the categories in the two variables. In the particular 3×2 example (three rows and two columns of primary information) entries can be designated as follows:

	UNIMPROVED	IMPROVED	TOTAL
Schizophrenia	f_o	f_o	f_r
Affective psychoses	f_o	f_o	f_r
Psychoneuroses	f_o	f_o	f_r
TOTAL	f_c	f_c	N

If all categories are numbered so that every frequency can be explicitly identified, with double subscripts denoting joint frequencies involving one category on one scale and another category on a second scale, then the preceding entries are:

	(1) UNIMPROVED	(2) IMPROVED	TOTAL
(1) Schizophrenia	f_{11}	f_{12}	f_{r1}
(2) Affective psychoses	f_{21}	f_{22}	f_{r2}
(3) Psychoneuroses	f_{31}	f_{32}	f_{r3}
TOTAL	f_{c1}	f_{c2}	N

It is apparent that there are three types of frequencies in the diagram. The f_r are the marginal frequencies in the rows. They are found by summing the cell frequencies row by row, and show the total distribution for one scale.

The f_c are the marginal frequencies in the columns. They represent sums of cell frequencies within columns and show the total distribution for the second scale.

The f_o are the observed cell frequencies. They constitute the primary information from which the f_c, the f_r, and N are found. It will be noted that $\Sigma f_r = \Sigma f_c = \Sigma f_o = N$.

Formula 2.4 for C is

$$C = \sqrt{1 - \dfrac{1}{\Sigma \dfrac{f_o{}^2}{f_r f_c}}}$$

Each f_o is to be squared and divided by the product of the two corresponding marginal entries, f_r and f_c. The sum of all values of $f_o{}^2/f_r f_c$ is found and divided into unity. The quotient is subtracted from 1. The square root of the result is C.

Computation. A convenient first step is to form a table of $f_r f_c$ products, one for each cell. Each f_o is then squared and divided by the corresponding $f_r f_c$ product. The quotients are then summed.

If a desk calculating machine with a "nonentry" feature is used, numbers can be squared in such machine space that the result is ready to use as a dividend without the entry of the multiplier into the quotient dials. By planning the work so that the machine decimal places remain constant, it is possible to accumulate $\Sigma(f_o{}^2/f_r f_c)$ without writing down individual quotients. On such machines, we need to record for each cell only f_o and $f_r f_c$. On other machines, we need also to record each quotient, $f_o{}^2/f_r f_c$.

Computational Checks. All diagrams should be checked prior to other computations by summing the three sets of frequencies and noting that all three sums equal N. That is,

$$\Sigma f_r = \Sigma f_c = \Sigma f_o = N$$

A second check, which should be executed before forming the quotients, is

$$\Sigma f_r f_c = N^2$$

It will be remembered that C cannot exceed $\sqrt{1 - 1/n'}$, in which n' is the smaller number of the two sets of categories. It attains the maximum value only when all cases in categories of one scale are also found in corresponding categories of the other scale.

Tabulation of Frequencies

	UNIMPROVED	IMPROVED	TOTAL
Schizophrenia	173	91	264
Affective psychoses	17	41	58
Psychoneuroses	24	71	95
TOTAL	214	203	417

Tabulation of Percentages Based on N

	UNIMPROVED	IMPROVED	TOTAL
Schizophrenia	41	22	63
Affective psychoses	4	10	14
Psychoneuroses	6	17	23
TOTAL	51	49	100

Tabulation of Percentages Within Diagnostic Categories

	UNIMPROVED	IMPROVED	TOTAL
Schizophrenia	65.5	34.5	100
Affective psychoses	29.3	70.7	100
Psychoneuroses	25.3	74.7	100

Numerical Steps in Finding C

		UNIMPROVED	IMPROVED	TOTAL
Schizophrenia	f_o	173	91	264
	f_o^2	29,929	8,281	
	$f_r f_r$	56,496	53,592	
	$f_o^2/f_r f_c$	.52975	.15452	
Affective psychoses	f_o	17	41	58
	f_o^2	289	1,681	
	$f_r f_c$	12,412	11,774	
	$f_o^2/f_r f_c$	.02328	.14277	
Psychoneuroses	f_o	24	71	95
	f_o^2	576	5,041	
	$f_r f_c$	20,330	19,285	
	$f_o^2/f_r f_c$	.02833	.26139	
TOTAL		214	203	417

Using the data in the accompanying tables,

$$\Sigma f_o = 173 + 91 + 17 + 41 + 24 + 71 = 417 \qquad \Sigma f_r = 264 + 58 + 95 = 417$$
$$\Sigma f_c = 214 + 203 = 417 \qquad\qquad\qquad\qquad N = 417$$

$$\Sigma f_r f_c = 56,496 + 53,592 + 12,412 + 11,774 + 20,330 + 19,285 = 173,889$$
$$N^2 = 173,889$$

$$\Sigma \frac{f_o^2}{f_r f_c} = .5298 + .1545 + .0233 + .1428 + .0283 + .2614 = 1.1401$$

Computation of C:

$$C = \sqrt{1 - \frac{1}{\Sigma \dfrac{f_o^2}{f_r f_c}}} = \sqrt{1 - \frac{1}{1.1401}} = \sqrt{1 - .8771} = \sqrt{.1229} = .35$$

Interpretation. In a 3×2 table, C has a maximum value of .707. The value of .35 appears to show definite relationship between the two scales.

If there were no relationship between type of psychiatric disorder and later status, it would be expected that patient status within each of the psychiatric categories would be distributed in the same proportion as in the total sample.

It will be noted in Example 2.2 that of the total group of 417 patients, 51 percent were reported unimproved and 49 percent improved. Accordingly, it would be expected, under the condition of no relationship between diagnosis and later status, that 51 percent of the schizophrenics, 51 percent of those with affective psychoses, and 51 percent of the psychoneurotics would be unimproved, while 49 percent in each diagnostic group would be improved.

That this is not true is apparent from an inspection of the percents based upon frequencies within diagnostic categories. Over 65 percent of the schizophrenics (as contrasted with an expectancy of 51 percent) are unimproved. On the other hand, less than 30 percent of those with affective psychoses and psychoneuroses are unimproved.

TWO HYPOTHETICAL EXAMPLES

Two hypothetical cases of the relationship between nominal scale I (categories A, B, C, and D), and nominal scale II (categories E, F, G, and H) are given as Examples 2.3 and 2.4. In Example 2.3, the frequencies of scale I are distributed within the categories of scale II in exact accordance with the total distribution of scale II, and vice versa. Thus, of the 35 cases in category A, 7 are in category E; 7 in F; 14 in G; and 7 in H. It will be

EXAMPLE 2.3

The hypothetical two-way distribution of two nominal scales with no association is given in the accompanying table.

	SCALE II				
SCALE I	E	F	G	H	TOTAL (f_r)
A	7	7	14	7	35
B	3	3	6	3	15
C	5	5	10	5	25
D	5	5	10	5	25
TOTAL (f_c)	20	20	40	20	$N = 100$

Computing C:

$$C = \sqrt{1 - \frac{1}{\sum \frac{f_o{}^2}{f_r f_c}}} = \sqrt{1 - \frac{1}{1}} = .00$$

readily seen that this type of relationship holds throughout the table. Accordingly, if this relation is typical of the population and if information as to where an individual falls on scale II is unknown, knowledge of the category in which he falls in scale I will give no inkling of his status on scale II. Scale I and scale II are independent and have no association.

In Example 2.3, where the cell frequencies for any category in either scale are exactly proportional to the marginal frequencies for the other scale, each of the cell frequencies can be reproduced by multiplying together the f_r, or marginal frequency in the same row, and the f_c, or marginal frequency in the same column, and dividing by N. This value, $f_r f_c/N$, is really f_e, the cell frequency to be expected by chance when there is no relationship between the variables. In Example 2.3, each f_o, or observed frequency, is equal to the corresponding f_e.

In Example 2.4 the situation is different. Here the distribution according to scale I is the same as in Example 2.3, but the relationship between the two scales is such that if we know the category on scale I, the category on scale II becomes known. If the sample used in constructing the table in Example 2.4 is truly representative of the population from which it was drawn, then we know that an individual in category A on scale I is necessarily also in category F on scale II, that an individual in category B is necessarily in category H, and so on. The relationship between the two scales is perfect, and the scales may be considered identical, at least in this sample.

EXAMPLE 2.4

The hypothetical two-way distribution of two nominal scales with perfect association is given in the accompanying table.

| | SCALE II | | | | |
SCALE I	E	F	G	H	TOTAL (f_r)
A	0	35	0	0	35
B	0	0	0	15	15
C	0	0	25	0	25
D	25	0	0	0	25
TOTAL (f_c)	25	35	25	15	$N = 100$

Computing C:

$$C = \sqrt{1 - \frac{1}{\sum \dfrac{f_o{}^2}{f_r f_c}}} = \sqrt{1 - \frac{1}{4}} = \sqrt{.75} = .87$$

THE NATURE OF C, THE CONTINGENCY COEFFICIENT

When, in each cell, f_e equals the corresponding f_o, it can be shown that $\Sigma(f_o^2/f_r f_c)^1 = 1.00$. This follows from certain algebraic relationships. When $f_r f_c/N = f_e = f_o$, then by multiplication by N, $f_r f_c = N f_o$. Accordingly, making simple substitutions and in the second term dividing both numerator and denominator by f_o, we have

$$\Sigma \frac{f_o^2}{f_r f_c} = \Sigma \frac{f_o^2}{N f_o} = \Sigma \frac{f_o}{N} = \frac{1}{N} \Sigma f_o = \frac{1}{N} N = 1$$

The formula for the contingency coefficient is

$$C = \sqrt{1 - \frac{1}{\Sigma \dfrac{f_o^2}{f_r f_c}}} \tag{2.4}$$

Inspection of this formula shows that when each f_e is equal to its corresponding f_o, the coefficient will be zero. This follows from the fact that, in that instance, $1/\Sigma(f_o^2/f_r f_c) = 1/1 = 1$.

The opposite situation exists when the frequencies in each category on one scale are concentrated in single categories on the second scale, as in Example 2.4. Here, $f_o = f_r = f_c$ and each $f_o^2/f_r f_c = 1.00$.

When the relationship between two scales is perfect, so that classification within one set of categories is predictable from knowledge of classification in the other set, the number of categories, designated as n', must be the same for both. Since there will be a value of $f_o^2/f_r f_c$ for each pair of categories in the two scales, and since this value will be 1.00, $\Sigma(f_o^2/f_r f_c)$ will equal n'.

This relationship is the basis for the formula for the maximum possible value of C for any n':[2]

$$C_{\max} = \sqrt{1 - \frac{1}{n'}} \tag{2.5}$$

By Formula 2.5 certain maximum values of C are as given in the following table.

In interpreting any obtained value of C, it is useful to compare it with the maximum C possible. Thus, an obtained C of .60 when $n' = 2$ would indicate a higher degree of relationship than when $n' = 9$. However,

---

[1] It should be noted that $\Sigma(f_o^2/f_r f_c)$ and $\Sigma \dfrac{f_o^2}{f_r f_c}$ are alternate ways of indicating the identical quantity.

[2] If the n' for the two variables differ, n' in Formula 2.5 refers to the smaller number of categories.

when numbers of categories are different, there is no commonly recognized method of comparing two obtained C's.

n'	C_{max}
2	.707
3	.816
4	.866
5	.894
6	.913
7	.926
8	.935
9	.943
10	.949

PREDICTION WITH CATEGORICAL DATA: THE EXPECTANCY CHART

Whenever information obtained by studying a sample is used as a basis for predicting the behavior of individuals, it is assumed, tacitly or explicitly, that the sample is truly representative of individuals later to be encountered.

In simplest form, prediction from categorical data involves:

1. Knowledge of the relationship, in a representative sample, between two variables;
2. Classification of an individual by determining that he belongs in a certain category of one of these variables; and
3. From these two ascertained facts, inferring the probability of the individual falling in one of the categories of the second variable.

The process is illustrated in Fig. 2.1. In the sample of 417 cases studied, 48.7 percent showed improvement one year after discharge. However, improvement was shown by only 34.5 percent of the schizophrenics, compared with 70.7 percent of those with affective psychoses, and 74.7

PSYCHIATRIC DIAGNOSIS	N	PERCENT SHOWING IMPROVEMENT
Schizophrenia	264	34.5%
Affective psychoses	58	70.7%
Psychoneuroses	95	74.7%
TOTAL	417	

FIG. 2.1. EXPECTANCY CHART: PROBABILITY OF IMPROVEMENT ONE YEAR AFTER DISCHARGE FROM MENTAL HOSPITAL. DATA FROM PASCAL ET AL. (5).

percent of the psychoneurotics. While it is exceedingly unlikely that any subsequent sample would show these identical percentages, it can be estimated that in future samples approximately 35 percent of the schizophrenics will show improvement, as contrasted with approximately 70 percent of those with affective psychoses and about 75 percent of the psychoneurotics. This is what is known as *group prediction*. From the proportion observed in a sample, the proportion in subsequent samples is predicted. Such prediction has been quite successful in forecasting highway accident rates, mortality rates by sex and age, and the like.

Prediction in individual instances follows identical logic. Using the relationship shown in Fig. 2.1, it can be said that if an individual is a schizophrenic about to be discharged from a hospital, the probability of his showing improvement a year from now is about .35. On the other hand, if he is a psychoneurotic under the same circumstances, the probability of his showing improvement is about .75. If only the categories of "improvement" or "no improvement" are used in the evaluation of outcome, any individual prediction will be either right or wrong. However, by predicting no improvement for the schizophrenics and improvement for the psychoneurotics, predictions will generally be right for a long series of cases.

Figure 2.1 shows forecasting a single criterion (improvement or no improvement a year after discharge) from a single predictor variable (diagnostic category). To improve prediction, it would be necessary to take more information into account. It is possible that data on age, sex, previous mental illness, physical condition, occupational level, and attitude of family toward the patient would be helpful in increasing the predictability of the criterion. Especially important, since it would contribute to making decisions with regard to the patient, would be information on the differential effects of various types of post-hospital care.

When predictors are measured in units that can be added; when the relationships between sets of measurements are best represented by straight lines; and, as always, if the trends in the sample adequately represent trends in the unknown population, an excellent statistical solution exists for the prediction of a criterion from a number of predictors. This is the technique of multiple correlation, treated in Chapter 7. Sometimes categorical information is transformed into simple scales, with pairs of classes being treated as the presence or absence of a trait. Such information then becomes amenable to treatment by multiple correlation.

Sometimes information on two or more nominal scales is used directly in the prediction of a criterion. A practical difficulty in predicting from a number of nominal scales simultaneously is that the number of subcategories increases rapidly as each new scale is added. In predicting a two-category criterion from four nominal scales, two with five categories each and two with four categories, the total number of subcategories of predictive information would be $5 \times 5 \times 4 \times 4 = 400$. For an average of 25 frequencies in each of the cells, prior to division according to the criterion variable, observations on 10,000 cases would be needed. Unless it is possible to develop generalizations that will group categories from two or more scales, such prediction is cumbersome.

PREDICTION FROM TWO NOMINAL SCALES JOINTLY

If two scales are predictive of a criterion and yet are independent or partly independent of each other, prediction from the two operating jointly is more effective than from either alone. Such is the case with the data presented in Example 2.5.

EXAMPLE 2.5

JOINT PREDICTION FROM TWO NOMINAL SCALES

(Eye Color of Father and Eye Color of Mother)

TABLE 2.1. PREDICTION OF CHILD'S EYE COLOR FROM THAT OF FATHER

FATHER'S EYES	CHILD'S EYES				PREDICTION	PROPORTION OF PREDICTIONS CORRECT
	BLUE	GRAY-GREEN	HAZEL	BROWN		
Brown	16	11	3	55	Brown	55/85 ($p = .647$)
Hazel	2	0	6	2	Hazel	6/10 ($p = .600$)
Gray-Green	12	15	1	9	Gray-Green	15/37 ($p = .405$)
Blue	41	11	4	7	Blue	41/63 ($p = .651$)

Remarks. Of 195 college students, 117 reported that they have the same eye color as their fathers. If this sample is representative of a population in which we wish to predict eye color, we can say that the probability of a child having the same eye color as his father is .60.

TABLE 2.2. PREDICTION OF CHILD'S EYE COLOR FROM THAT OF MOTHER

MOTHER'S EYES	CHILD'S EYES				PREDICTION	PROPORTION OF PREDICTIONS CORRECT
	BLUE	GRAY-GREEN	HAZEL	BROWN		
Brown	13	9	3	47	Brown	47/72 ($p = .653$)
Hazel	6	2	7	8	Hazel[a]	7/23 ($p = .304$)
Gray-Green	11	15	3	11	Gray-Green	15/40 ($p = .375$)
Blue	41	11	1	7	Blue	41/60 ($p = .683$)

[a] Not quite the best prediction based on this sample only, but perhaps the most reasonable prediction.

Remarks. Of 195 college students, 110 reported that they have the same eye color as their mothers. Based on this sample, the probability of a child having the eye color of his mother is .56.

TABLE 2.3. RELATIONSHIP BETWEEN EYE COLOR OF MOTHERS AND FATHERS

	FATHER'S EYE COLOR				
MOTHER'S EYE COLOR	BLUE	GRAY-GREEN	HAZEL	BROWN	TOTAL
Brown	19	13	3	37	72
Hazel	5	4	4	10	23
Gray-Green	12	9	2	17	40
Blue	27	11	1	21	60
TOTAL	63	37	10	85	195

Remarks. In contrast with the data in Tables 2.1 and 2.2, no relationship is apparent here. The value of C shows some association between eye color of the two parents. A hypothesis that such an association exists is reasonable, as the relationship could result from a tendency of individuals with similar racial backgrounds to marry. Whether the association in this sample represents a trend in the population represented by the sample, or whether it can be ascribed to sampling error, is treated in Chapter 3.

TABLE 2.4. EYE COLOR OF CHILDREN IN RELATION TO EYE COLOR OF BOTH PARENTS

(Within each cell, frequencies of eye color of children are given in the order: brown, hazel, gray-green, blue, and total.)

MOTHER'S EYE COLOR	CHILD'S EYE COLOR	FATHER'S EYE COLOR				CORRECT PREDICTIONS
		BLUE	GRAY-GREEN	HAZEL	BROWN	
Brown	Brown	6	7[a]	2[a]	32[a]	
	Hazel	1	1	1	0	50/72
	Gray-Green	3	3	0	3	($p = .694$)
	Blue	9[a]	2	0	2	
	TOTAL	19	13	3	37	
Hazel	Brown	0	0	0	8[a]	
	Hazel	2	0	4[a]	1	17/23
	Gray-Green	2	0	0	0	($p = .739$)
	Blue	1[a]	4[a]	0	1	
	TOTAL	5	4	4	10	
Gray-Green	Brown	1	1	0	9[a]	
	Hazel	0	0	1	2	24/40
	Gray-Green	4	7[a]	0	4	($p = .600$)
	Blue	7[a]	1	1[a]	2	
	TOTAL	12	9	2	17	
Blue	Brown	0	1	0	6	
	Hazel	1	0	0	0	41/60
	Gray-Green	2	5	0	4	($p = .683$)
	Blue	24[a]	5[a]	1[a]	11[a]	
	TOTAL	27	11	1	21	
CORRECT PREDICTIONS		41/63 ($p = .651$)	23/37 ($p = .622$)	8/10 ($p = .800$)	60/85 ($p = .706$)	132/195 ($p = .677$)

[a] Predictions according to rules stated in the text.

In Table 2.1 are exhibited the cross tabulations of eye color of father and child. Inspection reveals a marked degree of relationship. Computations for the contingency coefficient are not shown, but $C = .60$ compared with a maximum possible value of .87. The best generalization over all categories is that the child tends to have the same eye color as his father. In this table, 117 cases fit the rule; 78 do not.

In Table 2.2 a similar cross-tabulation is presented of the relationship between the eye color of mother and child. Again the best generalization to be abstracted from the data is that the eye color of the child is likely to be the same as the eye color of the parent (in this tabulation, that of the mother). It is to be noted, however, that the hazel-eyed mothers have eight children with brown eyes compared with only seven children with hazel eyes. Accordingly, a brief could be made for predicting brown-eyed children in such cases. However, the difference is only a single case, and could represent inadequate sampling. The discrepancy is not large enough to require revision of the generalization. Of the 195 cases, 110 agree with the stated principle, contrasted with 85 exceptions. The contingency coefficient for these data is .55, again indicating substantial relationship.

Table 2.3 shows a different situation. If there is a tendency for the eye color of mothers to be associated with the eye color of fathers, it is slight.[3] This is confirmed by a contingency coefficient of .27.

In the study as a whole, the two independent variables, eye color of father and eye color of mother, are both predictive and more or less independent, so that we have reason to believe that the combination will be more predictive than either singly.

In Table 2.4 is presented the trivariate distribution of eye color of mothers, fathers, and children. The presentation should be considered a three-dimensional diagram and, as such, could be shown as a set of four two-dimensional diagrams, one for each of the four categories of one of the scales.

Study of the table gives a basis for joint prediction. Within each of the 16 groupings by parent eye color, the most frequent color of children's eyes helps in the formulation of an appropriate generalization.

Four generalizations based on the sample seem to be pertinent for making predictions:

1. If both parents have the same eye color, predict that color (67 of 77 instances correct, or 87 percent).
2. If one parent is blue-eyed, predict blue eyes (34 of 66 instances correct,

---

[3] It should be remembered that any observed relationship may be a function of the group in which the observations are made. The eye color of mothers might be very substantially associated with eye color of fathers in one subracial group and not at all in another.

or 51 percent). Note: Blue-eyed fathers and hazel-eyed mothers in this sample do not follow this rule, but the generalization is apparently as good as any.

3. If one parent is brown-eyed and neither is blue-eyed, predict brown eyes (26 of 43 instances correct, or 60 percent).
4. If one parent has hazel eyes and the other gray or green eyes, predict blue eyes (5 instances of 6 correct, or 83 percent). Note: Instances are too few to be comfortable about this generalization. It can be regarded as tentative, pending further observations.

These results are summarized in the table. In this sample of 195, rules based on two independent variables lead to 132 correct placements of children in eye color categories, compared to 110 and 117 correct placements when information on only one parent is used. The increase of accuracy is of the order of 20 percent, and may be considered substantial.

DIFFERENTIAL EFFECTIVENESS OF PREDICTION

It is to be noted that parts of a nominal scale may be more predictive than other parts. For example, as shown in Table 2.1, 65 percent of brown-eyed children had brown-eyed fathers, while only 41 percent of gray or green-eyed children had gray or green-eyed fathers. Accordingly, with brown-eyed fathers there is better information about the probable eye color of their children than with gray or green-eyed fathers. With joint prediction, the same situation applies. With two parents with identical eye color, prediction should be correct in about 87 percent of the cases, while with the rule of predicting blue eyes when only one parent is blue-eyed, a rate of only about 51 percent of correct prediction is to be anticipated.

The principle of differential likelihood has wide application in clinical psychology. When a few facts about a patient are reasonably predictive, as in some kinds of mental deficiency, decisions may be made quickly. When, however, the information is in categories or parts of scales that are not highly predictive, and when there is hope that further investigation will yield new and pertinent facts, it may be appropriate to postpone a decision until further information is available.

Research applicable to clinical psychology consists in large part of finding ways of classifying people in categories and of determining the improvement to be expected under different types of treatment. Classification is by no means limited to nominal scales, although nominal scales are almost always involved. As probabilities of desirable outcome increase in defined categories, a rational basis for clinical practice is established.

NEED FOR CROSS-VALIDATION

When rules for prediction are developed in one sample, they cannot be considered as established until tested in one or more subsequent samples. The process of trying out on a new group a predictive method developed in one group is called *cross validation*. Because of fluctuations in the composition of successive samples, fluctuations in the success of the predictive system are to be anticipated. In addition, predictive rules in one sample may capitalize on associations that occur in that sample, but may not occur in the population. Accordingly, when the rules developed in one sample are applied to cases previously unobserved, prediction is likely to be less effective than in the sample used in formulating the rules.

SUMMARY

The concepts of N, frequencies within classes, percentages and proportions, permeate descriptive statistics. While various statistical procedures based on ranking or measurement along a scale in terms of additive units are not applicable to categorical data, all types of observations can be arranged in categories and treated by methods described in this chapter. Accordingly, these methods are fundamental in descriptive statistics.

The matter of determining from categorical data the likelihood that the obtained distribution is in accordance with some hypothesis is treated in the next chapter.

EXERCISES

1. The following data are reported by Hunter (3):

Distribution of Entries in Various Sections of
Psychological Abstracts, Volume 25

	ENTRIES
1. General and statistics	1024
2. Physiological psychology	597
3. Receptive processes	779
4. Response processes	252
5. Complex processes	897
6. Developmental psychology	505
7. Social psychology	1149
8. Clinical psychology	1215
9. Behavior deviations	2030
10. Educational psychology	857
11. Personnel psychology	387
12. Industrial psychology	371

Convert the frequencies by section to percentages (nearest whole number) and to proportions (correct to three places of decimals).

2. The number of impairments for males and females in the United States has been reported as follows (7):

	NUMBER OF IMPAIRMENTS (IN THOUSANDS)	
	MALE	FEMALE
Blindness	382	578
Other visual impairment	1,053	1,011
Hearing impairments	3,276	2,547
Speech defects	706	392
Paralysis	487	453
Absence of fingers or toes	1,195	233
Absence of major extremities	210	72
Impairment of lower extremities	1,823	1,331
Impairment of upper extremities	1,023	659
Impairment of limbs, back, or trunk	2,433	2,593
All other impairments	582	777
ALL IMPAIRMENTS	13,170	10,646

Within each group of impaired individuals (the male group and the female group), compute the proportion that have each type of impairment.

3. In a study of 138 highway accidents, Barmack and Payne (1) report the following data relating accident site to driver condition:

	DRIVER CONDITION	
ACCIDENT SITE	NOT DRINKING	DRINKING
Straightaway	26	30
Curve	8	37
Intersection	15	22

For each accident-site category, compute the proportions of drivers in each driver condition category.

4. Wickert (8) reports the following answers on feelings about supervision of 96 employees still with the company as contrasted with 48 employees who have left:

	SUPERVISION REGARDED AS POOR OR AVERAGE	SUPERVISION REGARDED AS GOOD
Still with company	13	83
Have left company	14	34

For each group find the proportion regarding the supervision as good.

5. Kurtz (4) presents the following data on the relationship between two categories of a special Rorschach scoring system and success as a district manager for life insurance sales:

	POORER MANAGERS	BETTER MANAGERS
Zero or positive Rorschach signs	11	12
Negative Rorschach signs	9	9

Compute and interpret C.

6. Gleason (2) reports the following two-way frequency distribution showing the relationship between scores on an information test on the Taft-Hartley law and attitude toward the law. While this information can be considered scaled, it is amenable to treatment by methods applicable to categorical data. Compute and interpret C.

SCORE ON INFORMATION TEST	ATTITUDE TOWARD TAFT-HARTLEY LAW		
	FAVOR	OPPOSE	NO OPINION
10–13	93	137	53
7–9	155	198	126
2–6	75	118	133

7. In a study on the prediction of attrition in trade school courses, Patterson (6) reports the following results:

ACTUAL CLASSIFICATION	PREDICTED CLASSIFICATION		
	FAIL	PASS	TOTAL
Pass	14	156	170
Fail	36	92	128
TOTAL	50	248	298

Compute and interpret C.

8. The following data are reported by Pascal *et al.* (5):

Status of 264 Schizophrenics One Year after Discharge from Mental Hospital

	UNIMPROVED	IMPROVED
Paranoid	87	36
Catatonic	38	38
Hebephrenic	29	3
Simple	5	6
Mixed	14	8

To study the relationship between type of schizophrenia and prognosis, compute C. What is the maximum possible value of C for a 5×2 diagram?

REFERENCES

1. BARMACK, J. E., AND PAYNE, D. E., "Injury-producing private motor vehicle accidents among airmen: psychological models of accident-generating processes," *J. Psychol.*, 1961, **52**, 3–24.

2. GLEASON, JOHN G., "Attitude vs. information on the Taft-Hartley Law," *Personnel Psychol.*, 1949, **2**, 293–299.

3. HUNTER, WALTER S., "Research interests in psychology," *Amer. J. Psychol.*, 1952, **65**, 627–632.

4. KURTZ, ALBERT K., "A research test of the Rorschach test," *Personnel Psychol.*, 1948, **1**, 41–51.

5. PASCAL, G. R., SWENSON, C. H., FELDMAN, D. A., COLE, M. E., AND BAYARD, J., "Prognostic criteria in the case histories of hospitalized mental patients," *J. Consult. Psychol.*, 1953, **17**, 163–171.

6. PATTERSON, C. H., "The prediction of attrition in trade school courses," *J. Appl. Psychol.*, 1956, **40**, 154–158.

7. United States Department of Health, Education and Welfare, Public Health Service, Washington, D.C. *Health Statistics from the U.S. National Health Survey*, 1959, B-9.

8. WICKERT, FREDERIC R., "Turnover, and employees' feelings of ego-involvement in the day-to-day operations of a company," *Personnel Psychol.*, 1951, **4**, 185–197.

AN INTRODUCTION
TO CHI SQUARE

3

THE FUNCTION OF CHI SQUARE IN COMPARING THEORY
AND FACT

Statistics that merely describe a particular sample are of preliminary interest only. Theoretical psychology requires generalized knowledge, that is,
principles and laws that relate to instances not yet observed. In generalizing
beyond specific samples and in making inferences about populations represented by them, the chi[1]-square test (the symbol for which is χ^2) is one of
the most serviceable techniques yet devised. Although it applies usually to
frequencies within categories, it is useful with data collected with all the
types of scales employed in psychological research.

This chapter is concerned principally with using chi square to make inferences from categorical data. Procedures with chi square, however, are
not affected by the type of measurement or description on which the classes
themselves are based. Later on, in Chapter 12, in connection with a discussion of the logic of various chance distribution curves, chi square will
be considered further.

---

[1] Chi rhymes with "try" and is pronounced with a hard "c" or "k" sound. The "h"
is silent.

STEPS IN TESTING HYPOTHESES WITH CHI SQUARE

The development and testing of hypotheses involving data tabulated in categories require seven steps:

1. Within some area of investigation the formulation of a hypothesis that relates to how frequencies are distributed into categories;
2. Collection of pertinent observations;
3. Classification of these data into categories and determining the actual class frequencies, denoted as the f_o's;
4. Determination of how the data would be distributed if the basic hypothesis were true, thus finding for each class the f_e, the expected or theoretical frequency;
5. Computation of χ^2, which is zero when each f_o equals its corresponding f_e, and increases as differences increase;
6. Determination of the likelihood that the particular value of χ^2 (or some greater value) would occur if each f_o differed from the corresponding f_e only by chance; and
7. Rejection of the basic hypothesis if the value of χ^2 is so large that it is highly improbable that it could have occurred by chance; or continuing the basic hypothesis as a possibility if χ^2 is small.

THE NULL HYPOTHESIS

Generally speaking, evaluation of the difference between the f_o's and f_e's is in terms of a "null hypothesis," which is most often not the basic hypothesis of the study (since the experimenter generally seeks true differences in frequency between categories). In connection with χ^2, the null hypothesis states that there is no difference between theoretical expectancy and empirical findings beyond what might reasonably be expected to occur by chance. The null hypothesis can never be proved, since if no difference is found in a series of investigations, a difference might still be found in an investigation yet to be conducted. On the other hand, if the differences between empirical findings and theoretical expectancies are greater than can reasonably be expected by chance, the null hypothesis is regarded as disproved, and it is necessary to take the view that something more than chance is responsible for the differences.

Actually, the null hypothesis is never completely rejected. It is rejected at a stated "level of significance," usually the 5 per cent level or the 1 per cent level. If an investigator is willing to make wrong decisions as often as 5 times in 100, by rejecting the null hypothesis when it should not be rejected, the 5 percent level is selected as critical. If one wishes a still higher degree of certainty, the 1 percent level can be used. Of course other levels can be selected, or in any given study, the precise probability can be stated that the difference between what is expected according to the basic hypothesis and the empirical findings represents a parameter value greater than zero.

As are other statistics of inference to be discussed in later chapters, chi square is not a direct measure of the degree of relationship. It is used in obtaining an estimate of the likelihood that some factor other than chance is operating in the area under investigation and is causing the obtained discrepancies between observed facts and the basic hypothesis. When the numerical value of chi square is larger than can reasonably be expected by chance, doubt is cast on the principle by which the theoretical frequencies were set up, and perhaps the principle will be actually rejected. If repeated investigations show no discrepancies beyond those that might reasonably be accounted for by chance, the principle receives support and may in time gain general acceptance.

In the case of data within categories, the following are examples of prior hypotheses that can be tested with chi square:

1. The hypothesis that cases are uniformly distributed among categories. In working with a multiple-choice maze, the hypothesis might be that without prior training, white rats are equally likely to choose any of, say, four alternative routes.

2. The hypothesis that cases follow a predetermined distribution. According to Mendelian principles of heredity, dominant and recessive characteristics at a certain stage of selective mating will be distributed in the proportion of three dominants to one recessive. With an appropriate sample of cases, the fit of observations to theory can be tested by chi square.

CHI SQUARE IN TESTING THE PRESENCE OF ASSOCIATION

A second use of chi square is similar to the function of testing hypothesis as to how frequencies are distributed, but is specifically concerned with determining whether an obtained relationship between two variables can be attributed to chance. Sometimes the hypotheses concern two nominal variables and the relationship between them as expressed by the contingency coefficient C.

In testing association with chi square, the theoretical frequencies are, in effect, provided by the null hypothesis rather than by the hypothesis in which the investigator is interested directly. In a study of the inheritance of eye color, for example, the investigator really wishes to determine whether eye color of the mother is related to the eye color of the child. However, this hypothesis lacks precision and does not lend itself to statistical testing. A better approach is to explore its converse. The first step is to determine the frequencies expected within the table if both marginal distributions were maintained, but without association between the two variables. If the value of chi square based upon the differences between observed and theoretical frequencies is greater than can be attributed to chance at a specified level of significance, we reject the null hypothesis, that is, the idea of no association between the variables is rejected. We can then accept the hypothesis that in the population represented by the sample, there is some association. No matter how large chi square may be, it never directly assesses the degree of such association, since chi square merely tests the presence of linkage. Measuring linkage requires other steps, such as finding C.

CHI SQUARE IN COMPARING TWO EMPIRICAL DISTRIBUTIONS

A third use of chi square is in testing two obtained distributions to see whether the differences between them can be attributed to chance.

Suppose that we draw two samples of individuals and record their religious preferences. The question is whether the two samples have similar distributions of religious preferences or whether the samples represent essentially different segments of the population.

The null hypothesis is that any difference between the two samples can be ascribed to sampling error. Identical categories must, of course, be used for the two samples and the procedure tests whether the differences within the distributions of the two samples can be attributed to chance.

FORMULAS FOR CHI SQUARE

The basic formula for chi square is

$$\chi^2 = \sum \frac{(f_o - f_e)^2}{f_e} \qquad (3.1)$$

in which f_o is any observed frequency and f_e is the corresponding frequency expected under some hypothesis. Because the differences between observed and expected frequencies are squared, chi square is always positive. Since each squared difference is divided by the expected frequency, chi square is, in a general way, a weighted average of the squared discrepancies. If there are no discrepancies at all, χ^2 is 0. As discrepancies increase, chi square increases, its maximum value increasing with the number of cases and decreasing with the number of categories. In working with chi square, it will be remembered that

$$\Sigma f_e = \Sigma f_o = N \qquad (3.2)$$

that is, the sum of the expected or theoretical frequencies equals the sum of the observed frequencies, and of course both sums equal N.

COMPUTING FORMULAS FOR CHI SQUARE

While Formula 3.1 indicates the nature of chi square, the following computing formula is usually more convenient:

$$\chi^2 = \sum \frac{f_o^2}{f_e} - N \qquad (3.3)$$

To develop Formula 3.3, each $(f_o - f_e)^2$ is expanded to $(f_o^2 - 2f_o f_e + f_e^2)$ and divided by f_e, yielding $(f_o^2/f_e - 2f_o + f_e)$. When this expression is summed, the result is $(\Sigma f_o^2/f_e) - 2 \Sigma f_o + \Sigma f_e$. Since, by Eq. 3.2, $\Sigma f_o = \Sigma f_e = N$, the expression can be simplified to Formula 3.3.

Chi square can be readily found if frequencies and expected frequencies are reported in proportions (p_o and p_e) or in percentages (percent f_o and percent f_e), both based on N. Then

$$\chi^2 = N \sum \frac{p_o^2}{p_e} - N \tag{3.4}$$

and

$$\chi^2 = \frac{N}{100} \sum \frac{\% f_o^2}{\% f_e} - N \tag{3.5}$$

In using these formulas, one more digit should be retained in the p or the

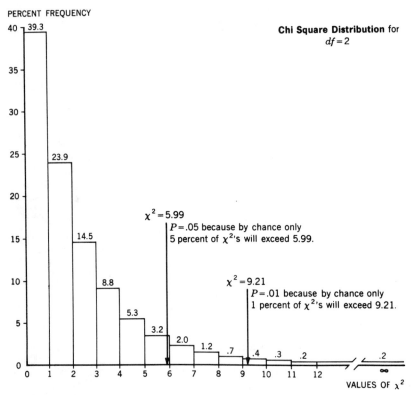

FIG. 3.1. THEORETICAL DISTRIBUTION IN HISTOGRAM FORM OF χ^2's FROM UNRELATED f_o's AND f_e's ($df = 2$, SINCE TWO OF THE DEVIATIONS ARE INDEPENDENT)

percent f than in the original frequencies, in order to reduce effects of rounding error.

In testing the independence of two variables, it is not necessary to compute the expected frequencies because we can use directly the row frequencies, the column frequencies, and the N on which the f_e are based.

Substitution of $f_r f_c/N$ for f_e in Formula 3.3 yields

$$\chi^2 = \sum \frac{f_o^2}{f_e} - N = \sum \frac{N f_o^2}{f_r f_c} - N = N \sum \frac{f_o^2}{f_r f_c} - N = N\left(\sum \frac{f_o^2}{f_r f_c} - 1\right) \quad (3.6)$$

DISTRIBUTIONS OF CHI SQUARE

For a statistic to be useful in making inferences about the population, its distribution must be known. One such distribution is shown in histogram form as Fig. 3.1, the chi square distribution for two degrees of freedom.

In finding the theoretical distribution of any statistic, it is assumed that, under the fixed set of conditions defining the statistic, only "chance" operates to produce variation. It can be shown that "chance," or better "probability," operates according to definite principles. If the possible range of variation of a statistic under stated conditions can be established, together with the relative frequency with which different values occur in the total plurality of values, the distribution of the statistic can be said to be established. This is accomplished by setting up the mathematical function that meets the stated conditions. The relative frequencies of different values can then be calculated. The use of these relative frequencies of chi square in comparing fact and theory is illustrated in Examples 3.1 and 3.2.

EXAMPLE 3.1

A χ^2 PROBLEM WITH $2df$

The theoretical distribution of χ^2 when $df = 2$ is derived to fit the condition that, when N is known for a three-category variate or when marginal frequencies are known for a 3×2 or a 2×3 bivariate[2] distribution, there are two and only two categories in which the frequencies can vary independently and freely within the overall limitations. This distribution in histogram form is shown in Fig. 3.1.

Consider a market survey in which 300 persons are asked to state their preference for one of three automobiles. The results are given in the accompanying table.

	PREFERRED BY
Car A	$115 = f_A$
Car B	$87 = f_B$
Car C	$98 = f_C$
TOTAL	$300 = N$

---

[2] The term *bivariate* refers to two variables considered simultaneously.

In a single variate distribution upon which a single restriction has been placed (in this case, a fixed N), the number of degrees of freedom is one less than the number of categories. Accordingly, in this example, $df = 2$. This means that within the limitation of the total number of cases, two categories are more or less independent. When N and the frequencies of any two categories are known, the frequency of the third category is readily deduced. Since $N = f_A + f_B + f_C$ it is easy to find any missing value from the other three values.

Two hypotheses are adopted:

1. The first is that in the population represented by this particular sample, preferences are evenly distributed. Theoretical or expected frequencies are always established on the basis of some tentative principle, and if the theory of even distribution is adopted, each f_e would be 100. Like the f_o, the f_e must add up to N.

2. The second is the "null hypothesis," which is tested directly by χ^2. In this case it states that there are no deviations from the theoretical frequencies beyond those that can be accounted for by chance.

It is permissible to compute χ^2 in either of two ways, by Formula 3.1 or by Formula 3.3, the latter being preferred when theoretical frequencies are decimal fractions or when a calculating machine is used. In the table below, all computations are written out in full. If the calculating machine has the "nonentry" feature so that numbers may be squared without affecting the quotient dials, $\Sigma(f_o{}^2/f_e)$ can be found without recording any of the f_o's or quotients of the type $f_o{}^2/f_e$.

PRE-FERRED CAR	f_o	f_e	$(f_o - f_e)$	COMPUTATIONS BY FORMULA 3.1		COMPUTATIONS BY FORMULA 3.3	
				$(f_o - f_e)^2$	$(f_o - f_e)^2/f_e$	$f_o{}^2$	$f_o{}^2/f_e$
A	115	100	15	225	2.25	13225	132.25
B	87	100	−13	169	1.69	7569	75.69
C	98	100	−2	4	.04	9604	96.04

$$\text{By Formula 3.1, } \chi^2 = 3.98 \qquad \Sigma(f_o{}^2/f_e) = 303.98$$
$$\text{By Formula 3.3, } \chi^2 = \Sigma(f_o{}^2/f_e) - N$$
$$= 303.98 - 300 = 3.98$$

The obtained chi square of 3.98 must be compared with the theoretical distribution of chi-square values that would be obtained purely by chance. Inspection of the curve for two degrees of freedom in Fig. 3.1 shows that $(5.3 + 3.2 + 2.0 + 1.2 + .7 + .4 + .3 + .2 + .2)$ percent, or 13.5 percent, of chi-square values would be greater than 4.00. Accordingly, P, the probability of obtaining purely by chance, a chi-square value as great as or greater than the obtained value is .135. In other words, there is approximately one chance in seven that a chi square as large as 3.98 could be obtained by chance alone if the a priori hypothesis of even distribution of choices among the three cars were true.

The P value that will cause rejection of the null hypothesis and thus cast doubt on the original theory depends on how much of a risk of an incorrect decision the investigator is willing to run. The most commonly accepted "levels of significance" in psychological research are the so-called 5 percent (meaning that P equals .05 or less) and the 1 percent level (meaning that P equals .01 or less). When these levels are accepted as a basis for rejecting the null hypothesis, we are taking 1 in 20, or 1 chance in 100, respectively, of an incorrect decision.

In the present instance, where $P = .135$, we probably would not regard the χ^2 as showing significant deviation from chance expectancy. In an unlimited population and with perfectly even distribution of choices among the three cars, chi squares as great as 3.98 would occur about one-seventh of the time. Accordingly, we are inclined to retain our tentative principle that in the population represented by the sample, there is no definite trend toward one car or the other.

EXAMPLE 3.2

A SECOND χ^2 PROBLEM WITH 2df

The following data are from Ellis (5) and show the results of a study of the relationship between improvement in certain patients during psychotherapy and their desire to achieve adjustment. The frequency f_o is shown for each cell.

	LITTLE OR NO IMPROVEMENT	DISTINCT IMPROVEMENT	CONSIDERABLE IMPROVEMENT	TOTAL (f_r)
Considerable desire to achieve adjustment	0	4	16	20
Moderate to no desire to achieve adjustment	10	7	3	20
TOTAL (f_c)	10	11	19	$N = 40$

In a two-way table, in which the hypothesis to be tested is that there is no association between the two variables, the f_e within each cell can be computed by multiplying the f_r for the row by the f_c for the column and dividing by N. For the cells in the upper row, the $f_r f_c$ are 200, 220, and 380. For the cells in the lower row, the $f_r f_c$ are also 200, 220, and 380. Since Formula 3.6 does not require f_e, only the $f_r f_c$ are needed. Squaring each f_o, dividing by the corresponding $f_r f_c$, and summing yields

$$\sum \frac{f_o^2}{f_r f_c} = \frac{16}{220} + \frac{256}{380} + \frac{100}{200} + \frac{49}{220} + \frac{9}{380} = 1.4928$$

By Formula 3.6, $\chi^2 = N [\Sigma(f_o^2/f_r f_c) - 1] = 40(1.4928 - 1) = 19.71$.

Since there are two rows and three columns, the number of degrees of freedom is: $df = (r - 1)(c - 1) = 1 \times 2 = 2$.

With 2df, Fig. 3.1 can again be used to find P. Inspection shows that a χ^2 of 19.71 is well beyond the upper 1 percent of the values, and hence it is significant at better than the 1 percent level. Accordingly, the null hypothesis of no association between the variables is rejected, and we are inclined to believe that there is association.

The degree of association is measured by the contingency coefficient. By the procedures of Chapter 2,

$$C = \sqrt{1 - \frac{1}{\sum \frac{f_o^2}{f_r f_c}}} = \sqrt{1 - \frac{1}{1.4928}} = \sqrt{1 - .6699} = \sqrt{.3301} = .57$$

It will be remembered that the distribution of chi square for $2df$ is only one of a number of chi-square distributions, and that in testing any particular value of chi square, it is essential to use the curve or values from a table appropriate to the df. As shown in the histogram of Fig. 3.1 with $2df$, approximately 39 percent of obtained values of chi square are expected to fall between 0 and 1.0, approximately 24 percent between 1.0 and 2.0, approximately 9 percent between 3.0 and 4.0, and so on. If there is no underlying association between the values of the frequencies and the expected values, 5 percent of the chi squares will still exceed 5.99. Similarly, if the association between expected and obtained frequencies is only by chance, about 1 percent of the chi-square values will be

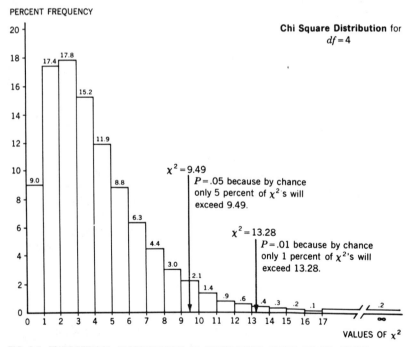

FIG. 3.2. THEORETICAL DISTRIBUTION IN HISTOGRAM FORM OF χ^2's FROM UNRELATED f_o's AND f_e's ($df = 4$, SINCE FOUR OF THE DEVIATIONS ARE INDEPENDENT)

greater than 9.21. This illustrates what is meant by the 5 percent and 1 percent levels of significance. If a computed chi square is 5.99 or over, such a value could be obtained on the basis of purely chance association only once in 20 times; hence the P value is .05. Similarly, for values of chi square of 9.21 or more, $P = .01$, or more precisely, $P < .01$ because by chance alone only 1 percent of chi squares will exceed 9.21.

The function yielding distributions of chi square was discovered by Pearson about 1900, and tables of the principal chi-square curves were prepared by W. P. Elderton. The concept of the degrees of freedom in relation to chi square was worked out by Fisher, who, together with Yates, produced a new set of chi-square tables oriented in terms of df and stated values of P rather than in terms of the number of categories and stated values of χ^2. For convenience, chi squares found in actual research are evaluated in terms of these tabled values rather than by direct use of a mathematical function.

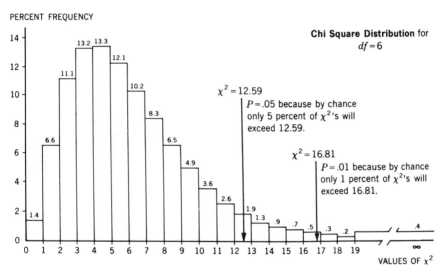

FIG. 3.3. THEORETICAL DISTRIBUTION IN HISTOGRAM FORM OF χ^2's FROM UNRELATED f_o's AND f_e's ($df = 6$, SINCE SIX OF THE DEVIATIONS ARE INDEPENDENT)

The distribution in Fig. 3.1 (χ^2 for $2df$) should be compared with the distribution in Fig. 3.2 (χ^2 for $4df$) and the distribution in Fig. 3.3 (χ^2 for $6df$). It will be noted that as the degrees of freedom increase, numerical values of chi square tend to increase, as might well be anticipated. The shape of the distribution changes, becoming more and more symmetrical. Beyond $df = 30$, the distribution of chi square is regarded as symmetrical and may be evaluated by means of tables of a symmetrical curve, as will be described in a later chapter.

DETERMINING THE SIGNIFICANCE OF χ^2

When we have the actual χ^2 distributions (or close approximations as in Figs. 3.1, 3.2, and 3.3), we can determine by inspection whether a given χ^2 represents a sufficiently unusual occurrence to indicate that something more than chance is operating to produce the discrepancies between observed and theoretical frequencies. Here, these distributions are available for 2*df*, 4*df*, and 6*df* merely to show the nature of the distributions and to clarify the logic underlying the χ^2 test. In actually carrying out research, one would want to find the significance of obtained chi squares from a source more compact than a series of charts, one for each *df*.

Figure 3.4, showing selected *P* functions for values of chi square up to 50 and for 1 to 30 degrees of freedom, can be used in evaluating obtained chi squares.

Entry is by means of chi square on the ordinate (vertical, or *y* axis) and the degrees of freedom on the abscissa (horizontal, or *x* axis). From the relation of the intersection of the lines from the two entries to the *P* value curves, an idea of *P* may be obtained.

VALUES OF χ^2

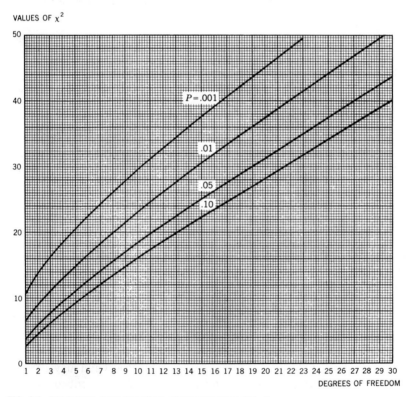

DEGREES OF FREEDOM

FIG. 3.4. DIAGRAM FOR FINDING SIGNIFICANCE OF χ^2

A few examples of the use of this graph are given below:

df	χ^2	LOCATION OF POINT OF INTERSECTION	INTERPRETATION
2	10.50	Between $P = .01$ and $P = .001$	$.01 > P > .001$: Discrepancies highly significant. Null hypothesis rejected at 1 percent level of significance.
6	5.40	Below $P = .10$	Discrepancies not statistically significant
7	18.30	Near $P = .01$	Table C (Appendix) should be consulted for exact value of χ^2 for $P = .01$
8	17.50	Between $P = .05$ and $P = .01$	$.05 > P > .01$: Null hypothesis rejected at 5 percent level of significance
10	2.00	Below $P = .10$	Discrepancies not statistically significant
14	5.10	Below $P = .10$	Discrepancies not statistically significant

In general, however, an obtained chi square is evaluated by means of a table such as Table C (Appendix), which shows how large a chi square must be to be significant at the 5 percent and 1 percent levels.

Illustrative problems involving the computation and interpretation of χ^2 with $4df$ are given in Examples 3.3, 3.4, and 3.5.

EXAMPLE 3.3

A χ^2 PROBLEM WITH $df = 4$

Another chi-square distribution curve is shown as Fig. 3.2, this one for four degrees of freedom. Like Fig. 3.1, its use is illustrative only, since in practice the significance of an obtained χ^2 is found from a chart such as Fig. 3.4 or from a table such as Table C (Appendix).

The χ^2 curve for $4df$ is useful in evaluating differences between obtained and theoretical frequencies when four categories (or, rather, four deviations) are free to vary independently. With a single categorical variable, this situation obtains when N is fixed and there are five categories. With two nominal variables, the number of cells for observed frequencies will be 2 by 5, 3 by 3, or 5 by 2; all of which, by the $(r - 1) (c - 1)$ principle, yield $4df$.

Testing Whether a Single Nominal Variable Differs from an a priori Distribution. In a market survey of soft drink preferences, 60 respondents might give first preferences as indicated under f_o in the table below.

	f_o	f_e	f_o^2/f_e
Brand I	14	12	16.333
Brand II	12	12	12.000
Brand III	11	12	10.083
Brand IV	9	12	6.750
Brand V	14	12	16.333

$$\Sigma \frac{f_o^2}{f_e} = 61.499$$

By Formula 3.3,

$$\chi^2 = \sum \frac{f_o^2}{f_e} - N = 61.499 - 60 = 1.499$$

The basic hypothesis in this case would be that there are no differences in preference for the five brands. Accordingly, in each case f_e is 12. The null hypothesis states that any discrepancies between the f_o and the f_e result from chance. With N fixed, four categories are left to vary, and accordingly, $df = 4$. Chi square is 1.499. Inspection of the curve for $4df$ and of the chart in Fig. 3.4 indicates that P is very high. Inspection of Table C (Appendix) shows that χ^2 for four degrees of freedom would have to be 9.488 to be significant at the 5 percent level of confidence. Accordingly, there is no reason to reject the null hypothesis, and it appears possible that the differences among the brands may result from sampling.

It should be remembered, of course, that the sample is small. Brands I and V have about 50 percent more first preferences than brand IV. If these same proportions were obtained in a considerably larger sample, it is likely that χ^2 would be found to be significant. In all cases, the question investigated is whether (in the particular set of data) discrepancies between theory and observation can be ascribed to chance.

EXAMPLE 3.4

A PROBLEM IN A 5 × 2 TABLE

In a study of the relationship of son's occupation to father's occupation, Jenson and Kirchner (6) reported numbers of sons following father's occupation and not following father's occupation for five occupational groups as shown in the table. Again, in each cell, f_o is given with $f_r f_c$ in parentheses below.

OCCUPATIONAL GROUP OF SONS	SONS NOT IN FATHER'S OCCUPATION	SONS IN FATHER'S OCCUPATION	TOTAL (f_r)
Operatives and allied	1,542 (9,499,340)	428 (3,282,020)	1,970
Craftsmen, foremen, and allied	1,156 (8,621,736)	632 (2,978,808)	1,788
Managers, officials, and proprietors (except farm)	773 (5,665,850)	402 (1,957,550)	1,175
Professional and technical	664 (3,920,286)	149 (1,354,458)	813
Clerical and allied	687 (3,577,924)	55 (1,236,172)	742
TOTAL (f_c)	4,822	1,666	$N = 6,488$

Check: $\Sigma f_r f_c = 9{,}499{,}340 + 8{,}621{,}736 + 5{,}665{,}850 + 3{,}920{,}286 + 3{,}577{,}924 +$ $3{,}282{,}020 + 2{,}978{,}808 + 1{,}957{,}550 + 1{,}354{,}458 + 1{,}236{,}172 = 42{,}094{,}144 = N^2$

$$\Sigma \frac{f_o^2}{f_r f_c} = 1.046438. \hspace{3cm} df = 4$$

By Formula 3.6,

$$\chi^2 = N[\Sigma(f_o^2/f_r f_c) - 1]$$

$$= (6488) \times (.046438) = 301.29$$

$$C = \sqrt{1 - 1/\Sigma(f_o^2/f_r f_c)} = \sqrt{1 - 1/1.046438}$$

$$= \sqrt{1 - .9556} = \sqrt{.0444} = .21$$

$\Sigma(f_o^2/f_r f_c)$ is computed in the usual way for contingency tables. First, the f_r and f_c are multiplied together in pairs, and the $f_r f_c$ products are entered in the cells under the f_o. The $f_r f_c$ are summed as a check, since $\Sigma f_r f_c = N^2$. Then each f_o is squared and divided by the $f_r f_c$ product. The sum of the quotients is $\Sigma(f_o^2/f_r f_c)$. The chi square of 301.29 is far beyond the graphed and tabled values, and is highly significant. The chance that there is no association between the two variables is exceedingly minute, and the null hypothesis can be rejected with considerable assurance.

However, as is always the case, the value of χ^2 is a function of N. With 6488 cases, a very small degree of association would be found to be statistically significant, in that the association would be too great to be ascribed merely to random variation in the particular sample. In this example, the relationship between occupational group and tendency to follow father's occupation is rather low, as shown by a contingency coefficient of .21, compared with a maximum possible C of .707 in a 5×2 table.

EXAMPLE 3.5

A χ^2 PROBLEM IN A 3×3 TABLE

Another example with $4df$ is based on data from Cohen (3) and involves a comparison of a psychologist's Wechsler-Bellevue pattern diagnoses and the corresponding neuropsychiatric criterion diagnoses. Three hundred cases were studied in all, with 100 in each of the following classes: psychoneurotic, schizophrenic, and brain-damaged. The results obtained are given in the accompanying table.

In each cell, $f_r f_c$ is written under the cell frequency (f_o). When each f_o is squared and divided by the appropriate $f_r f_c$, the result is $\Sigma(f_o^2/f_r f_c) = 1.067$. $\chi^2 = N[\Sigma(f_o^2/f_r f_c) - 1] = (300)\,(.067) = 20.10$. From the curve of χ^2 for $4df$, it is apparent that P is less than .01. Accordingly, the null hypothesis is rejected at better than the 1 percent level, and it can be believed that there is association between the two variables in the population represented by the sample.

The degree of association in the sample is measured by the contingency coefficient of .31, compared with a maximum possible of .816 for a 3×3 diagram.

| PSYCHOLOGIST'S DIAGNOSIS | NEUROPSYCHIATRIC CRITERION | | | TOTAL (f_r) |
	PSYCHO-NEUROTIC	SCHIZO-PHRENIC	BRAIN-DAMAGED	
Brain-damaged	20 (9100)	28 (9100)	43 (9100)	91
Schizophrenic	24 (8600)	33 (8600)	29 (8600)	86
Psychoneurotic	56 (12,300)	39 (12,300)	28 (12,300)	123
TOTAL (f_c)	100	100	100	$N = 300$

EXAMPLE 3.6

A PROBLEM WITH 6df

A third histogram showing chi square under the condition of no correspondence between obtained and theoretical frequencies is exhibited as Fig. 3.3. It is for six degrees of freedom; that is, six of the deviations are independent. Accordingly, it can be applied to test whether the distribution of a single variable with seven categories is in accordance with some hypothesis, or it can be used to test association in contingency tables of the following forms: 2×7, 3×4, 4×3, and 7×2.

The data in the table, from Patterson (8), represent passing and failing in seven trade school courses. In each cell, f_o is given with $f_r f_c$ in parentheses below.

SCHOOL COURSE	FAIL	PASS	TOTAL (f_r)
Automobile general	22 (5723)	37 (9853)	59
Building construction, drafting, and estimation	11 (3201)	22 (5511)	33
Electric general	12 (3977)	29 (6847)	41
Machine shop	8 (3201)	25 (5511)	33
Mechanical drafting	19 (3007)	12 (5177)	31
Printing	6 (1843)	13 (3173)	19
Radio and electronics	19 (4656)	29 (8016)	48
TOTALS (f_c)	97	167	$N = 264$

By χ^2 it is possible to test whether there is an association between type of course and success in training.

The $f_r f_c$ are checked by summing and comparing with N^2.

$$\Sigma f_r f_c = 69,696 = N^2$$

Then,

$$\Sigma\left(\frac{f_o{}^2}{f_r f_c}\right) = 1.04463$$

$$\chi^2 = N[\Sigma\left(\frac{f_o{}^2}{f_r f_c}\right) - 1] = 264 \times .04463 = 11.78$$

Figure 3.3 shows that with $6df$, more than 5 percent of chi squares obtained by chance exceed 11.78. Accordingly, by the conventional standard, there is no need to reject the null hypothesis of no association between type of course and success in training.

COMBINING CATEGORIES WHEN f_e ARE SMALL

The way in which the distributions of χ^2 are derived places restrictions on its use.

In the first place, theoretical or expected frequencies must not be too small. The dividing line "too small" is arbitrary and varies with different mathematical statisticians, from 5 to 20. The consensus favors 5 as the smallest f_e permissible. Sometimes the only recourse is to gather sufficient data so that all cells have a minimum f_e of 5. In other cases, however, where categories may be logically combined, the total number of categories can be reduced by consolidation, making all cells meet the requirement. Such is the situation in Exercise 8 at the end of this chapter, where certain information from Example 2.5 has been revised. In Example 2.5 there were too few cases of hazel eyes to permit the chi square test to be made in the total 4 by 4 table. By combining the categories of brown eyes and hazel eyes (various shades of off-brown), the test could be appropriately applied.

It should be noted that there is no restriction on the size of f_o, which may be zero.

YATES' CORRECTION FOR CONTINUITY FOR $1df$

A special case comes in a 2×2 diagram when one f_e is less than 5. Here there is no way to combine categories. Instead, the "correction for continuity" developed by Yates is applied. It brings the computation of χ^2 into closer harmony with its mathematical development, which involves a continuous function rather than discrete frequencies. A numerical example is given as Example 3.7.

EXAMPLE 3.7

YATES' CORRECTION FOR CONTINUITY (HYPOTHETICAL EXAMPLE)

Method I. If there is a single smallest f_o (as in this example), it is increased by .5, and all other f_o are adjusted so that f_c and f_r are unchanged.

After the cell frequencies have been corrected, computation of χ^2 proceeds exactly in the normal routine. Values of corrected f_o, of $f_r f_c$, of $\Sigma(f_o{}^2/f_r f_c)$ and of χ^2 are given in the table.

VARIABLE I		VARIABLE II		f_r
		C	D	
A	Obtained f_o	4	10	
	Corrected f_o	4.5	9.5	14
	$f_r f_c$	(168)	(210)	
		a	b	
		c	d	
B	Obtained f_o	8	5	
	Corrected f_o	7.5	5.5	13
	$f_r f_c$	(156)	(195)	
	f_c	12	15	$N=27$

As a check:

$$\Sigma f_r f_c = 168 + 210 + 156 + 195 = 729 = N^2$$

Using corrected f_o,

$$\Sigma\left(\frac{f_o{}^2}{f_r f_c}\right) = 1.066$$

$$\chi^2 = N\left[\Sigma\left(\frac{f_o{}^2}{f_r f_c}\right) - 1\right] = (27)(.066) = 1.782$$
$$df = 1.$$

From Fig. 3.4 and Table C (Appendix), it can be noted that χ^2 is not large enough for significance at the 5 percent level.

Method II. Method II is generally applicable, even when there are two or three smallest f_o.

Let the four observed frequencies be a, b, c, and d as indicated in the table. The absolute sum of $ad - bc$, that is, sum without regard to sign, is reduced by $N/2$ and squared. The square is multiplied by N, and the result is divided by the product of the four marginals: $(a + b)$, $(c + d)$, $(a + c)$, and $(b + d)$. The result is χ^2. Thus

$$\frac{(|ad - bc| - N/2)^2 N}{(a + b)(c + d)(a + c)(b + d)} = \frac{(60 - 13.5)^2 \times 27}{14 \times 13 \times 12 \times 15} = \frac{58,380.75}{32,760} = 1.782$$

In this expression, $|ad - bc|$ is evaluated as $+60$ even though $(4 \times 5) - (10 \times 8) = -60$, since the absolute rather than the algebraic sum of the two products is needed.

An important property of chi square is that it is additive. Under certain conditions, chi squares can be added together or, conversely, separated into portions, thus permitting more precise analyses of the data.

RELATIONSHIP BETWEEN χ^2 AND C

If N and χ^2 are known, the contingency coefficient C may be found from the following formula:

$$C = \sqrt{\frac{\chi^2}{\chi^2 + N}} \qquad (3.7)$$

Similarly, if N and C are known, χ^2 can be found as follows:

$$\chi^2 = \frac{NC^2}{1 - C^2} \qquad (3.8)$$

SUMMARY

By discussion and example, the logic of chi square has been developed. Applied to frequency data, consisting of independent observations in which each individual is represented by a tally in a single cell, chi square provides a method of determining the probability that we would be wrong in rejecting an a priori hypothesis as to the distribution of the frequencies as well as the probability that we would be wrong in accepting the hypothesis of association between two categorical variables.

Chi square thus provides a method of making inferences, at a stated degree of certainty, about the population represented by the sample.

The use of χ^2 is not restricted to nominal data. It can be used whenever observations are grouped into categories. Accordingly, it is a convenient and useful tool in much quantitative psychological research. However, when original data are values on an ordered variable rather than frequencies, there may be loss of information and precision in using χ^2 instead of a procedure specifically applicable to ordered variables.

EXERCISES

1. Consider a primary campaign in which five candidates are running for the nomination. A poll reports the following preferences from a random sample of voters.

CANDIDATE	PREFERENCES
A	45
B	50
C	40
D	53
E	27

Test the hypothesis that differences among the first four candidates are the result of sampling differences only.

2. In a study of students entering Wellesley in 1892, Calkins (2) reported the following data on the relationship between pseudo-chromesthesia and mental "forms."

	NOT REPORTING PSEUDO-CHROMES-THESIA	REPORTING PSEUDO-CHROMES-THESIA	TOTAL
Reporting mental "forms"	44	17	61
Not reporting mental "forms"	127	15	142
TOTAL	171	32	203

Test the association of pseudo-chromesthesia with mental "forms" by use of chi square.

3. In an experiment on perception, Bruner and Minturn (1) reported the following data:

	NUMBER OF SUBJECTS DRAWING A BROKEN-B STIMULUS FULLY OR PARTLY CLOSED, OR OPEN, UNDER THREE CONDITIONS OF EXPECTATION	
EXPECTATION	SEEN FULLY OR PARTLY CLOSED	SEEN OPEN
Number	2	22
Number or letter	8	16
Letter	16	8

Test with chi square whether there is a relationship between expectation and perception of the stimulus.
Compute C directly and compare the result with C as found by Formula 3.7.

4. In a study of interpersonal trust and communication, Mellinger (7) reported the following data (slightly modified) on the relationship between accuracy in perceiving another's attitude and actual level of agreement in attitude.

ACCURACY OF PERCEIVING	LEVEL OF AGREEMENT				TOTAL
	0 or 1	2	3	4	
4	6	5	28	40	79
3	8	21	64	13	106
2	8	25	3	4	40
0 or 1	17	0	0	2	19
TOTAL	39	51	95	59	244

By chi square, test whether there is a relationship between accuracy of perceiving another's attitude and actual level of agreement.

5. Sloan and Harmon (9) reported that of 332 feeble-minded with mental ages less than three who showed changes in I.Q. on retest, 102 gained in I.Q. and 230 lost. Test the hypothesis that in the population represented by the sample, half will gain and half will lose in I.Q.

Of the 102 gainers, 51 were male and 51 were female; of the 230 who lost in I.Q., 132 were male and 98 were female. Test whether there is an association between sex and direction of change in I.Q.

6. At a psychological research unit during World War II (4) recommendations for different types of training for aviation cadets and for student officers were made as follows:

| | STATUS | |
TYPE OF TRAINING	AVIATION CADETS	STUDENT OFFICERS
Bombardier	1,401	47
Navigator	3,393	65
Pilot	15,775	813

Using the chi-square test, determine whether the type of training recommended was related to status as aviation cadet or student officer.

7. Two samples of 5000 aviation cadets each reported previous flying experience as follows (4):

	SAMPLE A	SAMPLE B
Held pilot's private or commercial license	648	509
Student pilot certificate, solo privileges	411	494
Student pilot certificate	175	206
Had been passenger in plane, no instruction	2984	2910
Never had been passenger in plane	718	784
Previous military flying instruction	64	97

Test the null hypothesis that there are no differences in previous flying experience in the two samples.

8. The following data are modified from Example 2.5, hazel eyes being combined with brown eyes to avoid cells with f_e below 5. Test with chi square whether there is association between eyes of father and eyes of mother.

| | FATHER'S EYES | | | |
MOTHER'S EYES	BLUE	GRAY-GREEN	HAZEL-BROWN	TOTAL
Hazel-Brown	24	17	54	95
Gray-Green	12	9	19	40
Blue	27	11	22	60
TOTAL	63	37	95	195

REFERENCES

1. BRUNER, J. S., AND MINTURN, A. L., "Perceptual identification and perceptual organization," *J. Gen. Psychol.*, 1955, **53**, 21–28.
2. CALKINS, MARY W., "A statistical study of pseudo-chromesthesia and of mental-forms," *Amer. J. Psychol.*, 1892–1893, **5**, 439–464.
3. COHEN, JACOB, "The efficacy of diagnostic pattern analysis with Wechsler-Bellevue," *J. Consult. Psychol.*, 1955, **19**, 303–306.
4. DUBOIS, P. H. (ed.), *The Classification Program.* Report 2, AAF Aviation Psychology Program Research Reports. Washington, D.C.: U.S. Government Printing Office, 1947.
5. ELLIS, ALBERT, "Effectiveness of psychotherapy with individuals who have severe homosexual problems," *J. Consult. Psychol.*, 1956, **20**, 191–195.
6. JENSON, PAUL G., AND KIRCHNER, WAYNE K., "A national answer to the question, 'Do sons follow their fathers' occupations?'" *J. Appl. Psychol.*, 1955, **39**, 419–421.
7. MELLINGER, GLEN D., "Interpersonal trust as a factor in communication," *J. Abnorm. Soc. Psychol.*, 1956, **52**, 304–309.
8. PATTERSON, C. H., "The prediction of attrition in trade school courses," *J. Appl. Psychol.*, 1956, **40**, 154–158.
9. SLOAN, WILLIAM, AND HARMAN, HARRY H., "Constancy of IQ in mental defectives," *J. Genet. Psychol.*, 1947, **71**, 177–185.

DESCRIPTION BY RANKING

4

THE NATURE OF ORDINAL DESCRIPTION

A type of description of much interest in psychology is ranking, the basis of what is often called the *ordinal scale*. The adjective "ordinal" refers to order or rank as the fundamental characteristic of the quantitative description involved.

Essentially, an ordinal scale is used whenever individuals are placed in order according to the degree to which they possess a characteristic, such as proficiency in tennis, ability to speak French, or skill in argumentation. Devices for assessing handwriting or composition, in which key specimens are arranged in order of merit, are examples of formal ordinal scales.

With nominal data, numbers are used chiefly for N, for frequencies, for proportions and percentages, and for values of statistics such as chi square and the contingency coefficient. Only occasionally is a number used to designate a class or category, and then the number carries no implication of rank or value. With ordinal scales, however, numbers are not only used for statistics, but also to describe categories as having more or less of some attribute or characteristic.

JUDGMENTS WITH NOMINAL AND ORDINAL SCALES

In using a nominal scale, as described in the preceding chapter, an individual is judged as to whether he should or should not be assigned to a certain category. If he cannot be placed in the first category examined, other categories are considered until one is found in which he can be correctly placed. The act of judgment required is essentially that of differentiating between "equal" and "not equal"; that is, whether or not the individual possesses the characteristic or attribute differentiating the class from other classes.

A formal ordinal scale generally requires these same judgments of equality, but in addition, since the numbers describing the categories represent relative magnitudes, judgments of "more than" or "less than" are essential both in building the scale and in using it. With an informal ordinal scale, as when a supervisor is asked to rank the men under him as to their usefulness to the company, discriminations of "better than" and "poorer than" or "more than" and "less than" are needed. Essentially, then, ordinal measurement in psychology involves judgments as to variation in the degree to which different individuals possess a characteristic, but there is no implication of measuring the characteristic in equal units. On a formal ordinal scale, all that is assumed is that of the characteristic described by the scale, one category involves more or less than another category. When individuals are ranked directly, there is implication of a characteristic that varies in degree, but the question of how many units of the characteristic possessed by each individual is ignored.

THREE METHODS OF RANKING

In practice, the use of ranking as measurement in psychology involves one of three procedures:

1. The establishment of a formal ordinal scale in which categories are defined (possibly by means of samples) and arranged in order. Each individual case is then judged as to the category to which it belongs. Order-of-merit scales for evaluating work products are of this type.

2. Ordering a group from high to low or from low to high with regard to a defined characteristic. It is a matter of convenience whether low or high numbers represent the greater merit, but it is generally the former. The scoring system for cross-country meets is based upon the order in which individuals finish the run, and hence uses an ordinal scale of this type.

3. The application of a device yielding numerical scores of some sort (often the number of items right, or some function of time or errors) and then treating the scores as though they correctly differentiate individuals as to relative order, with ties permitted, but with no requirement that the original scores represent units. This is a method frequently used with psychological test data and constitutes the foundation of the use of percentiles in descriptive statistics.

All the statistics applicable to nominal scales (N, class frequencies, percentages and proportions, the mode, the contingency coefficient, and chi square) apply generally also to ordinal scales (although some of these would not ordinarily be used with a set of N ranks, as described below). In addition, there is a new family of descriptive statistics which can be used with ordinal data but not with nominal categories. Of these, the most fundamental is rank order, with the percentile as probably the statistic of widest application.

FOUR DESCRIPTIVE STATISTICS BASED ON RANKING

The use of order as a means of description makes possible four important statistics.

1. Rank or rank order. The N individuals in a sample may be assigned ranks, beginning with 1 and continuing through 2, 3, 4, and so on to N, using as the basis for the assignment some estimated or measured characteristic. Thus, each individual is described by his rank order in the sample. If the same individual is ranked in the same reference group with respect to several characteristics, the ranks in different characteristics may be compared numerically. For a given characteristic, however, the meaning of a rank changes both with the population sampled and the size of the sample. To be the best student in a section of freshman mathematics in a liberal arts college may not represent the same attainment as being the best in a freshman section in an engineering college. Placing second in a group of 10 may not represent the same achievement as placing second in a group of 200. Accordingly, when rank is used to reflect a psychological characteristic, both size and composition of the group in which rank is determined should be stated, as well as the nature of the measuring device.

If two or more individuals in a group are tied, the customary procedure is to make an adjustment so that the sum of the ranks is maintained. Suppose, for example, that after the first two individuals have been ranked, two are tied for third place. The two vacant ranks corresponding to the two ties are averaged, giving each the rank of 3.5. The next individual would be assigned the rank of 5. The series would thus be: 1, 2, 3.5, 3.5, and 5. Similarly, if these five were followed by three individuals tied for next place, the vacant ranks would be 6, 7, and 8, and the three would be assigned the average rank (sometimes called the *midrank*) of 7.

2. Percent position or percent rank. In order to make ranked data comparable, irrespective of the size of the reference group, rank orders may be translated into "percent position" or "percent rank," in which higher values represent the more desirable standing. The conversion formula is

$$\text{Percent rank} = \frac{100(N + .5 - R)}{N} \tag{4.1}$$

in which R is the original rank (with 1 at the more desirable end of the scale) and N is the number of cases in the sample.

By formula 4.1 a person standing fourth in a group of 11 would have a percent rank of $100(11.5 - 4)/11$, or (to the nearest whole number) 68. The interpretation is that he is theoretically higher than 68 percent of the group but that 32 percent are higher than he. The term *theoretically* refers to the fact that the individual's own rank is partly assigned to the higher group and partly to the lower. This is a convention by which the entire array of ranks is divided into just two groupings instead of three, and by which the percent of N belonging to the individual's own rank is eliminated from influencing the statistic. Actually, percent ranks are exactly the same in theory and in interpretation as the percentile ranks to be described below, except that they are derived directly from ranks instead of from measures that have been placed in order.

3. A percentile may be defined as the point below which a given percent of the scores or values in a frequency distribution theoretically fall. The theory of the frequency distribution when data are treated as ordinal, the method of making frequency distributions, and the computation, interpretation, and application of percentiles form the major portion of this chapter.

4. A percentile rank is closely allied to the percentile. There is an important difference. With a percentile, we start with a certain percentage of N and find the theoretical point in the distribution below which the scores fall. With a percentile rank, we start with some score or value that actually occurs in the distribution and find the theoretical percentage of the distribution that falls below it.

With percentiles, the percent of N is generally integral, while the equivalent theoretical score is a decimal fraction; with percentile ranks, the score is customarily integral, while the percentage equivalent, or percentile rank, could be taken to several decimal places. With psychological data, however, two digits of value for percentile ranks are generally considered sufficient.

THE FREQUENCY DISTRIBUTION IN ORDINAL DESCRIPTION

MAKING A FREQUENCY DISTRIBUTION

A frequency distribution is a means of classifying the scores of a single variable. Scores are grouped in categories defined by *step intervals*, each of which is a set of contiguous possible scores. In the frequency distribution shown in Example 4.1, the step interval is 5, which means that five different but contiguous values are grouped together as a single class.

EXAMPLE 4.1

MAKING A FREQUENCY DISTRIBUTION

Nature of a Frequency Distribution. A variable with values that indicate the order of the cases may be divided into a number of categories or "steps." Each step generally corresponds to a certain number of values on the original scale. The number of values in a step is known as the step interval and is denoted as i. In the distribution in Table 4.1, $i = 5$ because a case is tallied in a given step if it has any one of five different integral values. For example, any score, 140, 141, 142, 143, or 144, is tabulated in the top step.

TABLE 4.1. DISTRIBUTION OF 200 SCORES ON AN APTITUDE TEST

STEPS	TALLIES[a]	f	SCALE DISTANCE (i/f) FOR EACH SCORE IN STEP	CUMULATIVE FREQUENCIES Cf^b	Cf^c
140–144		1	5.000	200	1
135–139		2	2.500	199	3
130–134		3	1.667	197	6
125–129		6	.833	194	12
120–124		8	.625	188	20
115–119		12	.417	180	32
110–114		15	.333	168	47
105–109		20	.250	153	67
100–104		23	.217	133	90
95–99		26	.192	110	116
90–94		24	.208	84	140
85–89		20	.250	60	160
80–84		16	.313	40	176
75–79		10	.050	24	186
70–74		7	.714	14	193
65–69		4	1.250	7	197
60–64		2	2.500	3	199
55–59		0		1	199
50–54		1	5.000	1	200

[a] The alternate system of making tallies for the first five steps would be:

STEPS	TALLIES
140–144	
135–139	
130–134	
125–129	
120–124	

[b] Cumulated upward from the bottom of the distribution.
[c] Cumulated downward from the top of the distribution.

The number of cases tabulated in any step is the frequency, denoted as f. In the top step, there is only one tally. Accordingly, $f = 1$. The exact value of the score represented by a tally cannot be known from the distribution. However, the loss of information as to precise values is compensated for by:

1. The fact that the general shape of the distribution becomes apparent from inspection of the tallies or frequencies; and
2. The fact that a convenient format becomes available for the computation of descriptive statistics.

Preferred Practices. Although methods used in making frequency distributions vary, most social scientists would find the following practices acceptable:

1. Use of 10 to 20 steps. The use of fewer than 10 steps tends to increase inaccuracies in computed statistics; the use of more than 20 steps tends to accentuate irregularities in the shape of the distribution. However, the rule is flexible, and practice may be modified to fit circumstances. As an example, when cases are few, the use of only three or four steps may be advisable in order to bring out a trend.

2. Higher values at the top of the distribution; lower values at the bottom. This is merely the convention that applies above the origin to the *y* axis of Cartesian coordinates.

3. A step interval of 1, 2, 3, 4, 5, 10, or a multiple of 10. These values have familiar multiples and hence their use reduces the possibility of error.

4. Indicated lower limit of each step a multiple of the step interval. In the example, the indicated lower limits of the top three steps are 140, 135, and 130. The use of indicated limits that are integers makes for ease in tallying.

5. True lower limit (the "partition value") of each step .5 below the indicated lower limit. In the example, the true lower limits of the top three steps are 139.5, 134.5, and 129.5. The need for the use of the true lower limit may be noted by careful examination of any step. Consider, for example, the five values that may be tabulated in the top step: 140, 141, 142, 143, and 144. The midscore is 142, which must be considered to be one-half of a step interval, or 2.5 units, above the true lower limit. Accordingly, the true lower limit must be (142 − 2.5), or 139.5, which is .5 below the indicated lower limit.

6. Tally marks made in groups of five. Generally, up to four cases are indicated by vertical tallies, with the fifth case indicated by a crossline. Alternately, four tallies are formed into a square, which is crossed by the fifth tally. Such grouping facilitates counting.

Checking the Distribution. In making a distribution, N should be ascertained independently of the tallying operation. Then, $\Sigma f = N$. The tallying operation should also be checked separately. Dots may be placed at the ends of tallies to indicate the second tabulation.

Original Data. When original values are used as a means of ranking cases and of identifying step limits and percentiles, each case within a step is regarded as occupying an amount of scale distance exactly the same as that occupied by every other case within the same step.

For example, the single case in the top step, 140–144, is conceived as occupying 5 units of the original scale; each case in the second step from the top, 135–139, 2.5 units; each of the three cases in the third step, 1.667 units; each of the six cases in the fourth step, .833 unit, and so on.

In treating a series of scores as ordinal data, they are not added or multiplied. Scale values, however, provide reference points, and the distance between reference points is sometimes treated by subtraction or division, as illustrated in Example 4.2.

Cumulative Frequencies. Examples of cumulative frequencies, denoted as *Cf*, are shown in the last two columns of Table 4.1. In one column frequencies are cumulated upward from the bottom of the distribution, and in the other, from the top downward. A cumulative frequency is merely the sum of the frequencies from one end of the distribution through the step on which it appears.

In the case in which the frequencies are cumulated from the bottom of the distribution, the lowest *f* is 1. Accordingly, the lowest *Cf* is 1. The next *f* is 0; so, the second *Cf* is also 1. The third *f* is 2; so, the *Cf* is $1 + 2 = 3$. The fourth *f* is 4; so, the corresponding *Cf* is $3 + 4 = 7$. The process continues to the top of the distribution, where the final *Cf* is 200, which is *N*. This type of cumulation is useful in finding percentiles, as illustrated in Example 4.2.

In the last column of Table 4.1 the frequencies are cumulated downward, a procedure sometimes useful in treating interval scale data, as discussed in Chapter 5. The first *f* is 1 and the first *Cf* is, of course, the same. The next *f* is 2, yielding a *Cf* of $1 + 2$, or 3. The third *f* happens to be 3; so, the third *Cf* is $3 + 3$, or 6, and so on. Again, the final *Cf* is 200, or *N*.

The grouping of scores in categories or steps is a measure of considerable economy. It provides a means by which the general characteristics of the collection of scores can be assessed more or less at a glance. A frequency distribution provides a convenient means of recording observed data, greatly simplifies the computation of descriptive statistics, and is useful in preparing graphs and charts.

Two different assumptions are made in utilizing information from frequency distributions:

1. All scores within a given step interval are distributed evenly throughout that step; and
2. All scores within a given step are concentrated at the midpoint.

Obviously these two assumptions are inconsistent. The first, however, is followed in description by ranking, as in computing percentiles, while the second is used in description by summation, as will be discussed in the next chapter. In both cases, however, the true bottom of the step, or the "partition value" between it and the next lower step, is considered to be .5 below the lowest score that could be tabulated on that step.

CHOOSING A STEP INTERVAL

In organizing observations into a frequency distribution, the first step is to choose an appropriate interval. If there are too many steps in a frequency distribution and *N* is not large, the curve tends to be irregular. On the other hand, if the number of steps is few, computations become inaccurate and essential characteristics of the distribution may be obscured. As a convenient working rule, the number of step intervals in a distribution for most research purposes should be between 10 and 20.

A good working procedure for choosing an appropriate step interval follows. First of all, the range is computed by subtracting the lowest score from the highest score and increasing by 1. This gives the total number of different scores possible. Suppose, for example, the highest obtained score is 143 and the lowest is 52. Then $143 - 52 + 1 = 92$, which means that within the total range, 92 different scores are possible. We now divide 92 by 10, yielding 9.2, and also by 20, yielding 4.6. Accordingly, the step interval should be somewhere between 9.2 and 4.6 in order to have 10 to 20 steps. The most frequently used step intervals are 1, 2, 3, 4, 5, 10, and the higher multiples of 10. Here 5 would seem to be a satisfactory choice. In Example 4.1, the step interval of 5 actually yields 19 different steps.

Tallying scores in a frequency distribution is essentially the same as in using a nominal scale except that each category is defined by two numbers, the upper and lower partition values, instead of by a verbal description. After all tallies have been made, they are counted within steps or categories to find the f and, of course, $\Sigma f = N$.

COMPUTATION OF POINT MEASURES

FINDING A PERCENTILE

In computing descriptive statistics when scores are regarded as means of ranking individuals, point measures are fundamental. The basis for all these point measures is the percentile (sometimes called *centile*). As stated earlier, a percentile may be defined as that theoretical point in a distribution below which lies a stated percentage of the scores. Thus, the 37th percentile, or P_{37}, is a theoretical point (generally a fractional score that actually does not exist) below which it is assumed that 37 per cent of the distribution lies.

When percentiles are calculated from frequency distributions, the assumption stated earlier is always followed, namely, that within any step, all the scores are considered to be evenly distributed from the lower step limit or partition value to the upper step limit. That is to say, the "density" of scores at any distance representing one unit in raw score is thought to be the frequency for that step divided by the step interval. For example, in Table 4.1, the frequency (denoted under f) for the step 105–109 is 20. Five possible scores are represented in this step, namely, 105, 106, 107, 108, and 109. In making the frequency distribution, the number of cases for each of these five scores has been lost. It is unlikely that there were exactly four cases for each of the five different scores. One or more of the scores may not have been represented at all. However, in computing point measures, the 20 scores are regarded as distributed evenly over the five possible scores, that is, four cases for each score. The "scale distance" for each score in this particular category is .25. By this we mean that if all 200 scores were arranged in order from the lowest to the highest, and with all scores within a category spread out evenly throughout the step, each score in this category would occupy .25 of a scale unit. The same assumption holds when the number of cases in a given step is not a multiple of the step interval. For example, in the step 100–104, in which the frequency is 23, the 23 cases would be regarded as divided evenly among the five possible scores, namely, 4.6 cases for each unit of the scale, or a scale distance of .217 for each case.

In a somewhat similar fashion, the variable represented by the scores is regarded as continuous even though only integral scores are included in the original data. The step interval 100–104, for example, is thought of as a continuum from 99.500 to 104.499 +, the last figure to be interpreted as almost, but not quite, 104.5.

Under these assumptions, it is relatively easy to compute percentiles and, by means of percentiles, the other point measures.

The procedure for finding any desired percentile may now be considered. In the distribution in Table 4.1 there are 200 cases. An illustrative problem would be finding the theoretical point below which 37 percent of the cases fall, that is, P_{37}.

Multiplying 200 by .37 yields 74.00. This is the theoretical number of scores falling below the 37th percentile, or P_{37}.

It will be noted that the next to the last column in Table 4.1 is denoted as Cf entries in which are the frequencies cumulated up from the bottom of the distribution. This cumulative frequency is helpful in finding point measures when a number of them are to be found from the same distribution. A quick inspection shows that the 74th score lies somewhere in the category or step 90–94. The Cf column shows that there are 60 scores below this step, while 84 scores include all the scale up to the limit of 94.499 +. We can be sure, then, that P_{37} is at least 89.5, but not so large as 94.5. On the assumption that the 24 scores are equally distributed throughout the entire step, we can take as many as are necessary to round out the needed 74 cases and find the equivalent in score terms. Of course not all 24 cases are required. The desired number of cases, 74, minus the number of cases below the step, 60, yields 14, the number of cases required among the 24 within the step limits. Accordingly, the fraction of the total step interval that is to be added to the bottom of the step is 14/24. Hence it is necessary to add 14/24 of the step interval of 5 (that is, 2.92) to the bottom of the step 89.5 to obtain P_{37}, which in this example is 92.42.

All of the "point measures" used in statistics are based on percentiles. Essentially, percentiles are used to define and to locate points in the original system of measurement. These points, in turn, are used to describe central tendency and variability of the original measurements. Computation of these measures is shown in Example 4.2.

THE MEDIAN AS A MEASURE OF CENTRAL TENDENCY

When a group of numbers represents a series of observations, there is need to simplify the information so as better to understand it. If a single number can be chosen to represent the series, the information is simplified. The three most common measures of central tendency in psychological statistics are the mode, the median, and the mean.

The mode was mentioned in connection with nominal data, where it is simply the class of greatest frequency. Since the categories have no fixed order, it is not a measure of central tendency. However, with ordinal data, the mode reveals something about the location of the middle of the distribution, provided the distribution is reasonably symmetrical. For a distribution such as that in Example 4.2, we can define the modal class as the most popular category. The largest f, 170, is in the step 180–199. Accordingly, this is the category that can be regarded as the most typical in the series.

Several formulas exist for finding a single numerical value for the mode, but these need not require the attention of the student of elementary statistics. Perhaps the most important use of the mode is as a term describing frequency curves. A distribution with a single point of greatest frequency is *unimodal;* one with two points of greatest frequency is *bimodal,* and one with several such points is *multimodal.* Just as a mountain chain can have major and minor peaks, so it is sometimes convenient to describe a frequency distribution as having major and minor modes.

Probably the most useful of the measures of central tendency is the mean, but since its computation involves addition and division of observed values, consideration of its properties will be reserved to Chapter 5.

A measure of central tendency that cannot be computed for nominal information, but which becomes possible when observations can be identified numerically and arranged in order, is the *median*. The median is defined as the theoretical point that divides the distribution into two groups with equal frequencies. It is therefore definable as the 50th percentile, above which there are, theoretically, exactly 50 percent of the cases and below which are 50 percent of the cases. Its computation is shown in Example 4.2.

EXAMPLE 4.2

THE COMPUTATION OF PERCENTILES AND POINT MEASURES

Nature of Data. To compute percentiles, values are grouped in categories in a frequency distribution. No assumption is made that the units are actually equal, but it is assumed that the original values are adequate for purposes of ranking and designating the percentiles. In this example, scores of 874 high school seniors on a test of academic achievement have been distributed in 14 categories, using a step interval of 20. In all instances, the true lower step limit, or partition value, is .5 below the indicated limit.

Formula for Any Percentile. Steps by which any percentile may be computed are indicated in the formula:

$$P_j = \text{lower limit of step} + \frac{[pN - Cf(\text{below the step})]i}{f} \tag{4.2}$$

in which P_j is any percentile, pN is the desired proportion (percent divided by 100) multiplied by N, i is the number of units in the step interval, and f is the frequency of the step containing the percentile. The expression "Cf(below the step)" refers to the number of cases below the lower limit of the step containing the percentile.

Finding P_{25}. As an example, consider the operations incident to finding P_{25}, sometimes called the *first quartile:*

1. Find 25% of N. To do this, 874 is multiplied by .25 to obtain 218.5. This is the pN of Formula 4.2.
2. Determine, from the frequencies cumulated in Table 4.2 from the bottom of the distribution, the interval that contains P_{25}. The Cf of 327 of the step 160–179 is greater than 218.5; the Cf of the step below is 185, which is less than 218.5. It is therefore clear that the step 160–179 includes the 25th percentile. The lower limit of this step, or lower partition value, is 159.5.
3. From pN is subtracted the number of cases below the step; that is 185 (the Cf of the step below) is subtracted from 218.5, yielding 33.5.
4. This value, 33.5, is multiplied by the step interval i, which is 20, and divided by the step frequency, or f, which is 142. (In effect, 33.5 is divided by 142 to find .2359, as the needed proportion of the interval. Then .2359i = 4.72.)
5. This result, 4.72, is added to the "lower limit of step," 159.5, to find P_{25}, which is 164.22.

Numerical operations for five representative percentiles are shown under the distribution in Table 4.2. All percentiles, including the median, which is P_{50}, or the 50th percentile, are computed in exactly the same fashion.

Point Measures of Variability. Once the appropriate percentiles have been found, point measures of variability are readily determined. Q, the semi-interquartile range, is the usual point measure of variability and is $(P_{75} - P_{25})/2$. In this distribution, exactly half the cases (when all are arranged in order under the conventions of ordinal measurement) lie between the limits of 223.41 and 164.22. Half this distance would seem to be an appropriate measure of dispersion or scatter.

Another measure of dispersion is D, a modified range that is merely $(P_{90} - P_{10})$, and in this case is 111.3.

Checking a Percentile. Any percentile may be checked by working from the top of the distribution. Four changes are necessary, but since the procedure is

TABLE 4.2. COMPUTATION OF PERCENTILES

(The data are the scores of 874 high school seniors on a test of academic achievement.)

STEPS	f	Cf^a	
320–339	1	874	
300–319	5	873	
280–299	14	868	
260–279	40	854	
240–259	70	814	(Step includes 90th percentile)
220–239	110	744	(Step includes 75th percentile)
200–219	137	634	
180–199	170	497	(Step includes 50th percentile)
160–179	142	327	(Step includes 25th percentile)
140–159	102	185	(Step includes 10th percentile)
120–139	64	83	
100–119	12	19	
80–99	6	7	
60–79	1	1	

Computations

$$90\% \text{ of } 874 = 786.6 \qquad P_{90} = 239.5 + \frac{(786.6 - 744)20}{70} = 251.67$$

$$75\% \text{ of } 874 = 655.5 \qquad P_{75} = 219.5 + \frac{(655.5 - 634)20}{110} = 223.41$$

$$50\% \text{ of } 874 = 437 \qquad P_{50} = 179.5 + \frac{(437 - 327)20}{170} = 192.44$$

$$25\% \text{ of } 874 = 218.5 \qquad P_{25} = 159.5 + \frac{(218.5 - 185)20}{142} = 164.22$$

$$10\% \text{ of } 874 = 87.4 \qquad P_{10} = 139.5 + \frac{(87.4 - 83)20}{102} = 140.36$$

$$\text{Median} = P_{50} = 192.4$$

$$Q = \frac{P_{75} - P_{25}}{2} = \frac{223.41 - 164.22}{2} = 29.6$$

$$D = P_{90} - P_{10} = 251.67 - 140.36 = 111.3$$

---

^{a} Cumulated up.

exactly analogous, the changes are merely those incident to working from a different direction. The logic is identical.

Instead of the "lower limit of step," the "upper limit" is used. Instead of pN, we use $(1 - p)N$; and instead of "Cf(below the step)," we use the number cases above the step. Instead of adding to the "lower limit of the step," we subtract from the upper limit. These operations are summarized as Formula 4.2a under the distribution in Table 4.3.

By this procedure, P_{25} is found as follows:

$$(1 - p)N = (.75 \times 874) = 655.5$$

Counting down from the top of the distribution, the step interval containing the desired percentile is found. Again it is the step 160–179, the upper limit of which is 179.5. Above this step are 547 cases. Thus $(655.5 - 547)$ times 20 and divided by the f for the step, 142, is 15.28. When 15.28 is subtracted from the upper step limit, 179.5, the result is 164.22, which is P_{25} found by the usual method.

TABLE 4.3. CHECKING A PERCENTILE

STEPS	f	Cf^a	
320–339	1	1	
300–319	5	6	
280–299	14	20	
260–279	40	60	
240–259	70	130	
220–239	110	240	
200–219	137	377	
180–199	170	547	
160–179	142	689	(Step includes P_{25})
140–159	102	791	
120–139	64	855	
100–119	12	867	
80–99	6	873	
60–79	1	874	

Computation

$$P_j = \text{upper limit of step} - \frac{[(1 - p)N - Cf\,(\text{above the step})]i}{f} \tag{4.2a}$$

$$P_{25} = 179.5 - \frac{[(.75)874 - 547]20}{142} = 179.5 - \frac{(655.5 - 547)20}{142} = 164.22$$

^{a} Cumulated down.

POINT MEASURES OF VARIABILITY: THE RANGE, D AND Q

Of a series of values representing psychological data, a second way in which to simplify the information is to report a measure of their variability, or spread, or scatter. If all values tend to be more or less identical with the measure of central tendency, then there is little variability. Such is the case with certain structural characteristics, such as the number of fingers. A few individuals have fewer than 10 fingers because of prenatal or postnatal accidents, and a few have polydactylism, a condition with more than 10 fingers. However, the human race as a whole shows remarkably little variability in the number of fingers.

There is more variability in other structural characteristics such as height (in which some adults are twice as tall as other adults) and in weight, where the ratio of extremes is greater than with height. In psychological traits such as intelligence, there is no way of comparing variability on any absolute basis, but from observing the low-grade feeble-minded on the one hand, and highly intelligent, creative individuals on the other, one would estimate that the variability of the human race in this respect is very great.

With a series of measurement, a measure of variability along with a measure of central tendency can be used better to describe or summarize the series. On the same measuring device, two groups may be equal in central tendency, but very different in variability, or vice versa.

Three measures of variability that can be computed with ordinal data are often useful. The first is the range, mentioned in connection with establishing the step interval for a frequency distribution. The second is D, a modified range, and the third is Q, the semi-interquartile range.

The range, as the highest value in the series less the lowest value (plus 1 if the total number of different possible values is wanted), give the maximum variability in the particular sample. Because the two extreme values are often determined by single scores, and because what scores happen to be the highest and lowest are greatly affected by the composition of the particular sample, the range is likely to vary considerably from sample to sample. Since successive samples tend to yield inconsistent values, the range is used only as a crude measure of variability or as a help in planning the computation of more reliable descriptive statistics.

The statistic D was proposed by Kelley (1) as a modified range to describe the variability of a group of values. It is defined as the 90th percentile less the 10th percentile $(P_{90} - P_{10})$. Since P_{90} and P_{10} are measures that are more stable than are the two extremes of the distribution, D is more consistent from sample to sample than is the total range. Although D is an easily defended descriptive statistic, it is seldom used, chiefly because the total range is more useful for the practical purpose of planning a frequency distribution and Q seems to convey more information about the variability of the sample.

The semi-interquartile range Q is defined as half the distance between the third and first quartiles, that is,

$$Q = \frac{P_{75} - P_{25}}{2} \tag{4.3}$$

One quarter of all the cases in the distribution are above P_{75}, with another quarter below P_{25}. Accordingly, if the distribution is symmetrical, the scale distance of $1.00Q$ above the median and $1.00Q$ below it will include 50 percent of the cases. If the cases are bunched close to the median, it is obvious that Q will be small, whereas if the cases scatter away from the median, Q will be large. Computation of Q, as does the computation of the median, the range, and D, requires original scale values, such as the raw scores on a psychological test, as reference points. From them the numerical values of the point measures are obtained.

In describing several samples of subjects measured on the same variable, medians can be used to rank the groups as to which stands highest, which next highest, and so on, while Q can be used to compare the variability of the groups. Groups that are alike in central tendency may still differ in variability, and vice versa. Furthermore, as will be discussed in Chapter 13, measures of variability are essential in evaluating obtained differences in measures of central tendency, although Q itself is seldom used for this purpose.

The point measures provide a convenient method of reducing obtained scores on psychological tests to a form facilitating comparison from individual to individual on the same test and from test to test for the same individual.

Sometimes tables of scores equivalents at selected percentile points, as in the following table, are given. Data represent the scores of 998 male engineering freshmen at the University of Minnesota Institute of Technology on the Minnesota paper form board test (3).

PERCENTILE	SCORE
99	62
95	59
90	57
80	55
75	54
70	53
60	50
50	49
40	47
30	46
25	44
20	43
10	39
5	36
1	30

Score equivalents have been rounded, so that no fractions are reported. By means of a table of this sort, obtained scores are quickly interpreted for guidance and other purposes. For example, a young man with a score of 52 on the test has a score as good or better than two-thirds of freshman engineers in the norm group.

PERCENTILE RANKS

Another method of norming tests is to provide for each possible score its percentile equivalent, or percentile rank, as demonstrated in Example 4.3.

EXAMPLE 4.3

THE CALCULATION OF PERCENTILE RANKS

The usual formula for a percentile rank computed from a frequency distribution is

$$\text{Percentile rank} = \frac{[Cf(\text{below the step}) + .5f]100}{N} \tag{4.4}$$

in which f is the step frequency and 100 is the multiplying factor to remove the decimals. This gives the percentile rank of the score at the midpoint of the step, which is often assigned to all the scores in the step. For more exact work, a step interval of 1 can be used.

An equivalent formula is

$$\text{Percentile rank} = \frac{(Cf - .5f)100}{N} \tag{4.4a}$$

in which Cf is the cumulative frequency of the step, the cumulations being made from the bottom of the distribution.

Computation. Two methods of calculating the percentile ranks, both with a step interval of 1, are illustrated. The first is for computations by hand. The second method was developed by Thurstone and permits fast computation when a calculating machine is available.

For the hand method, the frequencies in column 2 of Table 4.4 are cumulated from the bottom of the distribution to form the Cf in column 3. Next, in each step, one-half of the frequency is subtracted from the Cf to form the $(Cf - .5f)$, which are in column 4. These figures are divided by N and multiplied by 100 to form the percentile ranks in column 5.

Machine Computation. In a method described by Thurstone (5), half of the reciprocal of N is determined. In this case, N is 179 and $1/2N$ is .002793. Since there are six places of decimals in the half-reciprocal, and it is desired to multiply by 100 to remove decimals in the part retained, four places of decimals are marked off in the product dials of the calculating machine. The half-reciprocal (or rate) is multiplied by each frequency twice, but since only the percentile ranks at the mid-points are desired, the result of the second multiplication at each step is disregarded. The multiplications begin at the bottom of the distribution, and both products and multipliers are allowed to accumulate. The first multiplication of .002793 by 4 gives the rounded percentile rank of 1. The second multiplication by 4 is disregarded. The next multiplication also happens to be by 4, the frequency of the second step. As a rounded percentile, it is recorded as 3, the percentile rank of the midpoint of the second step. The process continues, alternately recording and discarding the cumulated results of the multiplications. When the two multiplications by the frequency of the top step have been completed, the accumulated sum of the multipliers should be $2N$, or 358, and the accumulated sum of the products should be 100.

In comparing the standing of the same individual on several tests, the percentile ranks can be compared to determine the areas in which he is strong and the areas in which he is weak. An entering freshman with a percentile rank of 90 on a verbal intelligence test might be an excellent risk for a liberal arts course, but with percentile ranks of 20 or so in numerical ability, spatial relations, and mechanical comprehension, he would be a poor risk in engineering.

TABLE 4.4. CALCULATION OF PERCENTILE RANKS

(The data represents the scores of 179 students on an achievement test.)

(1) SCORE	(2) f	(3) Cf	(4) $Cf - .5f$	(5) PERCENTILE RANK
83	1	179	178.5	100
82	1	178	177.5	99
81	2	177	176	98
80	1	175	174.5	97
79	1	174	173.5	97
78	6	173	170	95
77	2	167	166	93
76	7	165	161.5	90
75	3	158	156.5	87
74	9	155	150.5	84
73	4	146	144	80
72	6	142	139	78
71	6	136	133	74
70	16	130	122	68
69	8	114	110	61
68	16	106	98	55
67	18	90	81	45
66	22	72	61	34
65	18	50	41	23
64	15	32	24.5	14
63	9	17	12.5	7
62	4	8	6	3
61	4	4	2	1

$N = 179$; $1/N = .005587$; $1/2N = .002793$.

In interpreting percentiles and percentile ranks, it will be noted that a difference of, say, ten percentile points near the middle of the distribution will involve fewer raw score points than a difference of the same number of percentile points at the top or bottom of the distribution. In the table of norms for the Minnesota paper form board test, it is seen that the difference between P_{60} and P_{50} is one raw-score point and between P_{30} and P_{20} it is three raw-score points, while the difference between P_{10} and P_1 is nine raw-score points.

This results from the fact that with most psychological measures, scores tend to pile up near the center of the distribution and to become rarer as the scores deviate from the median.

DISTRIBUTION OF A SET OF PERCENTILE RANKS

In contrast with obtained scores, a distribution of percentile ranks (if based on an exceedingly large number of different raw scores) yields a "rectilinear" or flat distribution. This can be readily understood from the concept of deciles, which are sometimes used for norming tests when there is not much varability in raw scores.

To convert scores into deciles, the following percentiles are computed: P_{90}, P_{80}, P_{70}, P_{60}, P_{50}, P_{40}, P_{30}, P_{20} and P_{10}. Then the group with raw scores above P_{90} are in the 10th decile group, the group with scores between P_{80} and P_{90} are in the 9th decile group, and so on to the group with scores below P_{10}, which are in the 1st decile group. It will be readily seen that, in theory at least, equal numbers (that is, 10 percent of N) will be assigned to each decile group. Thus, with identical f in each of the ten categories, the distribution of decile scores will be flat or "rectilinear." The same basic principle applies to percentile ranks, which are finer subdivisions than are decile groups. Accordingly, a distribution of percentile ranks is theoretically a flat or rectilinear distribution. In practice, however, it can be truly rectilinear only when both N and the range are large. The principle, however, must be kept in mind when percentiles or percentile ranks are used in interpretations of psychological test scores.

RANK CORRELATION

SPEARMAN'S ρ

Just as the contingency coefficient is a means of describing association between two nominal variables, so rank correlation is a method for describing how two ordinal variables tend to vary together. There are two important methods for rank correlation, Spearman's rho (the symbol[1] for which is ρ) and Kendall's tau (the symbol for which is τ).

The computation of ρ, which varies from -1.00 through .00 to $+1.00$, is illustrated in Examples 4.4 and 4.5. If $\rho = -1.00$, the highest rank in one variable is associated with the lowest rank in the second variable, the next highest rank in the first variable is associated with the next to the lowest rank in the second variable, and so on. This would be perfect inverse relationship: the higher the standing in one variable, the lower in the other.

---

[1] In order to follow the convention of Roman letters for descriptive statistics, Greek letters for parameters, some authors have discarded ρ as the symbol for rank correlation in the sample. However, many psychologists continue to follow Spearman's original usage of ρ and to use τ for Kendall's coefficient.

EXAMPLE 4.4

COMPUTATION OF SPEARMAN'S ρ TO MEASURE RANK CORRELATION

INDIVIDUAL	RANK IN X	SCORE IN Y	RANK IN Y	D	D^2
A	1	25	3	2	4
B	2	30	1.5	.5	.25
C	3	30	1.5	1.5	2.25
D	4	15	5	1	1
E	5	15	5	0	0
F	6	15	5	1	1
G	7	10	7	0	0

$$\Sigma D^2 = 8.50$$

To compute ρ, paired observations must be expressed in ranks. In these hypothetical data, variable X consists of ranks; variable Y is in score form, but is converted to ranks. Any scores that are tied are assigned the midrank, that is, the different ranks required for the ties are summed and divided by their number. Thus, the two values of 30 are tied for first place. The corresponding ranks, 1 and 2, are summed and divided by 2, yielding a rank of 1.5 each. The next score is 25, with a rank of 3. Then three scores, all with a value of 15, are tied. The corresponding ranks are 4, 5, and 6, which when summed and divided by 3 yield a midrank of 5. The final rank is 7.

Strictly speaking, ρ does not apply when there are ties, but the midrank method is generally accepted for treating ties. Rank correlation is often used in psychology and education when there are only a few cases and a general idea of the relationship is wanted.

In the column headed D appears the difference between the rank in X and the rank in Y without regard to sign. These differences are squared and entered in the column headed D^2.

In rank correlation it is often necessary to square numbers ending in .5. A simple rule, which can be verified algebraically by expanding $(X + .5)^2$, is to multiply the number, X, by $(X + 1)$ and add .25. Thus, $(1.5)^2$ is 2.25; $(2.5)^2$ is 6.25; and $(8.5)^2$ is 72.25.

The sum of the D^2 is 8.50. The computation of ρ follows:

$$\rho = 1 - \frac{6\Sigma D^2}{N(N^2 - 1)} = 1 - \frac{6 \times 8.5}{7 \times 48} = 1 - \frac{8.5}{56} = 1 - .15 = .85$$

This shows a substantial relationship between the two variables. However, since ρ is based on only seven cases, it may not truly represent the relationship in the population from which the sample has been drawn. The evaluation of obtained ρ in terms of what is to be expected in a series of samples is reserved to a later chapter.

EXAMPLE 4.5

CORRELATION BETWEEN TWO SETS OF RANKS

CATEGORY	RANK IN FATHERS' REPORTS	RANK IN MOTHERS' REPORTS	D	D^2
Companionship	1	2	1	1
Personality characteristics	2	1	1	1
Intellectual abilities	3	3	0	0
Fact of having	4	13	9	81
Child rearer	5	5	0	0
Endearing mannerisms	6	15	9	81
Relatives' relations with child	7	10	3	9
Motor ability, coordination	8	12	4	16
Growth, developmental progress	9.5	14	4.5	20.25
Artistic abilities, interest	9.5	11	1.5	2.25
Relationships with siblings	11	9	2	4
Social relationships	12	4	8	64
School progress	13.5	6	7.5	56.25
Routines	13.5	7	6.5	42.25
Interests, hobbies	15	8	7	49

$$N = 15. \qquad \Sigma D^2 = 427$$

$$\rho = 1 - \frac{6\Sigma D^2}{N(N^2 - 1)} = 1 - \frac{6 \times 427}{15 \times 14 \times 16} = 1 - \frac{61}{80} = 1 - .76 = .24$$

A comparison of the order in which categories of "satisfactions" in child rearing are ranked in fathers' and mothers' reports is made in the preceding table by means of Spearman's ρ. Data are modified from Tasch (4). Categories are taken from a list of 35, but only categories rated in the top ten by fathers or mothers are included. Ranks are based on reports of 544 mothers and 85 fathers. The coefficient of .24 reflects a low, positive relationship between fathers' and mothers' reported satisfactions in child rearing.

Perfect positive relationship, in which the two sets of ranks are identical, results in a ρ of +1.00. If there is no association between the two variables, so that the rank in one gives no indication of the rank in the other, ρ is .00.

The formula for ρ is

$$\rho = 1 - \frac{6\Sigma D^2}{N(N^2 - 1)} \qquad (4.5)$$

in which N is the number of ranked cases and ΣD^2 is the sum of the squares of the differences in ranks.

KENDALL'S τ (TAU)

A second coefficient used to describe the relationship between two sets of ranks is τ (tau), proposed by Kendall (2). As does ρ, τ varies from -1.00, indicating perfect inverse relationship, through .00, indicating no relationship, to $+1.00$, indicating perfect relationship. At intermediate points, the correspondence between the two coefficients is only fair, with τ being smaller in absolute magnitude. The computation of τ (for an instance without ties) is shown in Example 4.6.

EXAMPLE 4.6

COMPUTATION OF KENDALL'S τ

When there are no ties, Kendall's τ can be found as follows:

1. One variable (in this case X) is arranged in order from 1 through N. Each rank in X continues, of course, to be associated with the corresponding rank in Y.

2. For each rank in Y (denoted as Y_i), the number of ranks is found that are below it in the same column and that are numerically greater than Y_i. This gives the number of pair-to-pair comparisons involving Y_i, which constitute agreements. In the example, these numbers are tabulated as "pair-to-pair agreements." The sum of them is then used in Formula 4.6.

It is to be noted that only ranks greater than Y_i and below Y_i in the same column are counted. This ensures that each pair of paired ranks is examined only once. If ranks greater than Y_i and above Y_i were counted, the result would be the number of disagreements, which still could be used to find τ but which would require a different formula.

Procedures involving tied ranks are given by Kendall (2).

The computation of τ for a case without ties follows:

CASE OR INDIVIDUALS	RANK IN X	RANK IN Y	NUMBER OF PAIR-TO-PAIR AGREEMENTS
A	1	3	9
B	2	1	10
C	3	2	9
D	4	5	7
E	5	4	7
F	6	7	5
G	7	6	5
H	8	12	0
I	9	9	2
J	10	8	2
K	11	10	1
L	12	11	0
			——
			57

The number of pair-to-pair agreements is 57, which is substituted in Formula 4.6. Then

$$\tau = \frac{4 \text{ (number of pair-to-pair agreements)}}{N(N-1)} - 1$$

$$= \frac{4 \times 57}{12 \times 11} - 1 = 1.73 - 1.00 = .73$$

The result indicates considerable agreement between the two variables. For the same data, $\rho = .89$.

Spearman's ρ has two advantages over τ. In the first place, it belongs to the family of product-moment coefficients described in Chapters 6, 7, 8, and 9; and, in fact, if there are no ties, ρ is precisely the product-moment correlation between the two sets of ranks. In the second place, ties are easier to handle with ρ than with τ, even though no theoretically perfect solution for tied ranks exists.

With τ, however, the solution for tied ranks is more satisfactory in that it is in accordance with the theory of the coefficient. Another advantage of τ is that its sampling distribution[2] is well understood, even when there are ties in ranks, and hence it is more useful in making inferences about the population from a knowledge of a sample.

The logic of τ is readily understood. Consider the case of any two pairs of paired ranks in which the two values of variable X are two different numbers of the series 1 through N, inclusive, and the two values of Y are also two numbers from the same series. Then, in the two pairs, the order is the same (agreement) or different (disagreement), as illustrated in the following table:

PAIR-TO-PAIR AGREEMENT		PAIR-TO-PAIR DISAGREEMENT	
RANK IN X	RANK IN Y	RANK IN X	RANK IN Y
2	3	2	5
5	4	5	4

With N the number of ranks in each variable, the total number of pair-to-pair comparisons is the number of combinations of N things taken two at a time, or $N(N-1)/2$. If all pair-to-pair comparisons represent agreements, then the relationship should be represented as $+1.00$; if all pair-to-pair comparisons are disagreements, then the relationship should be represented as -1.00. If agreements and disagreements are equally divided, then the relationships should be represented as .00. Kendall's τ is a coefficient designed to measure the relationship between two sets of ranks by

---

[2] If a descriptive statistic were computed in each one of an indefinitely long series of equivalent samples, drawn at random from the same unlimited population, the result would be a "sampling distribution." Certain characteristics of sampling distributions are treated in Chapter 13.

a ratio that meets these conditions. It is simply the number of pair-to-pair agreements less the number of pair-to-pair disagreements, with the result divided by the total number of pair-to-pair comparisons. Since numbers of agreements and disagreements add to $N(N-1)/2$, τ can be found from either. A convenient formula uses only the number of agreements:

$$\tau = \frac{4 \text{ (number of pair-to-pair agreements)}}{N(N-1)} - 1 \qquad (4.6)$$

SUMMARY

When description is by ranking rather than by assignment to defined categories, a second system of statistics becomes possible. All the statistics applicable to nominal data can be used with ordinal information, plus the descriptive statistics based on percentiles. Central tendency is measured by the median, and variability by the range and by Q. Although numerical values for these statistics are in terms of obtained values, the measuring instrument is thought of as essentially a device for ranking the observations.

Percentiles and percentile ranks are convenient means of norming tests, so that standing of the same individual on different tests or of different individuals on the same test can be easily compared.

Spearman's ρ and Kendall's τ are descriptive statistics for showing the relationship between two sets of ranks.

Rank correlation requires only ranks, and hence it can be used with ordinal measurement. Values from more advanced types of measurement can, of course, be converted into ranks and rank correlation can be applied.

Rank correlation is a convenient descriptive statistic when N is small, and a quickly obtained measure of relationship is needed as an aid in planning further investigation.

Rank correlation is also a good introduction to other measures of correlation to be discussed in later chapters.

EXERCISES

1. The following represent scores on a reading comprehension test:

34, 34, 33, 32, 32, 31, 31, 31, 31, 30, 30, 30, 30, 29,
29, 29, 29, 29, 28, 28, 28, 28, 28, 28, 27, 27, 27, 27,
27, 27, 26, 26, 26, 26, 26, 26, 26, 26, 25, 25, 25, 25,
25, 25, 25, 25, 25, 25, 24, 24, 24, 24, 24, 24, 24, 24,
24, 24, 24, 24, 23, 23, 23, 23, 23, 23, 23, 23, 23, 23,
22, 22, 22, 22, 22, 22, 22, 21, 21, 21, 21, 21, 21, 21,
21, 20, 20, 20, 20, 19, 18, 18, 18, 18, 18, 18, 17, 17,
17, 17, 16, 14, 14, 14, 13, 13, 13, 13, 12, 12, 12, 11,
11, 11, 10, 9, 9, 9, 9, 8, 7, 7, 6, 5, 5.

Make a distribution of these scores, using a step interval of 2. Find the median, D, and Q.

2. Using a step interval of 1 and the data of Exercise 1, prepare a table of percentile ranks.

3. Given the following distribution, find P_{45}, the median, and Q.

STEPS	f
42–44	1
39–41	2
36–38	4
33–35	7
30–32	10
27–29	9
24–26	4
21–23	5
18–20	4
15–17	3
12–14	1

4. For the following distribution, find percentile ranks corresponding to raw scores.

X	f	X	f
103	3	87	72
102	5	86	68
101	8	85	58
100	10	84	50
99	15	83	43
98	25	82	43
97	23	81	33
96	30	80	20
95	36	79	15
94	49	78	17
93	58	77	18
92	77	76	10
91	95	75	8
90	132	74	7
89	129	73	5
88	85	72	3

5. For the following distribution of scores, prepare a table of percentile norms. To do this, compute the following percentiles: P_{99}, P_{95}, P_{90}, P_{80}, P_{75}, P_{70}, P_{60}, P_{50}, P_{40}, P_{30}, P_{25}, P_{10}, P_5, and P_1. Round each percentile to the nearest integral score.

STEP LIMITS	f
170–179	1
160–169	0
150–159	3
140–149	11
130–139	19
120–129	24
110–119	38
100–109	49
90–99	66
80–89	86
70–79	90
60–69	52
50–59	27
40–49	18
30–39	10
20–29	4
10–19	2

6. In three sections of high school mathematics taught by different instructors, distributions of final grades were as follows:

GRADE	SECTION I	SECTION II	SECTION III
A	5	10	0
B	14	12	18
C	8	10	10
D	8	0	7
F	2	0	5
TOTALS	37	32	40

The principal, who was taking a course in statistics, decided to compute the median for each section by assigning numerical values as follows: A = 4; B = 3; C = 2; D = 1; and F = 0. He considered the step interval to be 1. As the partition value between A and B, he used 3.5. He used 2.5 as the partition value between B and C, 1.5 as the partitition value between C and D, and .5 as the partition value between D and F. He reported the medians at a teachers' meeting, correct to two places of decimals. What were his results?

7. In two practice heats, a squad of cross-country runners finished as follows:

NAME	1ST HEAT	2ND HEAT
Jack	1	1
Roger	2	7
Lon	3	3
Sid	4	5
Bob	5	2
Doug	6	11
Chuck	7	8
Jud	8	6
Frank	9	9
Stu	10	4
John	11	10
Paul	12	13
Stan	13	12
Glenn	14	14

Find ρ and τ.

8. For the following data on two variables, compute ρ:

INDIVIDUAL	VARIABLE I	VARIABLE II
A	35	6
B	25	12
C	45	7
D	45	9
E	20	15
F	35	12
G	35	8
H	30	11
I	50	8
J	40	10

REFERENCES

1. KELLEY, TRUMAN LEE, *Statistical Method*. New York: The Macmillan Company, 1923. xi + 390.
2. KENDALL, MAURICE G., *Rank Correlation Methods*, Second Edition. London: Charles Griffin, 1955. viii + 196.
3. LIKERT, R., AND QUASHA, W. H., *The Revised Minnesota Paper Form Board Test*. New York: The Psychological Corporation, 1948.
4. TASCH, RUTH J., "Interpersonal perceptions of fathers and mothers," *J. Genet. Psychol.*, 1955, **87**, 59–65.
5. THURSTONE, L. L., "Note on the calculation of percentile ranks," *J. Educ. Psychol.*, 1927, **18**, 617–620.

DESCRIPTION
BY AVERAGING

5

Test scores, errors made by a rat in learning a maze, ages of children—in fact, most of the varieties of numerical information of interest in psychology and education—are commonly summarized by averaging. An average, which takes into account the actual values of all the numbers in a series, is generally a highly representative and dependable summarization. This chapter is concerned with three averages:

1. The arithmetic mean, used as a measure of the central tendency, or the "center of gravity";
2. The variance, which is the mean of the squares of the differences between a set of values and their arithmetic mean; and
3. The standard deviation, the most useful of the direct measures of variability. It is the positive square root of the variance.

INTERVAL SCALES AND RATIO SCALES

If the mean, the variance, and the standard deviation are to be appropriate statistics, the variable must have values such that addition is a meaningful operation. The chief requirement is that the characteristic be measured along a scale, the units of which can be considered equal. This is clearly the case with months of chronological age, even though months do differ as much as 10.7 percent in length. Since the different parts of a maze may usually be considered to be equally difficult, errors in a maze are also taken as additive. Whether a set of psychological or educational test scores (generally the number of items successfully completed, or the number of correct items less a proportion of the items answered incorrectly) can meaningfully be added is less easily decided. In some cases attempts are made to develop tests so that two conditions are met:

1. All the items measure slightly different aspects of the same general trait or quality; and
2. Equal score differences at different positions in the range represent equal differences in ability.

While the second objective is seldom, if ever, attained, addition is a convenient tool in summarizing scores on educational and psychological tests. Accordingly, such tests are customarily treated as if they constituted interval scales, in which measurement is in units that are equal but which lack a true zero point.

In physics, the Fahrenheit and centigrade thermometers constitute interval scales. In neither case, however, does zero represent absence of heat, since 0° is an arbitrary reference point. Accordingly, one cannot say that a day on which the temperature is 90° F is twice as hot as one on which the temperature is 45° F. However, as in the case with all interval scales, degrees of temperature are additive. If on three separate occasions the temperature is observed to be 68°, 75°, and 70°, it is permissible to add the three readings, to divide by 3, and to take the mean, 71°, as representative of the three separate figures.

REQUIREMENT OF A TRUE ZERO FOR A RATIO SCALE

A ratio scale meets an additional requirement. It has a true zero point, representing complete absence of the characteristic. Physical measurements of time, distance, and weight are on ratio scales, so-called because ratios and percentages are meaningful. Measurements of weight can reveal whether one boy is twice as heavy as another; but, since measures of intelligence, reading comprehension, and the like are not on ratio scales, there is no way of knowing that one person is twice as intelligent as another or has twice as much reading comprehension. This is because measurements on psychological and educational tests have no true zero point. To illustrate, a student might take an examination in mathematics far beyond his training. If no questions are answered correctly, his obtained score would be zero. However, such a score would not necessarily indicate complete ignorance of mathematics. Rather it might mean that the items are too difficult for him and he is unmeasured.

Measuring devices in psychology and the social sciences certainly yield ranks along defined dimensions and thus are at least ordinal scales. In most cases they appear also to qualify reasonably well as interval scales, permitting summarization through addition. This is fortunate, since addition is a versatile basis for descriptive and inferential statistics.

THE ARITHMETIC MEAN AND ITS PROPERTIES

The arithmetic mean, found by adding all the values in a series and dividing by the number of cases, is perhaps the only important statistic that is universally familiar. In statistical notation the formula is

$$\overline{X} = M_x = \frac{\Sigma X}{N} \tag{5.1}$$

or, with better identification of the summing operation,

$$\overline{X} = M_x = \frac{1}{N} \sum_{i=1}^{N} X_i \tag{5.1a}$$

This formula, which requires no derivation, defines the mean by indicating the operations that are performed in order to arrive at it. The variable, denoted as X, is summed over all N cases. The sum is divided by N, considered a constant because it does not vary within a sample. The quotient is the mean. This formula describes precisely the way the mean is found from observed values or "raw scores." A computing formula, for the specific purpose of finding the mean from a frequency distribution, is given in connection with Example 5.3.

EXAMPLE 5.1

M_x, V_x, AND s_x FROM ORIGINAL VALUES OF X

With an N of any size, it is always appropriate to find the mean, the variance, and the standard deviation by using original values and their squares. Appropriate procedures, discussed in the text, are summarized as Formulas 5.1, 5.3a, 5.3b, 5.6, 5.8, and 5.8a.

Because of greater accuracy and ease of computation, raw score techniques are preferable with small N to methods involving coding within a frequency distribution, as described in Examples 5.3 and 5.4.

When N is large, there is little difference in precision between raw score and frequency distribution methods. Original values and their squares can be handled with speed and accuracy on desk calculators, the one disadvantage being that a frequency distribution is not available for visual inspection. Punch card machines and electronic computers generally use raw-score methods in processing large masses of data. If desired, frequency distributions can sometimes be made more or less automatically as by-products of the computations.

With computing machinery, individual squares are seldom recorded. With a desk calculator, each X is entered in the keyboard and multiplied by itself. The accumulation of multipliers is ΣX; and of products, ΣX^2. Some machine routines find ΣX^2 through special summation techniques that do not involve individual values of X^2. In the numerical example the X^2 values are written out only to clarify the general method.

The scores in the table represent the number of errors made on an objective test in psychological statistics.

INDIVIDUAL	X	X^2	INDIVIDUAL	X	X^2
A.A.	29	841	P.J.E.	25	625
G.J.B.	16	256	B.R.S.	21	441
C.B.	31	961	S.L.K.	40	1600
A.T.B.	37	1369	E.N.P.	25	625
J.E.B.	35	1225	J.A.P.	51	2601
R.P.C.	17	289	I.G.S.	15	225
V.L.C.	34	1156	T.D.S.	39	1521
C.S.C.	28	784	J.S.T.	28	784
R.A.C.	22	484	W.L.W.	33	1089
R.C.C.	12	144	J.A.Z.	36	1296
O.J.E.	21	441			

$$N=21 \qquad \Sigma X = 595 \qquad \Sigma X^2 = 18757$$

By Formula 5.1,

$$M_x = \frac{\Sigma X}{N} = \frac{595}{21} = 28.33$$

By Formula 5.3a,

$$V_x = \frac{\Sigma X^2}{N} - M^2 = \frac{18,757}{21} - (28.33)^2 = 893.19 - 802.59 = 90.60$$

By Formula 5.3b,

$$V_x = \frac{N\Sigma X^2 - (\Sigma X)^2}{N^2} = \frac{(21 \times 18,757) - (595)^2}{(21)^2}$$

$$= \frac{39,872}{441} = 90.42$$

By Formula 5.6,

$$s_x = \sqrt{V_x} = \sqrt{90.42} = 9.51$$

The variance as computed by Formula 5.3a differs slightly from that computed by its exact algebraic equivalent, Formula 5.3b. In using Formula 5.3a, the mean has been rounded to two places of decimals and then squared. As computed, the square of the mean is 802.59 instead of the correct figure of 802.77. If M^2 is taken as 802.77, results by the two formulas are identical.

The reason why Formula 5.3b gives somewhat better results is that rounding occurs only at the end. It is a good calculating principle to postpone division as long as possible.

Of course, as in generally true, the discrepancy in the results has no practical importance. Often, however, computing errors are easier to detect when intermediate rounding error is avoided.

The mean is a single number that in a general way represents a whole group of numbers. It can be regarded as a "measure of central tendency," similar in intent to the median discussed in Chapter 4. If there are a few values in the series that are so extreme that they would change the mean markedly, or if definite values for some of the cases at the ends of the distribution cannot be ascertained, the median is preferred to the mean as a statistic indicating the central point. In most instances, however, if it is permissible to add the scores, the mean is definitely preferable to the median.

The mean has the following characteristics:

1. Every value in the series for which a mean is computed affects it.

2. It is a unique point in a set of numbers, namely, the point around which the deviations[1] sum of zero. In all cases the sum of the positive deviations from the mean equals the sum of the negative deviations.

3. The mean is also the point around which the sum of the squares of the deviations is a minimum.

4. The mean is affected directly by any systematic arithmetical change in the variable. Thus, if all values in a variable are increased or decreased by a constant, the mean is increased or decreased by exactly that amount. Similarly, if all values are multiplied or divided by a constant, the mean is changed in precisely the same way. This principle is important in the conversion of variables to standard scores, as discussed later in this chapter.

DEVIATIONS FROM THE MEAN AS INDICATORS OF VARIABILITY

As implied in the preceding discussion, a deviation from M_x (denoted by x) is merely the original value (denoted by X) minus the mean of all the values in the series. Thus, by definition,

$$x = X - M_x \tag{5.2}$$

Provided knowledge of the mean is retained, a value in deviation form actually preserves all the information in the original score. By adding the mean to a deviation from the mean, the original value is restored.

Since most psychological and educational tests lack a true zero point, and since the obtained mean is determined by somewhat arbitrary factors such as the number and difficulty of the items that happen to compose the

---

[1] Any variable can be converted into a set of deviations from a constant by subtracting the constant from each of the values. The constant used as a reference point in forming deviations is generally the mean; consequently, unless otherwise specified, the term *deviation* refers to a deviation from the mean.

test, it appears that translation of all scores to a series with a predetermined mean could be useful. If an entire series of original scores were translated into deviations, the sum of the deviations (and hence their mean) would be zero. This is easily demonstrated by summing all the terms in Formula 5.2. While Formula 5.2 indicates only a single case, it applies generally to all values in the series. Conceptually, the process of summing involves adding together N of these equations, one for each case. The summing of variables is indicated by the summation sign (Σ). When a constant is summed (in this instance, M_x), the constant is added N times, which is the same as multiplying it by N. Substituting $\Sigma X/N$ for M_x and canceling N from the numerator and denominator of the fraction, it is seen that the sum of the deviations from the arithmetic mean is necessarily zero. In notation:

$$\Sigma x = \Sigma X - NM_x = \Sigma X - \frac{N\Sigma X}{N} = \Sigma X - \Sigma X = 0$$

The most important function of the deviations is in indicating the degree to which the values in a series of numbers tend to vary. It is apparent that if all the deviations are zero, all original values are exactly alike; that if the deviations tend to be small, then the original values vary little one from another; while if the deviations are large, there is considerable variability among the original values.

The magnitudes of the deviations, then, reflect the variability of the original values. Some method of summarizing these magnitudes is needed, but since the deviations necessarily sum to zero, their arithmetic mean is necessarily zero. In the early days of statistics the "average deviation," or "mean deviation," was computed by summing the deviations as though all were positive and then dividing by the number of cases. Involving an operation of questionable mathematical merit and not fitting into a generally accepted family of descriptive statistics, the "average deviation" or AD is seldom encountered in present-day research.

THE VARIANCE AND THE STANDARD DEVIATION

Two exceedingly useful statistics based on deviations are the variance and the standard deviation. The variance is the more important in theoretical studies, since it lends itself to analysis into component parts, while the standard deviation is useful in making scores from different sources comparable.

FORMULAS FOR THE VARIANCE

By definition, the variance is the mean of the squares of the deviations; that is,

$$V_x = \frac{\Sigma x^2}{N} \tag{5.3}$$

The formula[2] indicates that the variance, here denoted by ^3V_x, is found by squaring each deviation, summing these squares, and dividing by the number of cases. While Formula 5.3 defines the variance, it is awkward for actual computation because time is required to find the deviations and because deviations are usually decimal fractions. Accordingly, a procedure for finding the variance from the mean of the original values and the sum of their squares is preferable.

Squaring Formula 5.2, which defines any deviation x as equal to $(X - M_x)$, yields

$$x^2 = X^2 - 2M_xX + M_x^2 \qquad (5.4)$$

Summing all terms,

$$\Sigma x^2 = \Sigma X^2 - 2M_x\Sigma X + NM_x^2 \qquad (5.5)$$

(In the middle term on the right-hand side of Formula 5.4, 2 and M_x are constants and X is a variable. The sum of such terms is the sum of the variable multiplied by the constants, so that the sum of $2M_xX$ is $2M_x\Sigma X$.)

All terms of Formula 5.5 are now divided by N:

$$\frac{\Sigma x^2}{N} = \frac{\Sigma X^2}{N} - 2M_x\frac{\Sigma X}{N} + \frac{NM_x^2}{N}$$

Changing $\Sigma X/N$ to M_x and canceling N in the final term, we have

$$\frac{\Sigma x^2}{N} = \frac{\Sigma X^2}{N} - 2M_x^2 + M_x^2 = \frac{\Sigma X^2}{N} - M_x^2$$

Accordingly, from Formula 5.3,

$$V_x = \frac{\Sigma X^2}{N} - M_x^2 \qquad (5.3a)$$

An alternate formula, that may be obtained by substituting $\Sigma X/N$ for M_x and by putting all terms over N^2, is

$$V_x = \frac{N\Sigma X^2 - (\Sigma X)^2}{N^2} \qquad (5.3b)$$

---

[2] In Chapter 13 it will be noted that the variance is computed by dividing Σx^2 by $(N-1)$ instead of by N. This procedure yields an estimate of a parameter, namely, the variance in the population. The parameter standard deviation is estimated similarly, as $\sqrt{\Sigma x^2/(N-1)}$. This chapter is concerned with variances and standard deviations of samples, where division by N is appropriate.

[3] The symbol V seems to be convenient and acceptable for the variance, although not widely used. Mathematical statisticians sometimes use "Var." Other symbols often encountered are s^2 and σ^2, which reflect the fact that the variance is the square of the standard deviation, symbols for which are s (in the sample) and σ (the parameter or population value).

The variance is difficult to interpret directly. It is not in the units of the original scale, and its absolute size is markedly affected by scale changes involving multiplication or division. Generally, it is merely an intermediate statistic used in finding another statistic of more direct interest. Analysis of a variance is always in terms of a ratio of variances, so that it is not necessary for the absolute magnitudes of variances to have significance. In correlation, as described in subsequent chapters, the variance, as a proportion of another variance, is a central tool in understanding relationships among variables.

STANDARD DEVIATION AS AN AVERAGE

The standard deviation is a measure of variability that can be directly interpreted. It is applicable to all scales that are in addable units.

The standard deviation[4] can be defined as the positive square root of the variance; that is,

$$s_x = \sqrt{V_x} \tag{5.6}$$

The procedure of taking the square root of the variance acts to restore the original scale of measurement so that the standard deviation, like the mean, can be directly interpreted in terms of original units.

An alternate method of interpreting the standard deviation is to regard it as an average of the deviations from the arithmetic mean.

One of the averages known to mathematics is the quadratic mean, or root mean square. Obtaining the quadratic mean is a convenient method of finding a measure of central tendency of a series in which some numbers are positive and some are negative, and for which an average of the magnitudes without regard to sign is of interest. Even though the arithmetic mean of the deviations is necessarily zero, their quadratic mean is an appropriate average. Each deviation is squared and the sum of the squared deviations is divided by N. The square root of the quotient is then found. The result, by definition, is the standard deviation; that is,

$$s_x = \sqrt{\frac{\Sigma x^2}{N}} \tag{5.7}$$

Like the variance, the standard deviation is more readily computed from obtained values than from actual deviations. To obtain a raw-score formula, it is necessary only to take the square root of both sides of Formula

---

[4] In addition to s, symbols used for the standard deviation in the sample include SD, S, and σ, which was used routinely by early writers, including Karl Pearson, and which is still often encountered. Most statisticians, however, prefer to reserve σ to indicate the standard deviation as a parameter.

5.3a. Accordingly,

$$s_x = \sqrt{V_x} = \sqrt{\frac{\Sigma X^2}{N} - M_x^2} \qquad (5.8)$$

An alternate formula is found by substituting $\Sigma X/N$ for M_x in Formula 5.8. Then,

$$s_x = \sqrt{\frac{\Sigma X^2}{N} - \left(\frac{\Sigma X}{N}\right)^2} = \sqrt{\frac{N\Sigma X^2}{N^2} - \frac{(\Sigma X)^2}{N^2}} = \frac{1}{N}\sqrt{N\Sigma X^2 - (\Sigma X)^2} \quad (5.8a)$$

FUNCTIONS OF THE STANDARD DEVIATION

The standard deviation has four important functions:

1. It is used in transforming obtained values of a variable into a new system of values with a predetermined standard deviation (and a predetermined mean). By such transformations, scores on different variables are made comparable. This use is discussed under the topic of standard scores.

2. The standard deviation is the measure of variability essential in correlation. All formulas for linear correlation include, in some form or other, the standard deviations of the two variables correlated. The term *correlation* applies to a description of the relationship between two variables after standard deviations have been equalized. This is explained in Chapter 6.

3. The standard deviation helps to define some of the theoretical frequency curves, especially the so-called normal curve discussed in Chapter 11.

4. The standard deviation is used in evaluating differences between means. This application is presented in Chapter 13.

STANDARD SCORES

Any variable for which it is appropriate to compute a mean and standard deviation may be transformed linearly[5] into a new set of values with an assigned mean and assigned standard deviation.

For theoretical purposes, the most useful of these transformations is the z score. To compute z scores, the difference between any value and the mean of the entire series is divided by the standard deviation. In symbols,

$$z_x = \frac{X - M_x}{s_x} \qquad (5.9)$$

---

[5] A "linear transformation" may be indicated as $Y = aX + b$, in which X is any original value, a and b are constants, and Y is the transformed value of X. $Y = aX + b$ is an equation of a straight line in which a is the slope and b the intercept.

Obviously, since $(X - M_x)$ is the deviation x, this may be written as

$$z_x = \frac{x}{s_x} \qquad (5.9a)$$

The z score indicates directly how many standard deviations the original score deviates from the mean. Thus, for z scores, the standard deviation itself becomes the unit of measurement. For scores above the mean, z scores are positive. For scores below the mean, they are negative.

When Formula 5.9a is summed, it is readily seen that $\Sigma z_x = \Sigma x / s_x$. However, since $\Sigma x = 0$, Σz_x, the sum of any set of z scores over the entire range of the variable is also precisely zero.

If both sides of Formula 5.9a are squared, summed, and divided by N, it appears that

$$\frac{\Sigma z^2}{N} = \frac{\Sigma x^2}{N s_x^2} = \frac{s_x^2}{s_x^2} = 1.00$$

Since the z scores are deviations from their mean, it follows that their variance is 1.00. Also, since the square root of unity is unity, it follows that the standard deviation is also 1.00 and that V_z and s_z are equal.

When actually used, z scores are generally reported to two places of decimals. For practical purposes they suffer from two disadvantages:

1. They are usually three-digit numbers, which are awkward to handle; and
2. They require an indication of their algebraic sign, since approximately half of them are negative and the other half positive.

Accordingly, standard scores for practical purposes, such as norming tests, generally follow a system of positive two-digit numbers. While any arbitrary mean greater than about three standard deviations can be used, one of the most popular systems is to assign a mean of 50 and a standard deviation of 10.

Any system of scores may be readily translated into standard scores (S.S.) by the use of the following formula:

$$\text{S.S.}_x = \left(\frac{X - M_x}{s_x} \right) s' + M' \qquad (5.10)$$

in which s' is the assigned standard deviation and M' is the assigned mean.

In this formula the effect of the expression $(X - M_x)/s_x$ is to reduce original values to z scores with mean of zero and standard deviation of unity. When these z scores are multiplied by s', the standard deviation will, of course, be s' instead of unity. The mean remains at zero. Now, by adding M' to each score, the standard deviation remains unchanged as s', while the mean becomes M'.

To convert values into a series with predetermined mean of 50 and standard deviation of 10, often called T scores,[6] Formula 5.10 becomes

$$\text{S.S.}_x = \left(\frac{X - M_x}{s_x}\right) 10 + 50 \qquad (5.10a)$$

For computing purposes, Formula 5.10 may be written as

$$\text{S.S.}_x = X\left(\frac{s'}{s_x}\right) + M' - \frac{s'M_x}{s_x} \qquad (5.10b)$$

or, in the specific instance of standard scores with an assigned M' of 50 and s' of 10,

$$\text{S.S.}_x = T = X\left(\frac{10}{s_x}\right) + 50 - \frac{10M_x}{s_x} \qquad (5.10c)$$

Since $(M' - s'M_x/s_x)$ is a constant, it need be computed only once. Conversion of a variable X into standard scores requires each X to be multiplied by the ratio of the arbitrary to the obtained standard deviation (s'/s_x). To this result, the constant $(M' - s'M_x/s_x)$ must be added. A method of rapidly converting raw scores into standard scores by means of a calculating machine is illustrated in Example 5.2.

EXAMPLE 5.2

CONVERSIONS OF X TO STANDARD SCORE FORM

The two systems of standard scores most frequently encountered are z scores (with $M' = .00$ and $s' = 1.00$) and T scores (with $M' = 50$ and $s' = 10$). A few examples of the conversion of X to z and T, if M_x happens to be 30.00 and s_x happens to be 8.00 are given in the table.

X VALUE	EQUIVALENT z SCORE	EQUIVALENT T SCORE
30	.00	50
34	+ .50	55
38	+1.00	60
46	+2.00	70
26	− .50	45
22	−1.00	40
6	−3.00	20

In the tabulation above only a few selected X values are shown. Only for an entire set of X would the means necessarily be .00 for z scores and 50 for T scores and the standard deviations 1.00 and 10, respectively.

---

[6] As originally proposed by McCall (2) T scores were normalized scores with M' of 50 and s' of 10 for a reference population of 12-year-olds.

It will be readily seen that the z scores indicate the number of standard deviations the X score is above or below the M_x of 30. Thus, the X of 46 is 16 points, or $2.00s$ above 30, and the X of 26 is four points or $.50s$ below 30 (and hence the z score is $-.50$).

Similarly, all T scores may be seen to be just as many s above or below their M' of 50 as the X scores are above or below their mean of 30. Thus, a T score of 60 is 10 units or $1s$ above 50 and corresponds to an X score of 38, which is 8 units, or $1s$, above 30.

The following artificial data, arranged in order for convenience, illustrate the conversion of an entire series of values to z scores and to T scores:

X	z	z^2	T	T^2
130	2.00	4.00	70	4900
115	1.50	2.25	65	4225
115	1.50	2.25	65	4225
100	1.00	1.00	60	3600
94	.80	.64	58	3364
91	.70	.49	57	3249
88	.60	.36	56	3136
85	.50	.25	55	3025
85	.50	.25	55	3025
73	.10	.01	51	2601
70	.00	.00	50	2500
70	.00	.00	50	2500
70	.00	.00	50	2500
67	$-.10$	.01	49	2401
55	$-.50$	.25	45	2025
55	$-.50$	.25	45	2025
52	$-.60$	.36	44	1936
49	$-.70$	.49	43	1849
46	$-.80$	.64	42	1764
40	-1.00	1.00	40	1600
25	-1.50	2.25	35	1225
25	-1.50	2.25	35	1225
10	-2.00	4.00	30	900

$\Sigma X = 1610$ $\Sigma z = .00$ $\Sigma z^2 = 23.00$ $\Sigma T = 1150$ $\Sigma T^2 = 59,800$

$\Sigma X^2 = 133,400$ $N = 23$

Before conversion to any system of standard scores, M_x and s_x must be known. In this case, by Formula 5.1,

$$M_x = \frac{\Sigma X}{N} = \frac{1610}{23} = 70$$

By Formula 5.3b,

$$V_x = \frac{(23 \times 133,400) - (1610)^2}{(23)^2} = \frac{476,100}{529} = 900$$

By Formula 5.6,

$$s_x = \sqrt{V_x} = \sqrt{900} = 30$$

Procedures in converting X to z follow:

1. Since the z have $M' = .00$ and $s' = 1.00$, Formula 5.10b is used as follows:

$$\text{S.S.} = X\left(\frac{S'}{s_x}\right) + M' - \frac{s'M_x}{s_x} = X\left(\frac{1}{s_x}\right) - \frac{M_x}{s_x}$$

2. Accordingly, each X is divided by s_x (or multiplied by the reciprocal, $1/s_x$) and the result is reduced by M_x/s_x. In the example, $1/s_x = .0333$ and $M_x/s_x = 2.3333$. Accordingly, for $X = 130$, $z = (130 \times .0333) - 2.3333 = 2.00$. All other z score equivalents can be found similarly.
3. A complete set of z scores can be checked by finding Σz (which must be .00, within rounding error) and Σz^2 (which must be N, also within rounding error). These are the conditions under which $M_z = .00$ and $V_z = s_z = 1.00$. In this instance the checks work.

Steps in converting X to T are similar:

1. With $M' = 50$ and $s' = 10$, Formula 5.10b becomes:

$$\text{S.S.} = X\left(\frac{s'}{s_x}\right) + M' - \frac{s'M_x}{s_x} = X\left(\frac{10}{s_x}\right) + 50 - \frac{10M_x}{s_x}$$

2. The factor by which X is to be multiplied (s'/s_x) is (10/30), or .3333. The ratio, s'/s_x, is often called the *rate*. The constant by which X times the rate is to be increased is $[50 - (10 \times 70)/30] = 26.6667$. To convert the X of 130 to T, 130 is multiplied by .3333, and 26.6667 is added to the product, yielding 70.
3. The entire series of T is checked as follows:

$$M_T = \frac{1150}{23} = 50$$

$$V_T = \frac{(23 \times 59,800) - (1150)^2}{(23)^2} = \frac{52,900}{529} = 100$$

Formula 5.10b fits nicely into any desk calculator, so that an entire series of obtained values can be quickly converted to standard scores. Steps are:

1. Compute the rate (s'/s_x).
2. Compute the constant ($M' - s'M_x/s_x$).
3. Enter the constant in the product dials, with the number of decimals equal to those to be used with the rate.
4. Enter the rate in the key board.
5. The machine should now read 0 in the quotient dials, while in the product dials is the equivalent standard score. As X entries are built up in the quotient dials, the rate adds in the product dials and builds up corresponding standard scores.

Note: Any negative scores would, of course, be read as complements. However, in the practice of psychology, individual z scores are rarely, if ever, used. The method works well with T scores and other standard scores that are positive throughout the range.

THE FREQUENCY DISTRIBUTION IN STATISTICS BY AVERAGING

A distribution used for computing the mean, the variance, the standard deviation, and other statistics obtained by summation or averaging is based on a convention somewhat different from that used in a distribution for computing percentiles and other "point measures."

In computing percentiles, all values within the step are thought of as being evenly distributed throughout the step. In computing statistics by averaging, all scores within the step are treated as though they fall exactly at the midpoint.

The same distribution may be used for computing percentile measures and then again for summation measures. However, in changing from statistics obtained by ranking to statistics obtained by summation, the concept of how the frequencies are distributed within the steps must be altered.

By regarding all the scores within a step as falling exactly at the midpoint, scores are in effect coded, thus considerably reducing the size of the numbers to be handled.

CODING AS A COMPUTATIONAL AID

It will be recalled that if a constant is added to or subtracted from all the scores in a series, the mean is correspondingly increased or decreased. Normally a constant is subtracted in order to reduce the numerical size of scores. However, in some cases, a constant is added in order to eliminate negative scores.

To find the mean for a series of scores that have been coded by adding or subtracting a constant, the coded scores are summed and divided by N in the usual fashion. Then comes a final step of adjusting the result by adding or subtracting the constant. For example, if 65 has been subtracted from all scores, then 65 must be added to the mean of the coded scores in order to correct it to the mean of the original scale.

Adding or subtracting a constant to all scores has no effect upon the standard deviation.

Scores may be coded also by multiplying or dividing by a constant. Such an operation affects both the mean and the standard deviation. After computations are made in the usual fashion, they are corrected by multiplication for scores coded by division, and by division for scores coded by multiplication. For example, if all scores have been coded by dividing them by 3, the obtained mean and standard deviation must be multiplied by 3 to find the mean and standard deviation of the original series.

Both types of coding may be used simultaneously. For example, in computations from a frequency distribution, the usual procedure is to code both by subtraction and by division. The midpoint of a step interval is taken as an arbitrary origin. In taking the origin at such a midpoint, we are in effect subtracting that value from all the scores. Also, all scores are handled as deviations in terms of step intervals from that midpoint, In so doing, the scores are, after the subtractive operation, divided by the step interval. Computations are then carried out in terms of coded scores taken as deviations in terms of step intervals from the assumed mean. These coded scores are, of course, much smaller than the original numbers. The arithmetical labor in handling them is much reduced over handling raw scores by hand methods. This principle is the basis of the methods of finding the mean and standard deviation illustrated in Examples 5.3 and 5.4.

EXAMPLE 5.3

M_x, V_x, AND s_x FROM A FREQUENCY DISTRIBUTION[7]

(Conventional Method)

Distribution of 200 Scores on an Aptitude Test

STEPS	TALLIES	f	d	x' (i.e., df)	x'^2 (i.e., d^2f)
140–144	|	1	9	9	81
135–139	||	2	8	16	128
130–134	|||	3	7	21	147
125–129	L┼┼ |	6	6	36	216
120–124	L┼┼ |||	8	5	40	200
115–119	L┼┼ L┼┼ ||	12	4	48	192
110–114	L┼┼ L┼┼ L┼┼	15	3	45	135
105–109	L┼┼ L┼┼ L┼┼ L┼┼	20	2	40	80
100–104	L┼┼ L┼┼ L┼┼ L┼┼ |||	23	1	23	23
95–99	L┼┼ L┼┼ L┼┼ L┼┼ L┼┼ |	26	0	+278	
90–94	L┼┼ L┼┼ L┼┼ L┼┼ ||||	24	−1	−24	24
85–89	L┼┼ L┼┼ L┼┼ L┼┼	20	−2	−40	80
80–84	L┼┼ L┼┼ L┼┼ |	16	−3	−48	144
75–79	L┼┼ L┼┼	10	−4	−40	160
70–74	L┼┼ ||	7	−5	−35	175
65–69	||||	4	−6	−24	144
60–64	||	2	−7	−14	98
55–59		0	−8		
50–54	|	1	−9	− 9	81
				−234	2108

$N = 200$ $\Sigma x' = 278 - 234 = 44$
$i = 5$ $\Sigma x'^2 = 2108$
$M' = 97$

---

[7] Since two variables are involved in the examples in Chapter 6, the notation for frequencies and computations involving coded scores is made more explicit. Thus, M', i, f, and d are written with a subscript to indicate the variable concerned; x' becomes $d_x f_x$, and x'^2 becomes $d_x^2 f_x$, to show more clearly the operations in finding $\Sigma x'$ and $\Sigma x'^2$.

The Data. The 200 scores on the aptitude test are considered to be addable. The scores are distributed on steps that extend from .5 below the stated lower limit to .5 above the stated upper limit. Accordingly, the true dividing points or partition values for the first five steps are 49.5, 54.5, 59.5, 64.5, 69.5, and 74.5. In computing the mean, the variance and the standard deviation, each score is treated as though it were exactly equal to the midpoint of the step in which it is classified.

Coding System. By distributing the scores into steps or classes and establishing the midpoint of one of the steps as the assumed mean (M'), all the scores are automatically coded. Thus:

1. Any score X is taken as the midpoint X' of the step in which it falls.
2. In effect, the assumed mean M' is subtracted from X' and the difference is divided by i, the step interval. This yields x', the number of step intervals the score deviates from the assumed mean. Thus, for any case,

$$x' = \frac{X' - M'}{i}$$

3. In practice, after the distribution has been made, coding is accomplished merely by writing the d's opposite the frequencies. Each d indicates the number of step intervals the scores in a class deviate from M', the assumed mean.
4. The midpoint of any class in the distribution can be chosen as M', but if a class near the center of the distribution is chosen, the computations will involve smaller numbers. In addition, if M' is below the true mean, the correction to M' to find M_x will be positive. To avoid all negative quantities, M' is often the midpoint of the bottom step, as in Example 5.4.

Identification of the Columns. For any single case, x' and d are identical. However, the column headed d is merely the coding apparatus. What is needed is the sum of the d values for the N cases. This sum is denoted as $\Sigma x'$. The column headed x' is, for each step, the sum of the x' for all the cases in that step or class. It is found by multiplying f, the class frequency, by d, the deviation of the class in step intervals from the assumed mean. Products corresponding to negative d's are negative.

The column headed x'^2 also carries sums; that is, the sum of the x'^2 or d^2 for all the cases in the step. These entries may be computed by multiplying each f by its corresponding d^2 (not indicated in the distribution) or by multiplying the entry in the d column by the corresponding entry in the x' column. Thus the first four entries are $1 \times 81 = 81$, $2 \times 64 = 128$, $3 \times 49 = 147$, and $6 \times 36 = 216$; or, more readily, $9 \times 9 = 81$, $8 \times 16 = 128$, $7 \times 21 = 147$, and $6 \times 36 = 216$.

Computation of the Mean. The mean computed from a frequency distribution is the mean of the X' or scores coded as midpoints. It is found by Formula 5.13 as follows:

$$M_x = M' + i\frac{\Sigma x'}{N} = 97 + \frac{5 \times 44}{200} = 98.10$$

Computation of the Variance. In finding the variance from a frequency distribution, each score X is again treated as though it were X', the value at the midpoint of the step in which it falls. With computations in terms of x' and x'^2 Formula 5.14 yields

$$V_x = i^2 \left[\frac{N\Sigma x'^2 - (\Sigma x')^2}{N^2} \right] = 25 \left[\frac{(200 \times 2108) - (44)^2}{(200)^2} \right] = 262.29$$

Computation of the Standard Deviation. The standard deviation is merely the square root of the variance. Thus

$$s_x = \sqrt{V_x} = \sqrt{262.29} = 16.20$$

Charlier's Check. Computations of $\Sigma x'$ and $\Sigma x'^2$ from a frequency distribution may be verified by Charlier's check. This usually involves new computations with an assumed mean one step interval lower than the assumed mean originally selected. The effect is to use a series of deviations, each of which is 1 greater than the d originally used. They may be denoted as x''. The check equations may be derived as follows. Let

$$x'' = x' + 1 \tag{5.11}$$

Summing 5.11,

$$\Sigma x'' = \Sigma x' + N \tag{5.11a}$$

Also, squaring 5.11,

$$x''^2 = x'^2 + 2x' + 1 \tag{5.11b}$$

Summing 5.11b,

$$\Sigma x''^2 = \Sigma x'^2 + 2\Sigma x' + N \tag{5.11c}$$

Charlier's check can be applied to the example as follows:

STEPS	f	d	d'	x''	x''^2
140–144	1	9	10	10	100
135–139	2	8	9	18	162
130–134	3	7	8	24	192
125–129	6	6	7	42	294
120–124	8	5	6	48	288
115–119	12	4	5	60	300
110–114	15	3	4	60	240
105–109	20	2	3	60	180
100–104	23	1	2	46	92
95–99	26	0	1	26	26
90–94	24	−1	0	+394	
85–89	20	−2	−1	−20	20
80–84	16	−3	−2	−32	64
75–79	10	−4	−3	−30	90
70–74	7	−5	−4	−28	112
65–69	4	−6	−5	−20	100
60–64	2	−7	−6	−12	72
55–59	0	−8	−7		
50–54	1	−9	−8	−8	64
				−150	+2396

Computations

$$\Sigma x'' = \Sigma x' + N$$
$$244 = 44 + 200$$
$$\Sigma x''^2 = \Sigma x'^2 + 2\Sigma x' + N$$
$$2396 = 2108 + 88 + 200$$

Since $\Sigma x''$ and $\Sigma x''^2$ as computed agree with $\Sigma x''$ and $\Sigma x''^2$ as found by the check equations, the computations are considered to be correct. While compensating errors might conceivably occur, their likelihood is exceedingly small.

EXAMPLE 5.4

M_x, V_x, AND s_x BY TWO CALCULATING-MACHINE METHODS

(Conventional Procedure)

STEPS	f	d	d^2	x' (i.e., df)	x'^2 (i.e., d^2f)
160–169	1	12	144	12	144
150–159	7	11	121	77	847
140–149	40	10	100	400	4,000
130–139	123	9	81	1,107	9,963
120–129	117	8	64	936	7,488
110–119	137	7	49	959	6,713
100–109	96	6	36	576	3,456
90–99	54	5	25	270	1,350
80–89	33	4	16	132	528
70–79	8	3	9	24	72
60–69	1	2	4	2	4
50–59	0	1	1	0	0
40–49	1	0	0	0	0

$$\Sigma x' = 4,495$$

$$N = 618 \qquad \Sigma x'^2 = 34,565$$

The Data. The distribution represents scores of 618 patrolmen who took a competitive merit pay examination.

Procedure. Except that the arbitrary origin (M') is the midpoint of the lowest step, the procedure is the same as that illustrated in Example 5.3. Frequencies are multiplied by d's (deviations from M' in step-interval units) to form the entries in the column headed x'. Each entry is the sum of the d's for all cases tabulated in the step. Similarly, the f's are multiplied with the d^2's to form the entries in the x'^2 column, which are sums of the d^2 for cases tabulated in the step. It is not necessary to write out the d^2 because x'^2 entries can be found by multiplying each d by the entry in the x' column.

Actually, a skillful calculating-machine operator can work directly from the frequencies, using them as multipliers of the successive natural numbers (1, 2, 3 ...) to form $\Sigma x'$ and of the squares of the successive natural numbers (1, 4, 9 ...) to form $\Sigma x'^2$.

Charlier's check, of course, applies. The procedure is to use the midpoint below M' for the new arbitrary origin.

Computations. By Formula 5.13,

$$M_x = M' + i \frac{\Sigma x'}{N} = 44.5 + \frac{10 \times 4495}{618} = 117.23$$

By Formula 5.14,

$$V_x = i^2\left[\frac{N\Sigma x'^2 - (\Sigma x')^2}{N^2}\right] = 100\left[\frac{618 \times 34{,}565 - (4495)^2}{(618)^2}\right]$$

$$= \frac{115{,}614{,}500}{381{,}924} = 302.7160$$

By Formula 5.6,

$$s_x = \sqrt{V_x} = \sqrt{302.7160} = 17.40$$

Cumulative Frequency Procedure. A procedure for finding $\Sigma x'$ and $\Sigma x'^2$ from cumulative frequencies was developed by DuBois (1). It is based on the algebraic principle that when two series of numbers are multiplied together in pairs, the sum of the products is identical under two conditions:

1. The two series are unmodified; or
2. One series is cumulated and the other consists of differences between terms. The differences between successive squares are successive odd numbers, as shown in the table column headed m (for multiplicand).

If the cumulative frequencies are found directly from the tallies, the f are not needed. Successive odd numbers beginning with 1 in the step above M' are multiplied by the corresponding Cf. The sum of the multipliers, that is, the Cf, is $\Sigma x'$; and of the products, that is, the mCf, is $\Sigma x'^2$. If a desk calculator is used, multipliers and products are allowed to accumulate and the entries headed mCf need not be written out. It is to be noted that N appears as the final Cf, and that $\Sigma x'$ and $\Sigma x'^2$ are found in a single series of machine operations. Charlier's check applies, with the usual shift in arbitrary origin.

Since the arbitrary origin M' is the same in both sets of computations, the $\Sigma x'$ are identical, as are the $\Sigma x'^2$. This procedure is illustrated in the table.

STEPS	f	Cf	m	mCf
160–169	1	1	23	23
150–159	7	8	21	168
140–149	40	48	19	912
130–139	123	171	17	2,907
120–129	117	288	15	4,320
110–119	137	425	13	5,525
100–109	96	521	11	5,731
90–99	54	575	9	5,175
80–89	33	608	7	4,256
70–79	8	616	5	3,080
60–69	1	617	3	1,851
50–59	0	617	1	617
40–49	1	618		

$$N = 618$$
$$\Sigma x' = \Sigma Cf = 4{,}495$$
$$\Sigma x'^2 = \Sigma mCf = 34{,}565$$

ERROR INTRODUCED BY CODING

A certain degree of error may be introduced by the coding process, since all the scores within a step are treated as falling exactly at the midpoint. When the number of cases is small, there may be considerable discrepancy between the mean and standard deviation, as computed by coding, when compared with the same statistics computed from raw scores. However, when the number of steps is reasonably large, say, ten or more, and the distribution is fairly regular and symmetrical, the error is negligible. A correction[8] exists to compensate for this "grouping error" in computing the standard deviation, but the amount of correction is small and of little practical consequence.

FORMULAS FOR M AND s BASED ON CODING

The use of coding results in computations using deviations from an arbitrary point (the "assumed mean") rather than deviations from the actual mean. If M' represents an assumed mean and x''' is any deviation from it, then

$$X = M' + x'''$$

Summing,

$$\Sigma X = NM' + \Sigma x'''$$

Dividing by N,

$$\frac{\Sigma X}{N} = M' + \frac{\Sigma x'''}{N} = M_x$$

In computations from a frequency distribution, an additional step is involved, namely, the coding of the deviations in step-interval units, denotes as x', which is the nearest whole number resulting when x''' (the deviation from the assumed mean) is divided by i (the step interval). In finding means and standard deviations from a frequency distribution, all work is done in step-interval units and is translated into raw-score units at the end of the computations.

It is approximately true and can be taken as true that

$$X = M' + ix' \tag{5.12}$$

Summing,

$$\Sigma X = NM' + i\Sigma x'$$

Dividing by N,

$$\frac{\Sigma X}{N} = M_x = M' + \frac{i\Sigma x'}{N} \tag{5.13}$$

---

[8] This adjustment is known as *Sheppard's correction*. Prior to extracting the root, the variance is reduced by $i^2/12$.

This is a preferred formula for finding the mean from a frequency distribution. Its use is illustrated in Examples 5.3 and 5.4.

For the standard deviation we first find a formula for the deviation x by the use of Formulas 5.12 and 5.13:

$$x = X - M_x = (M' + ix') - \left(M' + \frac{i\Sigma x'}{N}\right) = i\left(x' - \frac{\Sigma x'}{N}\right) \qquad (5.13a)$$

Squaring both sides,

$$x^2 = i^2\left[x'^2 - 2\frac{\Sigma x'}{N}x' + \left(\frac{\Sigma x'}{N}\right)^2\right]$$

Summing and dividing by N,

$$\frac{\Sigma x^2}{N} = V_x = i^2\left[\frac{\Sigma x'^2}{N} - 2\frac{\Sigma x'\Sigma x'}{N^2} + \left(\frac{\Sigma x'}{N}\right)^2\right] = i^2\left[\frac{\Sigma x'^2}{N} - \left(\frac{\Sigma x'}{N}\right)^2\right] \qquad (5.14)$$

Extracting square roots and identifying $\sqrt{V_x}$ as the standard deviation,

$$s_x = \sqrt{\frac{\Sigma x^2}{N}} = i\sqrt{\frac{\Sigma x'^2}{N} - \left(\frac{\Sigma x'}{N}\right)^2} \qquad (5.15)$$

or

$$s_x = \frac{i}{N}\sqrt{N\Sigma x'^2 - (\Sigma x')^2} \qquad (5.15a)$$

Formula 5.15 is sometimes preferred for computations by hand, while Formula 5.15a fits better into a desk calculator.

PROPERTIES OF THE STANDARD DEVIATION

Properties of the standard deviation may be summarized as follows:

1. It is a number, in original scale units, that represents the variability of a series.
2. Mathematically, it is an average (the "quadratic mean" or "root mean square") of the deviations from the arithmetic mean.
3. Since it takes into account the magnitudes of all values in the series, it is a more stable measure of variability than those based upon points in the distribution, such as the range and Q.
4. It is closely related to other descriptive statistics that summarize data through summation. The mean helps define the standard deviation, which is the square root of the variance; and, as will be seen later, the standard deviation helps to define the correlation coefficient and the normal distribution curve.

VISUAL CHECKS OF M AND s

After a mean has been computed from a frequency distribution, it can be checked by inspection. If the distribution is reasonably symmetrical, the mean should be close to median; that is, close to the point dividing the distribution into two halves. If there is marked discrepancy between the mean and P_{50}, either the distribution is definitely asymmetrical or there has been an error in computation.

The standard deviation can also be checked visually for plausibility. If the distribution is symmetrical and if there is the usual concentration of the larger frequencies around the midpoint, then approximately two-thirds of the cases will be included in the limits of one standard deviation above and one below the mean ($\pm 1s$). More precisely, half of the distance between P_{84} and P_{16} should be fairly close to the standard deviation. Any marked discrepancy should result in further checking and in re-computation of the standard deviation.

COMBINING STATISTICS FROM DIFFERENT SAMPLES

Means, variances, and standard deviations of the same variable in different samples may be used to find the mean, variance, and standard deviation for the total sample. Let N_a, $N_b \cdots N_n$ be the numbers of cases in the n samples; M_a, $M_b \cdots M_n$, the means; and V_a, $V_b \cdots V_n$, the variances. By writing out raw-score formulas, manipulating them so that they can be added, and building up the required sums, appropriate formulas result. For the total mean,

$$M_x = \frac{N_a M_a + N_b M_b + \cdots + N_n M_n}{N_a + N_b + \cdots + N_n} \qquad (5.16)$$

Accordingly, to find a mean for the total group, we multiply each mean by the number of cases used in finding it; then the products are summed and the result is divided by the total number of cases.

Somewhat similarly, for the total variance,

$$V_x = \frac{N_a(V_a + M_a{}^2) + N_b(V_b + M_b{}^2) + \cdots + N_n(V_n + M_n{}^2)}{N_a + N_b + \cdots + N_n} - M_x{}^2 \quad (5.17)$$

This formula requires that each variance and the square of the corresponding mean be added together. Then, in each case, the resultant sum must be multiplied by the number of cases in the sample. These products are summed and divided by the total number of cases. From the result, the square of the total mean is subtracted.

Computation of the standard deviation of the total group is identical with the computation of the variance except for the final step of taking a square root. Procedures are illustrated in Example 5.5.

EXAMPLE 5.5

M_x, V_x, AND s_x FOR COMBINED GROUPS

Consider the following statistics for Groups A, B, and C:

	N	M	V
Group A	42	10.0	13.00
Group B	20	15.5	19.75
Group C	28	12.5	13.75

To find M_x for the total group, Formula 5.17 is applied as follows:

$$M_x = \frac{N_a M_a + N_b M_b + N_c M_c}{N_a + N_b + N_c}$$

$$= \frac{(42 \times 10.0) + (20 \times 15.5) + (28 \times 12.5)}{42 + 20 + 28}$$

$$= \frac{1080}{90} = 12.0$$

The variance of the combined sample is found from Formula 5.18:

$$V_x = \frac{N_a(V_a + M_a^2) + N_b(V_b + M_b^2) + N_c(V_c + M_c^2)}{N_a + N_b + N_c} - M_x^2$$

$$= \frac{42[13.00 + (10.0)^2] + 20[19.75 + (15.5)^2] + 28[13.75 + (12.5)^2]}{42 + 20 + 28} - (12.0)^2$$

$$= \frac{14{,}706}{90} - 144.00 = 163.40 - 144.00 = 19.40$$

It is to be noted that the variance of the entire group is almost as large as the largest variance, that of Group B. Such a finding should not be surprising, since, as Formula 5.17 indicates, the total variance is a function of the group variances and the squares of the group means, both weighted in accordance with the group N. Actually, if means were markedly different and had little variation around them, the total variance could be chiefly a function of the group means.

To find the standard deviation of the total group, Formula 5.6 is used:

$$s_x = \sqrt{V_x} = \sqrt{19.40} = 4.4$$

THE MEAN OF THE SUM OF SEVERAL VARIABLES

An entirely different problem exists when we have the means of several variables on the *same sample* and desire the mean of the variable obtained by summing for every case the values on the several variables. Thus, knowing the means for the several parts of an achievement test, we might wish to know the mean score for the test as a whole. Designating the several variables as $X_1, X_2 \cdots X_n$ and their means as $M_1, M_2 \cdots M_n$, and designating the total or sum variable as X_t. and its mean as M_t, it can be stated that

$$X_1 + X_2 + \cdots + X_n = X_t$$

Summing,

$$\Sigma X_1 + \Sigma X_2 + \cdots + \Sigma X_n = \Sigma X_t$$

Dividing by N,

$$M_1 + M_2 + \cdots + M_n = M_t \qquad (5.18)$$

Accordingly, the mean of a sum variable is merely the sum of the means of its constituent variables.

Procedures for finding the variance and the standard deviation of a sum variable are discussed in Chapter 9.

SUMMARY

Many of the varieties of numerical information used in psychology are summarized by averaging. The arithmetic mean, which is the sum of all the values in a series divided by the number of cases, is the most frequently used measure of central tendency. The variance, defined as the mean of the squares of the deviations from the arithmetic mean, is a measure of variability, which can sometimes by analyzed into component parts. Its square root is known as the *standard deviation*, the most useful of the direct measures of variability.

Obtained values can be transformed linearly into a new set of values with assigned mean and standard deviation. For theoretical purposes, the most useful of these transformations is the z score with mean of .00 and variance of 1.00. For practical purposes, two-digit standard scores with no negative values are more convenient. Of these, the most common is the T score, with assigned mean of 50 and assigned standard deviation of 10.

This chapter is concerned in part with computing methods, including the finding of statistical constants from obtained values and scores coded by procedures applicable to frequency distributions.

EXERCISES

1. Using a step interval of 5, make a distribution of the following scores from a chemistry placement test:

65	44	28	78	44
39	52	78	34	28
68	52	78	68	56
34	76	18	68	39
34	76	23	48	61
61	76	68	23	72
39	28	72	72	52
56	61	68	48	52
65	34	28	65	72
52	48	78	56	79
34	34	68	39	65
61	61	48	56	78
48	48	76	61	61
23	72	52	78	52
61	72	39	34	28
65	61	76	48	65
34	56	68	34	56
52	52	68	44	44
72	65	78	76	34
23	34	52	48	52

Find M_x, V_x, and s_x.

2. For the following distribution, find $\Sigma x'$ and $\Sigma x'^2$ from any arbitrary origin and then apply Charlier's check to verify the results. Find M_x, V_x, and s_x.

STEPS	f	STEPS	f
42–43	1	28–29	12
40–41	3	26–27	5
38–39	7	24–25	3
36–37	11	22–23	0
34–35	18	20–21	2
32–33	20	18–19	2
30–31	16		

3. For the following distribution, find $\Sigma x'$ and $\Sigma x'^2$ by the conventional method and also from cumulative frequencies and the successive odd numbers. Use the midpoint of the lowest step as the arbitrary origin. Compute M_x, V_x, and s_x.

STEPS	f
42–44	3
39–41	3
36–38	6
33–35	8
30–32	10
27–29	15
24–26	12
21–23	7
18–20	4
15–17	2

4. If the mean of a set of values is 18.2 and the standard deviation is 3.9, compute the rate (s'/s_x) and the additive constant $(M' - s'M_x/s_x)$ to convert the original values to standard scores with a mean of 50 and standard deviation of 10. What standard score corresponds to an obtained value of 26?

5. In a sample of 200 cases, the following M and s were found for three parts of a test:

	M	s
Part I	40.8	10.3
Part II	30.7	8.2
Part III	29.5	9.5

If the total score is found by summing the three part scores, what is the total mean? Is enough information available to find the total standard deviation?

6. Find the mean and standard deviation of the following scores (words recalled) on a memory test consisting of 25 words: 22, 22, 18, 18, 17, 17, 16, 14, 13, 20, 19, 18, 18, 17, 17, 16, 15, 15.

7. Convert the following set of raw scores to z scores and also to T scores: 37, 71, 49, 88, 21, 64, 55, 19, 42, 54.

8. Group 1, consisting of 30 women, has a mean weight of 122 pounds and standard deviation of 8 pounds. Group 2, consisting of 40 men, has a mean weight of 155 pounds and standard deviation of 12 pounds. Find the mean and standard deviation of the combined group.

REFERENCES

1. DUBOIS, PHILIP H., "A statistical time-saver for means and sigmas," *J. Consulting Psychol.*, 1939, **3**, 80–82.
2. MCCALL, WILLIAM A., *How to Measure in Education*. New York: The Macmillan Company, 1922. xii+416.

LINEAR CORRELATION AND REGRESSION: TWO VARIABLES

6

THE NATURE OF CORRELATION

Science comprises statements of relationship between variables. Examples include: the association between temperature and the state of a substance, such as water or a metal; and the relationship between pressure and the volume of a gas, temperature remaining constant. A relationship in physics can often be stated as a mathematical function with minimal error, but in constructing a science of the behavior of human beings, variables are difficult to identify; the number of variables operant simultaneously is large; and relationships between pairs of variables are far from perfect.

An important statistic for describing relationships in the social sciences is *product-moment*[1] correlation, which involves fitting a straight line to a two-dimensional plot of the observations in a manner such that the best possible fit is obtained.

---

[1] Karl Pearson, who developed the formula in common use, taught applied mathematics at University College, London. He referred to certain functions of deviations as *moments*, a term taken from mechanics. His formula involves finding the average of the products of pairs of deviations, modified so that the standard deviations of the two variables are equal. As applied to two observed variables, the formula yields "zero order *r*."

REGRESSION AND CORRELATION

1. The relationship between two variables is expressed as the equation of a straight line, the *regression*[2] equation.

2. The degree of correlation is unaffected by linear conversion of one of the variables, or both, entering into the correlation. However, numerical values of constants in the regression equation used for predicting values in one variable from a knowledge of values in the other are based on: (1) the degree of relationship; and (2) the means and standard deviations of the two variables.

3. When the variables have been modified so that their standard deviations are equal, the slope of the line indicates the degree of relationship.

4. Without implying that one variable is the cause of the other, we may, for convenience, arbitrarily call one the *independent* variable and the other, the *dependent* variable. In the sample in which the correlation is computed, each value of the dependent variable may be divided uniquely into two uncorrelated portions: a part perfectly correlated with the independent variable and a part uncorrelated with it.

5. In using the regression equation to predict values of the dependent variable, or *criterion*, in cases for which values of only the independent variable are available, the proportion of the variance of the dependent variable that can be predicted can, under certain assumptions, be stated precisely.

6. In general, correlation requires paired sets of measurements on scales amenable to addition. Most frequently, in education and psychology, the measurements that are paired are of the same individual, and the correlation is a summary of the relationship existing in a sample of N individuals. It is impossible to find a correlation from a single pair of observations or between a variable observed in one sample and a different variable observed in a second sample.

LINEAR AND NONLINEAR RELATIONSHIPS

There is nothing in psychological and educational measurement that makes fitting straight lines better than fitting curved lines. It is conceivable that many relationships between psychological variables may ultimately turn

---

[2] Sir Francis Galton, who first described correlation, introduced the term *regression*. In applying the principle of correlation to characteristics of children paired with parents, he noted that children tend to regress toward the mean. For example, while the children of tall parents tend to be above average in height, they are closer to the mean of all children than their parents are to the parents' mean. Similarly, children of short parents tend to be below average in height, but again closer to the mean of all children in the group than their parents are to the parents' mean. This phenomenon always appears when two variables are linearly related and when the relationship is less than perfect.

out to be curvilinear rather than linear. Up to the present time, however, age is perhaps the only variable showing consistent curvilinear relationships with psychological variables. Excluding relationships with age, most correlations so far found appear to be linear. Because of this fact, linear correlation is used in psychological investigations almost to the exclusion of curvilinear correlation.

GRAPHING THE RELATIONSHIP BETWEEN TWO VARIABLES

Consider the following five pairs of values, X_0 and X_1, and their z score equivalents:

CASE	X_0	z_0	X_1	z_1
A	8	$-.50$	1	-1.50
B	2	-1.50	3	$-.50$
C	14	$+.50$	4	$.00$
D	11	$.00$	5	$+.50$
E	20	$+1.50$	7	$+1.50$

These data are plotted on Cartesian coordinates in Fig. 6.1. The dependent variable, z_0, is represented on the vertical axis, or ordinate; the independent variable, z_1, on the horizontal axis, or abscissa. Each of the five plotted points (denoted as five circles identified by letters) represents the two z-score values for a single case: a value in z_1 as shown by its

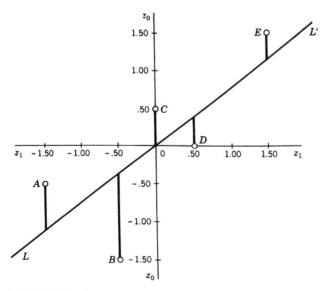

FIG. 6.1. A REGRESSION LINE. (THE LINE LL' IS THE LINE OF BEST FIT CONNECTING OBSERVATIONS IN z_1 WITH THE OBSERVATIONS IN z_0. SINCE z SCORES ARE PLOTTED, r_{01} IS THE SLOPE OF THE LINE.)

projection on the horizontal axis; and a value in z_0 as shown by its projection on the vertical axis.

Sometimes the plot of points indicates no relationship at all between the
two variables. Under such circumstances the points tend to fall in a circular
area. In Fig. 6.1 they fall approximately in an ellipse, indicating some degree
of relationship. Since low values in z_1 tend to be associated with low
values in z_0, and vice versa, the correlation is positive. Had low values in
one variable been associated with high values in the other (as indicated
by points running from upper left to lower right), the association would
have been negative. If all points fall exactly on a straight line, then knowledge of a value in one variable leads to precise knowledge of the corresponding value in the other variable. In such instances, correlation is
perfect.

In psychological research, high correlations appear chiefly when a group
of individuals is measured twice with the same instrument or with two
equivalent measuring devices. Correlations between most psychological
variables tend to be moderate or low.

r AS THE SLOPE OF THE LINE OF BEST FIT

A coefficient of correlation, denoted as r, is the slope of a straight line of
best fit when two variables have been modified (if necessary) so that their
standard deviations are equal, and when pairs of scores have been plotted
as single points on Cartesian coordinates, as in Fig. 6.1.

A generally accepted mathematical convention, known as "least
squares," states that the line of best fit can be defined as the line
around which the sum of the squares of the errors in fitting (that is to say,
the "misses," or residuals) is at a minimum.

In Fig. 6.1, consider the line LL'. This is the line used to predict z_0 scores
(values of the dependent variable or criterion) from z_1 scores (values of the
independent variable). Denoting as $\tilde{z}_0$ the score in z_0 predicted from z_1, we
wish to establish the slope of this line such that the sum of the squares
of the residuals, $\Sigma(z_0 - \tilde{z}_0)^2$, be as small as possible. When plotted on
Cartesian coordinates, a line is thought to consist of points, each having
two values, one of which is its projection on the y axis and the other of
which is its projection on the x axis. The slope of a straight line passing
through the origin is any nonzero y value divided by the corresponding
x value.

All the z_0 values of points on the line LL' are $\tilde{z}_0$'s as obtained from the
equation $\tilde{z}_0 = \beta z_1$, in which β, as the slope of the line, can take any value
between -1.00 and $+1.00$. The problem is to find the value of β such that
the sum of the squares of the differences between the observed values z_0
and the values of $\tilde{z}_0$ (on the line LL') is as small as possible.

A rigorous derivation[3] of the formula for r, the coefficient of correlation, consists of finding the value of β under the stated condition.

DERIVATION OF r

In any particular case the difference between z_0 and $\tilde{z}_0$ can be written as

$$z_0 - \tilde{z}_0 = z_0 - \beta z_1$$

Squaring both sides, and summing and dividing by N,

$$\frac{\Sigma(z_0 - \tilde{z}_0)^2}{N} = \frac{\Sigma z_0^2}{N} - 2\beta \frac{\Sigma z_0 z_1}{N} + \beta^2 \frac{\Sigma z_1^2}{N}$$

Since the variances of z scores are unity, 1.00 can be substituted for $\Sigma z_0^2/N$ and $\Sigma z_1^2/N$:

$$\frac{\Sigma(z_0 - \tilde{z}_0)^2}{N} = 1 - 2\beta \frac{\Sigma z_0 z_1}{N} + \beta^2$$

On the right-hand side of the equation, $(\Sigma z_0 z_1/N)^2$ can be subtracted and added as follows:

$$\frac{\Sigma(z_0 - \tilde{z}_0)^2}{N} = 1 - \left(\frac{\Sigma z_0 z_1}{N}\right)^2 + \left(\frac{\Sigma z_0 z_1}{N}\right)^2 - 2\beta \frac{\Sigma z_0 z_1}{N} + \beta^2$$

The last three terms now form a perfect square and can be factored:

$$\frac{\Sigma(z_0 - \tilde{z}_0)^2}{N} = 1 - \left(\frac{\Sigma z_0 z_1}{N}\right)^2 + \left(\frac{\Sigma z_0 z_1}{N} - \beta\right)^2$$

It is now seen:

1. If $\Sigma(z_0 - \tilde{z}_0)^2/N$ is as small as possible, then $\Sigma(z_0 - \tilde{z}_0)^2$ will also be a minimum.
2. This condition will obtain if $[(\Sigma z_0 z_1/N) - \beta]^2$, the last expression on the right-hand side of the equation, equals zero.
3. If $\beta = \Sigma z_0 z_1/N$, then $[(\Sigma z_0 z_1/N) - \beta]^2$ will equal zero and $\Sigma(z_0 - \tilde{z}_0)^2$ will be as small as possible. Accordingly, the required slope is $\Sigma z_0 z_1/N$.

When the slope of the line is the mean of the products of the z scores in the two variables (that is, $\Sigma z_0 z_1/N$), it can be denoted as r_{01}, the coefficient of correlation, or with slight change in notation, as

$$r_{xy} = \frac{\Sigma z_x z_y}{N} \tag{6.1}$$

---

[3] The usual derivation involves differentiating $y = 1 - 2\beta(\Sigma z_0 z_1/N) + \beta^2$ with respect to β, and setting the first derivative equal to zero. The exposition in the text accomplishes the same result by what is mathematically the identical procedure, but which is in an algebraic idiom. See Treloar (4).

in which x is any variable and y is any other variable for which paired measurements exist. This coefficient varies from -1.00 (indicating perfect inverse relationship) through $.00$ (indicating no relationship) to $+1.00$ (indicating perfect, positive relationship).

The derivation of r given above assumes nothing about the shape of the true line of best fit. The true line of best fit might be a parabola or some other curve. What is actually fitted is a straight line. If the regression is linear, then the line fitted by the correlation technique would be the line of best fit. If the regression is not linear, then the straight line with slope of r is not the best possible function connecting the two variables. In that case, the coefficient r does not provide an adequate description of the relationship.

To find r for the data of Fig. 6.1, the mean z-score product can be found as follows:

CASE	z_0	z_1	z_0z_1
A	$-.50$	-1.50	$.75$
B	-1.50	$-.50$	$.75$
C	$+.50$	$.00$	$.00$
D	$.00$	$+.50$	$.00$
E	$+1.50$	$+1.50$	2.25
			$\Sigma z_0z_1 = 3.75$

By Formula 6.1,

$$r_{01} = \frac{\Sigma z_0 z_1}{N} = \frac{3.75}{5} = .75$$

In Fig. 6.1, the line LL' has been drawn so that its slope is $.75$; that is, for every point on the line (except at the origin), the $\tilde{z}_0$ value divided by the corresponding z_1 value is $.75$. In making predictions of z_0 from z_1, the vertical distance between the z_1 point on the horizontal axis and the corresponding point on the regression line, or line of best fit, is the value of the predicted score, $\tilde{z}_0$.

It will be noted that in this particular instance, none of the points representing pairs of original observations falls precisely on the line LL'. The deviations, or $(z_0 - \tilde{z}_0)$ distances, are shown as vertical heavy lines connecting the points with the regression line. It is the sum of the squares of these distances that has been minimized. From a line plotted with slope other than r, the sum of the squares of the residuals would necessarily be greater.

THE TWO-VARIABLE REGRESSION EQUATION

In product-moment correlation, then, a straight line is, in effect, fitted to plotted pairs of observations, although with conventional computing techniques, points are seldom plotted and the line itself is seldom explicit. If the line passes near the points so that the residuals or discrepancies in fitting the line are small, the correlation is high; if the points tend to lie away from the line, the correlation is low. The correlation coefficient, a pure number that is independent of the units in which the two variables are measured, is both the slope of the line of best fit and an indication of the goodness of fit.

If X_0 and X_1 are known to be positively related, one might suppose that the z_1 value would be the best estimate of the corresponding value in z_0. While the derivation given above of the formula for r shows that this is not the case, a numerical illustration may be of interest. In the tables below, for the data used for Fig. 6.1, are z_0 and z_1 values, their differences, the differences squared, the $\tilde{z}_0$ values from the regression equation ($\tilde{z}_0 = r_{01}z_1$), the residuals around the regression line ($z_0 - \tilde{z}_0$), and the residuals squared.

DISCREPANCIES BETWEEN OBSERVED VALUES

CASE	z_0	z_1	$(z_0 - z_1)$	$(z_0 - z_1)^2$
A	−.50	−1.50	1.00	1.00
B	−1.50	−.50	−1.00	1.00
C	+.50	.00	.50	.25
D	.00	+.50	−.50	.25
E	+1.50	+1.50	.00	.00

$$\Sigma(z_0 - z_1)^2 = 2.50$$

DISCREPANCIES BETWEEN OBSERVED AND PREDICTED VALUES

CASE	z_0	$\tilde{z}_0$, i.e., $r_{01}z_1$	$(z_0 - \tilde{z}_0)$	$(z_0 - \tilde{z}_0)^2$
A	−.50	−1.125	.625	.391
B	−1.50	−.375	−1.125	1.266
C	+.50	.000	.500	.250
D	.00	.375	−.375	.141
E	+1.50	+1.125	+.375	.141

$$\Sigma(z_0 - \tilde{z}_0)^2 = 2.189$$

It will be seen that the sum of the squares of the residuals around the regression line is less than the sum of the squares of the differences between pairs of observed values. This is necessarily true in all situations in which r is less than 1.00.

RAW-SCORE REGRESSION EQUATION

The regression equation in z form is not particularly useful for making predictions in practical instances, since in handling educational and psychological data, obtained values are seldom converted into z scores. It is possible, however, to modify the z score regression equation into a form suitable for predicting values in X_0 from obtained values in X_1.

It will be recalled that a z score is merely the number of standard deviations that a value is above or below the mean, and that z_1, for example, is $(X_1 - M_1)/s_1$. Designating the predicted X_0 value as $\tilde{X}_0$, $(\tilde{X}_0 - M_0)/s_0$ is substituted for $\tilde{z}_0$, and $(X_1 - M_1)/s_1$ for z_1. If the regression equation is written as

$$\tilde{z}_0 = r_{01}z_1 \qquad (6.2)$$

then

$$\frac{(\tilde{X}_0 - M_0)}{s_0} = r_{01} \frac{(X_1 - M_1)}{s_1}$$

Multiplying both sides by s_0, and adding M_0 to both sides of the equation,

$$\tilde{X}_0 = r_{01} \frac{s_0}{s_1} X_1 + M_0 - r_{01} \frac{s_0}{s_1} M_1 \qquad (6.3)$$

This is the equation[4] of a straight line with slope of $r_{01}s_0/s_1$ and intercept (the X_0 value when $X_1 = 0$) of $(M_0 - r_{01}M_1s_0/s_1)$.

A regression equation provides a procedure for predicting a score in a second variable when the score in the first is known. In a particular sample, the means and standard deviations of the two variables and the correlation between them can be organized as an equation for making predictions for cases not in the original sample, but for which the score on one of the variables is available.

Suppose, for example, in a representative sample the relationship between an intelligence test and success in a course of training has been ascertained. To a new applicant we can: (1) administer the test; and (2) make a prediction as to his probable training success. Obviously, the higher the correlation, the more closely the prediction is likely to approximate the criterion value, when and if the criterion value is determined.

For a more precise description of prediction, it is necessary to consider the division of the criterion variance into two portions: the variance of the predictions and the variance of the residuals.

---

[4] Other forms of the regression equation are possible. To develop the *deviation* form, for example, $\tilde{x}_0/s_0$ is substituted for $\tilde{z}_0$ and x_1/s_1 for z_1 in Formula 6.2. This yields $\tilde{x}_0 = (r_{01}s_0/s_1)x_1$, a form of the regression equation that could be used for predicting deviations in X_0 from deviations in X_1. Since, in making predictions, one may be interested in relative standing without predicting actual criterion values, the equation could be modified so that predicted values would be standard scores with an assigned mean and standard deviation.

DIVISION OF V_0 INTO $\tilde{V}_0$ AND $V_{0.1}$

If any variable is transformed into z scores, its variance is 1.00. This variance can be represented as V_0, which can be divided into two parts, $\tilde{V}_0$ and $V_{0.1}$, where $\tilde{V}_0$ represents the variance of the predicted scores. To find the value of this variance, both sides of the regression equation, $\tilde{z}_0 = r_{01}z_1$, are squared. This gives

$$\tilde{z}_0{}^2 = r_{01}{}^2 z_1{}^2$$

Summing and dividing by N, and dropping out the variance of z_1, which is 1.00,

$$\tilde{V}_0 = r_{01}{}^2 \tag{6.4}$$

The value of the variance of the residuals, $V_{0.1}$, can be found somewhat similarly:

$$z_{0.1} = z_0 - \tilde{z}_0 = z_0 - r_{01}z_1 \tag{6.5}$$

Squaring,

$$z_{0.1}{}^2 = z_0{}^2 - 2r_{01}z_0 z_1 + r_{01}{}^2 z_1{}^2$$

Summing and dividing by N,

$$\frac{\Sigma z_{0.1}{}^2}{N} = \frac{\Sigma z_0{}^2}{N} - 2r_{01}\frac{\Sigma z_0 z_1}{N} + r_{01}{}^2 \frac{\Sigma z_1{}^2}{N}$$

Considering that $\Sigma z_0 z_1/N = r_{01}$ and that the variance of a set of z scores is unity, it can be stated that

$$V_{0.1} = 1 - 2r_{01}r_{01} + r_{01}{}^2 = 1 - r_{01}{}^2 \tag{6.6}$$

It is now apparent that

$$V_{0.1} + \tilde{V}_0 = 1 = V_0 \tag{6.7}$$

Generalizing, it can be said that any z score, z_0, can be divided into two portions: the predicted value $\tilde{z}_0$, and the residual $z_{0.1}$. The predicted score $\tilde{z}_0$ is correlated perfectly with the predictor variable z_1, since it is merely z_1 multiplied by a constant. The residual $z_{0.1}$ is uncorrelated with z_1. This can be shown by multiplying Formula 6.5 by z_1, with the result:

$$z_1 z_{0.1} = z_0 z_1 - r_{01}z_1{}^2$$

Summing and dividing by N,

$$\frac{\Sigma z_1 z_{0.1}}{N} = \frac{\Sigma z_0 z_1}{N} - r_{01}\frac{\Sigma z_1{}^2}{N} = r_{01} - r_{01} = .00$$

Since the sum of products of z_1 and $z_{0.1}$ is zero, their correlation is zero.

With original X_0 values, V_0 in general does not equal 1.00, but the principle that the total variance is divisible into two uncorrelated portions is still applicable; that is,

$$V_0 = \tilde{V}_0 + V_{0.1} \qquad (6.7a)$$

PREDICTABLE VARIANCE OF THE CRITERION

Of the total variance of the criterion, represented as V_0, a certain proportion is generally predictable from an outside variable such as X_1. If r_{01}, the correlation between X_0 and X_1 is zero; then no part of X_0 is predictable from X_1. On the other hand, if r_{01} is ± 1.00, then X_0 is completely predictable from X_1. These are the two extremes.

Since with z scores, $\tilde{V}_0 = r_{01}{}^2$, it follows that $\tilde{V}_0/V_0 = r_{01}{}^2/1 = r_{01}{}^2$. If original values are used, the predicted variance becomes $r_{01}{}^2 V_0$, in which V_0 refers to a variance in original units. Accordingly, the proportion of the variance predicted by X_1 is $r_{01}{}^2 V_0/V_0$ or $r_{01}{}^2$, just as with the z score formulation.

UNPREDICTED VARIANCE

The same reasoning applies to the unpredicted variance. The portion of the variance of the criterion that is unpredictable from a knowledge of the predictor is $V_{0.1}$. In z scores reduced by Formula 6.5, $V_{0.1}$ is $(1 - r_{01}{}^2)$, and in original units it is $V_0(1 - r_{01}{}^2)$. In either case, $V_{0.1}$ represents the variance of the residuals around the regression line and $(1 - r_{01}{}^2)$ is the proportion of the criterion variance unpredictable from the independent variable.

This variance of the residuals is also known as a *partial* variance, and its square root is a *partial standard deviation*. It reflects the variability that remains in X_0 when the variability associated with X_1 has been removed by subtraction.

HOMOSCEDASTICITY AROUND THE REGRESSION LINE

Figure 6.2 represents a two-variable scatter diagram for 49 cases (artificial data). The two scales are such that $V_0 = V_1 = 8$. Since the two standard deviations are equal, the slope of the regression line LL' is r_{01}. It has a numerical value of .707. As in most correlation diagrams, this line is not actually shown.

From column to column in Fig. 6.2, the variability is the same, since there is one X_0 unit between successive cases. In each column the mean would be exactly on the regression line. Accordingly, a straight line is the line of best fit, and the regression is linear. Also, the variance of the values in each column is exactly 4. The vertical arrays show homoscedasticity, meaning that the variability from column to column is the same.

It will be seen that there are seven different X_1 values and that corresponding $\tilde{X}_0$ values (values exactly on the regression line) are 3, 4, 5, 6, 7, 8, and 9. The variance of these $\tilde{X}_0$ values is 4. Formula 6.6a holds, and

$$V_0 = \tilde{V}_0 + V_{0.1} = 4 + 4 = 8$$

Again the variance of the criterion has been divided into two portions: the predicted variance $\tilde{V}_0$, and the unpredicted or residual variance $V_{0.1}$. In the specific instance, $\tilde{V}_0 = V_{0.1}$, but this happens only when $r = .707$. When r is greater than or less than .707, the predicted variance is greater than or less than the residual variance.

X_0	X_1 0	$\sqrt{2}$	$2\sqrt{2}$	$3\sqrt{2}$	$4\sqrt{2}$	$5\sqrt{2}$	$6\sqrt{2}$	f_0
12								1
11								2
10								3
9								4
8								5
7								6
6								7
5								6
4								5
3								4
2								3
1								2
0								1
f_1	7	7	7	7	7	7	7	$N = 49$

FIG. 6.2. SCATTER DIAGRAM SHOWING HOMOSCEDASTICITY IN THE VERTICAL DIRECTION

In this artificial example, there are seven cases in each column (or vertical array). Since the regression for the 49 cases is perfectly linear, the mean of each set of seven cases corresponds to the $\tilde{X}_0$ value for the column and falls exactly on the regression line. The variances of the seven sets of seven cases each are identical. Accordingly, the seven standard deviations of the "errors of prediction" (that is, values obtained by subtracting predicted values from observed values) are all identical. Thus, in predicting X_0 from X_1, the bivariate distribution is homoscedastic around the regression line.

If an observed sample of cases is taken as representative of cases not yet observed, then (on the further assumption of homoscedasticity) the standard deviation of the residuals in the sample can be taken as the standard deviation of errors in making predictions of X_0 values when only

X_1 values are known. It is then called the *standard error of estimate*. The formula is easily developed. In z form, the variance of the residuals, $V_{0.1}$, is $1 - r_{01}^2$. To find this variance in raw-score form, $(1 - r_{01}^2)$ is multiplied by the variance of the criterion in raw-score form, which yields $V_0(1 - r_{01}^2)$. The square root of this variance is the standard deviation of the residuals when X_0 is predicted, and becomes the standard error of estimate, denoted as $s_{\text{est } 0}$. Thus

$$s_{0.i} = s_{\text{est } 0} = s_0\sqrt{1 - r_{0i}^2} \tag{6.8}$$

in which the subscript 0 refers to the criterion variable, and the subscript i refers to any predictor.

If the errors in fitting the straight line connecting the two variables have widely differing standard deviations within the columns, Formula 6.8 will not be a good estimate of the standard deviations of the errors of prediction in different parts of the range. However, when the sample used in computing r is representative of samples yet to be studied, when regression is linear, and when homoscedasticity can be assumed, the formula for $s_{\text{est } 0}$ helps in the interpretation of r. The smaller $s_{\text{est } 0}$, the more accurate the predictions. When r is 1.00 (or -1.00), there is no error in estimation; and, at the other extreme, when r is .00, the standard deviation of the errors equals the standard deviation of the criterion. It is to be noted that the sign of the correlation coefficient has no effect on the standard error of estimate. Prediction on the basis of a negative r is just as effective as prediction on the basis of a positive r of the same absolute magnitude.

THE COVARIANCE AS AN AVERAGE

In connection with the derivation of r it was noted that $\Sigma(z_0 - \tilde{z}_0)^2$, the sum of the squares of the deviations from the regression line, is minimal when the slope of the line is $\Sigma z_0 z_1/N$. This gives the basic formula (from Formula 6.1) for r as

$$r_{01} = \frac{\Sigma z_0 z_1}{N} \quad \text{or} \quad r_{ij} = \frac{\Sigma z_i z_j}{N}$$

or $\tag{6.1a}$

$$r_{xy} = \frac{\Sigma z_x z_y}{N}$$

Inspection of this formula shows that a coefficient of correlation is the arithmetic mean of the products of pairs of z scores in the two variables. If each z_0 equals its corresponding z_1, then $r = \Sigma z_0 z_1/N = \Sigma z_0 z_0/N = 1.00$, which is the upper limit of the correlation coefficient. If each z_0 equals its corresponding z_1 in absolute magnitude, but is opposite in sign, then $r = \Sigma z_0 z_1/N = \Sigma z_0(-z_0)/N = -\Sigma z_0^2/N = -1.00$, which is the lower limit of r. If the $z_0 z_1$ terms do not vary together, but sum to zero, then $r = .00$, indicating no linear relationship between the two variables.

When deviation scores in two variables are multiplied together in pairs and summed and divided by N, the result is known as a *covariance*. Since a z score is a deviation score indicating the number of standard deviations a case is above or below the mean, r is the z score covariance.

A covariance is one way of stating the relationship between two variables. When there is no linear relationship, the covariance is .00. However, the maximum value of a covariance is a function of the standard deviations of the two variables concerned. Accordingly, a covariance is generally interpreted as a proportion of a variance, or it is converted into a correlation coefficient by division by the standard deviations of the two variables from which it derives.

Since covariances can sometimes be added together and sometimes fractionated into components, they are crucial in the study of relationships involving more than two variables. The concept of a correlation as a covariance of z scores with mean of zero and variance of unity is particularly convenient in the formulation of multiple and partial correlation, as discussed in Chapters 7 and 8, and in the treatment of sum variables (that is, variables obtained by adding case by case the values on two or more constituent variables), as discussed in Chapter 9.

COMPUTING FORMULAS FOR r

Formula 6.1a can be easily modified to find r from deviations in original score units. For each z, its equivalent, x/s_x, is substituted. Then,

$$r_{ij} = \frac{\Sigma z_i z_j}{N} = \frac{\Sigma \dfrac{x_i x_j}{s_i s_j}}{N} = \frac{\Sigma x_i x_j}{N s_i s_j} \qquad (6.1b)$$

The final expression is obtained by placing the constants s_i and s_j outside the summation sign. This is justifiable, since the sum of a variable with each term multiplied by a constant is the constant times the sum of the variable. If the variables are denoted as x and y, Formula 6.1b becomes

$$r_{xy} = \frac{\Sigma xy}{N s_x s_y} \qquad (6.1c)$$

Neither Formula 6.1a, nor 6.1b, nor 6.1c is very useful for computational purposes. Both z scores and deviations require conversion from the original values. Since the mean is generally a decimal fraction, each z score and each deviation is also a rather awkward decimal fraction. For greater accuracy, and especially for use with calculating machines, formulas in terms of original values are far more convenient.

TABLE 6.1. COMPUTATION OF r FROM RAW SCORES BY ALTERNATE FORMULAS

X_i = score on algebra test X_j = score on arithmetic reasoning test $N = 20$ Candidates for admission to a liberal arts college

CANDIDATES	X_i	X_j	X_i^2	X_j^2	X_iX_j	$(X_i - X_j)$	$(X_i - X_j)^2$	$(X_i + X_j)$	$(X_i + X_j)^2$
A.A.	7	22	49	484	154	−15	225	29	841
G.J.B.	1	12	1	144	12	−11	121	13	169
C.B.	6	18	36	324	108	−12	144	24	576
A.W.B.	34	40	1156	1600	1360	−6	36	74	5476
J.E.B.	13	19	169	361	247	−6	36	32	1024
R.P.C.	33	24	1089	576	792	9	81	57	3249
V.L.C.	12	13	144	169	156	−1	1	25	625
C.S.C.	7	13	49	169	91	−6	36	20	400
R.J.D.	8	12	64	144	96	−4	16	20	400
R.C.D.	13	7	169	49	91	6	36	20	400
O.J.E.	3	15	9	225	45	−12	144	18	324
P.J.E.	7	21	49	441	147	−14	196	28	784
B.R.J.	4	14	16	196	56	−10	100	18	324
S.L.K.	3	12	9	144	36	−9	81	15	225
E.N.P.	4	6	16	36	24	−2	4	10	100
J.A.P.	7	24	49	576	168	−17	289	31	961
I.G.S.	9	8	81	64	72	1	1	17	289
T.D.S.	20	17	400	289	340	3	9	37	1369
J.S.T.	0	6	0	36	0	−6	36	6	36
W.L.W.	6	13	36	169	78	−7	49	19	361

Sums

$\Sigma X_i = 197$
$\Sigma X_j = 316$
$\Sigma X_i^2 = 3591$
$\Sigma X_j^2 = 6196$

$\Sigma X_iX_j = 4073$
$\Sigma(X_i - X_j) = -119$
$\Sigma(X_i - X_j)^2 = 1641$
$\Sigma(X_i + X_j) = 513$
$\Sigma(X_i + X_j)^2 = 17{,}933$

Checks

$\Sigma X_i - \Sigma X_j = \Sigma(X_i - X_j)$
$197 - 316 = -119$

$\Sigma X_i + \Sigma X_j = \Sigma(X_i + X_j)$
$197 + 316 = 513$

$\Sigma(X_i - X_j)^2 = \Sigma X_i^2 - 2\Sigma X_iX_j + \Sigma X_j^2$
$1641 = 3591 - 8146 + 6196$

$\Sigma(X_i + X_j)^2 = \Sigma X_i^2 + 2\Sigma X_iX_j + \Sigma X_j^2$
$17{,}933 = 3591 + 8146 + 6196$

RAW-SCORE FORMULAS

A raw-score equivalent for Formula 6.1c can be developed by noting that the deviation x_i is $(X_i - M_i)$ or $(X_i - \Sigma X_i/N)$ and that x_j is $(X_j - \Sigma X_j/N)$ Then,

$$x_i x_j = \left(X_i - \frac{\Sigma X_i}{N}\right)\left(X_j - \frac{\Sigma X_j}{N}\right) = X_i X_j - X_j \frac{\Sigma X_i}{N} - X_i \frac{\Sigma X_j}{N} + \frac{\Sigma X_i}{N}\frac{\Sigma X_j}{N}$$

Summing and dividing by N,

$$\frac{\Sigma x_i x_j}{N} = \frac{\Sigma X_i X_j}{N} - \frac{\Sigma X_i}{N}\frac{\Sigma X_j}{N} - \frac{\Sigma X_j}{N}\frac{\Sigma X_i}{N} + \frac{\Sigma X_i}{N}\frac{\Sigma X_j}{N} = \frac{N\Sigma X_i X_j - \Sigma X_i \Sigma X_j}{N^2}$$

Dividing by $s_i s_j$ and their equivalents, as given by Formula 5.8a, so as to build the left-hand term up to Formula 6.1b,

$$\frac{\Sigma x_i x_j}{N s_i s_j} = r_{ij} = \frac{N\Sigma X_i X_j - \Sigma X_i \Sigma X_j}{\sqrt{N\Sigma X_i{}^2 - (\Sigma X_i)^2}\sqrt{N\Sigma X_j{}^2 - (\Sigma X_j)^2}} \tag{6.9}$$

To utilize this formula, we need N, the number of cases; $\Sigma X_i X_j$, the sum of the cross-products; ΣX_i and ΣX_j, the sums of the values in the two variables; and $\Sigma X_i{}^2$ and $\Sigma X_j{}^2$, the sums of the values squared. The use of the formula is illustrated in Example 6.1.

EXAMPLE 6.1

ALTERNATE FORMULAS IN THE COMPUTATION OF r FROM RAW SCORES

In finding correlations from raw scores, each X is, in effect, taken as a deviation from 0 in terms of a step interval of 1. Means of cross-products and means of squares are, in effect, corrected to find covariances and variances.

In Table 6.1 are shown the individual values of $X_i, X_j, X_i{}^2, X_j{}^2, X_i X_j, (X_i - X_j)$, $(X_i - X_j)^2, (X_i + X_j)$ and $(X_i + X_j)^2$. Since only sums of these values (readily obtained with a desk calculator) are of interest, there is actually no need to write out the individual values of squares or cross-products. The information on differences, sums, and their squares is presented to show certain checking procedures and to illustrate the use of alternate formulas.

Computations of Variances and Standard Deviations

$$V_i = \frac{N\Sigma X_i{}^2 - (\Sigma X_i)^2}{N^2} = \frac{(20 \times 3591) - (197)^2}{400} = \frac{33011}{400} = 82.53$$

$$s_i = \sqrt{V_i} = 9.08$$

$$V_j = \frac{N\Sigma X_j{}^2 - (\Sigma X_j)^2}{N^2} = \frac{(20 \times 6196) - (316)^2}{400} = \frac{24,064}{400} = 60.16$$

$$s_j = \sqrt{V_j} = 7.76$$

$$V_{i-j} = \frac{N\Sigma(X_i - X_j)^2 - (\Sigma X_i - X_j)^2}{N^2} = \frac{(20 \times 1641) - (-119)^2}{400} = \frac{18,659}{400} = 46.65$$

$$V_{i+j} = \frac{N\Sigma(X_i + X_j)^2 - (\Sigma X_i + X_j)^2}{N^2} = \frac{(20 \times 17,933) - (513)^2}{400} = \frac{95,491}{400} = 238.73$$

Computation of r

By Formula 6.9,

$$r_{ij} = \frac{N\Sigma X_i X_j - \Sigma X_i \Sigma X_j}{\sqrt{N\Sigma X_i^2 - (\Sigma X_i)^2}\sqrt{N\Sigma X_j^2 - (\Sigma X_j)^2}} = \frac{(20 \times 4073) - (197 \times 316)}{\sqrt{(20 \times 3591) - (197)^2}\sqrt{(20 \times 6196) - (316)^2}}$$

$$= \frac{19,208}{28,185.57} = .68$$

By Formula 6.10,

$$r_{ij} = \frac{V_i + V_j - V_{(i-j)}}{2s_is_j} = \frac{82.53 + 60.16 - 46.65}{2 \times 9.08 \times 7.76} = \frac{96.04}{140.92} = .68$$

By Formula 6.11,

$$r_{ij} = \frac{V_{(i+j)} - V_i - V_j}{2s_is_j} = \frac{238.73 - 82.53 - 60.16}{2 \times 9.08 \times 7.76} = \frac{96.04}{140.92} = .68$$

Generally, only formulas involving sums of cross-products, such as Formula 6.9, are used for computing r from raw scores. If each set of X_i and X_j is entered simultaneously in the keyboard of a desk calculator that has, say, seven places between the decimal positions of each, and then multiplied by the same X_i and X_j, (also with seven places between the decimal positions), then in repeated operations ΣX_i and ΣX_j will accumulate in the multiplier dials (with seven places between decimal positions), and ΣX_i^2, $2\Sigma X_i X_j$, and ΣX_j^2 will accumulate in the product dials (also with seven places between decimal positions). (Some machines have squaring devices that permit keyboard entries to be used both as multiplicands and as multipliers.)

Formula 6.9 is also generally used when the intercorrelations of a number of variables are needed. If the variables are X_i, X_j ... X_n, then ΣX_i and ΣX_i^2 need be found only once for each variable (except perhaps for checking), while each sum of cross-products (such as $\Sigma X_i X_j$) is found again as $\Sigma X_j X_i$. If cross-products check, it is generally assumed that sums of squares are correct.

FORMULAS FOR CODED SCORES

A parallel development yields a formula for r in terms of scores coded as x'_i and x'_j, the number of step intervals from "assumed means." The derivation involves using Formula 5.13a to set up equivalents of x_i and x_j the true deviation scores in the two variables, as follows:

$$x_i x_j = i_i\left(x'_i - \frac{\Sigma x'_i}{N}\right)i_j\left(x'_j - \frac{\Sigma x'_j}{N}\right)$$

in which i_i is the step interval used to code variable i, and i_j is the step interval used to code variable j.

Multiplying terms, summing, writing equivalents, and dividing by the standard deviations (in the form given by Formula 5.15a), the following formula for r is obtained:

$$r_{ij} = \frac{N\Sigma x'_i x'_j - \Sigma x'_i \Sigma x'_j}{\sqrt{N\Sigma x'^2_i - (\Sigma x'_i)^2}\sqrt{N\Sigma x'^2_j - (\Sigma x'_j)^2}} \qquad (6.9a)$$

If the derivation of this formula is written out in full, it will be seen that i_i and i_j, representing the two step intervals, drop out from both the numerator and denominator. The use of this formula[5] is demonstrated in Examples 6.2 and 6.3.

EXAMPLE 6.2

THE COMPUTATION OF r FROM A SCATTER DIAGRAM

(Conventional Method)

Theory. While the computation of r, using original raw scores, may be regarded as yielding maximum accuracy, there is actually little loss in precision if the correlation is found through the use of coded scores. The coded scores demonstrated in this example are of the kind employed in Example 5.3 for the computation of the mean and the variance. Here, however, two variables are treated simultaneously, instead of only one. While not needed in solving for r, means and standard deviations for the two variables can be readily found from the scatter diagram (Table 6.2).

Preparation of Scatter Diagram. It is sometimes stated that 10 to 20 steps are needed to code each variable if the obtained correlation is to be a close approximation of the r obtained from raw scores. However, empirical studies have shown that as few as nine steps can adequately represent a variable when N is large, say, 1000 or more.

Table 6.2 shows the scores of 20 first-year law students in two tests: vocabulary and reading comprehension. As explained in Chapter 5, the high and low scores (marked H and L) are used in determining the approximate number of categories any step interval will yield. Here, only five steps are used in X and only six in Y. For serious research, both the N of 20 and the numbers of categories would, of course, be regarded as inadequate.

---

[5] Few formulas appear in different statistics texts in as wide a variety of guises as this one. Sometimes numerator and denominator have been divided by N^2 so that the first term in each pair appears divided by N; the second term, by N^2. Sometimes $\Sigma x'/N$ appears as c, a correction term. Often, terms involving x' appear as df and terms involving x'^2 as d^2f, the d representing the deviation in terms of step intervals and the f representing frequencies. However, all formulas involving summation of cross-products of coded scores are fundamentally the same.

TABLE 6.2. SCORES OF 20 INDIVIDUALS ON TWO TESTS

INDIVIDUAL	VOCA-BULARY TEST (Y)	LEVEL OF READING COMPRE-HENSION (X)	INDIVIDUAL	VOCA-BULARY TEST (Y)	LEVEL OF READING COMPRE-HENSION (X)
B.A.	46	23	S.K.	56	24
D.A.	42	27	C.L.	42	21
P.A.	54	24	D.L.	50	30
H.B.	44	24	M.L.	59 (H)	28
R.B.	43	20	P.L.	34 (L)	18 (L)
A.C.	48	28	B.S.	48	19
R.G.	48	22	I.S.	56	30 (H)
A.H.	47	23	R.S.	43	24
B.J.	37	21	A.T.	39	23
D.J.	45	18(L)	F.W.	49	27

The 20 Scores Tallied in a Scatter Diagram

Y VOCABULARY TEST, $i_y = 5$	X LEVEL OF READING COMPREHENSION, $i_x = 3$				
	18–20	21–23	24–26	27–29	30–32
55–59			I	I	I
50–54			I		I
45–49	II	III		II	
40–44	I	I	II	I	
35–39		II			
30–34	I				

It is readily seen from Table 6.2 that each tally mark represents two scores, one in Y and the other in X. Thus, the first pair of scores, for B.A., is represented as one of the three tallies in the cell corresponding to a Y score of 45–49 and an X score of 21–23. In effect, it is coded at the two midpoints, 47 and 22. As N and the numbers of categories increase, the grouping error in a scatter diagram becomes negligible, just as with a frequency distribution.

In making a two-dimensional plot of tallies corresponding to two sets of values, it is often convenient to use a straightedge on which are indicated the step limits of X. As this straightedge is positioned in accordance with the Y value, the correct placing of the tally within the proper cell is facilitated.

Computation of r. Finding a correlation coefficient from a scatter diagram is demonstrated in Table 6.3. The following notation is used:

d_x = deviation in step-interval units from M'_x, the assumed X mean.

d_y = deviation in step-interval units from M'_y, the assumed Y mean.

$d_x d_y$ = the product of the X and Y deviations (both in step-interval units).

f_x = frequency of any X step.

f_y = frequency of any Y step.

f_{xy} = frequency within any cell.

TABLE 6.3. COMPUTATION OF r_{xy} FOR 20 INDIVIDUALS ON TWO TESTS
(Together with M_x, M_y, s_x and s_y.)

Y	X 18–20	21–23	24–26	27–29	30–32	f_y	d_y	d_yf_y	$d_y{}^2f_y$	$d_xd_yf_{xy}$
55–59			(10) 1	(15) 1	(20) 1	3	5	15	75	45
50–54			(8) 1		(16) 1	2	4	8	32	24
45–49	2	(3) 3		(9) 2		7	3	21	63	27
40–44	1	(2) 1	(4) 2	(6) 1		5	2	10	20	16
35–39		(1) 2				2	1	2	2	2
30–34	1					1	0	0	0	0
f_x	4	6	4	4	2	$N=20$	Sums: 56		192	114
d_x	0	1	2	3	4			($\Sigma y'$)	($\Sigma y'^2$)	($\Sigma x'y'$)
d_xf_x	0	6	8	12	8	Sums: 34 ($\Sigma x'$)				
$d_x{}^2f_x$	0	6	16	36	32	90 ($\Sigma x'^2$)				

By Formula 6.9a,

$$r_{xy} = \frac{N\Sigma x'y' - \Sigma x'\Sigma y'}{\sqrt{N\Sigma x'^2 - (\Sigma x')^2}\ \sqrt{N\Sigma y'^2 - (\Sigma y')^2}}$$

$$= \frac{(20 \times 114) - (34 \times 56)}{\sqrt{20 \times 90 - (34)^2}\ \sqrt{20 \times 192 - (56)^2}}$$

$$= \frac{376}{\sqrt{644}\ \sqrt{704}} = .56$$

By Formula 5.13,

$$M_x = M'_x + \frac{i_x\Sigma x'}{N} = 19 + \frac{3 \times 34}{20} = 24.1$$

$$M_y = M'_y + \frac{i_y\Sigma y'}{N} = 32 + \frac{5 \times 56}{20} = 46.0$$

By Formula 5.15a,

$$s_x = \frac{i_x}{N}\sqrt{N\Sigma x'^2 - (\Sigma x')^2} = \frac{3}{20}\sqrt{20 \times 90 - (34)^2}$$

$$= \frac{3}{20}\sqrt{644} = 3.81$$

$$s_y = \frac{i_y}{N}\sqrt{N\Sigma y'^2 - (\Sigma y')^2} = \frac{5}{20}\sqrt{20 \times 192 - (56)^2}$$

$$= \frac{5}{20}\sqrt{704} = 6.63$$

With conventional numbers of categories, say, ten or more, the assumed means are often taken near the center of each distribution, thus reducing the numerical size of the constants entering into the formula for r. Here, for convenience and to avoid all negative values, the assumed means are taken as the midpoints of the lowest step in each distribution.

Step Frequencies. The f_x and f_y are found by summing the cell frequencies (f_{xy}) in columns and in rows. Then $\Sigma f_x = \Sigma f_y = N$.

Step frequencies are multiplied by corresponding d's to form $d_x f_x$ and $d_y f_y$ products, which are then summed to find $\Sigma x'$ and $\Sigma y'$, respectively. In Table 6.3, $\Sigma d_x f_x = \Sigma x' = 34$ and $\Sigma d_y f_y = \Sigma y' = 56$.

The $d_x f_x$ are multiplied by the corresponding d_x to form the $d_x^2 f_x$ products which, when summed, yield $\Sigma x'^2$ (in this case, 90). Similarly, $\Sigma y'^2$ is found as $\Sigma d_y^2 f_y$, or 192.

$\Sigma x'y'$ is found as $\Sigma d_x d_y f_{xy}$. In each cell the product of the two d's is shown in parentheses. When this $d_x d_y$ is multiplied by the corresponding cell frequency (f_{xy}), the sum of the products is the sum of the cross-products of the coded scores. In Table 6.3, $\Sigma d_x d_y f_{xy} = \Sigma x'y' = 114$.

Below the table, Formula 6.9a has been applied to find r_{xy}, Formula 5.13 to find M_x and M_y, and Formula 5.15a to find s_x and s_y.

Checking Procedures. The bivariate distribution of Table 6.2 may be checked by making a completely new diagram or by placing a dot at the end of the appropriate tally as each pair of scores is examined. A good way of checking the computations is to rework them on a new copy of the scatter diagram, using a different M' in both X and Y.

Comparison of Computations with Raw and Coded Scores. Although N is small and steps are few, results by coding (Formulas 5.13, 5.15a, and 6.9a) do not seem to differ much from results by raw-score methods (Formulas 5.1, 5.8a, and 6.9), as shown in the table below:

	RESULTS WITH CODED SCORES	RESULTS WITH RAW SCORES
M_x	24.1	23.7
M_y	46.0	46.5
s_x	3.8	3.6
s_y	6.6	6.3
r_{xy}	.56	.58

A Second Problem. A bivariate distribution based on 582 cases is presented in Table 6.4 together with computations leading to r_{xy}, M_x, M_y, s_x, and s_y. Because the assumed means are chosen near the sample means, a large proportion of the d is negative; and the resulting negative values of $d_x f_x$, $d_y f_y$, and $d_x d_y f_{xy}$ are summed with proper attention to sign. All values of $d_x^2 f_x$ and $d_y^2 f_y$ are, of course, positive.

Steps in preparing a scatter diagram, such as the one shown in Table 6.4,

TABLE 6.4. COMPUTATION OF r FROM A SCATTER DIAGRAM (CONVENTIONAL METHOD)

(N = 582 freshmen entering a university; X = reading comprehension; Y = reading rate.)

X = reading comprehension across columns; values shown as frequency with the $d_x d_y$ cross-product in parentheses.

Y	70–79	80–89	90–99	100–109	110–119	120–129	130–139	140–149	150–159	160–169	170–179	180–189	190–199	200–209	210–219	f_y	d_y	$d_y f_y$	$d_y^2 f_y$	$d_x d_y f_{xy}$ (+)	$d_x d_y f_{xy}$ (−)
84–87												(28) 1				1	7	7	49	28	
80–83											(18) 2	(24) 3		(36) 1	(42) 1	7	6	42	252	186	
76–79										(10) 1	(15) 3	(20) 3	(25) 4	(30) 1		12	5	60	300	245	
72–75								1		(8) 4	(12) 11	(16) 7	(20) 6	(24) 1		30	4	120	480	420	
68–71					(−9) 1	(−6) 1	(−3) 1	1	(3) 13	(6) 6	(9) 8	(12) 6	(15) 6	(18) 3		46	3	138	414	363	−18
64–67				(−8) 2	(−6) 1	(−4) 2	(−2) 6	10	(2) 12	(4) 6	(6) 17	(8) 15	(10) 5	(12) 1		77	2	154	308	332	−42
60–63			(−5) 1	(−4) 1	(−3) 1	(−2) 4	(−1) 9	12	(1) 18	(2) 25	(3) 14	(4) 13	(5) 2	(6) 1		101	1	101	101	178	−29
56–59	1	1	1	3	6	9	14	18	20	12	8	5	2			100	0	0	0		
52–55			(5) 1	(4) 6	(3) 4	(2) 13	(1) 21	13	(−1) 10	(−2) 8	(−3) 4	(−4) 4				84	−1	−84	84	88	−54
48–51		(12) 1	(10) 4	(8) 8	(6) 6	(4) 6	(2) 10	14	(−2) 5	(−4) 8						62	−2	−124	248	196	−42
44–47	(21) 2		(15) 2	(12) 5	(9) 2	(6) 4	(3) 8	6	(−3) 3	(−6) 1	(−9) 1					34	−3	−102	306	198	−24
40–43		(24) 1	(20) 2	(16) 1	(12) 3	(8) 4	(4) 3	3		(−8) 1						18	−4	−72	288	160	−8
36–39		(30) 1	(25) 2		(15) 1		(5) 1	2								7	−5	−35	175	100	
32–35		(36) 1														1	−6	−6	36	36	
28–31		(42) 1	(35) 1													2	−7	−14	98	77	
f_x	2	6	14	26	25	43	73	80	81	72	68	57	25	9	1	N = 582					
d_x	−7	−6	−5	−4	−3	−2	−1	0	1	2	3	4	5	6	7						
$d_x f_x$	−14	−36	−70	−104	−75	−86	−73	0	81	144	204	228	125	54	7						
$d_x^2 f_x$	98	216	350	416	225	172	73	0	81	288	612	912	625	324	49						

Sums:
+385 $(\Sigma x')$
4441 $(\Sigma x'^2)$

Sums:
+185 $(\Sigma y')$
3139 $(\Sigma y'^2)$
2607 $\Sigma x'y'$ = +2390
−217

$i_x = 10$
$i_y = 4$

By Formula 6.9a,
$$r_{xy} = \frac{N\Sigma x'y' - \Sigma x'\Sigma y'}{\sqrt{N\Sigma x'^2 - (\Sigma x')^2}\sqrt{N\Sigma y'^2 - (\Sigma y')^2}}$$

$$= \frac{(582 \times 2390) - (385 \times 185)}{\sqrt{582 \times 4441 - (385)^2}\sqrt{582 \times 3139 - (185)^2}} = .63$$

By Formula 5.13,
$$M_x = M'_x + \frac{i_x\Sigma x'}{N} = 144.5 + \frac{10 \times 385}{582} = 151.12$$

$$M_y = M'_y + \frac{i_y\Sigma y'}{N} = 57.5 + \frac{4 \times 185}{582} = 58.77$$

By Formula 5.15a,
$$s_x = \frac{i_x}{N}\sqrt{N\Sigma x'^2 - (\Sigma x')^2} = \frac{10}{582}\sqrt{582 \times 4441 - (385)^2} = 26.82$$

Similarly,
$$s_y = \frac{4}{582}\sqrt{582 \times 3139 - (185)^2} = 9.20$$

and in solving for r, follow:

1. Choose i_x and i_y, the two step intervals, so that appropriate numbers of categories result.

2. Make and check the bivariate distribution.

3. Sum the f_{xy}'s in the rows to find the f_y's and in the columns to find the f_x's. Check: $\Sigma f_x = \Sigma f_y = N$.

4. Find $\Sigma x'$ as the sum of the f_x's multiplied by the d_x's and $\Sigma y'$ as the sum of the f_y's multiplied by the d_y's.

5. Find $\Sigma x'^2$ as the sum of the $d_x f_x$'s multiplied by the d_x's and $\Sigma y'^2$ as the sum of the $d_y f_y$'s multiplied by the d_y's. (When a calculating machine is being used, writing of individual products such as the $d_x f_x$'s should be avoided. In that case the f_x's can be multiplied by the squares of the d's; that is, by the d_x^2's, and products accumulated).

6. Enter the $d_x d_y$'s in the individual cells, with proper attention to sign, and multiply by the f_{xy}'s. The sum of the products is $\Sigma x'y'$.

7. All work should be checked before applying formulas to find r and other constants. In both variables, Charlier's check (as described in Chapter 5) applies. There are also more or less obvious alternate ways of finding $\Sigma x'y'$, such as multiplying the f_{xy}'s within rows by the corresponding d_x's and recording the sums, row by row; and subsequently multiplying each of these summed $d_x f_{xy}$'s by the d_y of the row. The overall sum will, of course, be $\Sigma d_x d_y f_{xy}$ or $\Sigma x'y'$.

Another method is to prepare a new diagram, using new assumed means. $\Sigma x'$, $\Sigma y'$, $\Sigma x'^2$, $\Sigma y'^2$, and $\Sigma x'y'$ will have different numerical values, but if the arithmetic is correct, the correlation and other constants will be precisely identical in the two sets of computations.

EXAMPLE 6.3

THE COMPUTATION OF r FROM A SCATTER DIAGRAM
(Cumulative Method)

Purpose. This cumulative method of finding r takes advantage of economies effected through the use of a calculating machine. It also provides an unusually convenient system of checks for sums, sums of squares, and the sum of the cross-products of the coded scores.

Comparison with Conventional Method. Both preparation of the scatter diagram and final computation of r_{xy}, M_x, M_y, s_x, and s_y are exactly the same as in the conventional method. If identical M' are used, then $\Sigma x'$, $\Sigma y'$, $\Sigma x'^2$, $\Sigma y'^2$, and $\Sigma x'y'$ will also be identical. The chief difference is that much of the multiplication is accomplished by addition, as in one of the methods of finding M_x and s_x demonstrated in Example 5.4.

Finding the Cumulative Frequencies. Cumulative frequencies, rather than frequencies, are found for both rows and columns. All work in either the X or Y variable starts as far from the origin as possible and is carried toward the origin. Starting with the first row in which there are tallies, the cell frequencies are added into the adding machine or calculator and the total of the cell frequencies in that row is entered in the column headed Cf_y. This sum is not cleared from the machine, but is added to the cell frequencies in the row below to form the cumulative frequency for that row. If a row has no tallies, the Cf_y is the same as that of the preceding row. The Cf_y of the bottom row is necessarily N, the number of cases. The procedure is readily apparent from an inspection of Table 6.5, in which the successive Cf_y are 3, 5, 12, 17, 19, and 20.

By a process exactly analogous, the cumulative frequencies in X are found. Tallies or f_{xy}'s in the column farthest to the right are added to find the first Cf_x. Without clearing the machine, the tallies or f_{xy}'s in the column to the left are added to find the next Cf_x, and so on across to the column containing the X origin, the Cf_x of which is N. Thus, in Table 6.5, the Cf_x's, beginning at the left, are 2, 6, 10, 16, and 20.

The Computation of $\Sigma y'$. To obtain $\Sigma y'$, the Cf_y's are added, excluding the entry in the step that contains the assumed mean. This method of computing the sum of the deviations in terms of step intervals from the arbitrary origin takes advantage of the principle that the sum of a series of cumulative frequencies is equal to the sum of the products of each frequency times its deviation from the origin in terms of step intervals. This fact is easily noted from the algebraic example below:

f_y	d_y	$d_y f_y$	Cf_y
a	n	na	a
.	.	.	.
.	.	.	.
.	.	.	.
h	3	$3h$	$a + \cdots + h$
i	2	$2i$	$a + \cdots + h + i$
j	1	j	$a + \cdots + h + i + j$

$$\Sigma Cf_y = na + \cdots + 3h + 2i + j$$

The frequencies are indicated in the column headed f_y and are $a \ldots h, i, j$. The column headed d_y gives the deviations in terms of step intervals from the arbitrary origin. The column headed $d_y f_y$ gives the products of the deviations in step intervals as obtained in the ordinary multiplicative method of computing the mean from an assumed mean. The column headed Cf_y gives the cumulative frequencies. Since there are n of these cumulative frequencies, in all of which a is represented, na will be a part of ΣCf_y. It is readily apparent, that irrespective of the number of terms or the values of the frequencies, the sums of the two columns $d_y f_y$ and Cf_y are identical. In summing the cumulative frequencies to obtain $\Sigma y'$, care must be taken not to include N in the step containing the origin.

Computation of $\Sigma y'^2$. To compute $\Sigma y'^2$, the Cf_y are multiplied by the successive odd numbers, beginning with unity in the step above the one that contains the assumed mean. The sum of these products is $\Sigma y'^2$. This method of computing the sum of the squares of the deviations in terms of step intervals from the arbitrary origin is an application of the fact that the sum of a series of odd numbers beginning with unity is equal to n^2 when n is the number of terms in the series. The algebraic basis of this principle is given in the table below:

f_y	$d_y{}^2$	Cf_y		m	mCf_y
a	n^2	a		$2n-1$	$(2n-1)a$
.	.	.		.	.
.	.	.		.	.
.	.	.		.	.
h	9	$a + \cdots + h$		5	$5a + \cdots + 5h$
i	4	$a + \cdots + h + i$		3	$3a + \cdots + 3h + 3i$
j	1	$a + \cdots + h + i + j$		1	$a + \cdots + h + i + j$
					$\Sigma mCfy = n^2 a + \cdots + 9h + 4i + j$

The successive odd numbers are denoted as m, or the multiplying factors. It will be seen that $\Sigma mCf_y = \Sigma d_y{}^2 f_y$. Again the cumulative frequency in the step containing the assumed mean is ignored.

Numerical Computation of $\Sigma y'$ and $\Sigma y'^2$. When a key-driven adding machine is used to compute $\Sigma y'$ and $\Sigma y'^2$, two series of operations are performed: the summing of the Cf_y's and summing of the products of each Cf_y with its corresponding m. When a calculating machine is used, the two quantities are found in one series of operations. Each m is placed in the keyboard and multiplied by the corresponding Cf_y. The accumulation of the multipliers is ΣCf_y, or $\Sigma y'$, and the accumulation of products in the product dials is ΣmCf_y, or $\Sigma y'^2$. Here, ΣCf_y is 56 and ΣmCf_y is 192. $\Sigma x'$ and $\Sigma x'^2$ are computed similarly. $\Sigma x'$ and $\Sigma y'$ are written twice in connection with Charlier's check on the sums of squares.

In Table 6.5, m's and m'''s are written out. If a calculating machine is used, the operator can put m's and m'''s in the keyboard successively, and they need not appear on the diagram showing the work. This practice is followed in Table 6.6, which also omits the d_x's and d_y's which would ordinarily appear only on pieces of cardboard used to facilitate computation.

TABLE 6.5. COMPUTATION OF r BY A CUMULATIVE METHOD
(Data are the same as in Table 6.2)

		X								
		18–20	21–23	24–26	27–29	30–32				
		d_x								
Y	d_y	0	1	2	3	4	Cf_y	m	m'	$C\Sigma d_x f_{xy}$
55–59	5			1	1	1	3	9	11	9
50–54	4			1		1	5	7	9	15
45–49	3	2	3		2		12	5	7	24
40–44	2	1	1	2	1		17	3	5	32
35–39	1		2				19	1	3	34
30–34	0	1					20		1	34
Cf_x		20 (N)	16	10	6	2	(N)			($\Sigma x'$)
m			1	3	5	7				
m'		1	3	5	7	9				
$C\Sigma d_y f_{xy}$		56 ($\Sigma y'$)	48	35	22	9				

$$\Sigma C\Sigma d_y f_{xy} = \Sigma C\Sigma d_x f_{xy} = \Sigma x'y' = 114(\surd)$$

$$r = \frac{N\Sigma x'y' - \Sigma x'\Sigma y'}{\sqrt{N\Sigma x'^2 - (\Sigma x')^2}\,\sqrt{N\Sigma y'^2 - (\Sigma y')^2}} = \frac{(20 \times 114) - (34 \times 56)}{\sqrt{20 \times 90 - (34)^2}\,\sqrt{20 \times 192 - (56)^2}} = .56$$

$$N = 20 \qquad\qquad N = 20$$
$$\Sigma Cf_x = \Sigma x' = 34(\surd) \qquad \Sigma Cf_y = \Sigma y' = 56(\surd)$$
$$\Sigma x' = 34 \qquad\qquad \Sigma y' = 56$$
$$\Sigma mCf_x = \Sigma x'^2 = 90(\surd) \qquad \Sigma mCf_y = \Sigma y'^2 = 192(\surd)$$
$$\overline{\Sigma m'Cf_x = 178} \qquad\qquad \overline{\Sigma m'Cf_y = 324}$$

TABLE 6.6. COMPUTATION OF r FROM A SCATTER DIAGRAM (CUMULATIVE METHOD)
(Data are the same as in Table 6.4)

Y \ X	70–79	80–89	90–99	100–109	110–119	120–129	130–139	140–149	150–159	160–169	170–179	180–189	190–199	200–209	210–219	Cf_y	$C\Sigma d_x f_{xy}$
84–87												1				1	11
80–83											2	3		1	1	8	91
76–79										1	3	3	4	1		20	224
72–75								1		4	11	7	6	1		50	539
68–71					1	1	1	1	13	6	8	6	6	3		96	976
64–67				2	1	2	6	10	12	6	17	15	5	1		173	1660
60–63			1	1	1	4	9	12	18	25	14	13	2	1		274	2516
56–59		1	1	3	6	9	14	18	20	12	8	5	2	1		374	3247
52–55		1	1	6	4	13	21	13	10	8	4	4				458	3801
48–51			4	8	6	6	10	14	5	8						520	4158
44–47	2		2	5	2	4	8	6	3	1	1					554	4338
40–43		1	2	1	3	4	3	3		1						572	4426
36–39		1	2	1	1			2								579	4455
32–35		1														580	4456
28–31		1	1													582	4459
Cf_x	582 (N)	580	574	560	534	509	466	393	313	232	160	92	35	10	1	(N)	(Σx')
$C\Sigma d_y f_{xy}$	4259 (Σy')	4251	4233	4174	4028	3886	3627	3174	2656	2037	1488	876	352	103	13		

$\Sigma C\Sigma d_y f_{xy} = \Sigma C\Sigma d_x f_{xy} = \Sigma x'y' = 34{,}898$

Results of Computations $r_{xy} = .63$ $M_x = 151.12$ $M_y = 58.77$

$s_x = 26.82$ $s_y = 9.20$

$N = 582$

$\Sigma Cf_x = \Sigma x' = 4{,}459\,(\checkmark)$
$\Sigma x' = 4{,}459$
$\Sigma m Cf_x = \Sigma x'^2 = 38{,}349\,(\checkmark)$
$\Sigma m' Cf_x = 47{,}849$

$N = 582$

$\Sigma Cf_y = \Sigma y' = 4{,}259\,(\checkmark)$
$\Sigma y' = 4{,}259$
$\Sigma m Cf_y = \Sigma y'^2 = 34{,}247\,(\checkmark)$
$\Sigma m' Cf_y = 43{,}347$

Charlier's Check. As already noted in connection with Example 5.3, the basic formula for Charlier's check is $\Sigma(y'+1)^2 = \Sigma y'^2 + 2\Sigma y' + N$. That is to say, if we drop the assumed mean just one step interval, and thereby increase the value of all deviations by 1, the new sum of squares will be equal to the old sum of squares plus twice the sum of the deviations from the old origin plus N. The successive odd numbers denoted by m' are designed for use with Charlier's check. The procedure used in determining ΣCf_y and ΣmCf_y is repeated, and the sum of the products of the m''s and the Cf_y's is entered as $\Sigma m'Cf_y$. When it appears that this value is equal to the sum of the four entries above it, a check is obtained on the computation of $\Sigma y'^2$. In Table 6.5, $20 + 56 + 56 + 192 = 324$.

Computation of $\Sigma x'y'$ (working within the columns). $\Sigma x'y'$ is computed twice. Working within columns, each cell frequency (designated as f_{xy}) is multiplied by the corresponding d_y and the sum of these products for the column at the right is entered in the row labeled $C\Sigma d_y f_{xy}$. Without clearing this sum from the machine, the cell frequencies in the next column nearer the origin are similarly multiplied by the d_y's, and the cumulative sum written in the appropriate row. The work is carried through the column that includes the X origin. The last entry is $\Sigma y'$, but this entry is used only as a check upon the previous computation of $\Sigma y'$. The sum of all the entries in this bottom row of the diagram, including the entry in the column containing the X origin, is $\Sigma C\Sigma d_y f_{xy}$, or $\Sigma x'y'$. In Table 6.5, the successive entries are $(5 \times 1) + (4 \times 1) = 9$; $9 + (5 \times 1) + (3 \times 2) \times (2 \times 1) = 22$; $22 + (5 \times 1) + (4 \times 1) + (2 \times 2) = 35$; $35 + (3 \times 3) + (2 \times 1) + (1 \times 2) = 48$; $48 + (3 \times 2) + (2 \times 1) = 56$. $\Sigma y'$ is 56 both in this operation and in the operation involving the Cf_y. $\Sigma C\Sigma d_y f_{xy} = \Sigma x'y' = 48 + 35 + 22 + 9 = 114$. It is to be noted that the entries in the row containing the Y origin are not used in computing the cross-products.

Computation of $\Sigma x'y'$ (working within the rows). The process of computing $\Sigma x'y'$ from the rows is exactly analogous to the process of computing $\Sigma x'y'$ from the columns. Beginning with the row farthest from the origin, work proceeds toward the origin in Y. Each cell frequency (f_{xy}) is multiplied by its corresponding d_x, and the product is entered in the extreme right-hand column headed by $C\Sigma d_x f_{xy}$. Without clearing the first entry from the machine, the entry for the next row is computed and entered in the allotted space. This continues through the row containing the origin in Y, in which case the entry is $\Sigma x'$ and becomes a check on the previous computation of this figure. The sum of the entries in the column, excluding the final entry, is $\Sigma C\Sigma d_x f_{xy}$, or $\Sigma x'y'$. In Table 6.5, $(2 \times 1) + (3 \times 1) + (4 \times 1) = 9$; $9 + (2 \times 1) + (4 \times 1) = 15$; $15 + (1 \times 3) + (3 \times 2) = 24$; $24 + (1 \times 1) + (2 \times 2) + (3 \times 1) = 32$; $32 + (1 \times 2) = 34$; and this entry is repeated for the final row. In computing $\Sigma x'y'$ from either the rows or the columns, it is convenient to use a strip of cardboard with the d's written on it.

Algebraic Explanation of the Computing Principle in Finding $\Sigma x'y'$. Consider a tally in a cell with a d_y value of a and a d_x value of b. When working in the columns, this tally takes on a value of a, and since cumulative sums are used, it appears in the $C\Sigma d_y f_{xy}$ row b times; hence it adds ab to the value of $\Sigma x'y'$. In a similar fashion the tally contributes ab to the $C\Sigma d_x f_{xy}$ column.

Comparison with Table 6.3. $\Sigma x'$, $\Sigma y'$, $\Sigma x'^2$, $\Sigma y'^2$, and $\Sigma x'y'$ are exactly the same in Table 6.5 and Table 6.3. This is to be expected, since the data are identical and identical assumed means are used.

Recapitulation. In the procedure described above, the suggested routine is as follows:

1. Sum all the cell frequencies in the rows, obtaining the cumulative frequencies in Y, the last entry being N.

2. Sum the frequencies in the columns, obtaining the cumulative frequencies in X, the last entry again being N.

3. Obtain $\Sigma y'$ by summing the cumulative frequencies down to, but not including, the step containing the assumed mean in Y and $\Sigma y'^2$ by multiplying the m's by corresponding Cf_y's. Check the results through the use of the Charlier formula. Repeat the routine to obtain $\Sigma x'$ and to obtain and check $\Sigma x'^2$.

4. Compute $\Sigma x'y'$ by multiplying the cell frequencies in each column by the corresponding d_y, cumulating all results toward the origin. The last entry in the row labeled $C\Sigma d_y f_{xy}$ is $\Sigma y'$. In the rows in which each cell frequency is multiplied by its corresponding d_x and the resulting sums are cumulated toward the Y origin, the $C\Sigma d_x f_{xy}$ are found. In this way, $\Sigma x'$ and $\Sigma x'y'$ are checked.

5. The coefficient of correlation is obtained by Formula 6.9a, the means by Formula 5.13, and the standard deviations by Formula 5.15a.

A Second Example. In Table 6.6, the data of Table 6.4 are reworked by this cumulative method. Since different arbitrary origins are used, the sums, sums of squares, and sums of cross-products of coded scores are also different; but final results are, of course, identical.

THE DIFFERENCE FORMULA AND THE SUM FORMULA FOR r

A coefficient of correlation may be computed from three variances (or standard deviations): the variances of the two variables being correlated, and either the variance of the differences between pairs of scores, or the variance of the sums of pairs of scores.

Consider two variables, x_i and x_j, measured as deviations from their respective means. Let V_i and V_j be their variances and C_{ij} their co-variance,[6] all in original score units. Then,

$$x_i - x_j = x_i - x_j$$

Squaring, summing, and dividing by N,

$$\frac{\Sigma(x_i - x_j)^2}{N} = \frac{\Sigma x_i^2}{N} - \frac{2\Sigma x_i x_j}{N} + \frac{\Sigma x_j^2}{N}$$

Writing equivalents yields

$$V_{(i-j)} = V_i - 2C_{ij} + V_j$$

---

[6] In mathematical statistics "Cov" is often used as the symbol for covariance. Here, C is used. While it is the same symbol that is used for the contingency coefficient, the two concepts should not be confused.

in which $V_{(i-j)}$ is the variance of the difference between X_i and X_j values. Since adding or subtracting a constant has no effect on the variance of a variable, the variance of raw-score differences is exactly the same as the variance of the differences in deviation scores.

Solving for C_{ij}, we have

$$C_{ij} = \frac{V_i + V_j - V_{(i-j)}}{2}$$

and dividing by $s_i s_j$ gives

$$\frac{C_{ij}}{s_i s_j} = r_{ij} = \frac{V_i + V_j - V_{(i-j)}}{2 s_i s_j} = \frac{s_i^2 + s_j^2 - s_{(i-j)}^2}{2 s_i s_j} \tag{6.10}$$

An exactly parallel development, starting with $(x_i + x_j)$ yields the sum formula:

$$r_{ij} = \frac{V_{(i+j)} - V_i - V_j}{2 s_i s_j} = \frac{s_{(i+j)}^2 - s_i^2 - s_j^2}{2 s_i s_j} \tag{6.11}$$

Formulas 6.10 and 6.11, which are applied in Example 6.1, also appear in various guises: in terms of deviations in step intervals from assumed means and in terms of raw scores. Many published correlation charts are based upon Formula 6.10, which requires no cross-products and a relatively small number of steps for the distribution of the differences. Incidentally, Formula 6.11 may be readily solved for $V_{(i+j)}$, giving the variance of a new variable found by adding X_i and X_j in pairs:

$$V_{(i+j)} = V_i + V_j + 2 r_{ij} s_i s_j = V_i + V_j + 2 C_{ij} \tag{6.12}$$

INTERPRETATION OF r

ROLE OF N, THE NUMBER OF CASES

As stated earlier, it is impossible to find a correlation for a single pair of observations. In that case, $N = 1$, and no variable has been established. With two pairs of observations, r is either 1.00 or -1.00. With three pairs of observations, r can take four different values, and as N increases without limit, so does the number of possible different values of r. However, the restriction remains that r cannot be greater than 1.00 nor less than -1.00.

One exceedingly important characteristic of a correlation is its reliability, that is, the degree to which it can be expected to be stable if computed from subsequent samples of the same size drawn at random from the same unlimited population. As developed in Chapter 13, reliability estimates are greatly affected by sample size. Accordingly, while the size of r is independent of N, the number of cases is of crucial importance in determining the significance of r.

THE ROLE OF UNITS OF MEASUREMENT

A correlation coefficient is a pure number, completely independent of the units used to measure either variable.

Any variable may be transformed linearly by adding or subtracting a constant, or by multiplying or dividing by a constant, or by both addition (or subtraction) and multiplication (or division), without in any way affecting the correlations of the variable.

Let X' be any linear function of X, so that

$$X' = bX + c \tag{6.13}$$

in which b and c are constants.

Summing,

$$\Sigma X' = b\Sigma X + Nc$$

Dividing by N and writing equivalents,

$$M_{x'} = bM_x + c \tag{6.14}$$

Subtracting Eq. 6.14 from Eq. 6.13 and writing the deviations, x' for $(X' - M_{x'})$ and x for $(X - M_x)$, yields

$$x' = bx \tag{6.15}$$

If we square both sides of Eq. 6.15, then sum and divide by N and extract square roots, it is seen that

$$s_{x'} = bs_x \tag{6.16}$$

This shows that multiplication (or division) of all scores by a constant will multiply (or divide) the standard deviation by that constant. However, addition (or subtraction) of a constant has no effect.

We can now compare the correlation of x and x' with y, defined as any third variable.

Multiplying both sides of Eq. 6.15 by y, then summing, and dividing by N, we have

$$\frac{\Sigma x'y}{N} = b\frac{\Sigma xy}{N} \tag{6.17}$$

By dividing both sides of Eq. 6.17 by $s_x \cdot s_y$ so as to correct the covariance on the left to correlation coefficient, we have

$$\frac{\Sigma x'y}{Ns_x \cdot s_y} = r_{x'y} = b\frac{\Sigma xy}{Ns_x \cdot s_y}$$

Substituting bs_x for $s_{x'}$ in accordance with Eq. 6.16, rearranging, and writing equivalents,

$$r_{x'y} = b\,\frac{\Sigma xy}{Nbs_x s_y} = \frac{b}{b}\,\frac{\Sigma xy}{Ns_x s_y} = r_{xy}$$

which proves that a linear conversion has no effect on the correlations of a variable.

By multiplying both sides of Eq. 6.15 by x and by proceeding by a similar development, it can be shown that X and X' correlate perfectly.

NORMALITY OF DISTRIBUTION AND CORRELATION

In mathematical treatments of correlation, it is sometimes assumed that the two variables are normally distributed and that the cases in the arrays also follow the normal[7] distribution. In Fig. 6.2, the X_1 distribution is perfectly "rectilinear"; that is, all steps have identical frequencies, and the overall shape of the distribution is flat. The X_0 distribution is symmetrical, with concentration of frequencies in the center, but (as compared with the normal distribution described in Chapter 11) is not perfectly normal.

In Fig. 6.2 the frequencies within each X_1 array are distributed in rectilinear fashion. While the distribution demonstrates homoscedasticity in the X_1 arrays (and hence is homoscedastic with reference to X_0 as a dependent variable), it does not show normality of distribution around the regression line.

In the derivation of the formula for r, no assumption was made about the shapes of the two distributions or about variation in variance along the regression line. It is only in applying the standard error of estimate in specific instances of prediction that the question arises as to whether the variation around the regression line is homoscedastic or heteroscedastic. In interpreting any single score by means of the standard error of estimate (as inferred from the standard deviation of the residuals), the distribution is assumed to be homoscedastic, since the standard error of estimate is conceived as uniform throughout the range.

r AS A MEASURE OF RELATIONSHIP

It has been seen that r can be defined as the slope of the straight line of best fit connecting two variables after their variances (and thus their standard deviations) have been equalized. Indirectly, r measures the degree of relationship between the two variables. As the variance[8] of the

---

[7] The "normal" distribution is described in Chapter 11. It is symmetrical, with the higher concentrations of frequencies close to the mean.
[8] As discussed earlier, the square root of this variance is taken as the "standard error of estimate."

errors of prediction (that is, the variance of the residuals around the regression line) decreases, r increases; as the variance of the errors of prediction increases, r decreases. These facts are summarized in the following formula (based on Formula 6.6), in which $V_{0.1}$ is the residual variance in z-form around the regression line:

$$r_{01} = \pm\sqrt{1 - V_{0.1}} \tag{6.18}$$

If there is no error of prediction, $V_{0.1}$ will be zero and r will be $+1.00$ or -1.00. If the variance of the errors of prediction equals the criterion variance, $V_{0.1}$ will be 1.00 and r_{01} will be zero. With intermediate degrees of error of prediction, r will have intermediate absolute values. Whether r is positive or negative is determined by the direction of slope of a regression line. The degree of association is independent of the sign of the correlation coefficient. One can predict just as efficiently from a negative r as from a positive r of the same absolute magnitude.

WHAT AFFECTS r

The correlation is changed systematically whenever the effective range in which it is computed is changed. If, to a certain group of cases, more cases are added which are either high or low in one of the variables being correlated, the correlation between the two variables will increase. On the other hand, if the upper or lower part of the group is dropped out, the correlation will decrease.[9] "Change in range" refers only to changes in the composition of the sample in which the correlation is computed. Such changes have a marked influence on values of the correlation coefficient, as contrasted with systematic changes in all the numerical values of one of the variables, or of both. Changes through linear conversion have, of course, no influence on the correlation coefficient.

The change in r with the group in which it is computed means that, in reporting correlation coefficients, the groups used should always be carefully defined.

Correlation is also affected by changes in the internal composition of the variables concerned.

If a variable, such as psychological test, is modified by dropping out or adding unreliable items, or by shortening or lengthening the test as a whole, or by changes in the conditions under which it is administered, its correlations tend to be altered. Any change that increases the internal consistency or reliability of a variable tends to raise its correlations with outside variables; and any change that decreases its reliability, lowers its correlations.

---

[9] Further discussion of this point, together with methods of estimating the changes in r, is presented in Chapter 10.

SUMMARY

Product-moment correlation is a technique useful for describing the relationship between two variables measured on scales that have values which can be added and multiplied. The joint function of two such variables can be described in terms of: (1) a covariance; (2) a correlation coefficient; or (3) a simple regression equation.

As the mean of paired deviation products, the covariance is useful chiefly as an intermediate step in finding other statistics. For example, when divided by a variance (as described in Chapter 7), a covariance becomes a regression coefficient, useful in regression equations; when divided by two standard deviations, it becomes a correlation coefficient, a pure number that is independent of the original units of measurement and which can be interpreted as an indication of the direction and degree of relationship between the two variables.

Although correlations vary from .00 to 1.00 (and negatively from .00 to −1.00), they cannot be considered as proportions (or percentages). Basically, an r is merely the slope of the best-fitting, least squares line, after the variance of the two variables have been equalized. Somewhat indirectly, r becomes a measure of relationship by indicating (when squared) the proportion of the variance in one variable predictable through knowledge of the values in the other.

The equation of the line of best fit is a means by which unknown values in one variable can be estimated from known values in the other. The regression equation, either in z form or in terms of original values, is a joint function of two variables of great practical importance in making predictions. The problem is treated more extensively in Chapter 10.

Another important application of correlation is in describing the reliability of a single variable; that is, the degree to which the device used to measure the variable yields consistent results, either from alternate forms or from repeated measurements. This application is amplified in Chapter 15.

The effects of "changes in range" on r are discussed in more detail in Chapter 10, and the effects of changes in reliability are taken up again in Chapter 15.

EXERCISES

1. Develop a formula for the correlation between two variables in the form of T scores, in which each mean is precisely 50 and each standard deviation is 10. (This may be accomplished by appropriate substitution of known values in one of the raw-score formulas for r.)

2. The following z scores for two variables should be first plotted on graph paper as a scatter diagram.

OBSERVATION	VARIABLE X	VARIABLE Y
A	1.50	.50
B	1.00	1.00
C	.50	1.50
D	.00	−.50
E	−.50	−1.50
F	−1.00	.00
G	−1.50	−1.00

(a) Fit a straight line, by eye, connecting the two variables.
(b) Measure the vertical distance between each actual z_y value and the fitted line. (These distances may be called the *crude* errors of prediction.)
(c) Find the sum of the squares of these crude errors.
(d) Compute the correlation coefficient between X and Y as the mean z score product.
(e) Using a distinctive color, plot the best-fitting straight line by the principle of least squares. (This line passes through the origin and has a slope equal to r_{xy}.)
(f) Measure the vertical distance between each actual z_y value and the new line. (These distances are the *true* errors of prediction, or residuals.)
(g) Find the sum of the squares of the true errors and compare it with the sum of the squares of the crude errors.

3. Consider the following z scores for two variables:

OBSERVATION	VARIABLE 0	VARIABLE 1
A	1.50	.50
B	.50	−.50
C	.00	1.50
D	−.50	.00
E	−1.50	−1.50

(a) Compute r_{01}.
(b) Compute the five values of $\tilde{z}_0$ as $r_{01}z_1$.
(c) Compute the five values of the residual $z_{0.1}$ as $z_0 - \tilde{z}_0$.
(d) Find the covariance between $\tilde{z}_0$ and $z_{0.1}$.
(e) Why is this covariance .00?
(f) Compute the variance of $z_{0.1}$. and determine whether it has the value of $(1 - r_{01}^2)$.

4. The following are the scores of 20 candidates for a police force on two tests: the police aptitude test and a space relations test:

CANDIDATE	POLICE APTITUDE	SPACE RELATIONS
A	89	66
B	80	70
C	80	49
D	97	67
E	96	81
F	98	79
G	91	39
H	78	59
I	74	45
J	83	31
K	99	81
L	89	28
M	64	19
N	110	66
O	106	77
P	64	10
Q	92	85
R	84	54
S	83	41
T	84	35

(a) Compute r by the raw-score product-moment formula (Formula 6.9).
(b) Compute r by the difference formula (Formula 6.10).
(c) Compute r by the sum formula (Formula 6.11).
(d) Observe whether or not the following check equations hold:

$$\Sigma(X + Y)^2 = \Sigma X^2 + 2\Sigma XY + \Sigma Y^2$$
$$\Sigma(X - Y)^2 = \Sigma X^2 - 2\Sigma XY + \Sigma Y^2$$

5. Sir Francis Galton (1) reports data on the heights of 205 women and their husbands, using three categories: short, medium, and tall (These data were collected about the time Galton was working out the theory of correlation. Today, in correlating continuous variables, one would use a number of steps appreciably greater than three.)

MARRIAGE SELECTION IN RESPECT TO STATURE

WIVES	HUSBANDS		
	SHORT	MEDIUM	TALL
Tall	12	20	18
Medium	25	51	28
Short	9	28	14

Compute product-moment r and decide whether Galton's conclusion, that there was no relationship between the two variables, is reasonable for these data.

6.

Data on age in relationship to highest audible tone were collected by Galton at his anthropometric laboratory and were reported by Koga and Morant (2). Here the data have been rearranged, but it has not been possible to change the partition values to accord with present practice.

Relationship Between Age and Highest Audible Pitch

X = age in years
Y = highest audible pitch in thousands of vibrations per second.

Y	5.5–11.5	11.5–17.5	17.5–23.5	23.5–29.5	29.5–35.5	35.5–41.5	41.5–47.5	47.5–53.5	53.5–59.5	59.5–65.5	65.5–71.5	71.5–77.5	77.5–83.5	f_y
33–34	1	1	1	1										4
31–32		2												2
29–30		1	1											2
27–28	1	7	7		1									16
25–26	4	19	14	3	1	1								41
23–24	10	64	72	15	3	8	4							165
21–22	48	270	467	115	45	43	16	4	1					957
19–20	26	227	439	213	81	42	31	7	2	1				1051
17–18	7	75	226	122	64	43	34	22	8					576
15–16	2	28	72	60	38	18	10	15	8	2	1			310
13–14		5	9	5	12	7	13	26	16	8	2			93
11–12		3	5	6	6	1	2	2	2	14	5	1	1	104
9–10				1				2	8		1	2	1	10
7–8		2	5	3	2	2	4	4	1	6	5	4		45
5–6			1	1					1					3
f_x	99	704	1319	545	253	165	114	80	46	31	14	7	2	$N = 3379$

(a) In each column in which the number of cases is more than 30, compute the mean. Does the regression appear to be linear?

(b) Compute r.

7. The following data are reported by Pearl (3).

Relationship Between Height and Weight of Cerebrum

$N = 308$ English males
$X =$ height in inches
$Y =$ weight of cerebrum in ounces

Y	58	59	60	61	62	63	64	65	66	67	68	69	70	71	72	f_y
50–51					1					2	1	2	1			7
48–49						1		3	1	3	5	2	2		1	19
46–47			1	1	1		1	3	4	6	2	3	1	3	3	31
44–45			2			1	3	2	10	4	6	3	6	4	3	42
42–43						1	1	6	8	12	10	4	5	2	4	55
40–41			1	1			3	5	6	8	8	5	7	3	3	52
38–39	1		2		1	2	3	3	10	8	6	6	5			45
36–37						1	2	4	3	6	6	2	4			26
34–35				1		2	2	4	5	5	4		2		1	20
32–33					2		1	1			1				3	3
30–31	1				1					1	1		1	1		5
28–29							1					1	1			3
f_x	2		6	3	6	9	20	31	47	47	44	28	34	13	18	$N = 308$

(a) Find r_{xy}.
(b) Find M_x, M_y, s_x, and s_y.
(c) Establish the raw-score regression equation for estimating weight of cerebrum from height.
(d) Find and interpret the standard error of estimate for these data.

8. For 1047 English-speaking U.S. Army recruits (white draft) in World War I, the following data on the relationship between two group intelligence tests were reported (5). (Step intervals for both variables have been increased.)

X = Army Alpha total score
Y = Army Beta total score

Y	X													f_y
	0–14	15–29	30–44	45–59	60–74	75–89	90–104	105–119	120–134	135–149	150–164	165–179	180–194	
110–119						1		1	1	2	2	1	1	9
100–109					1	4	6	3	9	5	5	4	2	39
90–99		1	1	3	14	12	18	17	13	13	6	2		100
80–89	1	6	8	17	35	32	34	20	12	8	2	3	1	173
70–79	1	16	30	28	33	30	18	6	3	1				156
60–69	5	38	37	32	23	14	8	5	5					145
50–59	4	32	34	21	16	5	1	1	1					121
40–49	25	26	20	11	1	1		1	1					92
30–39	28	15	16	4	2	1		1						77
20–29	50	3	9	1	2									78
10–19	31	1	2	2			1							39
0–9	17													18
f_x	162	138	157	119	127	100	86	55	45	29	15	10	4	$N = 1047$

(a) By inspection, what can be said about linearity of regression?

(b) Is the bivariate distribution homoscedastic either vertically or horizontally?

(c) Compute r for the total group.

(d) Compute r for the subgroup with Beta scores below 90.

(e) Compute r for the subgroup with Beta scores of 90 or more.

(f) Why are the r for the truncated groups ("restricted in range") less than the r in the uncurtailed range?

REFERENCES

1. GALTON, FRANCIS, *Natural Inheritance*. New York: The Macmillan Company, 1889, 206.

2. KOGA, Y., AND MORANT, G. M., "On the degree of association between reaction times in the case of different senses," *Biometrika*, 1923, **15**, 346–372.

3. PEARL, RAYMOND, "Variation and correlation in brain weight," *Biometrika*, 1905–1906, **4**, 13–104.

4. TRELOAR, ALLAN E., *Elements of Statistical Reasoning*. New York: John Wiley & Sons, Inc., 1939, 114.

5. YERKES, ROBERT M. (ED.), "Psychological examining in the United States Army," *Memoirs of the National Academy of Sciences*. Washington, D.C.: U.S. Government Printing Office, 1921, **15**, 621.

MULTIPLE CORRELATION

7

THE NATURE OF MULTIPLE R

A major aim of science is such precise description of phenomena and their relationships that accurate forecasts of future findings or happenings become possible. In astronomy, for example, eclipses are predicted with a high degree of accuracy. Similarly, in chemistry it is often possible to state properties of a compound before the substance is actually in existence. Psychology aims to understand human behavior. While it seems extremely unlikely that human behavior will ever be completely predictable, statistical techniques may be advantageously used in forecasting the behavior of both individuals and groups.

The simple regression equation involving two variables, described in Chapter 6, can be used for prediction, but more typically in applied psychology, a criterion such as school achievement or success on a job is forecast by means of a number of measurements, typical of which are test scores and biographical data. The problem is to combine information from several sources in such a fashion that the errors in prediction will be as small as possible. The statistical device by which a number of predictors are combined to yield a single score having the highest possible correlation with a criterion is the multiple regression equation, summarized by the coefficient of multiple correlation.

Like all other types of correlation, a multiple correlation shows the relationship between two and only two variables. It is a product-moment correlation which (with considerable unnecessary effort) could actually be computed by means of a basic formula for r. It is the correlation between an unmodified variable (the "dependent variable" or "criterion") and a second variable consisting of the weighted sum of scores in two or more "independent" or "predictor" variables (the weights of which are such that the correlation of the sum variable with the unmodified criterion is at a maximum for the particular sample of observations used in computing it).

Like all r's, a coefficient of multiple correlation is the slope of the least squares line of best fit connecting two variables of equal variability. However, since computing methods involve the extraction of a square root conventionally taken as positive, the multiple is regarded as varying between .00 and 1.00 rather than from -1.00 to 1.00.

The criterion may be denoted as variable 0, and the predictors used in determining the weighted sum as variables $1, 2, 3 \cdots n$. The objective in multiple correlation, then, is to determine how to weight variables $1, 2, 3 \cdots n$ in such a way that the correlation of their sum with variable 0 will be as high as possible. In any sample of N cases, and using information as to the degree of rectilinear relationship between pairs of variables, there is a unique solution to this problem.

R AND THE MULTIPLE REGRESSION COEFFICIENTS

The multiple correlation may be indicated as $R_{0(12 \cdots n)}$, in which the capital letter indicates a coefficient involving differential weighting of the components of a sum variable so as to maximize the correlation. In this expression, the criterion variable is indicated as a subscript outside the parentheses, while the predictors are shown within the parentheses. The general expression $(12 \cdots n)$ refers to n predictors, commas being omitted from subscripts unless needed for clarity. The order of the subscripts within the parentheses is immaterial. Thus, if variables 1 and 2 were the only predictors, the multiple could be indicated either as $R_{0(12)}$ or as $R_{0(21)}$.

Regression coefficients or regression weights applied to predictor variables are known as *beta coefficients* (denoted with the Greek letter β) if the variables have unit variance, as is the case with z scores. They are known as b coefficients or b weights if the variables have original variances, as with deviation scores or raw scores. In this chapter only the betas are of interest, since b weights are used chiefly in practical prediction problems, as discussed in Chapter 10.

If no confusion is likely to result, a regression coefficient may have a single subscript indicating only the variable to which it is applied. Thus a multiple regression equation with four predictors may be written as

$$\tilde{z}_0 = \beta_1 z_1 + \beta_2 z_2 + \beta_3 z_3 + \beta_4 z_4 \qquad (7.1)$$

in which the tilde over z_0 indicates a predicted rather than an obtained value.

Formula 7.1 represents a scheme for finding the most likely criterion value for a particular case from the four z scores for the four predictors, together with four constant weights, the β coefficients. When, for a sample of cases, the ten intercorrelations of the five variables are known, it is possible to determine the numerical values of $\beta_1, \beta_2, \beta_3$, and β_4. In the sample, all z_0 values are, of course, known. The regression equation can be used for predicting z_0 for new cases for which z_0 is unknown but for which values are available for the four predictors.

For greater precision, beta coefficients can be written with subscripts indicating all the variables involved in the multiple. Of the two "primary" subscripts (written before the period) the first designates the criterion, and the second designates the variable to which the beta is applied when a predicted value is computed. The "secondary" subscripts, written after the period, indicate all other variables used in finding the beta. Thus, $\beta_{02.1345}$ is the beta to be applied to variable 2 in predicting variable 0 as a criterion when the predictors are variables 1, 2, 3, 4, and 5. Accordingly, the precise method of writing the betas for a problem with four predictors is

$$\tilde{z}_0 = \beta_{01.234} z_1 + \beta_{02.134} z_2 + \beta_{03.124} z_3 + \beta_{04.123} z_4 \qquad (7.1a)$$

The "order" of the beta is the number of secondary variables. Thus, $\beta_{01.234}$ is a third-order beta. If there are no secondary variables, as in predicting values in a criterion from a single predictor, the beta is of "zero order." The n betas used in a regression equation based on n predictors are all of the $(n-1)$st order.

The multiple R is precisely the product-moment correlation between actual criterion values (in z form, denoted as z_0) and the predicted values (denoted as $\tilde{z}_0$). However, if all the intercorrelations among the predictors and the correlations of the predictors with the criterion are known, this correlation can be inferred exactly without using the individual values of the criterion and without computing the individual predicted values. In fact, the multiple correlation can be determined before the final beta coefficients are available, and hence before it is possible to find the predicted values. To understand the way in which this is done, it is convenient to employ the concept of a "residual" variable.

PROPERTIES OF A RESIDUAL VARIABLE

In Chapter 6, certain properties of a variable "residualized" with respect to another variable were described. By Formula 6.2, the value of z_0 as predicted from z_1 is $\beta_{01} z_1$, and by Formula 6.4, $\tilde{z}_0$ has a variance of r_{01}^2.

By Formula 6.5, the residual $(z_0 - \tilde{z}_0)$, or $z_{0.1}$, is equal to $(z_0 - \beta_{01}z_1)$, and by Formula 6.6, its variance is $(1 - r_{01}{}^2)$.

Since predicted scores and residuals are uncorrelated, every criterion value z_0, can be divided uniquely into two uncorrelated portions, $\tilde{z}_0$ and $z_{0.1}$. Similarly, as summarized by Formula 6.7, the total variance of the criterion V_0, is the sum of the predicted variance $\tilde{V}_0$, and the unpredicted variance $V_{0.1}$.

Any variable can be modified so that it becomes a residual variable in relation to any number of outside variables. It is then uncorrelated with each of the outside variables as well as with their weighted sum.[1]

Thus, "residualization" of variable 0 with respect to variables 1, 2, 3 $\cdots$ n yields

$$z_{0.12\cdots n} = z_0 - \tilde{z}_{0(12\cdots n)}$$
$$= z_0 - \beta_{01.23\cdots n}z_1 - \beta_{02.13\cdots n}z_2 - \cdots - \beta_{0n.12\cdots(n-1)}z_n$$

in which $\tilde{z}_{0(12\cdots n)}$ represents prediction of z_0 from the best-weighted combination of scores in variables 1, 2 through n. The residual variable, $z_{0.12\cdots n}$, is not only uncorrelated with $\tilde{z}_{0(12\cdots n)}$, but it is also uncorrelated, both singly and in combination, with variable 1, variable 2, and the other outside or independent variables, including variable n, with respect to which it has been "residualized."

The variance of this "higher order" residual variable is $(1 - R^2_{0(12\cdots n)})$, while the variance of the corresponding predicted scores, the $\tilde{z}_0$, is $R^2_{0(12\cdots n)}$. Just as with zero-order r, the variance of the residuals plus the variance of the predicted values equals the variance of the criterion in z form; that is,

$$V_0 = R^2_{0(12\cdots n)} + V_{0.12\cdots n} \qquad (7.2)$$

The N values for the N cases involved in a residual variable could actually be found. In practice, however, values of residuals for individual cases are seldom needed; rather summary statistics are used: variances[2] and standard deviations describing separate variables; and covariances and correlations involving pairs of residual variables.

FINDING THE VARIANCES AND COVARIANCES OF RESIDUAL VARIABLES

Formula 6.6 can be used to find the variance of a set of residuals in "higher-order" z form (that is, with mean of zero, but with variance less than 1.00). If original, or "zero-order" variables are in z form (with mean of zero and variance of 1.00), then the variance of the residuals around the regression line connecting any two variables, denoted here as 0 and 1, is $(1 - r_{01}{}^2)$.

---

[1] A proof of this principle is given by Kendall (3).
[2] The role of variances and covariances in conceptualizing multiple R is discussed by DuBois (2).

This formula, however, can be improved by writing it in the notation that is convenient in finding variances of orders higher than the first. Since, in the zero-order case, correlation coefficients, betas, and covariances of z scores are numerically identical, $\beta_{01}C_{01}$ can be substituted for r_{01}^2 in Formula 6.6. Since in original z form, any variance is 1.00, V_0 can be used instead of 1.00. Accordingly, Formula 6.6 becomes

$$V_{0.1} = 1 - r_{01}^2 = V_0 - \beta_{01}C_{01} \qquad (7.3)$$

Formula 7.3 is cognate with a more general formula useful for finding a higher-order variance (or covariance) of any order from the corresponding variance (or covariance) of immediately lower order and the product of a beta and a covariance. This formula is

$$E' = E - \beta C \qquad (7.4)$$

in which E' is the variance or covariance of higher order and E, β, and C all involve residual variables of the next lower order.

To be specific, let i represent a variable that has been residualized with respect to any number of other variables, collectively represented as q. Its variance is thus $V_{i.q}$. To find the variance of a still higher order of residuals, $V_{i.(q+k)}$, two coefficients of the same order as $V_{i.q}$ are needed: a beta, $\beta_{ik.q}$, and a corresponding covariance, $C_{ik.q}$, which involves two residual variables, $z_{i.q}$ and $z_{k.q}$. Formula 7.4 then becomes

$$V_{i.(q+k)} = V_{i.q} - \beta_{ik.q}C_{ik.q} \qquad (7.4a)$$

Similarly, for covariances of order $(q + k)$ from coefficients of order q, Formula 7.4 may be written as

$$C_{ij.(q+k)} = C_{ij.q} - \beta_{ik.q}C_{jk.q} \qquad (7.4b)$$

Formulas of this type become the basis of a computing routine in which step-by-step substitution of values in the formulas is not necessary. In effect, the routine replaces what would be an involved system of formulas. In finding R by reduction of criterion variance, as demonstrated in Example 7.1, the first matrix[3] is of zero-order coefficients. From it is produced a second matrix with one less row and one less column, and consisting of coefficients involving first order residual variables; that is, variables from which a single outside variable has been partialed out. Another matrix is then produced, involving the elimination of another row and another column, and consisting of second-order coefficients; that is, variances and covariances of variables from which two variables have been partialed out.

---

[3] A matrix is simply an arrangement of data in rows and columns of assigned meaning. In correlational analysis, each variable gives meaning to a row and again to a column.

The procedure then continues until a matrix of one row and one column is found. The single element of this matrix is $V_{0.12\ldots n}$, the partial variance of the criterion.

EXAMPLE 7.1

COMPUTATION OF MULTIPLE R WITH TWO PREDICTORS

The following matrix represents two predictor variables, variables 1 and 2, and a criterion, variable 0. Their z score variances of 1.00 are in the main diagonal. Above the diagonal, in appropriate rows and columns, are the covariances in z form among the three variables, each precisely equal to the correlation.

VARIABLE	2	1	0
2	1.00	.20	.50
1		1.00	.58
0			1.00

The first step is to compute a required column of intermediate beta coefficients. In all matrices this is accomplished by dividing the covariances of the top row by the variance in that row. Since the variance (V_2) is 1.00, the matrix now becomes:

VARIABLE	2	1	0
2	1.00	.20	.50
1	.20	1.00	.58
0	.50		1.00

The next step is to form a variance-covariance matrix of residual variables, which in this case will be $z_{1.2}$ and $z_{0.2}$. Variable 2 is "eliminated" from the matrix by subtracting from all elements not involving variable 2 the product of the beta in the same row (and in the first column) and the covariance in the same column (and the top row). Thus, from V_1 in the second row and second column, $(.20 \times .20)$ is subtracted. From C_{01}, which is .58, $(.20 \times .50)$ is subtracted; while from V_0, in the last row and column, $(.50 \times .50)$ is subtracted. This procedure produces a new matrix of the variances and the covariances of variables $z_{1.2}$ and $z_{0.2}$ as follows:

VARIABLE	1.2	0.2
1.2	.96	.48
0.2		.75

The next step is to produce beta coefficients by dividing the covariance(s) in top row by the variance in that row. Since this is a 2×2 matrix of two rows and two columns only, one beta is required. It is .50, found by dividing the partial covariance between $z_{1.2}$ and $z_{0.2}$, which is .48, by the partial variance of $z_{1.2}$, which is .96. This partial covariance can be designated $C_{01.2}$, while the partial variance is $V_{1.2}$. The matrix now reads:

VARIABLE	1.2	0.2
1.2	.96	.48
0.2	.50	.75

The matrix is reduced again, this time eliminating variable 1.2. Subtraction from $V_{0.2}$ (.75) of the product of the beta in the first column (.50) and the covariance in the top row (.48) yields the final partial variance, .51. This is $V_{0.12}$, the variance of the criterion with the variance associated with both predictor variables removed.

Since the sum of this partial variance and $R^2_{0(12)}$ is 1.00, it is now known that the predicted proportion of the criterion variance, or $R^2{}_{0(12)}$, is .49. Consequently, $R_{0(12)}$ is .70. The same result is obtained by the use of Formula 7.5.

Of course, in actually finding R, the successive matrices are placed one underneath the other. All the numerical work described above is shown below:

VARIABLE	2	1	0
2	1.00	.20	.50
1	.20	1.00	.58
0	.50		1.00
1.2		.96	.48
0.2		.50	.75
0.12			.51

$$R_{0(12)} = \sqrt{1 - V_{0.12}} = \sqrt{1 - .51} = \sqrt{.49} = .70$$

A STRATEGY FOR FINDING $R_{0(12\ldots n)}$

In multiple correlation, as demonstrated in Examples 7.1 and 7.2, the variance of the criterion is taken as 1.00. It is reduced successively by the removal of the proportion of the criterion variance predictable from the first predictor; by the proportion of the variance predictable from the second predictor, less that portion associated with the first; by the proportion predictable from the third predictor, less the portions associated with the first and second; and so on, until the portions of the criterion variance associated with all predictors have been removed.

EXAMPLE 7.2

COMPUTING AND CHECKING MULTIPLE R AND THE FINAL BETA COEFFICIENTS

Purpose. This example extends the computation of multiple R to the case of four predictor variables and includes finding the four final-order betas. The analytic solution in Table 7.1, which is exactly parallel to the numeric solution in Table 7.2, can by analogy be expanded to any number of variables. Complete checks are provided. All elements in all matrices have identifiable statistical meaning, and each operation can be expressed as a formula.

TABLE 7.1. ANALYTIC SOLUTION OF MULTIPLE R

In the original matrix, the variances and covariances are of zero-order z scores, with mean of zero and unit variance. In subsequent matrices, the coefficients are in terms of higher-order z scores, with mean of zero but with variance generally less than unity.

4	3	2	1	0	CHECK SUM
$=\beta_{04.123}$ V_4	C_{34}	C_{24}	C_{14}	C_{04}	$C_{4(0+T)}$
$-\beta_{03.124} \times \beta_{34}$	V_3	C_{23}	C_{13}	C_{03}	$C_{3(0+T)}$
$-\beta_{02.134} \times \beta_{24}$		V_2	C_{12}	C_{02}	$C_{2(0+T)}$
$-\beta_{01.234} \times \beta_{14}$			V_1	C_{01}	$C_{1(0+T)}$
β_{04}				V_0	$C_{0(0+T)}$
$=\beta_{03.124}$ $V_{3.4}$	$C_{23.4}$	$C_{13.4}$	$C_{03.4}$		$C_{3(0+T).4}$
$-\beta_{02.134} \times \beta_{23.4}$	$V_{2.4}$	$C_{12.4}$	$C_{02.4}$		$C_{2(0+T).4}$
$-\beta_{01.234} \times \beta_{13.4}$		$V_{1.4}$	$C_{01.4}$		$C_{1(0+T).4}$
$\beta_{03.4}$			$V_{0.4}$		$C_{0(0+T).4}$
$=\beta_{02.134}$ $V_{2.34}$	$C_{12.34}$	$C_{02.34}$			$C_{2(0+T).34}$
$-\beta_{01.234} \times \beta_{12.34}$	$V_{1.34}$	$C_{01.34}$			$C_{1(0+T).34}$
$\beta_{02.34}$		$V_{0.34}$			$C_{0(0+T).34}$
Computations		$V_{1.234}$	$C_{01.234}$		$C_{1(0+T).234}$
		$\beta_{01.234}$	$V_{0.234}$		$C_{0(0+T).234}$
			$V_{0.1234}$		$C_{0(0+T).1234}$

Final Check: $C_{0(0+T).1234} = V_{0.1234}$

Multiple R: $R_{0(1234)} = \sqrt{1 - V_{0.1234}}$

Back solution for β weights as indicated in the boxes:

$$\beta_{02.134} = \beta_{02.34} - \beta_{01.234}\beta_{12.34}$$
$$\beta_{03.124} = \beta_{03.4} - \beta_{01.234}\beta_{13.4} - \beta_{02.134}\beta_{23.4}$$
$$\beta_{04.123} = \beta_{04} - \beta_{01.234}\beta_{14} - \beta_{02.134}\beta_{24} - \beta_{03.124}\beta_{34}$$

Coefficients. The three types of coefficients used in the cells of the successive matrices of the analytic solution are: variances denoted as V, covariances denoted as C, and betas denoted as β.

In the original matrix the variables are considered to be in conventional z form, with all variances unity, with all covariances equal to corresponding correlations, and with any beta as a covariance divided by the variance of one of the variables concerned, also equal to a correlation.

Subsequent matrices consist of variances and covariances of residual variables in higher-order z form; that is, with means equal to zero, but with variances generally less than unity. Intermediate betas, used in developing the subsequent matrix, are formed from the covariances and the variance in the top row of each new matrix. In this zero-order matrix, columns and rows are designated from 4 down to 0, with an additional column for the sum variate, T. The arrangement coincides with an order of work from left to right and from top to bottom.

TABLE 7.2. NUMERIC SOLUTION

Computing and checking multiple R for four predictors. Data are from Rosen and Van Horn (4)

4	3	2	1	0	CHECK SUM	VARIABLE
=.0360	1.0000	.3900	.3700	.2500	.3000	2.3100	(4)
−(.1854) × .3900	1.0000		.3500	.0800	.3500	2.1700	(3)
−(.3853) × .3700		1.0000		.4400	.5500	2.7100	(2)
−(.1967) × .2500			1.0000		.3900	2.1600	(1)
.3000				1.0000		2.5900	(0)
=.1854	.8479	.2057	−.0175	.2330	1.2691	(3.4)
−(.3853) × .2426	.8631		.3475	.4390	1.8553	(2.4)
−(.1967) × − .0206		.9375		.3150	1.5825	(1.4)
.2748			.9100		1.8970	(0.4)
=.3853	.8132	.3517	.3825	1.5474	(2.34)
−(.1967)× .4325	.9371		.3198	1.6086	(1.34)
.4704		.8460	1.5483	(0.34)

Identification of Variables

4. Verbal score
3. Quantitative score
2. High school rank
1. Application blank
0. 1st semester grade point average

	1	0	CHECK SUM	VARIABLE
	.7850	.1544	.9393	(1.234)
	.1967	.6661	.8204	(0.234)
		.6357	.6356	(0.1234)

$$R_{0(1234)}^2 = 1 - .6357 = .3643 \qquad R_{0(1234)} = .60$$
$$\beta_{01.234} = .1967$$
$$\beta_{02.134} = .4704 - (.1967 \times .4325) = .3853$$
$$\beta_{03.124} = .2748 - (.1967 \times - .0206) - (.3853 \times .2426) = .1854$$
$$\beta_{04.123} = .3000 - (.1967 \times .2500) - (.3853 \times .3700)$$
$$- (.1854 \times .3900) = .0360$$
$$R_{0(1234)}^2 = (.0360 \times .3000) + (.1854 \times .3500) + (.3853 \times .5500)$$
$$+ (.1967 \times .3900) = .3643$$

In forming each new matrix after the first, one of the variables in the preceding matrix has been "eliminated," which means that all variables remaining in the new matrix have been "residualized" with respect to the variable "eliminated," or "partialed out."

Thus, the second matrix consists of variances and covariances of first-order residual variables (with one variable eliminated); the third matrix of variances and covariances of second-order residuals (with two variables eliminated); and so on. Betas, derived from the top row of coefficients, are written underneath the V. Each beta is found by the formula: $\beta = C/V$.

Forming the New Matrices. In forming each new matrix, the computing formula is

$$E' = E - \beta C$$

in which E' is the element (variance or covariance) of higher order, E is the corresponding element in the preceding matrix, β is the beta in the same row but first column of that matrix (under the variance used in computing the column of betas), and C is the covariance in the same column but top row.

When variate 4 is partialed out of the matrix, 4 disappears as a primary sub-script. Its appearance as a secondary subscript in all coefficients in subsequent matrices shows that the variance associated with variate 4 has been subtracted from each value of each remaining variate.

After variate 4 has been partialed out, the variables forming the new matrix of variances and covariances are the following higher-order z scores: $z_{3.4}$, $z_{2.4}$, $z_{1.4}$, and $z_{0.4}$. Similarly, after $z_{3.4}$ has been partialed out, the resultant matrix is of variances and covariances of second-order z scores: $z_{2.34}$, $z_{1.34}$, and $z_{0.34}$. Next $z_{0.34}$ is partialed out, leaving a matrix involving only two variables, $z_{1.234}$ and $z_{0.234}$. The final, single element matrix is the variance of the fourth-order residuals, $z_{0.1234}$.

Check Sum. In the column headed T appear the coefficients of an artificial variable developed, in effect, by summing the z scores of the original variables. In the first matrix, values are obtained by summing all the terms pertaining to a variable, pivoting on the variance. In subsequent matrices, values are obtained just as though T were an additional variate (except that no betas are found), and these computed values are compared with those obtained by summation within the matrix. Discrepancies in the final decimal place may be expected, but other discrepancies indicate that an error has been made.

Finding Final-Order Betas. With n predictors, the regression equation based on all of them requires n betas of the $(n-1)$st order. In the forward solution one is available as the beta in the nth matrix. In the back solution, a second beta comes from the $(n-1)$st matrix, a third from the $(n-2)$nd matrix, and so on up to the first matrix, which yields the nth beta of $(n-1)$st order. The rule is invariant. Each beta of the required order is the beta in the matrix applicable to predicting the criterion, less the sum of the products of betas of the $(n-1)$st order already found and corresponding betas in the matrix. Betas are regarded as corresponding when they share a primary subscript. In the analytic solution, appropriate formulas for final-order betas are shown as equations and also as operations within boxes.

Computation of R. Formulas 7.2 and 7.5 indicate that when one starts with a matrix of coefficients of variables in z form, the square of any multiple R is unity less the variance of the criterion after variance associated with all predictors has been removed. This relationship is the basis of Table R in the Appendix, which gives two-place values of multiple R corresponding to four-place values of partial variances.

Checking R and the Final Betas. $R^2_{0(12\ldots n)}$, found as $(1 - V_{0.12\ldots n})$ can be checked by multiplying each validity coefficient by the corresponding final-order beta and summing the products. That is to say, $R^2_{0(12\ldots n)} = \Sigma\beta_{0i}C_{0i}$, in which i represents each predictor variable in turn. The procedure checks both R and the final betas.

Computations. In Table 7.2, the numeric solution, are shown the computations corresponding to the analytic solution in Table 7.1. Variables are identified at the right. At the left in boxes are the intermediate betas used for computations within matrices as well as the final-order betas found in the back solution. Steps in the procedure follow:

1. Write a triangular matrix of coefficients of $(n+1)$ variables, with variances

(1.0000) in the main diagonal and covariances (equal to r) above the diagonal. (Strictly speaking, the matrix has $(n + 1)^2$ terms, but since it is symmetrical, covariances below the diagonal need not be written.)

2. Find the entries in the check sum column by summing down each column and pivoting on the variance. Thus, $1.0000 + .3900 + .3700 + .2500 + .3000 = 2.3100$; and $.3900 + 1.0000 + .3500 + .0800 + .3500 = 2.1700$.

3. Find the column of intermediate betas by dividing the covariances of the top row by the variance in that row. Thus, $.3900/1.0000 = .3900$; $.3700/1.0000 = .3700$; etc.

4. Compute the entries of the new matrix by the $(E' = E - \beta C)$ formula. Thus, $1.0000 - (.3900 \times .3900) = .8479$; $.3500 - (.3900 \times .3700) = .2057$; $.0800 - (.3900 \times .2500) = -.0175$; $.3500 - (.3900 \times .3000) = .2330$; and $2.1700 - (.3900 \times 2.3100) = 1.2691$. It is to be noted that the procedure with the sum variable is the same as with the other variables.

5. Sum down each column and across each row of the new matrix, pivoting on the variance. Each sum should agree with the result of the computation involving the sum variable. As examples, $.8479 + .2057 - .0175 + .2330 = 1.2691$, and $.2057 + .8631 + .3475 + .4390 = 1.8553$.

6. Continue the sequence of steps until a single element matrix has been found, the partial variance of the criterion, after variance predictable from all the independent variables has been removed. Except for rounding error, it should be identical with the final entry in the check sum column. In this case, $V_{0.1234}$ is .6357; the final check is .6356.

7. Find the multiple by the use of Table R (Appendix) or Formula 7.5.

8. Compute the final-order betas, using the single beta in the (2×2) matrix and the intermediate betas in the preceding matrices.

9. Check the final betas by multiplying each by the corresponding validity coefficient. Here $(.0360 \times .3000) + (.1854 \times .3500) + (.3853 \times .5500) + (.1967 \times .3900) = .3643 = R^2_{0(1234)}$.

In this procedure the original matrix is considered to consist of:

1. Zero-order z score variances in the main diagonal (all are 1.00); and
2. Zero-order z score covariances above the diagonal (each precisely equal to the corresponding r).

The term *zero order* refers to the fact that the variables at this stage are unmodified by the process of forming residuals. In the second matrix, the variances and covariances are of first-order residuals (that is, variables with the variance associated with one variable removed); in the third matrix they are of the second order, with variance associated with two variables removed, and so on.

Mathematically, as explained in Chapter 16, each matrix is square, and except for the final matrix consisting of a single residual (or partial) variance, there are covariances below the diagonal as well as above it. However, since the original and all succeeding matrices are symmetrical, it is not necessary to write out the covariances below the diagonal. This space then becomes a convenient place to write certain beta coefficients, used in applying Formula 7.4.

The final partial variance, which is the only element in the final matrix, is the proportion of the criterion variance not predictable from the predictors. It is also the variance of the criterion variable (in z form) "residualized" with respect to all the predictors. It is found by repeated applications of Formula 7.4, together with a routine for finding certain required beta coefficients by dividing a partial covariance (the covariance between two residual variables) by the variance of one of the variables concerned.

In this routine, the variable represented in the top row and first column of any matrix is "eliminated" in forming the subsequent matrix. By "elimination" is meant the process of transforming each variable entering into the new matrix by subtracting from each value that portion perfectly correlated with the eliminated variable. The residual variables so formed are uncorrelated with all variables previously eliminated.

COMPUTATION OF A MULTIPLE R FROM A PARTIAL VARIANCE

Each new matrix, as it is computed, includes the variance of the criterion less those portions associated with the variables previously eliminated. This partial variance is the proportion of the criterion variance that is not predicted by the "eliminated" predictors. Subtraction of this partial variance from 1.00 results in the predicted proportion of the criterion variance, and this predicted proportion is the square of a correlation coefficient. The correlation is the multiple. Accordingly, to find multiple R corresponding to a group of "eliminated" predictors (that is, the correlation between the criterion and a group of independent variables each weighted in the best possible fashion), it is necessary merely to subtract the partial variance of the criterion (after these variables have been "eliminated") from 1.00 and take the square root of the result.

This is an application of Formula 7.2, which may be written as

$$R_{0(12 \cdots n)} = \sqrt{1 - V_{0.12 \cdots n}} \qquad (7.5)$$

Formula 7.5 yields the multiple between the criterion and all the variables that have been "eliminated." It can be applied at any step of a solution, and is also applicable to the partial variances in the diagonal of each successive matrix. Thus, after variables 4 and 3 have been eliminated, $R_{1(34)}$, for example, can be found from $V_{1.34}$.

FINDING THE BETA COEFFICIENTS

As already pointed out, when only two variables are concerned, each of the beta coefficients (for estimating z_0, given z_1, and for estimating z_1, given z_0) is exactly equal to the correlation between the two variables, r_{01}.

When three variables are concerned, there are six possible regression coefficients, none of which is necessarily equal to any of the others. If variables 0, 1, and 2 comprise the system, the six betas are $\beta_{01.2}$, $\beta_{02.1}$ (for use when variable 0 is the criterion and to be applied to z_1 and z_2, respectively), $\beta_{10.2}$ and $\beta_{12.0}$ (when variable 1 is the criterion), and $\beta_{20.1}$ and $\beta_{21.0}$ (when variable 2 is the criterion).

In the solution of a multiple correlation problem, it is by no means necessary to find all the possible beta coefficients, which become very numerous as the number of variables increases. Final-order betas are found by routines that correspond precisely to the solution of simple, simultaneous linear equations. However, the computation of each of the betas used in the forward solution for multiple R can be expressed as the division of a partial covariance by a partial variance of the same order. Let i and j represent any two variables; let q represent any number of variables with respect to which i and j have been "residualized." Then, in higher-order z form, $C_{ij.q}$ is the covariance between $z_{i.q}$ and $z_{j.q}$, both residuals of the same order and from which variance associated with the same set of variables has been removed. Then

$$\beta_{ij.q} = \frac{C_{ij.q}}{V_{j.q}} \tag{7.6}$$

and

$$\beta_{ji.q} = \frac{C_{ij.q}}{V_{i.q}} \tag{7.6a}$$

It is apparent from Formulas 7.6 and 7.6a that the variance used as the divisor is the partial variance derived from the original variable to which the beta would be applied in a regression equation; that is, $\beta_{ij.q}$ would be applied to z_j in predicting z_i as a criterion, while $\beta_{ji.q}$ would be applied to z_i in predicting z_j as a criterion.

In the "back" solution, the complete set of betas required for a single regression equation is found. With n predictors, n betas of the $(n-1)$st order are required. In such a set of betas, all are of the same order, all are based on the same set of predictors, and all are in reference to the same variable as a criterion. However, each is the beta applied to a different predictor, and the set of eliminated or secondary variables is different in each case.

One of these betas appears in the forward solution, in the 2×2 matrix, just preceding the single-element matrix consisting of the final partial variance of the criterion. Each of the preceding matrices yields another final beta, each of which is a lower-order beta less one or more products between betas in the matrix and the final-order betas already found.

To find final-order betas involving four predictors, operations are summarized in the following formulas:

$$\beta_{02.134} = \beta_{02.34} - \beta_{01.234}\beta_{12.34} \tag{7.7}$$

$$\beta_{03.124} = \beta_{03.4} - \beta_{01.234}\beta_{13.4} - \beta_{02.134}\beta_{23.4} \tag{7.7a}$$

$$\beta_{04.123} = \beta_{04} - \beta_{01.234}\beta_{14} - \beta_{02.134}\beta_{24} - \beta_{03.124}\beta_{34} \tag{7.7b}$$

The computing routine involves:

1. Identification of the final-order beta in the 2 by 2 matrix. This is the beta that, in a z-score regression equation, would be applied to the last predictor eliminated.

2. Computation of a second final-order beta from the 3 by 3 matrix. This is the beta that, in a z-score regression equation, would be applied to the predictor eliminated next to the last. It is found by subtracting from the beta at the bottom of the first column the product of the final-order beta already found and the beta in the cell next to the bottom of the first column.

3. Computation of the other final-order betas by the same general method. Each is the beta at the bottom of the first column less the products of the final-order betas already found and the betas used in the elimination process. Always the work is from the bottom, and each final-order beta is always used in a row appropriate to the variable to which, in a z-score regression equation, the beta would be applied.

This routine is demonstrated in Example 7.2.

The n final-order betas of the $(n - 1)$st order can be checked by multiplying each by the corresponding validity or correlation between the criterion and the variable to which the beta is applied in the regression equation. The result is $R_{0(12\cdots n)}^2$, the square of the multiple correlation between the criterion and the weighted sum of the n predictors. The value of $R_{0(12\cdots n)}^2$ must correspond with the value formed by subtracting from 1.00 the partial variance of the criterion after variance associated with the n predictors has been subtracted.

Algebraically,

$$\begin{aligned} R_{0(12\cdots n)}^2 &= 1 - V_{0.12\cdots n} \\ &= \beta_{01.2\cdots n}r_{01} + \beta_{02.1\cdots n}r_{02} + \cdots + \beta_{0n.1\cdots(n-1)}r_{0n} \end{aligned} \tag{7.8}$$

SELECTING A HIGHLY VALID COMBINATION OF VARIABLES

A slight modification in the procedure for finding multiple R results in a logical method for selecting out of a pool of predictors a limited number of variables that in combination will have a high correlation with the criterion. In psychological and educational research, there is often considerable overlap among predictors, so that four or five well-chosen variables may have almost as high a composite validity as eight or ten predictors.

If the variable with the highest correlation with the criterion is selected as the first predictor, a good start will have been made in picking an effective team of predictors. When all variables remaining in the matrix have been "residualized" with respect to this first variable, the task then becomes one of choosing that predictor which at that point will add most to the multiple.

This second variable can be readily identified. The partial covariance between each predictor and the criterion is squared and divided by the partial variance of that predictor. The variable with the highest ratio so derived is the one that, at this stage, will add the most to the multiple. Actually, these ratios are the squares of the correlations between the criterion and the predictors "residualized" with respect to the variables first "eliminated" from the matrix. Hence, the identification procedure consists merely of comparing a set of r^2's. The variable with the highest $C_{0i.q}^2/V_{i.q}$ ratio is then eliminated.

The third variable to be used in the team is identified similarly; the square of each partial covariance between each remaining variable and the criterion is divided by the partial variance of the variable. The residual variable with the highest resultant ratio, and hence the highest correlation with the criterion, is selected to be the next variable to be eliminated. Each cycle adds a predictor to the team, and the process may be continued for as many cycles as one wishes. After a time, however, if the original group of predictors have considerable overlap, the ratios may be small and the gain in multiple R will be negligible. When this happens, the selected team may be almost as useful as the original group of predictors. The procedure is illustrated in Example 7.3.

EXAMPLE 7.3

SELECTING A HIGHLY VALID COMBINATION OF PREDICTORS[4]

Purpose. A subset of n' predictors may be nearly as valid as the total group of n predictors. At any stage of elimination, the variable that will add most to multiple R can be identified as the one having the highest $C_{0i.q}^2/V_{i.q}$ ratio, in which 0 is the criterion, i is the predictor, and q designates all variables previously eliminated.

In the original matrix, where all variances are unity, the variable with the highest validity has the highest $C_{0i.q}^2/V_{i.q}$ ratio.

Procedure. Steps are:

1. Eliminate the variable with the highest validity.

---

2. Test the remaining variables by computing $C_{0i.q}^2/V_{i.q}$ for each, thus determining the variable that, at this stage, will add most to the multiple.
3. Eliminate this variable.
4. Again test the remaining variables by finding $C_{0i.q}^2/V_{i.q}$ for each, and continue the process until it appears that no remaining variable will add appreciably to the multiple, as indicated by Formula 7.9. (Sometimes, however, n', the number of predictors in the subgroup, is determined for reasons of convenience rather than on the basis of purely statistical considerations.)

After the n' predictors have been chosen, the sum of the square of the validity of the first predictor and of the $C_{0i.q}^2/V_{i.q}$ ratios of the other selected predictors yields R^2. The related final-order betas must be found from a back solution involving only the n' predictors and the criterion.

If the procedures are to be completely in the model of finding multiple R as demonstrated in Example 7.2, each successive matrix is arranged so that the variable selected for elimination (and hence for inclusion in the team of predictors) is in the first row and column, and then this variable is eliminated throughout the matrix.

An Accelerated Procedure. Considerably faster is the procedure demonstrated in Table 7.3. The steps follow.

1. Each variable chosen for the multiple is eliminated immediately only from the variances in the diagonal and the covariances involving the criterion.
2. When a variable discovered by the $C_{0i.q}^2/V_{i.q}$ technique is to be added to the multiple, then
   (a) All covariances involving that variable are computed for the second matrix and subsequent matrices through the one from which it is to be eliminated.
   (b) Intermediate betas are found, as always, by dividing covariances by the variance of the variable to be eliminated. For convenience the betas are placed in a column at the left.
3. Entries for the new matrix are found by the regular formula, $E' = E - \beta C$. The difference from the procedure described in connection with Example 7.2 is that the required covariance is not necessarily in the top row. It is in the column or row assigned to the variable to be eliminated.

In Table 7.3 it happens that the first two variables to be eliminated, z_{10} and $z_{9.10}$, are in the first row and first column of their respective matrices. In the third matrix it is found that $z_{5.9,10}$ will, at that stage, add most to the multiple. Accordingly, covariances involving $z_{5.10}$ are computed for the second matrix, followed by the covariances involving $z_{5.9,10}$ for the third matrix. In any matrix, rows and columns involving previously eliminated variables are omitted.

4. In the fourth matrix it is seen that $z_{5.6,9,10}$ will add most to the multiple. If the decision is made that only four predictors are needed, no further elimination is required.

5. The square of the multiple R is $r_{0,10}^2 + C_{09.10}^2/V_{9.10} + C_{05.9,10}^2/V_{5.9,10} + C_{06.5,9,10}^2/V_{6.5,9,10}$ or $.152 + .085 + .025 + .017 = .279$. While third-order betas could be found from the forward solution, the multiple is recomputed, final-order betas are found, and the work is checked in Table 7.4, using the procedures described in Example 7.2.

TABLE 7.3. SELECTING n' PREDICTORS YIELDING A HIGH MULTIPLE R

Data are slightly modified from Sprunger (5). Scales of MMPI variables (1, 2, 4, and 5) reversed so as to make all correlations positive. Original r's corrected to two places of decimals. N = 114.

VARIABLE	10	9	8	7	6	5	4	3	2	1	0	CHECK SUM
10 Self-description blank	1.0000	.2500	.2800	.4900	.5100	.3000	.3500	.2100	.3200	.3000	.3900	4.4000
9 Reading vocabulary	.2500	1.0000	.6800	.3000	.2100	.2600	.3500	.5800	.2300	.4200	.3800	4.6600
8 Arithmetic reasoning	.2800	.6800	1.0000	.3900	.2400	.3400	.3700	.6300	.2400	.4400	.3700	
7 Group contribution inv.	.4900	.3000	.3900	1.0000	.4600	.4300	.4400	.2700	.4300	.5200	.3600	
6 Personal inventory	.5100	.2100	.2400	.4600	1.0000	.2700	.3700	.1200	.4400	.2600	.3500	
5 Psychopathic deviate scale	.3000	.2600	.3400	.4300	.2700	1.0000	.6200	.1100	.6000	.5200	.3200	4.7700
4 Schizophrenia scale	.3500	.3500	.3700	.4400	.3700	.6200	1.0000	.1900	.8100	.8400	.3100	
3 Pattern analysis	.2100	.5800	.6300	.2700	.1200	.1100	.1900	1.0000	.1600	.2600	.3100	
2 Psychasthenia scale (part)	.3200	.2300	.2400	.4300	.4400	.6000	.8100	.1600	1.0000	.6000	.2800	
1 Validity score	.3000	.4200	.4400	.5200	.2600	.5200	.8400	.2600	.6000	1.0000	.2700	
0 Group contribution rating	.3900	.3800	.3700	.3600	.3500	.3200	.3100	.3100	.2800	.2700	1.0000	4.3400

2nd MATRIX

VARIABLE												$C_{0i.q}^2 / V_{i.q}$
9.10	.9375	.6100	.1775	.0825	.1850	.2625	.5275	.1500	.3450	.2825	3.5600	.085
8.10	.6507	.9216			.2560					.2608		.074
7.10	.1893		.7599		.2830					.1689		.038
6.10	.0880			.7399	.1170					.1511		.031
5.10	.1973				.9100	.5150	.0470	.5040	.4300	.2030	3.4500	.045
4.10	.2800					.8775				.1735		.034
3.10	.5627						.9559			.2281		.054
2.10	.1600							.8976		.1552		.027
1.10	.3680								.9100	.1530		.026
0.10	.3013									.8479	2.6240	

3rd MATRIX

VARIABLE											$C_{0i.q}^2 / V_{i.q}$
8.9, 10	.1552	.5247		.1356	.4632	−.0571	.4744	.3619	.0770	2.7476	.011
7.9, 10	.2839	.7263		.2480					.1154		.018
6.9, 10	.1153		.7326	.1007					.1262		.022
5.9, 10	xx			.8735					.1473		.025
4.9, 10	.5303				.8040				.0944		.011
3.9, 10	−.0654					.6591			.0691		.007
2.9, 10	.5431						.8736		.1100		.014
1.9, 10	.4143							.7830	.0490		.003
0.9, 10	.1686								.7628	1.5514	

4th MATRIX

VARIABLE											$C_{0i.q}^2 / V_{i.q}$
8.5, 9, 10	.5037	xx	xx	xx	xx	xx	xx	xx	.0541		.006
7.5, 9, 10		.6559		xx					.0736		.008
6.5, 9, 10			.7210	xx					.1092		.017
4.5, 9, 10				xx	.5584				.0163		.000
3.5, 9, 10				xx		.6554			.0787		.009
2.5, 9, 10				xx			.6160		.0300		.001
1.5, 9, 10				xx				.6331	−.0120		.000
0.5, 9, 10				xx					.7380	1.0882	

TABLE 7.4 COMPUTING AND CHECKING R AND FINAL BETAS FOR FOUR SELECTED PREDICTORS

(Predictors Selected in Table 7.3)

VARIABLE	β	10	9	6	5	0	CHECK SUM
10	.2029	1.0000	.2500	.5100	.3000	.3900	2.4500
9	.2582	.2500	1.0000	.2100	.2600	.3800	2.1000
6	.1515	.5100		1.0000	.2700	.3500	2.3400
5	.1511	.3000			1.0000	.3200	2.1500
0		.3900				1.0000	2.4400
9.10		.2582	.9375	.0825	.1850	.2825	1.4875
6.10		.1515	.0880	.7399	.1170	.1511	1.0905
5.10		.1511	.1973		.9100	.2030	1.4150
0.10			.3013			.8479	1.4845
6.9, 10			.1515	.7326	.1007	.1262	.9596
5.9, 10			.1511	.1375	.8735	.1473	1.1215
0.9, 10				.1723		.7628	1.0363
5.6, 9, 10					.8597	.1299	.9896
0.6, 9, 10					.1511	.7411	.8710
0.5, 6, 9, 10						.7215	.7215

$R = \sqrt{1 - V_{0.5, 6, 9, 10}} = \sqrt{1 - .7215} = .53$
$R^2 = 1 - V_{0.5, 6, 9, 10} = 1 - .7215 = .2785$
$\beta_{05.6, 9, 10} = .1511$
$\beta_{06.5, 9, 10} = .1723 - (.1511 \times .1375) = .1515$
$\beta_{09.5, 6, 10} = .3013 - (.1511 \times .1973) - (.1515 \times .0880) = .2582$
$\beta_{0, 10.5, 6, 9} = .3900 - (.1511 \times .3000) - (.1515 \times .5100) - (.2582 \times .2500) = .2029$
$R^2 = \Sigma \beta_i C_{0i} = .2786$

Cross Validation. The procedure for finding multiple R obtains a maximum relationship between the criterion and the weighted team of predictors only in the sample. As indicated by Formula 7.9, shrinkage in subsequent samples is to be anticipated. Table 7.5 shows the process of applying the betas from Table 7.4 to a new sample of cases measured on the same variables.

The intercorrelations of the four predictors with unity in the diagonal cells are regarded as a variance-covariance matrix, and the four validity coefficients are considered covariances. To find the correlation between the criterion and the weighted sum of the predictors, the following operations are required:

1. Each validity must be multiplied by the corresponding beta. The sum of the products is the covariance between the criterion and the wighted sum of the predictors.
2. Each of the intercorrelations must be multiplied by two betas (one for each predictor variable).
3. Each variance in the diagonal must be multiplied by the square of the corresponding beta.

4. The square root of the sum of the results of the operations with the predictors (steps 2 and 3) is the standard deviation of the weighted sum of the predictors. When divided into the covariance of the weighted sum with the criterion (which retains its standard deviation of 1.00), the quotient is the cross-validated multiple.

TABLE 7.5. APPLICATION OF BETAS AND OF UNIT WEIGHTS IN CROSS-VALIDATION SAMPLE

Data Slightly Modified from Sprunger (5). $N = 112$

		PREDICTORS				CRITERION
VARIABLE	BETA	10	9	6	5	0
10	$\beta_{0,\,10.5,\,6,\,9} = .20$	1.00	.25	.48	.14	.27
9	$\beta_{0,\,9.5,\,6,\,10} = .26$	.25	1.00	.12	.21	.22
6	$\beta_{0,\,6.5,\,9,\,10} = .15$	.48	.12	1.00	.23	.23
5	$\beta_{0,\,5.6,\,9,\,10} = .15$	.14	.21	.23	1.00	.20
	Column sums	.3580	.3595	.3117	.2671	.1757
	Column sum × beta:	.0716	.0935	.0468	.0401	

$$r = \frac{.1757}{\sqrt{.0716 + .0935 + .0468 + .0401}} = .35$$

Application of unit weights (from matrix above):

Variable:	10	9	6	5	0
Column sums:	1.87	1.58	1.83	1.58	.92

$$r = \frac{.92}{\sqrt{1.87 + 1.58 + 1.83 + 1.58}} = .35$$

In Table 7.5 these operations are performed by summing products of betas and coefficients, column by column; multiplying these column sums of products involving the predictors by the beta appropriate to the column; extracting the square root of the sum of these products; and dividing into the weighted column sum of the validities.

In cross-validation, the correlation is .35, a marked drop from the obtained multiple of .53. In this study, the coefficients are not stable, and the highest validity, .27, for any of the four predictors in the second sample is less than the lowest validity, .32, in the first sample.

It is also to be noted that, within the group of four predictors, little is gained by differential weighting according to the betas. If all weights are taken arbitrarily as 1.00, then, by the procedure outlined above (summing the validities and dividing by the square root of the sum of the entries in the predictor matrix), the overall validity is again .35.

Within an observed sample, it is not difficult to maximize, or approximately to maximize, the correlation of a weighted sum of predictors with a criterion. However, for such maximized coefficients to be stable from sample to sample, the correlations on which they are based must be reasonably stable.

It should not be supposed, however, that when n' variables are selected by this method from a total pool of n predictors that the n' so chosen necessarily constitute the best team of n' predictors for estimating criterion values. The team of n' predictors will tend to be the best combination, but theoretically at least, one might start with a predictor that does not have the highest correlation with the criterion and select a still more valid combination. In fact, the best single predictor may not enter the most valid combination at all. To select the most valid team of n' variables from a pool of n predictors, there seems to be no direct solution other than the comparison of the validities of combinations of the variables, taking n' at a time. However, the procedure of selecting a highly valid group of predictors, beginning with the most valid, generally leads to a reasonably good solution.

SUPPRESSOR VARIABLES AND NEGATIVE BETAS

Occasionally in multiple correlation one encounters a "suppressor" variable. One example is a variable that has zero correlation with a criterion, but a high correlation with a valid predictor. Such a variable increases the multiple by "suppressing" some of the invalid variance of the valid predictor.

Consider a criterion that is relatively "pure," for example, a criterion comprising mostly mechanical ability. Suppose a predictor was "mixed," requiring both verbal and mechanical abilities. The presence of the verbal admixture could be thought of as lowering the correlation from what it would have been had a predictor measuring only mechanical ability been available.

A "pure" verbal test might have a high correlation with the "mixed" predictor, but a zero or near-zero correlation with the criterion.

If the multiple correlation under such circumstances is computed, it is found that the addition of the invalid test actually adds to the prediction beyond the validity of the "mixed" test. The beta coefficient of the invalid measure is necessarily negative.

Variables that have negative betas in a regression equation are, to some degree at least, suppressors. This phenomenon is of interest when a team of highly valid predictors is being selected. A variable could have a zero covariance with a criterion at a given stage, but still add to the multiple later on. This would be true if it had a definite degree of relationship with one or more other predictors that were still valid. When a variable has neither validity nor a definite relationship with a valid predictor, it can add nothing to the prediction of the criterion.

SHRINKAGE OF MULTIPLE R

A multiple correlation is computed for a particular sample of cases. Each of the predictors is so weighted that the correlation between the weighted sum of the predictors and the criterion is as high as possible.

In finding the betas, observed correlations based upon the observed values of the variables are used. The weighting proceeds as though all variability were true variance; that is, the random error in each variable as well as the true component is weighted so as to make the correlation with the criterion as high as possible.

In a subsequent sample (or in the population), one would expect the random error to be differently disposed. Accordingly, if the beta weights found in one sample are applied to the same predictors in another sample, it is to be expected that the correlation between the weighted sum of the predictor and the criterion will decrease. This phenomenon is generally observed and is known as the *shrinkage of the multiple*.

A formula[5] for estimating the correlation in the population between the criterion and the weighted sum of the predictors is

$$R' = \sqrt{\frac{(N - 1)R^2 - (n' - 1)}{N - n'}} \tag{7.9}$$

in which R' is the shrunken multiple, N is the number of cases, and n' is the number of predictor variables selected at any stage.

It will be noted that the shrinkage decreases as N increases, but increases when the number of predictor variables becomes large. The formula indicates what is to be expected when maximizing procedures are used in one sample of cases and the weights are then applied in a new sample.

Many personnel psychologists handle this problem by cross-validation. A procedure involving maximization, whether by working out regression weights or by selecting highly valid combinations of test items, is not considered to yield the true correlation with the criterion. Weights obtained are applied to a subsequent sample of cases, and the validity found therein is taken as a better indication of the true validity.

CONSIDERATIONS IN UNDERSTANDING MULTIPLE *R*

If the predictors more or less duplicate one another (as evidenced by high intercorrelations), the multiple will tend to be a little higher than the validity of the most valid predictor. If there are a number of predictors and they are more or less independent (as evidenced by intercorrelations approximating zero), the multiple will be considerably higher than the validity of the best predictor. On the assumption that all validities of n predictors (indicated as r_{0i}) are equal to one another, and that all intercorrelations (indicated as r_{ij}) are also equal to one another, but the validities and intercorrelations are not necessarily equal, one can find the effect of

---

[5] Developed by Wherry (7).

different sets of validities on different sets of intercorrelations from the following formula:

$$R = r_{0i}\sqrt{\frac{n}{1 + (n - 1)r_{ij}}} \tag{7.10}$$

Under the assumptions stated above, this is an exact formula for multiple R. For example, for n predictors of equal validity and intercorrelations of .00, the multiple is $\sqrt{n}$ times the validity of a single predictor. If all intercorrelations are 1.00, one predictor is as good as the whole team. Consider also a specific case of 16 predictors, with all intercorrelations .20 and all validities .25. Multiple R would be .50. Sometimes, when conditions are met reasonably well, Formula 7.10 can be used to estimate the multiple, but the more validities or intercorrelations depart from equality, the less useful the formula is for this purpose.

A final word—it should be apparent that the multiple can never be less than the absolute value of the highest validity. If only one variable is useful in predicting the criterion, it alone will be weighted, and the weights of the other predictors will be zero.

SUMMARY

A coefficient of multiple correlation represents the relationship between a single variable on the one hand and a weighted combination of variables on the other, the weights being determined in such a manner that the correlation is a maximum in the sample in which it is computed.

Such correlations are subject to "shrinkage" in subsequent samples. Consequently, no computed multiple R should be regarded as descriptive of a generally obtaining relationship. When the weights obtained in one sample are applied to the predictors in a subsequent sample, the correlation between the criterion and the weighted composite is a better indication of the true relationship than the original multiple R.

Beta coefficients are weights applicable to z-scores in finding a weighted composite.

Variances of residual variables (partial variances) and covariances between pairs of residual variables (partial covariances) are intermediate statistics useful in finding a multiple R and the related betas.

Intercorrelations remaining the same, multiple R increases as validities increase. Validities remaining the same, multiple R increases as intercorrelations decrease. In other words, the less predictor variables overlap among themselves and the more they overlap the criterion, the better the criterion can be forecast.

1. The following artificial variables are expressed as z-scores:

CASE	z_2	z_1	z_0
A.A.	1.50	1.00	1.50
B.B.	1.00	-1.50	.00
C.C.	.50	.00	1.00
D.D.	.00	.50	$-.50$
E.E.	$-.50$	$-.50$	-1.00
F.F.	-1.00	1.50	.50
G.G.	-1.50	-1.00	-1.50

(a) Compute the matrix of intercorrelations, remembering that $r_{xy} = \Sigma z_x z_y / N$.

(b) Find $R_{0(12)}$ and related betas.

(c) By means of the regression equation, $\tilde{z}_0 = \beta_{01.2} z_1 + \beta_{02.1} z_2$, find the seven values of $\tilde{z}_0$.

(d) Find the variance of $\tilde{z}_0$, which should be $R^2_{0(12)}$.

(e) Find the correlation between $\tilde{z}_0$ and z_0, which should be $R_{0(12)}$.

2. Let three predictor variables be X, Y, and W. Let the criterion be K. Using appropriate subscripts for all variances, covariances, and betas, write algebraically the successive matrices that can be used to find the partial variance of the criterion after variance predictable from X, Y, and W has been removed. In the same notation, write a formula for multiple R, computing formulas for final-order betas and the regression equations in z form.

3. Using Formula 7.10, $R = r_{0i} \sqrt{n/[1 + (n-1)r_{ij}]}$, which applies when all validities (r_{0j}) are equal and when all intercorrelations (r_{ij}) are also equal, construct a table of R for cases in which n, the number of predictors, is 4. If the formula yields a value of R that is imaginary or greater than 1.00, the corresponding constellation of correlations is impossible, and an appropriate indication should be entered in the table. The following format is suggested:

TABLE OF R FOR FOUR PREDICTORS WITH EQUAL INTERCORRELATIONS (r_{ij})

EQUAL VALIDITIES (r_{0i})	INTER CORRELATIONS								
	$-.80$	$-.60$	$-.40$	$-.20$	$-.00$	$-.20$	.40	.60	.80
.90	—	—	—	—	—	—	—	—	—
.80	—	—	—	—	—	—	—	—	—
.70	—	—	—	—	—	—	—	—	—
.60	—	—	—	—	—	—	—	—	—
.50	—	—	—	—	—	—	—	—	—
.40	—	—	—	—	—	—	—	—	—
.30	—	—	—	—	—	—	—	—	—
.20	—	—	—	—	—	—	—	—	—
.10	—	—	—	—	—	—	—	—	—
.00	—	—	—	—	—	—	—	—	—

4. An aptitude test of 50 items has a mean item-item correlation of .30. The mean of the item validities against an external criterion is .15.

   (a) If it is assumed that all item-item correlations are equal to their mean of .30 and that all item validities are equal to their mean of .15, what is the validity of the complete instrument?

   (b) What would be the estimated validity under the same assumptions if the test were reduced to 25 items?

5. Use the sum variable as a check while finding multiple R for the following matrix of correlations from Breimeier (1). Also compute and check the final order betas.

VARIABLES	3	2	1	0
4 ACE psychological examination	.15	.05	.35	.31
3 Strong vocational interest (ministry)		.36	.42	.11
2 Kuder preference (musical)			.12	.19
1 Kuder preference (literary)				.12
0 Grade point average (theological school)				

6. The following hypothetical example is designed to show how a suppressor variable might function:

	1	0
2 Mechanical aptitude[a]	.707	.350
1 Verbal aptitude		.000
0 Mechanical occupation		

   [a] With items written in verbal context.

   (a) How much does a nonvalid test (verbal aptitude) add to the prediction of the valid test (mechanical aptitude)?

   (b) Is this situation reasonable?

7. (a) In sample A in the following data from Taylor and Tajen (6), apply the Wherry-Doolittle method to find a highly valid subset of three predictors.

   (b) For these three predictors, find R and related betas.

   (c) Apply these betas to the sample B and find the correlation between the three variables so weighted and the criterion. Has there been shrinkage?

   (d) For the same three predictors in sample B, compare the correlation so found with R.

Sample A: $N = 96$

	4	3	2	1	0
5 Clerical speed	.48	.61	.22	.46	.44
4 Word meaning		.65	.21	.56	.48
3 Arithmetic			.04	.50	.53
2 Figure cancellation				.14	.06
1 Figure classification					.53
0 Grade in course					

Sample B: $N = 97$

	4	3	2	1	0
5	.45	.49	.35	.41	.43
4		.55	.32	.48	.38
3			.29	.38	.36
2				.30	.24
1					.48

8. Below is the matrix of intercorrelations for the 11 variables in the cross-validation sample in the study described in Example 7.3 (5). $N = 112$.

	9	8	7	6	5	4	3	2	1	0
10	.25	.32	.27	.48	.14	.36	.25	.32	.29	.27
9		.65	.26	.12	.21	.30	.50	.30	.33	.22
8			.32	.22	.11	.26	.60	.24	.26	.41
7				.28	.44	.33	.11	.29	.51	.34
6					.23	.43	.19	.50	.35	.23
5						.53	.04	.51	.60	.20
4							.17	.81	.83	.16
3								.20	.12	.24
2									.63	.05
1										.28

By the Wherry-Doolittle procedure illustrated in Example 7.3, find a highly valid team of four predictors in this sample and cross-validate the multiple in the original sample.

REFERENCES

1. BREIMEIER, KENNETH H., *The Prediction of Academic Success in a Theological Seminary*, Master's Thesis, St. Louis: Washington University, 1948.
2. DUBOIS, PHILIP H., *Multivariate Correlational Analysis*, New York: Harper and Row, 1957.
3. KENDALL, MAURICE G., *The Advanced Theory of Statistics*, London: Charles Griffin, 1943.
4. ROSEN, NED A., AND VAN HORN, JOHN W., "Selection of college scholarship students: statistical vs. clinical methods," *Personnel Guid. J.*, 1961, **40**, 150–154.
5. SPRUNGER, JAMES A., "The ability of the individual to contribute to his group," *Personnel Psychol.*, 1961, **14**, 317–330.
6. TAYLOR, E. K., AND TAJEN, CLAIRE, "Selection for training: tabulating equipment operators," *Personnel Psychol.*, 1948, **1**, 341–348.
7. WHERRY, R. J., "A new formula for predicting the shrinkage of the coefficient of multiple correlation," *Ann. Math. Statist.*, 1931, **2**, 440–451.
8. WHERRY, R. J., IN STEAD, W. H., AND SHARTLE, C. L., *et al.*, *Occupational Counseling Techniques*, New York: American Book Co. 1940, Appendix 5.

STATISTICAL
CONTROL
AND PARTIAL
CORRELATION

8

INDEPENDENT AND DEPENDENT VARIABLES

Many psychological studies can be understood as an attempt to ascertain the relationship between two variables. Generally, one of the two can be identified as the "independent" variable; the other, as the "dependent" variable.

In a laboratory experiment, there may be a series of trials (or two or more groups of individuals) for each of which there is a different degree of an independent variable, which is usually under the direct control of the investigator. The experimenter may be interested in discovering any systematic variation in the dependent variable corresponding to changes he makes in the independent variable.

Thus, in a study of factors influencing the perception of a shape, the experimenter may vary area as an independent variable and determine the degree to which correctness of identification (the dependent variable) is related to variation in the independent variable.

He may do this for a sample of shapes, using a single observer, or he may carry out the study with a group of observers, exposing each to a different variant of the stimulus (that is, the independent variable). More than likely, however, he would employ a combined approach, using varying degrees of the independent variable with a number of subjects, and averaging results in order that the general trend might emerge more clearly and reliably.

If both variables can be conveniently scaled, results of such a study can be presented in the form of a graph. The vertical axis of pair of coordinates can be laid off to represent varying degrees of the dependent variable, say in percent of correct recognitions, while the horizontal axis may represent the varying degrees of the area of the stimulus.

An alternative procedure is to find a mathematical function to represent the relationship. Simple mathematical functions, which seem to be most appropriate for psychological data, may be graphed as straight lines or smooth curves. When raw data are plotted, irregularities in trend lines are generally taken as representing sampling or observational errors.

In Chapter 6 the fitting of a straight line connecting two variables by the method of least squares was described. To define a straight line precisely, relative to a pair of coordinate axes, two constants are needed: the slope and the intercept. In the z form of the regression equation connecting two variables, z_0 and z_1, the slope is r_{01} and the intercept is zero. In the raw-score form of the regression equation, the slope is the regression coefficient $(r_{01}s_0)/s_1$, and the intercept is the constant term, $[M_0 - (r_{01}s_0M_1)/s_1]$. By somewhat similar principles a parabola or other curve can be established to represent the relationship between two variables. Procedures for fitting curves are presented in advanced texts in statistics, such as Lewis (3).

An important fact in all types of experiments involving human beings is that in addition to the independent variable, there are almost always various other variables that may, directly or indirectly, affect variation within the dependent variable. In the study of the perception of shape, such factors, in addition to size, include configuration, color, and illumination as well as variables within the observers, such as familiarity, visual skills, and intelligence.

CONTROL OF EXTRANEOUS VARIABLES

Any variable not of direct interest in an investigation, but which may affect the results, may be tagged as an "extraneous" variable. "Control" refers to methods of eliminating or at least reducing the influence of such extraneous variables. There are five methods of experimental control through modification of the situation or through selection of cases. In addition to these five experimental methods, there is statistical control, the main topic of this chapter. The present discussion of experimental control emphasizes the control of a single variable in an experiment. Normally, however, attempts are made to control two or more variables simultaneously, and different control methods may be used in the same study. The five methods are:

1. Eliminating a variable completely;
2. Eliminating a variable by selecting or modifying cases so that all have a uniform degree of the characteristic;
3. Matching cases and distributing them into two or more groups according to values on a variable;
4. Balancing cases; and
5. Randomization in the assignment of cases to groups.

COMPLETE ELIMINATION AS A CONTROL

When a variable is controlled through elimination, it means that within the experimental situation there is complete uniformity with respect to the characteristic in question.

By eliminating a variable completely, the degree of a characteristic is reduced to zero in all instances. Thus, if one were studying the relationship of different concentrations of table salt to the speed of recognizing a watery solution as salty, one would ordinarily use the purest salt and the purest water obtainable, thus eliminating completely the effect of other chemicals that would ordinarily be in the salt or in the water.

Elimination by reducing the variable to zero in all cases is more practical in psychological studies when the variable characterizes situations than when it describes people. In a series of situations there can be zero degrees of light or noise or vibration; and, in experiments on taste and smell, zero amounts of specified chemical elements. On the other hand, temperature of a solution can be eliminated as a variable only by using a constant temperature. In a study in which it is necessary to control variation in temperature, a certain degree of heat (say, 18°C) may be specified.

SELECTION OF CASES OF A UNIFORM DEGREE OF A CHARACTERISTIC

This is a second method of control, in which a variable is eliminated by selecting only instances that have a uniform degree of the characteristic to be controlled. .

This type of control is feasible with attributes of individuals. Theoretically it is possible to conduct a study in which all subjects are of the same chronological age, the same I.Q., or same achievement in reading. However, there are two difficulties: one practical, the other theoretical.

While in some instances it is relatively easy to find numerous children who are, say, within two months of their tenth birthday, it is very difficult to find substantial numbers that are within, say, two days of their tenth birthday. Instead of uniformity in respect to age or I.Q., or reading achievement, the best that can be expected in practice is a narrow range of the variable. This may reduce its effect considerably, but does not completely eliminate it.

On the theoretical side, the variables on which it is feasible to control may not be the variables that need to be controlled. If one controls on sex, by using only boys in a study, there still may be a wide range of variation in variables related to sex, such as interests and physical characteristics, and which may also be related to the experimental variables.

MATCHING OF CASES

The third method of control is by matching precisely the cases assigned to two or more groups. If there are two groups, corresponding to two degrees of the experimental variable, cases that are identical on the variable to be controlled are paired. One member of the pair is assigned at random to each of the groups. If there are three or more groups, then clusters of three or more cases are located, all identical on the variable to be controlled.

Consider, for example, a study of the effect of different incentives on learning. Normally there would be at least one "experimental" group and one "control" group. In the experimental group a special incentive might be introduced, whereas in the control group there would be no special motivation. As an alternative, there might be several groups, each representing a different degree of the experimental variable.

Obviously, if the groups vary at the start of the study in some way that is related to the variables under scrutiny, it will be difficult or impossible to draw valid conclusions.

Suppose there are three groups in the study, two experimental groups and a single control group, with the experimental variable in three degrees and varying with group membership. To control a variable such as reading comprehension, steps might be as follows:

1. Measurement of the reading comprehension of all individuals who might be used in the experiment;
2. Arrangement of all individuals in order on this variable;
3. Selection of sets of three cases with more or less identical scores; and
4. Assignment of the three cases in each set to the three groups at random. This may be accomplished by devices such as dice or by a table of random numbers.

Matching of subjects is relatively easy on a single control variable, when assignments are made to a limited number of groups, and when there are relatively large numbers of subjects from which to choose. Matching becomes progressively more difficult as more groups are involved, as an attempt is made to match on two or more variables simultaneously, and when the pool of potential subjects is limited. When feasible, matching is an excellent method of control in that nonlinear as well as linear correlation between any matched variable and the independent variable becomes zero.

BALANCING OF CASES

When the pool of potential subjects is limited, or when it is desired to use more than two experimental groups, or when an attempt is made to control on two or more variables simultaneously, balancing of cases is more flexible than matching. In balancing, subjects are assigned so that the mean of each controlled variable is identical in each of the groups.

There is no exact formula for balancing. One procedure is to tally cases by groups as they are assigned and note whether the means remain more or less identical. Of course, before assignments are considered final, identity of group means should be demonstrated.

In addition to balancing on mean values, it is generally desirable in making the assignments to balance so that variances also become equal. This can be accomplished by noting the dispersions of the distributions during the process of assignment.

In actual experimentation, how much departure from equality of means and variance can be tolerated is a matter of judgment. Clearly, no group differences in either means or variances should be significant by statistical tests discussed in Chapter 13. Obviously, the closer the group means and variances are to being identical, the better the job that has been done in controlling the variable.

When variables are controlled by balancing, linear correlation between any controlled variable and any experimental variable is zero. However, it is conceivable that even with careful balancing, some sort of nonlinear relationship may exist between a controlled and experimental variable.

RANDOMIZATION OF CASES

A fifth method of control is to assign cases to groups by chance. Various systems can be used for this purpose, such as tossing coins or drawing lots. Probably the most satisfactory way is through the use of a table of random numbers and a predetermined formula.

Consider 200 subjects to be assigned at random to four groups, that is, 50 cases to each group. The first step would be to number the cases in any convenient way from 001 to 200. The second step would be to establish a rule for assignment to groups, such as using the last two digits of every fifth number in a table of random numbers, and assigning group membership on the basis of the remainder when these two digits are divided by four. A remainder of 1 might mean assignment to group 1; a remainder of 2, assignment to group 2; a remainder of 3, assignment to group 3; and remainder of zero, assignment to group 4. Each case would be studied in order, and the corresponding random number would be consulted in making the disposition of the case. In all probability the four groups would not be filled simultaneously. Suppose group 1 were filled first, with 50 cases. Thereafter, numbers with a remainder of 1 would be disregarded. The rule would then be to go on to the next random number until a second group was filled, and so on until 50 cases were allotted to each of the four groups. The use of a table of random numbers is shown in Example 8.1.

E X A M P L E 8.1

CONSTRUCTION AND USE OF A TABLE OF RANDOM DIGITS

Purpose. In psychological research, tables of random numbers are useful in replacing human judgments with a method of decision that lacks the possibility of systematic bias.

In many cases the mathematical model used in making inferences assumes that the sample being studied has been drawn at random from an unlimited population. The use of a table of random numbers to reduce bias in selecting the sample makes the mathematical model more appropriate.

In other cases, where a total sample is to be divided into subgroups, a table of random numbers may be useful. A useful method of controlling a variable in *n* subgroups is to:

1. Rank all cases on the variable;
2. Divide the *N* cases in order of rank into subsets of *n* each;
3. Use a table of random numbers in deciding which case of each subset is to be assigned to each of the *n* subgroups.

Construction of a Table of Random Numbers. Random multidigit numbers are simply aggregations of random digits. In the decimal system, a universe of random digits would consist of equal proportions of the ten digits with equal likelihood of any digit being drawn at any particular time.

Various mechanical devices can be used as sources of random digits, one of them being described in the volume by the Rand Corporation (5) from which the 2500 digits of Table 8.1 were selected by chance.

The decision as to where to enter a table of random numbers is generally made on the basis of some sort of a mechanical lottery, such as tossing one or more coins or using dice.

In the present instance, after developing a general plan that called for selecting 2500 of the 1 million digits of the Rand table, it was decided to insert a pointer blindly into the table to locate a key line of random numbers (ten blocks of five digits each). Other prior decisions were:

1. The first digit that was a 1, 2, 3, or 4 encountered in the first block would determine the series of fourth pages used in developing the sample of digits. If a 1 was first encountered, then the series of pages would be 1, 5, 9···; if 2, then the series would be 2, 6, 10···; and so on.

2. In the Rand tables there are 50 lines on a page. Accordingly, it was decided that the first digit in the second block would determine the tens digit of the line to be selected on each fourth page, 0 being paired with 6, 1 with 7, 2 with 8, and so on.

3. It was decided that the initial digit of the third block would be taken as the units digit of the designating line.

TABLE 8.1. A TABLE OF 2500 RANDOM DIGITS

00	04037	19964	00602	61524	00433	65116	23203	83826	50417	22746
01	79953	66662	14151	90774	79794	78578	27636	02703	09625	52336
02	73242	18669	03501	77640	26604	46306	23441	79886	63469	23592
03	86266	03223	59805	41477	49099	30208	30688	97429	93758	52013
04	68343	46283	82476	71647	37125	83863	61719	92232	07524	93974
05	72085	99528	43941	60685	83970	49905	47003	65139	40433	25054
06	86485	58168	96225	03088	98901	61695	48872	45422	11384	47546
07	73038	93790	24248	10861	08275	55599	42125	89577	06970	92692
08	12063	34851	74151	58394	98630	71851	79859	26319	23004	96680
09	46404	29297	81242	49268	69012	14515	89622	92470	60037	33129
10	86951	62495	61701	27395	65802	12184	46027	26755	62140	35208
11	99334	93261	04026	47377	58321	76789	60389	79438	73204	55594
12	64993	29279	68514	50076	42086	61216	48346	33844	52312	48912
13	53819	78628	04115	22867	53435	55014	48208	97953	38760	69207
14	30151	27420	80825	51422	41699	43411	79717	09995	60463	75768
15	82592	67181	19381	55046	54932	20744	89716	18591	95941	36410
16	63705	72019	39624	88518	76551	70846	58446	55085	62770	25747
17	10319	31485	96662	45788	39884	86037	11675	70936	15812	84941
18	26175	19661	47630	95737	68746	92421	51834	04141	87053	77748
19	19354	29305	22744	15825	01434	30056	18743	98753	54852	63170
20	37422	54758	19421	02704	24468	81992	09925	16328	05772	25638
21	54494	14592	91870	34236	11037	51387	85738	00706	25671	82382
22	28895	76678	71452	17152	17133	11287	17558	39950	91829	42711
23	53514	55089	37713	81714	55035	60828	12715	42834	84053	42111
24	46730	05308	29434	27904	53888	32737	52789	11359	16579	26175

25	70335	10817	16885	21308	29885	27733	47176	43013	32034	33972
26	47734	82585	85281	76634	81765	89362	62106	99324	85560	37796
27	70744	16985	16365	02482	22467	77415	60414	11590	52175	43964
28	41643	63919	95797	25291	01005	90568	15522	14517	20939	10466
29	18247	15105	43534	88643	43887	39654	87707	36889	10295	46770
30	17812	62885	75390	10263	39677	64934	97268	34346	47478	44462
31	96969	58500	42267	43197	41211	97323	77459	39620	24618	27403
32	68901	84279	90224	93240	33698	07116	73471	70043	52025	13543
33	46261	61216	32538	05665	89233	83901	67119	56367	60753	15905
34	09986	15581	63428	92310	80030	64195	47947	47119	28432	82840
35	55544	38379	68140	41492	16003	18783	34304	24591	61831	01403
36	01458	35565	26959	80660	59518	74890	67365	22141	84519	74587
37	07377	33463	81668	43720	56837	07762	64699	02366	63168	68372
38	73201	35959	14748	69985	52657	95411	05078	36453	11844	74024
39	90224	34604	53193	45721	48476	60754	98552	17879	01839	74987
40	38892	99784	14106	81602	71305	83637	96483	72863	73604	74282
41	11793	24645	47112	14970	30305	35240	94322	07374	27267	01558
42	20266	94585	95176	96288	65295	13349	92778	83432	68667	29211
43	25983	57459	86344	39396	87330	62666	48692	81936	79183	51316
44	96167	80698	89567	43738	50113	65339	69077	87101	84821	29996
45	11266	61844	82911	57007	60798	68124	48372	44290	12922	00490
46	23652	11934	95023	26134	42483	61787	11783	77201	21777	50869
47	97607	44037	00278	12728	02911	67869	11239	19011	19503	61699
48	81056	99779	80415	95761	54974	16692	74246	96370	76651	63891
49	08907	72067	75237	31592	20307	28518	99983	68509	50552	50406

4. Since only 25 digits were to come from each selected line of 50 digits, it was decided that if the first digit in the fourth block were odd, the odd sequence 1, 3, 5 ··· would be used; if it were even, then the even sequence.

Prior to entering the table with a pointer, a toss of a coin was used in deciding whether the pages to be inspected would be odd or even. The decision was for an even page, and the book entered accordingly.

Entry into the table resulted in automatic decisions:

1. To use pages with page numbers divisible by four without remainder;
2. That the tens digit of the line number would be 8;
3. That the units digit of the line number would be 2; and
4. That the even sequence of numbers on lines designated as xx82 would constitute the table.

Following a plan determined by chance, the pool of 2500 digits reported as Table 8.1 was selected.

Testing a Table of Random Digits. Tests to determine whether a table of digits really is random can be of many varieties, but all would resemble those to be described in Chapter 13.

Testing the Diversity Between Observation and Hypothesis. If a table is random, conditions such as the following would be true within sampling error:

1. Intercorrelations of rows and intercorrelations of columns would be .00.
2. Distributions of the ten digits for the table as a whole and for larger subdivisions would be rectangular.
3. Sequences and particular number combinations would occur no more and no less frequently than expected by chance.
4. The distribution of identical digits (pairs, triplets, and the like) within successive groups of n digits would be predictable on the basis of probability theory.

Using a Table of Random Digits. In psychological research one generally uses published tables such as the Rand table. The use of a table of random digits was illustrated in the decisions made in constructing Table 8.1. Within the framework of an investigation, the decisions that are to be free of the bias of the experimenter are catalogued, and then chance is involved as a basis for these decisions. Rules for applying the devices, such as coins or dice or roulette wheels or random numbers, are established arbitrarily in advance; then the chance devices are followed in making the decisions. The range of possible applications is vast.

As a method of control, randomization makes for easy decisions on the part of the experimenter. It also circumvents any prejudices he may have which might affect assignment to groups. Theoretically, the correlations between extraneous variables and the experimental variable associated with group membership is of the magnitude to be expected by chance.

When methods exist for the measurement of variables to be controlled, randomization is hardly to be recommended: complete elimination, elimination by the use of a constant value, matching and balancing are all much better. However, after one or more variables are controlled in arranging the cases in sets, then a chance procedure for final assignment to groups has much to recommend it.

CONTROL THROUGH FORMING RESIDUAL VARIABLES

As noted in the preceding chapter, any variable measured over N cases (on a scale for which linear correlation is an appropriate statistic) can be "residualized" with respect to any other variable or any group of variables measured over the same N cases. Residualization greatly resembles the methods of control described above. It results in variables that are linearly uncorrelated with one or more other variables, and thus eliminates variance associated with these "outside" variables.

Ordinarily, residual variables are not used in making assignments to groups; rather we partial out one or more variables to be controlled from the independent variable, the dependent variable, or both. This is usually effected by computing correlations in which one or both of the two variables entering into the correlation have been modified so that all values are residuals with respect to one or more outside or "secondary" variables.

In generalized notation let $z_{i.jk...n}$ refer to a variable in higher-order z form; that is, with mean of zero, but variance less than unity. Variable i is a primary, observed variable. In effect, scores in variable i have been divided into two portions: $\tilde{z}_{i(j)}$, which is predictable from z_j and perfectly correlated with z_j; and $z_{i.j}$, which is uncorrelated with z_j. In a two-variable scatter diagram, the $\tilde{z}_{i(j)}$ values are all exactly on the regression line, the least squares line of best fit, while all the $z_{i.j}$ values are residuals, that is, distances between the observed values and the regression line.

After the z_i values have been modified to form the $z_{i.j}$ values, the latter can be "residualized" again with respect to $z_{k.j}$. This results in a new variable, $z_{i.jk}$, a second-order residual variable, whihc is uncorrelated with both variable j and variable k and which comprises the variance remaining in variable i after the variance predictable from the best weighted team of variables j and k has been subtracted out. The numerical value of each case can be expressed as the original value less a portion predicted through the use of the regular regression equation:

$$z_{i.jk} = z_i - \tilde{z}_{i(jk)} = z_i - \beta_{ik.j}z_k - \beta_{ij.k}z_j$$

The process can be continued until an observed variable has been made uncorrelated with respect to any number of secondary variables, as indicated by the general notation $z_{i.jk...n}$.

While the individual values may sometimes be of interest, the correlation of residuals is of more importance in unraveling complex relationships among observed variables.

RATIOS AS RESIDUAL VARIABLES

Actually, a residual variable falls into the same statistical domain as a ratio or quotient. If a ratio, such as an intelligence quotient, has been properly constructed, it will correlate zero with the denominator variable. This is necessarily true in the original group in which the system of quotients has been developed, provided the relationship between the numerator and denominator variables is linear, and provided the standard deviation of the numerator variable is greater than the standard deviation of the denominator variable by a factor of $1/r$. The intent of the intelligence quotient, in which mental age is the numerator variable and chronological age is the denominator variable, is to obtain a measure of intelligence that has been purified by subtracting from the original measure that portion which is predictable from a knowledge of chronological age alone. If an intelligence quotient is constructed so that it correlates zero with chronological age, it will tend to be constant as the child grows older, which is one of its desirable characteristics. Although numerically quite different, a set of I.Q.'s for a standardization group, in which the regression of chronological age on mental age is linear, will correlate more or less perfectly with a set of residuals formed by subtracting from the mental age the portion predictable from chronological age.

In order to construct a set of ratios that will correlate zero with the denominator variable (designated as Y), both variables can be converted to standard scores with identical and positive means (such as as 50 or 100) and with the standard deviation of the numerator variable X, equal to s_y/r_{xy}. Such a set of ratios will correlate almost perfectly with the residual, $z_{x.y} = z_x - r_{xy}z_y$. The equivalence of ratios and residuals is demonstrated in Example 8.2.

EXAMPLE 8.2

EQUIVALENCE OF RATIOS AND RESIDUALS

Two variables ($N = 5$) in z form, z_x and z_y, are shown below. X' is a linear conversion of z_x and Y is a linear conversion of z_y. X'/Y is the ratio formed from these converted scores, multiplied by 100 and rounded to the nearest integer. Also shown are $\tilde{z}_x$ as predicted from z_y, and the residual variable $z_{x.y}$.

	z_x	z_y	X'	Y	X'/Y	$\tilde{z}_x$	$z_x - \tilde{z}_x$ or $z_{x.y}$
A.A.	1.50	.50	65	53	123	.30	1.20
B.B.	.50	1.50	55	59	93	.90	−.40
C.C.	.00	.00	50	50	100	.00	.00
D.D.	−.50	−1.50	45	41	110	−.90	.40
E.E.	−1.50	−.50	35	47	74	−.30	−1.20

By computing $\Sigma z_x z_y/N$, it can be seen that $r_{xy} = .60$. X' and Y have been formed with identical means. However, a standard deviation of 6 has been assigned to Y, and of $(s_y/r_{xy} = 6/.60 = 10)$ to X'. The result is that X'/Y correlates approximately .00 with Y. (The actual correlation is $-.012$.)

The correlation of X'/Y and the residual $z_{x.y}$ is .997, so that as a variable, X'/Y has statistical properties almost identical with those of $z_{x.y}$.

In practical instances, the residual is probably to be preferred to a ratio, since it correlates precisely .00 with the eliminated variable. It is also a simple matter to transform a set of residuals to standard scores with any desired M' and s'.

PARTIAL CORRELATION

As a descriptive statistic, a partial correlation is the Pearson product-moment correlation between two residual variables, both of which have been "residualized" with respect to an identical set of secondary variables. A partial correlation may be used to estimate what the correlation between the two primary variables would be in groups homogeneous with respect to the secondary variables. Suppose, for example, there is a series of groups, none of which shows variability in a third variable, but which collectively exhibit the entire range of the third variable. It would be expected that the partial correlation between the two primary variables, with the third partialed out (that is, the correlation between the two primary variables after variance predictable from the third variable has been removed), would be representative of the series of correlations between the two primary variables in the several groups homogeneous with respect to the third variable. The partial correlation could then be considered as a measure of the relationship between the two primary variables freed of the influence of the secondary variable.

As an example, consider the relationship between a reading comprehension test and an intelligence test in grade school children. Scores on both tests increase with age. For a group of pupils of varying age, the correlation between reading and intelligence will be spuriously high because of the extraneous variable (namely, age) that is related to both. If the correlation is obtained between reading and intelligence scores (modified so that as residual variables they are uncorrelated with age), the partial r so obtained can be taken as an estimate of the correlation between obtained reading and intelligence scores in groups homogeneous with respect to age.

The experimental approach to this problem parallels the statistical. In several groups of pupils, each of which is homogeneous as to age, the typical correlation in these groups should be substantially the same as that obtained by partial correlation over all groups. A comparison of partial correlation and zero-order correlation within groups is presented in Example 8.3.

EXAMPLE 8.3

COMPARISON OF PARTIAL r WITH r WITHIN GROUPS

Purpose of Partial r. A partial r may be considered an estimate of the cor-relation between two variables in groups homogeneous with respect to the variable(s) "partialed out." As a descriptive statistic, it is the Pearson product-moment r between two sets of residuals, both of which, by the fact of being residual variables, are uncorrelated with the variable(s) partialed out.

r Within Groups. In Table 8.2 are displayed nine scatter diagrams for nine groups homogeneous with respect to the pilot aptitude score (pilot stanine) for 3000 Air Force cadets (1). The correlations, in descending order, between bombardier and navigator stanine are shown in the table.

STANINE GROUP	N	r_{BN}
7	359	.688
8	218	.641
2	204	.636
9	224	.632
3	295	.627 (median)
5	536	.614
6	511	.614
4	571	.572
1	82	.546
TOTAL	3000	

The r for the Total Group. In Table 8.3 are the three scatter diagrams for the intercorrelations of three variables: bombardier stanine B, navigator stanine N, and pilot stanine P. The first diagram shows the correlation between the same variables, B and N, as reported in Table 8.2, but consolidated as one group of 3000, heterogeneous with respect to the pilot stanine. Here the r is .716, which may be compared with a median of .627 for the nine groups separately. The other correlations for the total group of 3000 are $r_{BP} = .737$ and $r_{NP} = .473$.

Computation of Partial r. For the special instance of a first-order partial (with the two primary variables residualized with respect to a single control variable), Formula 8.1a may be translated into zero-order variances, covariances, and betas, and then into zero-order r's as follows:

$$r_{ij.q} = \frac{C_{ij.q}}{\sqrt{V_{i.q}}\sqrt{V_{j.q}}} = \frac{C_{ij} - \beta_{iq}C_{jq}}{\sqrt{V_i - \beta_{iq}C_{iq}}\sqrt{V_j - \beta_{jq}C_{jq}}} = \frac{r_{ij} - r_{iq}r_{jq}}{\sqrt{1 - r_{iq}^2}\sqrt{1 - r_{jq}^2}} \quad (8.1)$$

Substituting the three correlations in Formula 8.1 yields

$$r_{BN.P} = \frac{r_{BN} - r_{BP}r_{NP}}{\sqrt{1 - r_{BP}^2}\sqrt{1 - r_{NP}^2}} = \frac{.716 - .737 \times .473}{\sqrt{1 - (.737)^2}\sqrt{1 - (.473)^2}} = .617$$

which is approximately the same as the median r_{BN} for groups homogeneous with respect to variable P.

TABLE 8.2. CORRELATIONS IN NINE GROUPS, EACH HOMOGENEOUS AS TO PILOT APTITUDE SCORE

Each group is designated by value of pilot stanine, navigator stanine is on X axis; bombardier stanine, on Y axis. These same 3000 cases appear also in the consolidated bivariate distributions in Table 8.3.

In each group: rows = B (bombardier stanine, 9 at top to 1 at bottom); columns = N (navigator stanine, 1–9).

Group 1 N = 82 r = .546

B	1	2	3	4	5	6	7	8	9
9									
8									
7									
6									
5		1			1		1		
4	1	1		1	3	3	1	2	
3	3	4	4			2			
2	5	3	7	6					
1	16	11	11						

Group 2 N = 204 r = .636

B	1	2	3	4	5	6	7	8	9
9									
8									1
7									
6					2	3	4	1	
5	1			3	11	8	1	1	
4	2	3	3	22	11	8			
3		8	16	6	6	1			
2	14	7	21	3	1				
1	18		15			2			

Group 3 N = 295 r = .627

B	1	2	3	4	5	6	7	8	9
9									1
8								1	
7							4	2	1
6					2	2	10	1	
5			2		17	10	7		
4	3		11	5	27	12	2		
3	5	7	35	19	19	12			
2	10	9	8	22	5				
1	7	4	2	6	1	1			

Group 4 N = 571 r = .572

B	1	2	3	4	5	6	7	8	9
9									1
8							1		1
7						4	2	2	1
6			2	1	7	18	16	10	
5		2	18	4	44	39	22	6	
4	1	3	42	24	38	35	12	2	
3	4	11	25	45	17	10	1	1	
2	7	24	7	37	1				
1	3	9	2	4					

Group 5 N = 536 r = .614

B	1	2	3	4	5	6	7	8	9
9	1								1
8									1
7				1			8	4	4
6		2	5	12	3	12	11	8	3
5		5	16	37	22	27	24	8	2
4	1	14	39	29	49	49	20	2	
3	1	11	18	10	32	11	5	1	
2	4	6	2	3	7	3			
1	1				1				

Group 6 N = 511 r = .614

B	1	2	3	4	5	6	7	8	9
9									2
8								1	5
7					1	3		9	3
6		1	3	1	14	35	6	23	
5		6	6	7	38	50	24	6	
4	1	8	18	20	52	33	20	4	
3	3	2	8	29	10	5	12	1	
2	2	2	4	23	3	1			
1	2		1	3					

Group 7 N = 359 r = .688

B	1	2	3	4	5	6	7	8	9
9									7
8								5	19
7						1	2	20	6
6					1	5	23	17	
5				3	18	27	28	5	
4				11	24	22	22	1	
3			4	12	17	14	3		
2		1	11	9	5	4			
1	1	2	3	1					

Group 8 N = 218 r = .641

B	1	2	3	4	5	6	7	8	9
9	1								20
8								6	12
7							7	14	2
6						1	7	6	
5					2	12	14	1	
4				2	9	24	11	2	
3			1	4	8	12	4		
2			2	4	7	4	1		
1	1	3	4	2	5	3			

Group 9 N = 224 r = .632

B	1	2	3	4	5	6	7	8	9
9									27
8							8	13	5
7						8	11	13	2
6					1	8	14	10	1
5				1	5	9	8	1	
4				2	15	12	6		
3			1	5	12	4			
2		1	2	5	4	2			
1	1	1	1	4	1				

TABLE 8.3. CORRELATIONS OF THREE VARIABLES (BOMBARDIER B
NAVIGATOR N AND PILOT P STANINES) FOR TOTAL GROUP. $N = 3,000$

B	N 1	2	3	4	5	6	7	8	9	f_B
9	1			1	1	10	18	25	57	113
8				3	5	28	56	62	42	196
7	1		5	15	59	111	93	65	18	367
6		7	19	54	106	143	105	33	7	474
5	2	16	66	116	200	156	77	17	3	653
4	13	38	109	134	129	83	28	6	1	541
3	21	49	101	97	60	36	6			370
2	38	38	44	27	18	5	2			172
1	45	24	29	10	4	2				114
f_N	121	172	373	457	582	574	385	208	128	3000

$$r_{BN} = .716$$

P	B 1	2	3	4	5	6	7	8	9	f_P
9			1	9	30	35	53	39	57	224
8			3	14	23	37	59	47	35	218
7		5	5	21	57	88	99	69	15	359
6		5	14	58	155	141	109	25	4	511
5	1	13	53	132	180	103	39	13	2	536
4	8	27	121	190	157	58	7	3		571
3	14	39	102	83	45	11	1			295
2	46	57	63	31	6	1				204
1	45	26	8	3						82
f_B	114	172	370	541	653	474	367	196	113	3000

$$r_{BP} = .737$$

N	P 1	2	3	4	5	6	7	8	9	f_N
9		1	1	3	11	10	32	34	36	128
8		2	5	20	23	44	48	29	37	208
7	2	6	23	54	68	63	78	44	47	385
6	8	22	37	106	102	127	73	56	43	574
5	5	31	71	108	114	118	68	32	35	582
4	14	34	52	115	92	83	39	10	18	457
3	16	55	58	95	80	40	16	8	5	373
2	15	18	23	49	38	19	5	3	2	172
1	22	35	25	21	8	7		2	1	121
f_P	82	204	295	571	536	511	359	218	224	3000

$$r_{NP} = .473$$

It is too much to expect that all investigations would show such a close correspondence between the partial *r* and *r*'s in homogeneous groups, but in this case the statistical method of control gives a result practically identical with that found by experimental control.

HIGHER-ORDER PARTIAL CORRELATION

A variable can be residualized with respect to any number of secondary variables. The residual variable so obtained is uncorrelated with each of the secondary variables and may be considered the part of the original variable that is independent of all the secondary variables.

When the correlation is found between two variables, both of which have been made into residuals with respect to an identical set of two or more secondary variables, the result is a partial correlation of the order indicated by the number of secondary variables. The interpretation is the same as for a first-order partial; that is, it can be taken as an estimate of what the correlation would be in groups homogeneous with respect to the secondary variables.

While multiple correlation is useful in making predictions for practical purposes, the value of partial correlation is as a tool in control and in understanding relationships obscured by the presence of correlated variables.

COMPUTATION OF PARTIAL *r*

Partial *r* of any order may be found rather simply by the same matrix routine as described in the preceding chapter for finding multiple *R*. In this routine, a matrix of variances and covariances of a given order is residualized with respect to one of its variables so as to form a matrix of variances and covariances of the next higher order. For any higher-order variance, the corresponding standard deviation is found merely by extracting the square root. To find any partial correlation, the covariance of two residual variables is divided by their standard deviations. Let i and j be any two variables that have been residualized with respect to any number of secondary variables, collectively represented as q. Then the basic formula for any partial *r* is

$$r_{ij.q} = \frac{C_{ij.q}}{\sqrt{V_{i.q}}\sqrt{V_{j.q}}} \tag{8.1a}$$

in which $C_{ij.q}$ is the partial covariance between the residual variables in z form, $z_{i.q}$ and $z_{j.q}$, and $V_{i.q}$ and $V_{j.q}$ are the two variances. In the matrix method, which is exhibited in Example 8.4, the three coefficients required for a partial *r* of a given order are all found in the same matrix, the matrix developed by the elimination of the secondary variables specified for the given partial.

EXAMPLE 8.4

COMPUTATION OF PARTIAL AND PART r

Strategy of Partial r. Except for the final steps, the matrix method of finding higher-order partial r is computationally the same as finding a multiple R. The steps are:

1. Write the matrix with r's (that is, covariances in z form) above the diagonal and the 1.00's (that is, variances in z form) in the diagonal. Variables to be partialed out are in the first rows and columns; variables for which residual r's are to be found are in the final rows and columns. As shown in Table 8.4, a sum variable may be developed to check on the accuracy of the arithmetic.

2. In each matrix the covariances in the top row are divided by the variance in that row to form a vector of betas, which, for convenience, are placed beneath the variance.

3. A new matrix is formed with one less row, and one less column by applying the formula $E' = E - \beta C$; that is, any element in the new matrix is the corresponding element in the original matrix less the product of the beta (in the same row but the first column) and the covariance (in the same column but the top row).

4. The process continues until the matrix of the desired order has been found, a matrix in which the variability associated with the secondary variables (that is, those to be "held constant") has been partialed out.

5. Each covariance is then divided by the square roots of the corresponding variances, one of which is in the same column and the other of which is in the same row. This yields the desired partial r.

In order to find a matrix of higher-order partial r's, corresponding lower-order partial r's need not be found. Only lower-order variances and covariances are needed.

When only a single partial r is needed, the initial matrix will consist of the secondary variables and the two primary variables. The partial r will be found from a 2 by 2 matrix consisting of a single partial covariance and two partial variances.

In Table 8.4 the primary variables are two scores on a learning test, a pretest in a course in Navy technical training and a final achievement measure in the same course. The secondary variables are three aptitude tests. It is to be noted that the process of partialing out the three aptitude tests influences the correlation between the two learning tests very little, but does reduce to a considerable degree other correlations among the primary variables. The third-order partial r's may be taken as estimates of the intercorrelations of the primary variables in groups homogeneous as to the three aptitude tests.

Computation of Part r. Table 8.5 shows the computation of first-order part r's, using data abstracted from Table 8.4. A matrix format is used in which variable 6 is eliminated from the covariances between variable 7 and the three aptitude tests. The partial variance of variable 7, after variability associated with variable 6 has been partialed out, is .8319. The square root of .8319, or .9121, is divided into the partial covariances in the column headed 7.6, to find the first-order

TABLE 8.4. COMPUTATION OF A MATRIX OF THIRD-ORDER PARTIAL r's
(Data from Manning (4); $N = 213$)

VARIABLE	1	2	3	4	5	6	7	CHECK SUM
1. General classification test	1.0000	.6300	.3600	.3000	.2700	.2600	.3300	3.1500
2. Arithmetic test		1.0000	.3800	.3100	.3000	.2100	.3200	3.1500
3. Mechanical test			1.0000	.4000	.4000	.3800	.4700	3.3900
4. Learning testI				1.0000	.7600	.1800	.2800	3.2300
5. Learning test II					1.0000	.2100	.3500	3.2900
6. Achievement pretest						1.0000	.4100	2.6500
7. Final achievement							1.0000	3.1600

VARIABLE	1	2	3	4	5	6	7	CHECK SUM
2nd MATRIX (1st-order residuals)								
2.1		.6031	.1532	.1210	.1299	.0462	.1121	1.1655
3.1		.2540	.8704	.2920	.3028	.2864	.3512	2.2560
4.1		.2006		.9100	.6790	.1020	.1810	2.2850
5.1		.2154			.9271	.1398	.2609	2.4395
6.1		.0766				.9324	.3242	1.8310
7.1		.1859					.8911	2.1205
3rd MATRIX (2nd-order residuals)								
3.12			.8315	.2613	.2698	.2747	.3227	1.9600
4.12			.3143	.8857	.6529	.0927	.1585	2.0512
5.12			.3245		.8991	.1298	.2368	2.1885
6.12			.3304			.9289	.3156	1.7417
7.12			.3881				.8703	1.9038

4th MATRIX (3rd-order residuals)

VARIABLE	Partial SD	4	5	6	7	CHECK SUM
4.123	(.8964)	.8036	.5681	.0064	.0571	1.4352
5.123	(.9009)		.8116	.0407	.1321	1.5525
6.123	(.9155)			.8381	.2090	1.0941
7.123	(.8632)				.7451	1.1431

Matrix of Third-Order Partial r's

VARIABLE	4.123	5.123	6.123	7.123
4.123				
5.123	.70			
6.123	.01	.05		
7.123	.07	.17	.26	

part r's in the last column. The procedure exploits the fact that in reduced z form, a part covariance and a partial covariance are numerically identical.

TABLE 8.5. COMPUTATION OF FIRST-ORDER PART r's
(Data from Table 8.4; $N = 213$)

VARIABLE		6	1	2	3	7	7.6
6. Achievement pretest	6	1.00	.26	.21	.38	.41	
1. General classification test	1	.26	xx	xx	xx	.33	.2234
2. Arithmetic test	2	.21		xx	xx	.32	.2339
3. Mechanical test	3	.38			xx	.47	.3142
7. Final achievement	7	.41				1.00	.8319

The three partial covariances and the partial variances in the column headed 7.6 are formed from the entries in the preceding column, as variance 6 is eliminated. Thus

$$C_{17.6} = .33 - (.26 \times .41) = .2234 \qquad r_{1(7.6)} = .24$$

$$C_{27.6} = .32 - (.21 \times .41) = .2339 \qquad r_{2(7.6)} = .26$$

$$C_{37.6} = .47 - (.38 \times .41) = .3142 \qquad r_{3(7.6)} = .34$$

Division by $\sqrt{V_{7.6}}$ or $\sqrt{.8319}$ yields the part r as indicated.

The part r's may be interpreted to mean that the aptitude tests are related to gain in the course.

By substituting the part r's for the zero-order r's in column 7, and disregarding the original entries involving variable 6, it would be possible to find the multiple correlation between the three aptitude tests and the residual criterion, $z_{7.6}$.

While partial r's are often lower than the corresponding zero-order r's, there is no necessity for the correlation to be decreased through partialing out one or more secondary variables. In some cases, it will increase. The limits of partial r, as are those of zero-order r, are -1.00 and $+1.00$.

PART CORRELATION

When one of the variables entering into a correlation is a residual and the other is not, the result is a part or semipartial correlation. In a part correlation, one of the variables has been modified by subtracting the portion or portions of each value correlated with one or more secondary variables, while the other is unmodified (except perhaps by a simple linear transformation that has no effect on a correlation). Thus $z_{0.12 \dots n}$ can be correlated with z_p, and the result may be indicated as $r_{p(0.12 \dots n)}$.

In $r_{p(0.12 \dots n)}$, any number of variables have been controlled insofar as they are related to variable 0, but their relationships with variable p are unchanged. The situation is somewhat analogous to control by matching or equating, in which the correlation between the independent variable (which varies with group membership) and any controlled variable is zero, but in which no restrictions are placed on the correlations of the controlled variables with the dependent variable.

To find a part r, as in finding any correlation, the covariance between the two variables concerned is divided by their standard deviations. It is especially helpful in working with part r to use matrices of variances and covariances of z scores and higher-order z scores. The reason is that, in higher-order z form, a part covariance (between an unmodified variable and a residual) happens to have the same numerical value as a partial covariance involving two sets of residuals (each with the same secondary variables). Also, in z form, the standard deviation of the unmodified variable is 1.00. Accordingly, to find a part r, the appropriate partial covariance is divided by a single partial standard deviation, the standard deviation of the residual variable. Thus

$$r_{p(0.12\ldots n)} = \frac{C_{0p.12\ldots n}}{\sqrt{V_{0.12\ldots n}}} \quad \text{or} \quad r_{p(0.q)} = \frac{C_{0p.q}}{\sqrt{V_{0.q}}} \tag{8.2}$$

The computation of part r from the general matrix solution was illustrated in Example 8.4.

APPLICATIONS OF PART CORRELATION

One application of part correlation is in the study of the correlates of change. In an experiment on learning, for example, gain can be defined as that portion of the proficiency measured at a second point in time, z_2, predicted from the proficiency measured at an earlier point in time, z_1. By defining gain as a residual, $z_{2.1}$, gain is that portion of z_2 that is uncorrelated with z_1. When $z_{2.1}$ is correlated with another variable, such as z_3, the result is a part correlation, $r_{3(2.1)}$, which gives the relationship between variable 3 and a score representing the change that occurs in variable 2 between the time that it is measured first and the time it is measured again.

Part correlation can be applied when there is decline in capacity, as in old age. It is also a way of handling measures of growth. Whenever we correlate a ratio (such as I.Q.) with an outside variable, we are, in effect, computing a part correlation. It will be actually a part correlation if the study is made in the group on which the I.Q. has been standardized and if the I.Q. has been constructed so that it correlates zero with chronological age.

The residual variable entering into a part correlation may be of any order that is, there may be any number of secondary variables, the number of which is the order of the part r.

MULTIPLE CORRELATION OF RESIDUAL VARIABLES

Residual variables can also be used in multiple correlations. In multiple partial r, a number of variables are residualized with respect to an identical set of secondary variables. One residual variable is then used as the criterion; the others, as predictors.

Somewhat similarly, multiple part r is possible, as when a residual is used as a criterion and a number of unmodified variables are the predictors; or when an unmodified variable is the criterion and a number of residual variables are the predictors. Other special varieties of correlation can be developed, if needed by the logic of the particular situation. In any application of the correlation of residuals, the particular coefficient needed is the one required by the logic of the situation. If we wish to deal with observed variables (as in most prediction problems in applied psychology), no residualization is needed. If we wish to infer what correlation might be expected if one or more outside variables were "controlled" or "held constant" (that is, if the correlation were computed in groups homogeneous with respect to the outside variables), then it may be of interest to residualize one of the variables, or both, entering into the correlation.

PRACTICAL APPLICATIONS OF RESIDUAL OR REGRESSED SCORES

Residual variables are seldom, if ever, used in regression equations. However, a residual or "regressed score," often in the form of a quotient, is sometimes of interest in estimating a psychological characteristic, when allowance is made for one or more correlated conditions.

Accomplishment quotients (educational age divided by mental age), educational quotients (educational age divided by chronological age), and other ratios have been advocated from time to time, but a persistent drawback has been their characteristic negative correlation with the denominator variable. This can be avoided if the derived scores are constructed so as to correlate perfectly with a set of scores representing the numerator variable residualized with respect to the denominator variable. One good method would be to find the residuals and then convert them into a series of standard scores with assigned mean and standard deviation.

COMPARISON OF MULTIPLE AND PARTIAL CORRELATION

Study of Examples 7.1 and 8.4 shows that the preliminary computational steps in multiple and partial correlation are exactly the same. A matrix of variances and covariances in z form are residualized with respect to one of the variables constituting the matrix. The process may be continued through successive matrices until the resultant partial variances and covariances are of the order of the desired partial r. At that time, the partial correlation is found by dividing a partial covariance by the partial standard deviations of two variables concerned. If a part r is desired, the partial covariance is divided by only a single partial standard deviation, that of the residual variable.

Multiple R's are found from partial variances. For every partial variance, which is the variance of a set of residuals, there is a corresponding r^2 if the partial variance is of the first order, or a corresponding R^2 if the partial variance is of the second order or higher. To find the r^2 or R^2, the partial variance (which in the matrix method is in reduced z score form) is subtracted from 1.00. Extracting the square root of the result yields r or multiple R. There is no point in finding r this way because r was known in order to find the partial variance. The situation is different, however, with R, which can be found only in some indirect fashion.

In general, when it is necessary to predict an unobserved criterion on the basis of an observed set of predictor variables, the multiple correlation (and corresponding regression weights) is used as worked out on an earlier sample of cases. When the aims of the investigation are scientific, that is, understanding relationships among the variables, some form of the correlation of residuals by which one or more variables are controlled statistically is often appropriate.

SUMMARY

In psychological investigations that attempt to ascertain the relationship between variables, the presence of sources of additional variation, either within the situation or within individuals, may obscure the results. Accordingly, methods have been developed which aim to reduce the influence of variables that are not of direct interest.

Experimental methods of control include complete elimination of a variable, use only of cases with a uniform degree of the variable, the sorting of matched cases into groups, the balancing of the means and standard deviations in two or more groups, and randomization. These experimental methods of control aim to reduce to .00 the correlation between an independent variable and a controlled variable.

Statistical control has a similar objective, but in effect it involves the modification of the values of the independent variable and the dependent variable, or both, so that the values become uncorrelated linearly with the variable or variables controlled or partialed out.

In partial r, both primary variables are modified so as to become uncorrelated with each of the variables controlled or partialed out. A partial r can be taken as an estimate of the correlation that would be found between the primary variables in groups in which there was no variation in the secondary or controlled variables.

In part r (sometimes called *semipartial r*), one of the variables is unmodified; the other is the same type of residual variable that enters into a partial r. In studies of change, as in learning, part r appears to be a more appropriate technique than partial r. In all cases the logic of the situation determines the appropriate type of coefficient to use.

EXERCISES

1. If the digits in Table 8.1 are truly random, then the expected correlation between any two columns is .00. However, it is extremely unlikely that any r would be precisely .00; rather, a large number of r would vary around a mean of .00, with a standard deviation of $1/\sqrt{N-1}$.

   Compute the correlation between the digits in one of the first five columns and the digits in another of the first five columns, and decide whether the obtained r constitutes evidence against the hypothesis of random arrangement.

2. In a learning study, the correct response varies among five choices: A, B, C, D, and E. Since the choices vary somewhat in difficulty, the decision has been made not to use A, B, C, D, and E completely at random, but rather to arrange them in cycles of 10, with each response being correct twice in each cycle.

   Devise a plan, involving a table of random numbers, so that the sequence of correct choices in each cycle of 10 will be developed at hazard. Apply the procedure in writing out a sequence of 10 cycles.

3. Sixty subjects have been arranged and numbered in order from 01 to 60 on a variable to be controlled experimentally. Devise a plan by which one member of each set of three subjects is to be assigned to group A, the second to group B, and the third to group C; then, with the help of a table of random numbers, make the assignments.

4. Consider the following variables, z_x and z_y, and corresponding standard scores X and Y, (with $M' = 30$ and $s' = 6$).

CASE	z_x	z_y	X	Y
A.A.	1.50	.50	39	33
B.B.	.50	1.50	33	39
C.C.	.00	−.50	30	27
D.D.	−.50	.00	27	30
E.E.	−1.50	−1.50	21	21

   (a) Compute values of the ratio X/Y, and correlate this ratio with Y. Why is this correlation negative?

   (b) Compute values of the modified ratio X'/Y (in which X' has a mean of 30 and standard deviation of s_y/r_{xy}), and correlate this ratio with Y. Why is this correlation approximately .00?

   (c) Correlate the modified ratio X'/Y with the residual variable $z_{x.y}$ or $(z_x - r_{xy}z_y)$. Why is this correlation approximately 1.00?

5. By use of methods to be discussed in Chapter 16, it can be proved that if, for any three variables i, j, and k, $(1 - r_{ij}^2)(1 - r_{ik}^2) - (r_{jk} - r_{ij}r_{ik})^2 \geq 0$, then first-order partial r's involving the three variables are possible. On the other hand, if the expression is negative, such partial r's are impossible.

   Develop a set of three correlations that meets the criterion, and another that does not. From the first set, compute a partial r and note that it falls within the limits of r, −1.00 and +1.00. Also, by computation, note that an attempt to find a partial r from the second set does not yield a coefficient within the limits for r.

6. By the partial correlation technique determine whether height appears to be related to success in basketball in groups homogeneous as to weight, age, and previous basketball experience. Data are from Jones (2). (Since $N = 42$, results should be considered very tentative.)

		2	3	4	5
1	Weight	.13	.28	.48	.36
2	Age		.52	.09	.45
3	Basketball experience			.00	.58
4	Height				.26
5	Success in basketball				

7. One application of part correlation is to explore the unique contribution of a variable in predicting a criterion. From the following matrix, reported by Stern and Gordon (7), determine the proportion of the variance of the criterion predicted uniquely by variable 1; that is, find $r^2_{0(1.2345)}$.

$N = 511$

VARIABLE		4	3	2	1	0
5	General classification test	.59	.41	.28	.54	.58
4	Arithmetic test		.25	.40	.59	.38
3	Mechanical test			.12	.36	.36
2	Clerical test				.36	.18
1	Oral directions test					.36
0	Recruit Achievement test					

8. Factor analysis (treated briefly in Chapter 17) may be conceived as partialing out one or more hypothetical variables until the original variables, residualized with respect to the hypothetical variables (or factors), have intercorrelations of .00 within sampling error.

For the following matrix, developed by Bonser in 1910 and quoted by Spearman (6), the correlations with g, the general factor, are given in the top row and first column. Partial-out g from the matrix and decide whether the first-order partial r's might differ from .00 only as much as might be expected by chance. (Precise tests for the significance of correlations are given in Chapter 13.)

$N = 757$

VARIABLE		g	1	2	3	4	5
g		1.00	.701	.672	.607	.550	.398
1	Mathematical judgment		1.000	.485	.400	.397	.295
2	Controlled association			1.000	.397	.397	.247
3	Literary interpretation				1.000	.335	.275
4	Selective judgment					1.000	.195
5	Spelling						1.000

REFERENCES

1. DUBOIS, P. H. (ED.), *The Classification Program.* Report No. 2, AAF Aviation Psychology Program Research Reports. Washington, D.C.: U.S. Government Printing Office, 1947.
2. JONES, EDWARD R., *Prediction of Basketball Success by Psychological Measurements*, Master's Thesis. St. Louis: Washington University, 1948.
3. LEWIS, DON, *Quantitative Methods in Psychology.* New York: McGraw-Hill Book Company, Inc., 1960.
4. MANNING, WINTON H., *Correlates of Change in Complex Functions*, Doctoral Dissertation. St. Louis: Washington University, 1959.
5. Rand Corporation, *A Million Random Digits with 100,000 Normal Deviates.* Glencoe, Illinois: The Free Press, 1955.
6. SPEARMAN, C., *The Abilities of Man.* New York: The Macmillan Company, 1927.
7. STERN, FERDINAND, AND GORDON, LEONARD V., "Ability to follow instructions as a predictor of success in recruit training," *J. Appl. Psychol.* 1961, **45**, 22–24.

SPECIAL MEASURES
OF RELATIONSHIP

9

ADDITIVE PROPERTIES OF VARIANCES AND COVARIANCES

It can be readily shown that when, for each individual or case, the scores on two or more variables are added to form a composite or sum variable, the variance of the new variable is a function of the variances and covariances of the constituent variables. If T is the sum or total variable and $X_1, X_2 \cdots X_n$ are the constituent variables, then

$$T = X_1 + X_2 + \cdots + X_n \tag{9.1}$$

Summing all terms and dividing by N,

$$\frac{\Sigma T}{N} = \frac{\Sigma X_1}{N} + \frac{\Sigma X_2}{N} + \cdots + \frac{\Sigma X_n}{N} \tag{9.2}$$

All terms in Eq. 9.2 are means, and each mean can be subtracted from the corresponding term in Eq. 9.1. Accordingly, as deviations from their respective means,

$$t = x_1 + x_2 + \cdots + x_n \tag{9.3}$$

Squaring both sides of Eq. 9.3, summing all terms, dividing by N, and arranging the terms in a square format or matrix,

$$\frac{\Sigma t^2}{N} = \frac{\Sigma x_1^2}{N} + \frac{\Sigma x_1 x_2}{N} + \cdots + \frac{\Sigma x_1 x_n}{N} \qquad (9.4)$$

$$+ \frac{\Sigma x_2 x_1}{N} + \frac{\Sigma x_2^2}{N} + \cdots + \frac{\Sigma x_2 x_n}{N}$$

$$\vdots \qquad \vdots \qquad \vdots$$

$$+ \frac{\Sigma x_n x_1}{N} + \frac{\Sigma x_n x_2}{N} + \cdots + \frac{\Sigma x_n^2}{N}$$

Substitution of variances (V) for terms involving sums of squares of deviations, and covariances (C) for terms representing sums of products of deviations yields

$$V_t = \quad V_1 + C_{12} + \cdots + C_{1n}$$

$$+ C_{21} + V_2 + \cdots + C_{2n}$$

$$\vdots \qquad \vdots \qquad \vdots \qquad (9.5)$$

$$+ C_{n1} + C_{n2} + \cdots + V_n$$

Each variable appears in both a row and a column. The variances form the main diagonal and can be designated as V or s^2. The table is symmetrical about the main diagonal in that $C_{ij} = C_{ji}$.

Since the procedure starts with raw scores and deviations from the means in terms of original units, the variances are not necessarily unity, and the covariances are not necessarily correlation coefficients. Since any covariance may be converted into an r by dividing by the standard deviations of the two variables concerned, any covariance, C_{ij}, can be replaced with $r_{ij} s_i s_j$.

The variances and covariances may be summed separately. Thus,

$$V_t = \sum_{i=1}^{n} V_i + 2 \sum_{i=1}^{n-1} \sum_{j=i+1}^{n} C_{ij} \qquad (9.6)$$

The expression

$$\sum_{i=1}^{n-1} \sum_{j=i+1}^{n} C_{ij}$$

refers to a special summation in which each covariance is added only once, although it appears twice in the total matrix.

Formula 9.5 is perfectly general. In the special instance in which variables i and j are added, the result is

$$V_{i+j} = V_i + 2C_{ij} + V_j \qquad (9.7)$$

or

$$V_{i+j} = s_i^2 + 2r_{ij}s_is_j + s_j^2 \tag{9.7a}$$

COVARIANCES OF COMPOSITE VARIABLES

A formula for the covariance between any variable and the sum can be found by multiplying all terms in Eq. 9.3 by the variable in deviation form, summing all terms and dividing by N. Let the variable be x_1. Then

$$\frac{\Sigma x_1 t}{N} = \frac{\Sigma x_1^2}{N} + \frac{\Sigma x_1 x_2}{N} + \cdots + \frac{\Sigma x_1 x_n}{N}$$

and

$$C_{1t} = V_1 + C_{12} + \cdots + C_{1n} \tag{9.8}$$

or, more generally, replacing variable 1 with variable i and summing the covariances,

$$C_{it} = V_i + \sum_{j=i+1}^{n} C_{ij} \qquad (i \neq j) \tag{9.9}$$

It is to be noted in Formula 9.9 that j refers to any variable except i. The correlation is found by dividing both sides of Formula 9.9 by $s_i s_t$. Then

$$\frac{C_{it}}{s_i s_t} = r_{it} = \frac{V_i + \sum_{j=i+1}^{n} C_{ij}}{s_i s_t} \qquad (i \neq j) \tag{9.10}$$

The covariances between two variables, each of which is a sum of two or more constituent variables, is simply the sum of all the covariances concerned. If one sum variable T_a is composed of n subvariables, and the other, T_b, is made up of m subvariables, the nm covariances must be summed to find the total covariance. The expression $t_a = x_i + x_j + \cdots + x_n$, which is in deviation form, is multiplied by $t_b = x_1 + x_2 + \cdots + x_m$. The nm products are summed and divided by N. This yields

$$\frac{\Sigma t_a t_b}{N} = \frac{\Sigma x_1 x_i}{N} + \frac{\Sigma x_1 x_j}{N} + \cdots + \frac{\Sigma x_1 x_n}{N}$$

$$+ \frac{\Sigma x_2 x_i}{N} + \frac{\Sigma x_2 x_j}{N} + \cdots + \frac{\Sigma x_2 x_n}{N}$$

$$\vdots \qquad \vdots \qquad \vdots$$

$$+ \frac{\Sigma x_m x_i}{N} + \frac{\Sigma x_m x_j}{N} + \cdots + \frac{\Sigma x_m x_n}{N}$$

which can be turned into a matrix arrangement of covariances as follows:

$$
\begin{aligned}
C_{t_a t_b} = \quad & C_{1i} + C_{1j} + \cdots + C_{1n} \\
& + C_{2i} + C_{2j} + \cdots + C_{2n} \\
& \quad \vdots \qquad \vdots \qquad\qquad \vdots \\
& + C_{mi} + C_{mj} + \cdots + C_{mn}
\end{aligned}
\tag{9.11}
$$

Formula 9.11 contains mn covariances, which, when summed, yield the covariance between the two sum variables. The corresponding r is found by dividing the covariance by the standard deviations of the two variables. These standard deviations are obtained by extracting the square roots of expressions of the type exhibited in Formula 9.5.

The use of raw-score variances and covariances to infer variances and correlations of combined variables is demonstrated in Example 9.1.

EXAMPLE 9.1

ADDITIVE PROPERTIES OF A VARIANCE-COVARIANCE MATRIX

The Basic Principle. From a variance-covariance matrix, such as Table 9.1, correlations of the weighted or unweighted sums of constituent variables may be found quickly and easily. Any composite variance or covariance is developed by adding all elements of the square or rectangular matrix of the basic coefficients. Prior to summation, any variable may be weighted positively or negatively by appropriate multiplication of elements involving the variable.

Similar operations are possible with a matrix of correlations with unity in the diagonal, as shown in Table 9.2. This may be considered a variance-covariance matrix of variables in z form. The correlations in Table 9.2 have been computed by dividing covariances shown in Table 9.1 by the square roots of the two corresponding variances.

TABLE 9.1. VARIANCE-COVARIANCE MATRIX OF SIX VARIABLES

($N = 239$)

	1	2	3	4	5	6
1. Reading test	3.176	2.455	1.867	1.820	1.395	.571
2. Linguistic test	2.455	3.646	1.748	1.625	.909	.324
3. Quantitative test	1.867	1.748	3.857	2.343	1.809	.592
4. Mathematic test	1.820	1.625	2.343	3.468	1.928	.757
5. Algebra test	1.395	.909	1.809	1.928	3.520	1.182
6. Grade in mathematics	.571	.324	.592	.757	1.182	1.177

An Illustration. Suppose the correlation is desired of the sum of the two verbal tests, variables 1 and 2, with the sum of the three numerical tests, variables 3,

4, and 5. This correlation is, of course, the covariance of the two sum variables, $C_{(1+2)(3+4+5)}$, divided by the two standard deviations, s_{1+2} and s_{3+4+5}, which are the square roots of corresponding variances. From Table 9.1, the covariance is found by Formula 9.11 as follows:

$$C_{(1+2)(3+4+5)} = C_{13} + C_{14} + C_{15} + C_{23} + C_{24} + C_{25}$$
$$= 1.867 + 1.820 + 1.395 + 1.748 + 1.625 + .909 = 9.364$$

The two variances follow:

$$V_{1+2} = V_1 + 2C_{12} + V_2 = 3.176 + 2(2.455) + 3.646 = 11.732$$
$$V_{3+4+5} = V_3 + V_4 + V_5 + 2(C_{34} + C_{35} + C_{45})$$
$$= 3.857 + 3.468 + 3.520 + 2(2.343 + 1.809 + 1.928) = 23.005$$

Accordingly,

$$r_{(1+2)(3+4+5)} = \frac{C_{(1+2)(3+4+5)}}{\sqrt{V_{1+2}}\,\sqrt{V_{3+4+5}}} = \frac{9.364}{\sqrt{11.732}\,\sqrt{23.005}} = .57$$

TABLE 9.2. MATRIX OF z SCORE VARIANCES AND COVARIANCES

(Original observations the same as for Table 9.1.)

		1	2	3	4	5	6
1.	Reading test	1.00	.72	.53	.55	.42	.30
2.	Linguistic test	.72	1.00	.47	.46	.25	.16
3.	Quantitative test	.53	.47	1.00	.64	.49	.28
4.	Mathematic test	.55	.46	.64	1.00	.55	.37
5.	Algebra test	.42	.25	.49	.55	1.00	.58
6.	Grade in mathematics	.30	.16	.28	.37	.58	1.00

Since the original variance-covariance matrix is in single-digit coded scores with approximately equal variances, correlations obtained from Table 9.2, where the variables are in z form, would be expected to differ very little. Here,

$$r_{(1+2)(3+4+5)} = \frac{.53 + .55 + .42 + .47 + .46 + .25}{\sqrt{2 + (2 \times .72)}\sqrt{3 + 2(.64 + .49 + .55)}} = \frac{2.68}{\sqrt{3.44}\,\sqrt{6.36}} = .57$$

In cases in which raw-score variances differ widely, results from simple summation may also differ considerably. However, by differentially weighting the variables in one matrix or the other, precisely identical results may be obtained.

A Correlation with Differential Weighting. Let it be presumed that there is some reason to find the correlation of twice the z-score in the algebra test less the z score in the reading test with the grade in mathematics. Since z scores are being weighted, the correlation matrix is used. Then,

$$C_{(2z_5 - z_1)} = 2C_{56} - C_{16} = (2 \times .58) - .30 = .86$$
$$V_{(2z_5 - z_1)} = 4V_5 - 4C_{15} + V_1 = 5 - 1.68 = 3.32$$

$$r_{(2z_5 - z_1)z_6} = \frac{C_{(2z_5 - z_1)z_6}}{\sqrt{V_{(2z_5 - z_1)}}\,\sqrt{V_6}} = \frac{.86}{\sqrt{3.32}\,\sqrt{1.00}} = .47$$

ADDITIVE PROPERTIES OF CORRELATION COEFFICIENTS

Since a correlation coefficient is the slope of a line (or the tangent of an angle), r's as such cannot be added to obtain an average or value representing several r's. However, when a correlation coefficient is considered as a covariance of z scores, it can be used in exactly the same fashion as any other covariance in inferring variances, covariances, and correlations of variables based on the summation of values of constituent variables. The process is illustrated in Table 9.2 in Example 9.1. With zero-order z scores, each variance is unity. If a matrix of correlations with unity in each of the diagonal cells is summed, each variable enters into the composite with equal weight. Formula 9.6 becomes

$$V_t = n + 2 \sum_{i=1}^{n-1} \sum_{j=i+1}^{n} r_{ij} \qquad (9.6a)$$

and Formula 9.7 becomes

$$V_{i+j} = 2 + 2r_{ij} \qquad (9.7b)$$

Similarly, the correlation between a single variable, i, and the composite of all the variables added together, with equal standard deviations, is (from Formula 9.10)

$$\frac{C_{it}}{s_i s_t} = r_{it} = \frac{1 + \sum_{i=1}^{n-1} r_{ij}}{\sqrt{n + 2 \sum_{i=1}^{n-1} \sum_{j=i+1}^{n} r_{ij}}} \qquad (i \neq j) \qquad (9.10a)$$

VARIANCES AND COVARIANCES OF WEIGHTED COMPOSITES

Variances entering into composites may be weighted, and appropriate variances and covariances readily obtained. In general,

$$t = w_i x_i \pm w_j x_j \pm \cdots \pm w_n x_n \qquad (9.12)$$

By squaring Formula 9.12 and summing and dividing by N, the variance of t is obtained. The correlations of t with simple or compound variables can be found by procedures similar to those used in developing Formula 9.11. It will be noted that in the regular matrix-like arrangements of Formulas 9.4, 9.5, and 9.11, each variable appears in a row or a column or in both a row and a column. Working within the matrix, we can, in effect, weight each score in a variable prior to adding the variable to a composite variance or covariance. To do this, each element in the row assigned to the variable and each element in the column assigned to the variable must be multiplied by the weight w_i. By this procedure, each covariance involving the variable is multiplied by w_i, but the variance is multiplied by w_i^2.

The matrix may be of variances and covariances of any type: raw scores; zero-order z scores (variances of 1.00 and covariances equal to r's); or the residual variances and covariances of multivariate correlation. The modified elements can now be added into combinations, in exactly the same fashion as in the addition of original elements.

The procedure of working from a complete matrix of variances and covariances is useful in theoretical work relating to the interrelationships of large numbers of variables, such as the items of a psychological test. Once the basic matrix is known, derived coefficients involving various combinations of the variables are determinate, and can be found through appropriate statistical operations.

VARIANTS OF PEARSON r: $r_{\mathrm{pt.bis}}$, ϕ and ρ

The Pearson product-moment formula for r, $r = \Sigma xy/Ns_x s_y$ or $r = \Sigma z_x z_y/N$, has three important algebraic variants: the point biserial r, the phi coefficient (denoted as ϕ), and ρ, the coefficient of rank correlation. These coefficients are alike in that each can be derived from the Pearson formula, usually in raw-score form, merely by substitution of equivalent expressions for certain parts of the formula. No violence would be done were the Pearson formula applied directly to the data to which one of these special formulas is applicable. In each instance the original formula and its modifiction yield identical results. The modifications are for convenience in computation. The formulas for the point biserial r and the phi coefficient take advantage of the fact that if a variable is dichotomous (that is, has only two possible values), its mean and standard deviation are known directly from the proportions of cases in the two categories. Somewhat similarly, the formula for ρ takes advantage of the fact that for a series of N different ranks, beginning with 1 (that is, $1, 2, 3 \cdots N$) the standard deviation is $\sqrt{(N^2 - 1)/12}$ and the mean is $(N + 1)/2$.

POINT BISERIAL r

A biserial correlation is a measure of relationship between a dichotomous variable on the one hand and a continuous variable on the other. Let the continuous variable be denoted as X and the dichotomous as Y. If all Y values are either 1 or 0, $\Sigma Y = N_p$, which is the number of cases "passing" or receiving a score of 1. Accordingly,

$$M_y = \frac{\Sigma Y}{N} = \frac{N_p}{N} = p \qquad (9.13)$$

p being the proportion of cases "passing."

If all Y values are either 1 or 0, then $\Sigma Y^2 = N_p$, since there are N_p cases with value of 1, and the square of 1 is 1. The value of the standard deviation, starting with the raw-score formula, is

$$s_y = \sqrt{\frac{\Sigma Y^2}{N} - \left(\frac{\Sigma Y}{N}\right)^2} = \sqrt{\frac{N_p}{N} - \left(\frac{N_p}{N}\right)^2}$$

$$= \sqrt{\frac{NN_p - N_p^2}{N^2}} = \sqrt{\frac{N_p N_q}{N^2}} = \sqrt{pq} \qquad (9.14)$$

In making the substitutions above, advantage is taken of the fact that $N = (N_p + N_q)$, in which N_q is the number of cases "failing," that is cases with value of 0.

From Formula 9.14 it is seen that the standard deviation of a dichotomous variable coded as 1 and 0 is the square root of the product of the two proportions. Since all values of Y are either 1 or 0, it is readily seen that $\Sigma XY = \Sigma X_p$, the sum of variable X for those cases with a Y value of 1.

The point biserial r makes no assumption about the shape of the distribution of the dichotomous variable. It is computed with the dichotomous variable distributed at two discrete points; hence the name, "point biserial." The values assigned to the scores at these points are actually immaterial, although for convenience sake, they may be regarded as 1 or 0.

The X variable is regarded as continuous, although, as in the derivation of the usual Pearson formula for r, no assumption is made as to whether or not it is distributed normally.

The raw-score formula for r can be modified into the point biserial as follows:

$$r_{\text{pt. bis.}} = \frac{\dfrac{\Sigma XY}{N} - M_x M_y}{s_x s_y} = \frac{\dfrac{\Sigma X_p}{N} - M_x \dfrac{N_p}{N}}{s_x \sqrt{\dfrac{N_p N_q}{N^2}}} = \frac{\Sigma X_p - M_x N_p}{s_x \sqrt{N_p N_q}} \qquad (9.15)$$

An alternate form is found by dividing numerator and denominator of Formula 9.15 by N_p:

$$r_{\text{pt. bis.}} = \frac{\dfrac{\Sigma X_p}{N_p} - M_x \dfrac{N_p}{N_p}}{s_x \sqrt{\dfrac{N_p N_q}{N_p^2}}} = \frac{M_p - M_x}{s_x} \sqrt{\dfrac{N_p}{N_q}} \qquad (9.15a)$$

in which M_p is the mean of variable X for the cases in which Y is 1.

There are many alternate formulas for the point biserial. The part involving the radical in Formula 9.15a can be written as $\sqrt{p/q}$. Table P, which includes this function, is in the Appendix. The computation of the point biserial is illustrated in Example 9.2.

EXAMPLE 9.2

COMPUTATION OF $r_{pt \cdot bis}$. AND r_{bis}.

On one part of an examination in educational psychology, students were marked satisfactory or unsatisfactory. Data for use in computing point biserial and biserial correlations between this part and the remainder of the examination, the continuous Y variable, follow:

$N = 75$	$N_p = 35$	$N_q = 40$
$\Sigma X = 5923$	$\Sigma X_p = 3084$	$\Sigma X_q = 2839$
$\Sigma X^2 = 501,395$	$M_p = 88.11$	$M_q = 70.98$
$M_x = 78.97$	$p = 35/75 = .467$	
$s_x = 21.18$	$y = .398*$	

* (Height of unit normal curve at the point of dichotomy, from Table P in Appendix.)

Computation of the Point Biserial. By Formula 9.15a,

$$r_{pt. bis.} = \frac{M_p - M_x}{s_x} \sqrt{\frac{N_p}{N_q}} = \frac{88.11 - 78.97}{21.18} \sqrt{\frac{35}{40}} = .41$$

Computation is facilitated by entering Table P (Appendix) with $p = .47$ and finding $\sqrt{N_p/N_q}$ or $\sqrt{p/q}$ as .94.

Computation of the Biserial. If, as in this case, it can be assumed that the variable underlying the dichotomy is normally distributed, r_{bis}. is an appropriate statistic with which to estimate the correlation that would be found if information on a continuous variable were substituted for the dichotomy.

Using the information given above, including the height of the unit normal curve at $p = .467$, then, by Formula 9.22,

$$r_{bis.} = \frac{(M_p - M_x)p}{y s_x} = \frac{(88.11 - 78.97)(.467)}{.398 \times 21.18} = .51$$

APPLICATIONS OF THE POINT BISERIAL AND OF BISERIAL r

The point biserial is used whenever a measure of relationship between a dichotomous variable and a continuous variable is needed and when it is inappropriate to assume that a normal distribution underlies the dichotomy.

To correlate sex (which is certainly dichotomous) with a continuous variable, we can arbitrarily assign values of, say, 1 to male and 0 to female, and compute the point biserial. The sign of the coefficient in this case is arbitrary and depends on the coding. Similarly, we can correlate race (if in two classes only) or any other two-class categorical or ordinal variable with a continuous variable.

When there is reason to believe that there is a normally distributed, continuous variable underlying the dichotomy and when there is need to estimate its correlation with the observed variable Y, the biserial correlation, discussed later in this chapter, is appropriate. While the biserial r is, strictly speaking, only an estimate of what would be found if more information were available, it has important uses. When a variable is imperfectly measured and only dichotomous information is available, the investigator may be more interested in the probable correlations of the underlying continuous variable than in the correlations of the observed dichotomous variable. In aviation training, for example, ability to learn to fly is probably a normally distributed trait, but in the military situation, only the fact of graduation or elimination from training may be available. The biserial r is more appropriate than the point biserial if the researcher is more interested in how the predictors are related to the basic underlying characteristic of "ability to learn to fly" than in how they are related to the fact of graduation or elimination from flying training. A formula for biserial r is given in a later section.

THE PHI COEFFICIENT

The phi coefficient (ϕ) is another algebraic variant of the Pearson product-moment formula for r. It is a measure of the relationship between two dichotomous variables, neither of which is considered to represent an underlying normal distribution. Each variable can be considered as having two possible values, 1 and 0, and this assumption facilitates the development of a convenient computing formula. However, any pair of discrete values may be used for either variable without affecting ϕ. If two such "point" variables are correlated by the ordinary Pearson formula, the result will agree precisely with the correlation as found by the formula for phi.

To develop a formula for ϕ, the four frequencies in a 2 by 2 diagram (illustrated in Fig. 9.1) may be taken as a, b, c, and d. For the Y variable, there are two values, 1 and 0, and $\Sigma Y = \Sigma Y^2 = (a + b)$, while M_y (or p_y) is $(a + b)/N$. Similarly, for the X variable, there are also two values, 1 and 0, and $\Sigma X = \Sigma X^2 = (b + d)$ and $M_x = p_x = (b + d)/N$. There are b cases that have scores of 1 in both X and Y. Accordingly, $\Sigma XY = b$. It is also to be noted that $(a + b + c + d) = N$.

Y	X 0	1	f_y
1	a	b	$a+b$
0	c	d	$c+d$
f_x	$a+c$	$b+d$	N

FIGURE 9.1 FREQUENCIES IN A 2 × 2 DIAGRAM. $N = a + b + c + d$

To find expressions for the standard deviations, we utilize the fact that for either dichotomous variable, $s = \sqrt{pq}$. Accordingly,

$$s_x = \sqrt{\frac{(b+d)}{N}\frac{(a+c)}{N}} = \frac{1}{N}\sqrt{(b+d)(a+c)}$$

$$s_y = \sqrt{\frac{(a+b)}{N}\frac{(c+d)}{N}} = \frac{1}{N}\sqrt{(a+b)(c+d)}$$

Substituting values for ΣXY, means and standard deviations in a raw-score formula for r,

$$r = \phi = \frac{\dfrac{\Sigma XY}{N} - M_xM_y}{s_xs_y} = \frac{\dfrac{b}{N} - \dfrac{(b+d)}{N}\dfrac{(a+b)}{N}}{\dfrac{1}{N}\sqrt{(b+d)(a+c)}\dfrac{1}{N}\sqrt{(a+b)(c+d)}}$$

$$= \frac{bN - (b+d)(a+b)}{\sqrt{(b+d)(a+c)}\sqrt{(a+b)(c+d)}} \tag{9.16}$$

When a matrix of phi coefficients is to be found, Formula 9.16 is convenient, since expressions of the type $(b+d)$ and $\sqrt{(b+d)(a+c)}$ can be found once for each variable. For each combination of two variables it is then necessary to find only b, the number of individuals in the "pass" categories of both variables.

An alternate to Formula 9.16 can be found by replacing N with $(a+b+c+d)$, multiplying out terms in the numerator and canceling where appropriate, and placing the terms in the denominator under a single radical. It thereupon appears that for two dichotomous distributions,

$$r = \phi = \frac{bc - ad}{\sqrt{(a+b)(a+c)(b+d)(c+d)}} \tag{9.16a}$$

Computation of ϕ is shown in Example 9.3.

EXAMPLE 9.3

COMPUTATION OF ϕ AND r_{tet}

Computation of ϕ. In a 2 by 2 diagram, such as the one below, ϕ or product moment r between two dichotomous variables may be found by Formula 9.16 or Formula 9.16a. Whenever a 2×2 measure is computed between variables that are truly dichotomous, or whenever a coefficient representing a 2×2 relationship is to be used in developing a regression equation, ϕ is appropriate.

Data. Among the items administered to 94 employees in a supermarket were:

X: "How do you like the kind of work you do?"

Y: "How do you rate this store as a place to work?"

Responses, originally obtained in multiple-choice form, were consolidated as follows:

Y	X WORK BORING OR ONLY FAIRLY INTERESTING		WORK LIKED VERY MUCH		TOTAL
Excellent place to work	7	(a)	(b)	18	25
Less satisfactory place to work	44	(c)	(d)	25	69
TOTAL	51			43	$N = 94$

By Formula 9.16,

$$\phi = \frac{bN - (b+d)(a+b)}{\sqrt{(b+d)(a+c)(a+b)(c+d)}} = \frac{(18 \times 94) - (43 \times 25)}{\sqrt{43 \times 51 \times 25 \times 69}}$$

$$= \frac{617}{\sqrt{3,782,925}} = .32$$

Formula 9.16a yields identical results, since the denominator is unchanged and the numerator is algebraically identical; that is, $(bc - ad) = (18 \times 44) - (7 \times 25) = 617$.

Computation of $r_{tet.}$ Strictly speaking, $r_{tet.}$ must be estimated rather than computed. For entry into the Cheshire-Saffir-Thurstone diagrams (1), frequencies must be reduced to proportions. The preceding example becomes:

Y	X WORK BORING OR ONLY FAIRLY INTERESTING	WORK LIKED VERY MUCH	TOTAL
Excellent place to work	.07	.19	.26
Less satisfactory place to work	.47	.27	.74
TOTAL	.54	.46	1.00

Four estimates of $r_{tet.}$ are made, based on the lower p (or q) in one variable, either proportion in the other, and the p_{xy} at the intersection as follows:

LOWER p (OR q) IN ONE VARIABLE	PROPORTION IN OTHER VARIABLE	p_{xy}	ESTIMATED $r_{tet.}$
.46	.26	.19	.46
.46	.74	.27	.56
.26	.54	.07	.58
.26	.46	.19	.53

Mean estimated $r_{tet.}$ .53

Actually, the diagrams use special notation and are self-explanatory. The point of interest here is that $r_{tet.}$ is obviously considerably higher than ϕ.

Pearson's Cosine[1] *Approximation of $r_{tet.}$* Pearson (2), who developed $r_{tet.}$, also presented a useful approximation:

$$r_{tet.} = \cos\left(\frac{180°}{1 + \sqrt{\dfrac{bc}{ad}}}\right) \tag{9.16b}$$

While various special tables for this function exist, any trigonometric table may be used. In this case,

$$r_{tet.} \doteq \cos\left(\frac{180°}{1 + \sqrt{\dfrac{18 \times 44}{7 \times 25}}}\right) = \cos\frac{180°}{3.127} = \cos 57.56° = .54$$

When working simultaneously with large numbers of dichotomous variables, it is sometimes convenient to use covariances in intermediate computations instead of r's or ϕ's. The development is the same as for Formula 9.16, except that $s_x s_y$ and equivalents are omitted. Accordingly, the covariance for dichotomous variables coded 1 and 0 is

$$C_{xy} = \frac{\Sigma XY}{N} - M_x M_y = \frac{b}{N} - \frac{(b+d)(a+b)}{N}\frac{}{N}$$

$$= \frac{bN - (b+d)(a+b)}{N^2} \tag{9.17}$$

APPLICATIONS OF ϕ AND $r_{tet.}$

Later in this chapter there is a discussion of tetrachoric $r(r_{tet.})$, which bears exactly the same relationship to ϕ as $r_{bis.}$ does to $r_{pt.\,bis.}$ If the correlation of two dichotomous variables is used to estimate what the correlation would have been if it had been based on continuously measured, normally distributed variables underlying the dichotomies, tetrachoric r is appropriate. Tetrachoric r is a good estimate of the correlation when continuous information has somehow been dichotomized and only the dichotomous information is available.

A great advantage of the phi coefficient is that, as a least squares solution without assumptions, it fits into any Pearson r system and it can be used in multiple and partial correlation and in computing regression equations. For this reason, the phi coefficient is generally preferable to $r_{tet.}$ in handling the statistics of items. In this connection one application is

---

[1] In trigonometry the cosine of an angle is defined as the ratio of two sides of a right triangle that incorporates the angle. It is the side adjacent to the angle divided by the hypotenuse.

that the variance of the total variable can be found by summing the variance-covariance matrix of the constituent items; that is, the matrix with variances equal to pq and with covariances as found by Formula 9.17.

When observed continuous distributions are highly skewed, and it is believed that the skewness results from defects in the measuring instrument, $r_{tet.}$ is sometimes computed to estimate what the correlation would have been if normally distributed variables had been obtained. However, when using information that falls naturally into dichotomies, such as sex, and sometimes race and marital status, the phi coefficient is generally preferable to $r_{tet.}$.

One characteristic of the phi coefficient is that it is markedly affected by the proportions in the upper and lower categories of the two variables and can reach a maximum of 1.00 only when $p_y = p_x$; that is, when points of dichotomy in the two variables are exactly the same.

SPEARMAN'S RANK CORRELATION COEFFICIENT

A third variant of the Pearson formula is Spearman's rank correlation coefficient, already discussed in Chapter 4. It is demonstrated in elementary algebra that the mean of a series of N ranks beginning with 1 is $(N + 1)/2$. It can also be shown that the sum of the squares of N ranks is $N(N + 1)$ $(2N + 1)/6$. Substitution of these values in a raw-score formula for the standard deviation yields

$$s_x = \sqrt{\frac{\Sigma X^2}{N} - M_x{}^2} = \sqrt{\frac{N(N + 1)(2N + 1)}{6N} - \left(\frac{N + 1}{2}\right)^2} = \sqrt{\frac{N^2 - 1}{12}} \quad (9.18)$$

Substituting Formula 9.18 and the value for the mean in a raw-score formula for r, and remembering that means and standard deviations are identical, for two sets of N ranks, we have

$$r = \frac{\frac{\Sigma XY}{N} - M_x M_y}{s_x s_y} = \frac{\frac{\Sigma R_x R_y}{N} - \frac{(N + 1)^2}{4}}{\sqrt{\frac{N^2 - 1}{12}} \sqrt{\frac{N^2 - 1}{12}}} = \frac{12\Sigma R_x R_y - 3N(N + 1)^2}{N(N^2 - 1)} \quad (9.19)$$

This is the "rank product" formula for ρ, the rank correlation coefficient, in which $\Sigma R_x R_y$ is the sum of the N products of the paired ranks. When there are no ties, it gives exactly the same result as the "rank difference" formula, which is a little easier to compute. The derivation of the rank difference formula starts with the difference formula for r (from Formula 6.10);

$$r_{xy} = \frac{V_x + V_y - V_{(x-y)}}{2s_x s_y}$$

Since any series of N ranks will sum to $N(N+1)/2$, the differences between two such series must sum to zero. Accordingly, to find the variance of the differences, it is necessary only to square each difference (denoted as D), sum, and divide by N. Accordingly, for a system of two sets of ranks ranging from 1 to N,

$$V_{x-y} = \frac{\Sigma D^2}{N} \qquad (9.20)$$

Substituting Formulas 9.18 and 9.20 in Formula 6.10 yields

$$r = \frac{\dfrac{N^2-1}{12} + \dfrac{N^2-1}{12} - \dfrac{\Sigma D^2}{N}}{2\sqrt{\dfrac{N^2-1}{12}}\sqrt{\dfrac{N^2-1}{12}}} = \frac{\dfrac{2(N^2-1)}{12} - \dfrac{\Sigma D^2}{N}}{\dfrac{2(N^2-1)}{12}} = 1 - \frac{6\Sigma D^2}{N(N^2-1)} \qquad (9.21)$$

This is the rank difference formula for r, denoted as ρ to show that it is computed from ranks instead of raw scores. It is seen that if the original data are two sets of ranks, Formula 9.21 yields the Pearson r between them. If, however, values on interval or ratio scales have been ranked, and then Formula 9.21 is applied, ρ is an approximation to the r that would have been found if the original scores had been correlated.

It is to be noted that the distribution of ranks, like the distribution of percentiles, is rectilinear. Accordingly, if a continuous variable is ranked prior to finding the correlation, some information is lost. In general, ρ will be a little smaller than r for the same data, but the difference is trifling. Since a major function of ρ is to obtain an estimate of the correlation from a small sample of cases, the difference between ρ and r is inconsequential. Computation of ρ is shown in Examples 4.4 and 4.5.

"AS IF" COEFFICIENTS: $r_{bis.}$, $r_{tet.}$

Both biserial r and tetrachoric r, in contrast to the point biserial and the phi coefficient described above, are "as if" coefficients in that they are estimates of what the correlation would be found to be if the dichotomous variables involved were actually continuously measured and normally distributed and if the more complete information were substituted for the dichotomous information at hand.

BISERIAL r

A convenient formula[2] for biserial r is

$$r_{bis.} = \frac{(M_p - M_x)N_p}{yNs_x} = \frac{(M_p - M_x)p}{ys_x} \qquad (9.22)$$

---

[2] A derivation of the formula for r_{bis} is given by Peters and Van Voorhis (4).

in which M_p is the mean score on the continuous variable of individuals in the upper group, N_p is the number of cases in that group, M_x and s_x are the mean and standard deviation of the continuous variable for the total group, and ^3y is the height of the unit normal curve at the point of dichotomy, as found from Table P (Appendix). Example 9.2 showed the computing steps.

While biserial r affords a useful estimate when the assumption of a normal variable underlying the dichotomy is justifiable, a computed $r_{bis.}$ cannot be considered exactly the same as the corresponding product-moment r. In the first place, its maximum value is not 1.00 but 1.25. In the second place, if the proportion of cases in one category or the other is less than .10, the coefficient is considered unreliable. In the third place, it may not be used in computing regression equations, since it does not belong to the Pearson family of correlation coefficients and since information for its use as a Pearson r is not available. It is strictly an estimate of what r would be if information not currently available became known.

It may be noted that a series of biserials has a high correlation with the series of points biserials computed from the same data. For analyzing item data in psychological tests, it rarely makes any difference which coefficient is used, since item data are evaluated relatively and since items that have high point biserials will have high biserials, and vice versa. However, in presenting research results against a dichotomous criterion, the choice of the appropriate coefficient is a matter of some concern. If the criterion is truly dichotomous, the point biserial is to be preferred. In personnel and clinical psychology, however, dichotomous criteria probably represent variables that are truly continuous. The point biserial is such an under-estimate of the biserial that the biserial is to be preferred if the correlation between a continuous predictor and a dichotomous criterion is to be accurately represented.

TETRACHORIC r

As does the biserial, $r_{tet.}$ involves an independent derivation of a formula for a relationship between two dichotomous variables rather than being an algebraic variant of the Pearson product-moment formula. Again, like biserial r, it is an "as if" coefficient in that it estimates what the correlation would be between two dichotomous variables if they were continuously and normally distributed and if complete information were available.

The formula for $r_{tet.}$, an infinite series of terms, is sufficiently complex that it is seldom used for computation, even with certain approximations. Instead, tetrachoric r's are usually found from computing diagrams, such

---

[3] It is to be noted that the meaning of y here has no particular relationship to y as a variable.

as those by Cheshire, Saffir, and Thurstone (1), which are published in a format that is fully self-explanatory. Some investigators dichotomize continuous data and then apply the diagrams to find the resultant tetrachoric *r*, which is then taken as the Pearson *r*. While the procedure is expeditious, it has doubtful merit, since the coefficient is far less stable than Pearson *r*.

There seems to be little justification for using $r_{tet.}$ in item analysis work, since it does not fit into the Pearson product-moment family of *r*, its computation is involved, and it is unlikely that the underlying variables are normally distributed. On the other hand, it is the appropriate coefficient whenever two dichotomous variables are correlated and the assumptions underlying its derivation are met.

Finding of $r_{tet.}$ was illustrated in Example 9.3.

CURVILINEAR CORRELATION

Almost exclusively, measures of relationship used in psychological statistics are based upon fitting a straight line to two sets of observations. The regression line, in the fitting of which the sum of the squares of the errors has been made as small as possible, is considered the "best-fitting" straight line. Its basic equation is

$$\tilde{y} = bx + a$$

in which $\tilde{y}$ is any value on the line, *b* is the slope, and *a* is its intercept. If all values are in *z* form, *b* becomes the correlation coefficient and *a* becomes zero.

It is easier to fit straight lines to bivariate distributions than it is to fit any other function. That fact, however, should not deter one from looking for other functions if they will better describe the relationship between the two variables under study.

Curvilinear correlation starts with the premise that the relationship between two variables can be better described by the equation of a curve than it can be by the equation of a straight line. The principle of least squares still applies. A straight line is actually a special, simple type of curve. A general method of curvilinear correlation will show that the best equation is a straight line when the straight line best fits the data; and in other cases it will give the equation of the curve of best fit by the least squares principle.

The first and perhaps most important technique of investigating the shape of the regression line is the inspection of the scatter plot. A glance at a correlation diagram can usually reveal whether or not there is a possibility that the line of best fit is not linear. One disadvantage of machine computation of descriptive statistics is that scatter plots must be obtained as an additional step rather than as basic to the computation of the correlation coefficient. Systematic psychological investigations should, however, include provision for the inspection of scatter plots. Ordinarily these can be obtained even when the primary mode of computation is by machine.

ETA AS A MEASURE OF CURVILINEAR CORRELATION

If the plot shows a tendency toward curvilinearity, the coefficient eta (η) may be computed. Eta supplies neither an equation of a line of best fit nor any statement of its shape. It is essentially a negative type of coefficient. When eta is higher than r, some line other than a straight line fits the data best. This line may or may not be a smooth curve.

Eta operates by determining the average variance within each column (or row) in a scatter diagram and comparing it with the total variance of the same variable. Computation is shown in Example 9.4.

EXAMPLE 9.4

COMPUTATION OF η THE CORRELATION RATIO

Nature of Eta. While the computation does not involve fitting a set mathematical function connecting two variables, η is often conceived as a measure of nonlinear correlation. A very irregular line of best fit can yield just as high an eta as will a smooth curve. The more the cell frequencies in the vertical arrays are concentrated, the higher one of the two etas, η_{yx}; while the greater the concentration in the horizontal arrays, the higher η_{xy}. If η's are markedly different from r, then a search can be made for a function connecting the two variables more appropriate than the straight line automatically fitted whenever a correlation is computed.

Data in Table 9.3. This table presents the bivariate distribution of the coded scores of 210 high school seniors on two achievement tests. The coded values, ranging from 0 through 9, are used directly as d_x and d_y. As in Example 6.2, each cell frequency is denoted as f_{xy}.

In either dimension, the total variance V_x or V_y can be shown to consist of two components: the variance of the means of the arrays V_{m_x} or V_{m_y}; and the variance around the means. By definition, η_{yx}^2 is the ratio V_{m_y}/V_y, and η_{xy}^2 is V_{m_x}/V_x. Somewhat similarly, r^2 is the ratio of the predictable variance to the total variance; that is, $r_{xy}^2 = \tilde{V}_x/V_x$. Since the predictable variance is of values on the regression line (which is necessarily straight), while the means within arrays used in finding η^2 may vary from a straight line, r^2 may equal η^2, but cannot exceed it.

The computation of η_{yx} involves the following steps:

1. Find the f_x's for the columns.
2. Within each column, multiply each cell frequency, f_{xy}, by its corresponding d_y, and sum.
3. Square each $\Sigma d_y f_{xy}$.

TABLE 9.3. COMPUTATION OF η, THE CORRELATION RATIO

$Y = d_y$	$X = d_x$										f_y	$\Sigma d_x f_{xy}$	$(\Sigma d_x f_{xy})^2$
	0	1	2	3	4	5	6	7	8	9			
9		1				1	1	1	1		5	27	729
8			1	2	5	1	3	2	1	3	18	100	10,000
7		1		3	3	8		3	2	1	21	108	11,664
6	3	2	3	3	4	2	3	3	1	1	25	99	9,801
5		2	8	4	8	4	1	1	1	1	30	112	12,544
4	4	2	4	8	10	3	3		1		35	115	13,225
3		2	7	5	8	4	1	1		1	29	105	11,025
2	5	8	4	1		2		1		1	22	45	2,025
1	3	3	3	4	1	3					17	40	1,600
0	1	2		3	2						8	19	361
f_x	16	23	30	33	41	28	12	12	7	8			
$\Sigma d_y f_{xy}$	47	71	114	128	190	136	71	74	46	47			
$(\Sigma d_y f_{xy})^2$	2209	5041	12,996	16,384	36,100	18,496	5041	5476	2116	2209			

$N = 210$

$\Sigma y' = \Sigma d_y f_y = 924$

$\Sigma y'^2 = \Sigma d_y^2 f_y = 5162$

$$\sum \frac{(\Sigma d_x f_{xy})^2}{f_y} = 4282.81$$

$\Sigma x' y' = \Sigma d_y (\Sigma d_x f_{xy}) = \Sigma d_x (\Sigma d_y f_{xy}) = 3858$

$$\eta_{yx} = \sqrt{\frac{210 \times 4282.81 - (924)^2}{210 \times 5162 - (924)^2}} = .45$$

$\Sigma x' = \Sigma d_x f_x = 770$

$\Sigma x'^2 = \Sigma d_x^2 f_x = 3192$

$$\sum \frac{(\Sigma d_y f_{xy})^2}{f_x} = 3056.28$$

$$\eta_{xy} = \sqrt{\frac{210 \times 3056.28 - (770)^2}{210 \times 3192 - (770)^2}} = .46$$

$$r_{xy} = \frac{(210 \times 3858) - (924 \times 770)}{\sqrt{210 \times 5162 - (924)^2}\,\sqrt{210 \times 3192 - (770)^2}} = .43$$

4. Divide each $(\Sigma d_y f_{xy})^2$ by the corresponding f_x and sum the quotients. This yields

$$\Sigma \frac{(\Sigma d_y f_{xy})^2}{f_x}$$

5. Multiply each f_y by the corresponding d_y and sum. This yields $\Sigma d_y f_y = \Sigma y'$. (If the cumulative method for finding $\Sigma y'$ is used, the Cf_y are found and summed, excluding the Cf in the 0 row.)

6. Compute $\Sigma y'^2$ by multiplying each f_y by d_y^2 (or by summing the products of the Cf_y and the m or successive odd numbers).

7. Find η_{yx} by the formula

$$\eta_{yx} = \sqrt{\frac{N\Sigma \dfrac{(\Sigma d_y f_{xy})^2}{f_x} - (\Sigma y')^2}{N\Sigma y'^2 - (\Sigma y')^2}} \tag{9.23}$$

which is the square root of the ratio V_{m_y}/V_y.

By parallel operations within the columns, η_{xy} can be found.

To find r_{xy}, the only additional information needed is $\Sigma x'y'$, which may be found as $\Sigma d_y(\Sigma d_x f_{xy})$; that is, multiplying each $\Sigma d_x f_{xy}$ by the corresponding d_y and summing. Alternately it may be found as $\Sigma d_x(\Sigma d_y f_{xy})$.

All computations are shown in Table 9.2.

Note on Testing the Significance of η. The greater the difference between η^2 and r^2, the greater is the departure from linearity of regression. Testing for the significance of the departure involves the F distribution, discussed in Chapters 12 and 14. In this case, F is found as follows:

$$F = \frac{(\eta^2 - r^2)/(n - 2)}{(1 - \eta^2)/(N - n)}$$

in which n is the number of row or column means and N is the total number of cases. In entering the F table, the degrees of freedom are $(n - 2)$ and $(N - n)$. The test may be applied both to η_{xy} and η_{yx}.

In each scatter diagram, two etas may be computed, one describing the regression of x on y, the other, the regression of y on x. If the information in x is informative with regard to y, the variability within the columns will be very small compared with the total variability of y, and η_{yx} will take a high value. If this value is much higher than r computed from the same data, it follows that the regression is curvilinear, but no equation of the line of best fit is available. There is a similar eta, η_{xy}, computed within the rows, for investigating the variability of x compared with the total variability. The values of η_{yx} and η_{xy} may be quite different.

FITTING A CURVILINEAR FUNCTION TO BIVARIATE DATA

More satisfactory than eta is a statement of the relationship between the two variables that will yield the equation of the curve of best fit. Theoretically, such an equation might be of any type of curve. One of the most versatile curves in mathematics is the parabola, since it can describe a wide variety of relationships. It would appear to be the most logical curve to select for the description of relationships departing from rectilinearity. Fitting a parabola to bivariate data is shown by Peters (3).

The interpretation of a curvilinear function of best fit parallels exactly the interpretation of the straight line of best fit. There is a standard error of estimate which is the square root of the variance of the residuals. The process of fitting the function is a process of minimizing the sum of the squares of these residuals. It is also possible to apply to curvilinear correlation theory the principles of multiple and partial regression. However, up to the present time, these have been applied very little in psychological research. If and when observed data require the curvilinear relationship of weighted sums and the curvilinear relationships of residuals, the required procedures are either available or can be readily worked out.

SUMMARY

Implicit in any complete variance-covariance matrix (of which a correlation matrix with 1.00's in the diagonal is a special case) are the variances, standard deviations, and correlations of new variables defined as the weighted or unweighted sums of the original variables.

The product-moment formula for r can be readily modified, for convenience in computation, to cover the case where one variable is dichotomous ($r_{pt.bis.}$), where both variables are dichotomous (ϕ), or when both variables consist of ranks (ρ).

If an estimate is needed of what the product-moment r would be if a single dichotomous variable were continuously and normally distributed, then $r_{bis.}$ may be used. For a similar estimate involving two dichotomous variables, the appropriate statistic is $r_{tet.}$.

If, for two continuously distributed variables a coefficient called η is markedly greater than r, the regression is not linear, and it is possible that some nonlinear function may better describe the relationship.

EXERCISES

1. Below is the complete variance-covariance matrix of eight arithmetic reasoning test items. $(N = 1000)$

	1	2	3	4	5	6	7	8
1	.194	.012	.032	.030	.032	.030	.014	.029
2	.012	.215	.016	.041	.026	.023	.018	.034
3	.032	.016	.234	.035	.059	.073	.032	.051
4	.030	.041	.035	.209	.209	.036	.033	.031
5	.032	.026	.059	.029	.238	.051	.033	.056
6	.030	.023	.073	.036	.051	.211	.036	.050
7	.014	.018	.032	.033	.033	.036	.250	.045
8	.029	.034	.051	.031	.056	.050	.045	.250

(a) Find the total variance of the eight-item test.
(b) Find the correlation of each item with the total score.
(c) Find the correlation between a test composed of the first four items and a test composed of the last four items.

2. Below are the intercorrelations of six tests used in screening applicants for admission to a college of engineering.

		2	3	4	5	6
1.	Reading test	.84	.41	.22	.11	.21
2.	Language test		.48	.38	.26	.34
3.	Reasoning test			.29	.27	.38
4.	Quantitative test				.29	.41
5.	Perceptual test					.63
6.	Mechanical test					

Find the correlations between each of the six variables and a composite formed by adding all the variables (with equal standard deviations).

3. Below are the joint frequencies (with total frequencies in the main diagonal) of six items on a reasoning test. $(N = 248.)$
(a) Find the variance-covariance matrix.
(b) Find the correlation matrix of ϕ coefficients.

	1	2	3	4	5	6
1	185	147	66	125	105	104
2	147	198	63	134	111	107
3	66	63	87	62	57	43
4	125	134	62	169	101	105
5	105	111	57	101	140	83
6	104	107	43	105	83	136

4. Compute ϕ for the following diagrams and then state the conditions under which $\phi = 1.00$.

	−	+
+		26
−	26	

	−	+
+	10	16
−	26	

	−	+
+		16
−	26	10

	−	+
+	5	26
−	16	5

	−	+
+		4
−	48	

	−	+
+	10	16
−	16	10

5. For the following artificial data, find $r_{\text{pt.bis.}}$ and $r_{\text{bis.}}$. In this case, are there good reasons why $r_{\text{bis.}} > 1.00 > r_{\text{pt.bis.}}$?

	X									
Y	1	2	3	4	5	6	7	8	9	10
Pass = 1						19	14	9	6	2
Fail = 0	2	6	9	14	19					

6. The following diagrams represent consolidations of the information in Table 6.4. Find $r_{\text{bis.}}$ and $r_{\text{tet.}}$ and compare with the r of .63 when the information is in 15 categories for each variable.

	X				
Y	70–99	100–129	130–159	160–189	190–219
1	1	13	83	145	32
0	21	81	151	52	3

	X	
Y	0	1
1	97	177
0	253	55

7. From the sum formula, $r_{xy} = (V_{x+y} - V_x - V_y)/2s_x s_y$, develop a formula for ρ that involves finding the variance of the sums of paired ranks.

8. For the data in Exercise 8, Chapter 6 (relationship between Army Alpha and Army Beta for 1047 recruits in World War I), compute η and test whether the regression is significantly nonlinear.

REFERENCES

1. CHESIRE, L., SAFFIR, M., AND THURSTONE, L. L., *Computing Diagrams for the Tetrachoric Correlation Coefficient*. Chicago: University of Chicago Bookstore, 1933.
2. PEARSON, K., "Mathematical contributions to the theory of evolution, VII. On the correlation of characters not quantitatively measurable." London: *Philos. Trans. Roy. Soc.*, 195A, 1901.
3. PETERS, CHARLES C., "A new descriptive statistic: The parabolic correlation coefficient," *Psychometrika*, 1946, **11**, 47–69.
4. PETERS, C. C., AND VAN VOORHIS, W. R., *Statistical Procedures and Their Mathematical Bases*. New York: McGraw-Hill Book Company, Inc., 1940.

FORECASTING
HUMAN BEHAVIOR

10

The psychologist who counsels clients on vocational choices, or who diagnoses maladjusted individuals in a psychological clinic, or who selects students for a professional school or employees for an industrial firm is making predictions about human behavior.

The counsellor bases his advice on information related to his client's probable success in different occupations. The clinical psychologist categorizes his patient, perhaps as mentally defective or as neurotic, and proceeds to predict changes that would occur under different types of education or therapy. The personnel psychologist, by his act of selection or classification, predicts success as a student or employee.

Forecasting human behavior is hardly novel; it has been practiced with varying degrees of success for thousands of years. Success in prediction has brought fame to soldiers and power to statesmen.

PSYCHOLOGICAL PREDICTION

Developments constituting the core of psychological methods of prediction include: procedures for measuring predictor variables; methods of scaling the criterion; and the use of quantitative methods within a sample to describe relationships useful in making predictions about cases yet to be observed.

Logically, psychological prediction involves four steps:

1. Selection of a sample believed to represent cases for which predictions are ultimately to be made.
2. Within the sample, observation of relationships between one or more predictor variables on the one hand and a dependent or criterion variable on the other. When there are two or more predictor variables, their interrelationships must be ascertained.
3. Observation of the predictor variables for new cases and the use of this information, together with information about their relationships, to make deductions about probable values in the unobserved dependent variable.
4. Verification by noting the degree to which predicted and actual criterion values agree in one or more new samples.

An appropriate sampling method is basic to the establishment of almost any psychological generalization. Certain sampling methods will be discussed in Chapter 13. This chapter concentrates on how forecasts are made and how a forecasting system may be tested.

THE CRITERION IN PREDICTION

Any time a nonzero relationship between two variables is discovered, one can, in a sense, "predict" one variable from the other. Often the relationship between a pair of variables is zero, and if no more information is available, such a relationship is useless for prediction. However, in the discussion of "suppressor" variables in Chapter 7, it was noted that under special circumstances and in combination with at least one other variable, a variable that is uncorrelated with another may be useful in predicting it.

When it is as easy to gather information simultaneously on two variables as on one, there is no need to set up a forecasting system, even though all required data are available. For example, a positive dependable relationship exists between height and weight in a defined group, such as 18-year-old males homogeneous as to racial, cultural, and socioeconomic background. Very easily, a system can be established for "predicting" height from weight or weight from height. With a large and well-defined sample, the proportion of error in such predictions can be ascertained, and the probability can be expressed that the discrepancy between a predicted and actual value will not exceed a stated amount. Ordinarily such "predictions" have little interest because values on both variables are at hand.

More usefully, forecasts are made in situations in which the predictive information is immediately available, but in which there is an interval of time before criterion data can be known. Typically, the applied psychologist has scores from psychological tests, or data from projective devices, or information about the past history of individuals, which he uses as a basis for decisions about people. When there are alternate candidates from whom to select for a training course or a position, or alternate possibilities for the treatment or placement of a person, the act of decision constitutes a prediction. Sometimes, especially in highly organized personnel programs, predicted criterion values are actually computed and recorded before decisions about individuals are made. In less formal programs, decisions reflect, more or less accurately, implicit predictions.

SCALES USED IN PREDICTION

Theoretically, any kind of scale can be used as a criterion: nominal, ordinal, interval, or ratio. Similarly, any type of scale can be used to predict information, either on the same or on a different kind of scale. When a physician uses symptoms to diagnose a disease, he may be combining several types of information: reaction to a physiological test as a nominal category; perspiration on an ordinal scale; and temperature on an interval scale. His objective may be classification into a disease category, belonging to a nominal scale.

In abnormal psychology, nominal scales are often used as criteria, as when responses to inkblots and personal inventories are used to differentiate psychiatric categories. Both in vocational counseling and in personnel classification, nominal scales can be used as criteria, but within each criterion group other scales may be used, such as degree of satisfaction with an occupation or degree of success on the job.

TESTING PSYCHOLOGICAL PREDICTIONS

Systematic testing of psychological prediction is possible when the criterion represents a single dimension of excellence. As far as the mechanics are concerned, it makes little difference whether the criterion is merely in two degrees, like the pass-fail criterion used in studies of predicting the ability to learn to fly an airplane, or a continuous variable such as the grade point average used in studies of academic success in college. In the first instance, prediction is in reference to broad categories; even when the predictors are not very valid, it may be that a large proportion of the predictions will turn out to be correct and that psychological procedures represent a considerable improvement over other forecasting methods. On the other hand, when a continuous variable is predicted, any deviation of the predicted score from the criterion score, when it becomes available, is likely to be considered an error. Sometimes the fact that a large proportion of the total variance turns out to be unpredictable is taken to indicate that psychological prediction methods are of little value. Actually, in real-life situations one is usually more concerned with making the decisions that will improve the caliber of personnel than in knowing precisely the eventual numerical evaluation the personnel will receive.

FORECASTING INSTRUMENTS

EXPECTANCY CHART

One of the simplest forecasting instruments is the expectancy chart, such as those illustrated in Figs. 10.1 and 10.2. In Fig. 10.2, one dichotomous variable is predicted from another; in Fig. 10.1 the criterion is dichotomous, but the predictor is nine steps and may be considered more or less continuous.

The basis of an expectancy chart is a scatter diagram showing the relationship between two variables. After a series of observations has been made, people are divided into categories according to the two variables. Usually there are two categories for the dependent or criterion variable and two or more for the independent or predictor variable. Either of the two categories of the criterion may be charted. In both Fig. 10.1 and Fig. 10.2 percentage of success is shown.

In Fig. 10.1 the nine categories represent different degrees of aptitude for pilot training. Actually, the nine-point pilot aptitude scale was based upon a battery of tests, weighted in accordance with the principles of multiple regression.

PILOT APTITUDE SCORE "(STANINE")"	NUMBER ELIMINATED	NUMBER GRADUATED	PERCENT GRADUATED
9	41	1048	96%
8	108	958	90%
7	271	1394	84%
6	590	1649	74%
5	815	1436	64%
4	800	927	54%
3	543	355	40%
2	37	16	30%
1	16	6	27%

0 10 20 30 40 50 60 70 80 90 100

FIG. 10.1. EXPECTANCY CHART FOR THE PREDICTION OF SUCCESS IN PILOT TRAINING FROM APTITUDE SCORE. Data from DuBois (1).

In using an expectancy chart in individual cases, information is available as to the person's score on the predictive measure but not, of course, on the outcome. What we want to predict is the individual's future. From Fig. 10.1 it can be said that the expectancy of the success of a young man with an aptitude rating of 9 is .96, whereas if his rating is only 1, the probability of his success is only .27. Thus, if conditions of training remain constant, then for 100 individuals who have the top rating, 96 will be expected to succeed and 4 to fail. Of 100 individuals with rating of 1, we may expect 27 to succeed and 73 to fail.

Of course one cannot be sure what will happen to any particular person. If, however, the high relationship observed during the course of the investigations continues to obtain, then the predictions in individual cases will tend to be correct. If the correlation were 1.00, both during the original investigation and subsequently, then all predictions would be perfectly accurate. If, on the other hand, the correlation were zero, predictions would be no better than blind guesses. With moderate degrees of correlation, predictions are better than chance.

GROUP PREDICTIONS AND INDIVIDUAL PREDICTIONS

Essentially there is no fundamental difference between predictions for individuals and the so-called *actuarial* predictions for groups. The group is made up of individuals. If we make N predictions for a group of N individuals, it is very likely that the mean of the predictions will come closer to the mean eventually obtained than will a prediction about a single individual be close to his eventual criterion score. However, the act of prediction is exactly the same in both instances. Suppose, for example, there are 100 individuals with a pilot aptitude rating of 3. Experience summarized in Fig. 10.1 shows that 40 of these men can be expected to succeed and 60 to fail; that is, each man has a probability of .40 of success.

When the 100 men are sent into training, it is likely that the yield will be reasonably close to the predicted yield of 40 men; that is, the mean score with success coded 1 and failure coded 0 will be close to .40. However, there is no way of identifying which 40 out of the 100 will succeed. Furthermore, by reason of differences in sampling, errors in the predictive measurements, and errors in measuring performance, the actual yield may be somewhat larger or smaller than .40. However, it has been found again and again that when actuarial predictions are made in large numbers of cases, the final results are not greatly different from what had been expected. This is the basis of prediction of death rates, voting behavior, and other group predictions in which there is more interest in averages than in what happens in the individual cases. In fact, in voting behavior, information as to the actual behavior of any specific individual when he goes to the polls is generally unavailable.

Prediction of Success of Deaf Children in Rotation Test

	N	PERCENT SUCCESSFUL IN ROTATION TEST
Success in Standing Test	39	85%
Failure in Standing Test	20	15%

Prediction of Success of Deaf Children in Standing Test

	N	PERCENT SUCCESSFUL IN STANDING TEST
Success in Rotation Test	36	92%
Failure in Rotation Test	23	22%

FIG. 10.2. EXPECTANCY CHARTS FOR DICHOTOMOUS VARIABLES.
Data from Worchel and Dallenbach (4).

What differs most from one case of prediction to another is the standard of accuracy. If we endeavor to predict a continuous variable, such as average grade in college, and if any discrepancy between the predicted average grade and the actual average grade is counted as an error, then predictions by means of regression equations are highly inaccurate. On the other hand, if the predictions are evaluated in broad categories, such as being successful in college as opposed to failure in academic work, then the errors may not be very numerous even though the correlation is fairly low.

PREDICTING ONE VARIABLE FROM ANOTHER

In the study summarized in Fig. 10.2, Worchel and Dallenbach (4) studied 59 deaf children with hearing loss ranging from 32 to 100 percent. Their "rotation test" involves sensitivity to motion in a rotation chair, as indicated by dizziness or nystagmus or compensatory adjustments.

The results indicate that information as to whether or not a deaf child can stand on one foot is valid in predicting whether or not he will be sensitive to the usual effects of rotation. It should be noted that correlation relates to concomitant variation rather than to cause and effect or even to identical underlying mechanisms. Using additional information as to the degree of hearing loss and as to whether the deafness was congenital or adventitious, Worchel and Dallenbach came to the conclusion that the two tests involve different physiological mechanisms: the rotation test, the semicircular canals; and the standing test, the macular organs of the utricle and saccule.

Originally the authors divided success on the standing test into four groups or categories and the rotation test into three, as shown in Table 10.1.

TABLE 10.1. OBSERVED VARIABLES

$X =$ ROTATION TEST

$Y =$ STANDING TEST	FAILURE ALL TRIALS	SUCCESS SOME TRIALS	SUCCESS ALL TRIALS	PERCENT WITH AT LEAST SOME SUCCESS
Immediate success	0	8	8	100
Success after practice	6	5	12	74
Failed: Average trial >4 seconds	7	1	2	30
Failed: Average trial <4 seconds	10	0	0	0

The product-moment r between the two variables is .62. A high degree of predictability of success on the rotation test from score on the standing test is indicated not only by the correlation coefficient but also by the percentages shown in the right-hand column. Such percentages could be the basis of an "expectancy chart," showing what percent of the cases in each category of one variable fall into a stipulated category in the second variable. As in this instance, the category in the second variable may be consolidated from two or more categories.

CONSOLIDATION INTO TWO DICHOTOMOUS VARIABLES

In Table 10.2 both variables have been made dichotomous as success-failure. Sometimes, when numbers of cases within the several cells are few, such a procedure results in a more accurate picture of the situation than when a number of steps are used with each variable. Here, however, it is done chiefly to illustrate the study of a pair of dichotomous variables.

TABLE 10.2. DICHOTOMIZED VARIABLES

$X =$ ROTATION TEST

$Y =$ STANDING TEST	TOTAL FAILURE	SUCCESS	TOTAL
Success	6 (a)	33 (b)	39
Failure	(c) 17	(d) 3	20
TOTAL	23	36	59

The computation of ϕ (product-moment r) by Formula 9.16a for dichotomies is

$$\phi = \frac{bc - ad}{\sqrt{(a+c)(b+d)(a+b)(c+d)}} = \frac{(17 \times 33) - (6 \times 3)}{\sqrt{23 \times 36 \times 39 \times 20}} = .68$$

The fact that ϕ is higher than the r computed in Table 10.1 is surprising because, when for identical data broader step intervals are used, r's tend to decrease. Actually, there are five other ways of dichotomizing the two variables of Table 10.1, and each yields a ϕ lower than that of Table 10.2, as shown in Table 10.3.

TABLE 10.3. ALTERNATE WAYS OF DICHOTOMIZING[a]

0	16
23	20

$\phi = .49$

8	8
29	14

$\phi = .16$

19	20
18	2

$\phi = .40$

13	36
10	0

$\phi = .57$

27	22
10	0

$\phi = .35$

[a] Data from Table 10.1.

Since the two sets of measurements are not interval scales, one is not justified in dichotomizing at any two points which happen to strike the fancy. Certainly there is no justification in dichotomizing at several pairs of points and then choosing the pair that happens to yield the highest numerical relationship.

In dichotomizing variables, one should either cut at the points that most logically separate the resultant categories, or cut as close to the two medians as possible. Table 10.2 probably meets both these criteria better than any of those shown in Table 10.3.

Table 10.2 is an example of the degree to which one dichotomous variable can be used to predict another. For two dichotomous variables, the technique of a regression equation can be justified mathematically; but no predicted score would correspond to one of the discrete values on a two-point scale. Rather, for all those "successful" on one scale, we should predict a fractional success score on the other; and for all those who "failed" on one scale, we should predict a fraction indicating failure on the other. Only when the predictor is a continuous variable do scores predicted from a regression equation make much sense. If the criterion is dichotomous, the predictors in continuous form are related to the probability of "success."

If the sample on which Table 10.2 is based is representative, our predictions would be accurate in most cases. By predicting "success" on a second variable for cases with "success" on the first, and "failure" on the second variable for cases with "failure" on the first $(33 + 17)/59$, or 85 percent, of the predictions would be expected to be correct and 15 percent incorrect. In 15 percent of the cases, then, one would expect to be completely wrong; but, of course, there is no way of identifying such cases in advance.

INCREASE IN CORRECT PLACEMENTS OVER CHANCE

If a 2 × 2 (or fourfold) table is used for prediction, as exemplified in the simpler scatter diagram from which a phi coefficient is computed, it is pertinent to inquire how much better the predictions are than sheer guessing.

When the four frequencies of the 2 × 2 table are labeled a, b, c and d, as in Table 10.4, the correct placements are b and c, and the incorrect placements are a and d. The method of estimating placement in cells on the basis of chance alone was discussed in Chapter 3 in connection with chi square. This method results in theoretical or expected cell frequencies that are proportional to both sets of marginal values, the f_r and the f_c. For any cell, the formula for the expected frequency is $f_e = f_r f_c / N$.

TABLE 10.4. PREDICTION FROM A 2 X 2 TABLE

VARIABLE Y	VARIABLE X		f_r
	$-$	$+$	
$+$	a	b	$(a + b)$
$-$	c	d	$(c + d)$
f_c	$(a + c)$	$(b + d)$	$N = a + b + c + d$

When one subtracts from b the number of correct placements expected in that cell by chance, $f_r f_c / N$ or $[(a + b)(b + d)]/N$, the result is $(bc - ad)/N$. The number of correct placements in the entire diagram, in addition to those expected by chance, is exactly double this amount, or $2(bc - ad)/N$.

Frequency in any cell expected purely on a basis of chance, that is, so that cell frequencies will be proportional to marginal entries, is $f_r f_c / N$.

The number of correct placements is $(b + c)$. The theoretical number of increases in correct placements because of a positive relationship between the two dichotomous variables is

$$b - \frac{(a + b)(b + d)}{N} + c - \frac{(a + c)(c + d)}{N} = \frac{2(bc - ad)}{N}$$

This formula may yield fractional values, since the theoretical frequencies may be fractional. The number of increases of correct placements in a single category can be shown to be $(bc - ad)/N$.

Table 10.5 explores the special instance in which both distributions are cut exactly in the middle. If the point of dichotomy is different for the two variables, results differ somewhat, but the general picture remains more or less the same.

It is seen from Table 10.5 that even a low correlation may increase the proportion of correct placements.

**TABLE 10.5. HYPOTHETICAL PREDICTIONS WITH PHI
(EQUAL DICHOTOMIES, N = 100)**

FREQUENCIES*				CORRECT PLACEMENTS	INCREASE IN CORRECT PLACEMENTS OVER CHANCE	INCREASE IN CORRECT PLACEMENTS IN UPPER CATEGORY OVER CHANCE	PHI
a	b	c	d				
25	25	25	25	50	0	0	.00
24	26	26	24	52	2	1	.04
23	27	27	23	54	4	2	.08
22	28	28	22	56	6	3	.12
21	29	29	21	58	8	4	.16
20	30	30	20	60	10	5	.20
19	31	31	19	62	12	6	.24
18	32	32	18	64	14	7	.28
17	33	33	17	66	16	8	.32
16	34	34	16	68	18	9	.36
15	35	35	15	70	20	10	.40
14	36	36	14	72	22	11	.44
13	37	37	13	74	24	12	.48
12	38	38	12	76	26	13	.52
11	39	39	11	78	28	14	.56
10	40	40	10	80	30	15	.60
9	41	41	9	82	32	16	.64
8	42	42	8	84	34	17	.68
7	43	43	7	86	36	18	.72
6	44	44	6	88	38	19	.76
5	45	45	5	90	40	20	.80
4	46	46	4	92	42	21	.84
3	47	47	3	94	44	22	.88
2	48	48	2	96	46	23	.92
1	49	49	1	98	48	24	.96
0	50	50	0	100	50	25	1.00

* In the 2 × 2 diagram

		−	+
+		a	b
−		c	d

b and c represent numbers of correct placements; a and d, numbers of incorrect placements.

Consider a situation in which 50 percent of the individuals working on a job were considered successful and for which a test was available that, when scored dichotomously, yielded a phi of .40 as a validity coefficient. Suppose we now hire only those who are above the median on the test and that work standards are not changed. It would now be expected that 35 instead of 25 of each 50 hired would be successful. Thus the percentage of successful employees would go from 50 to 70 percent. The increase in the efficiency of the organization as a result of better selection could thus be considerable.

PREDICTION WITH A CONTINUOUS VARIABLE

The method of establishing a basis for predicting one continuous variable from another is illustrated in Example 10.1. Within a sample of cases the relationship between the variables is summarized by a coefficient of correlation.

When only two variables are concerned, the predicted score, $\tilde{z}_0$ or $\tilde{X}_0$, is merely a linear transformation of the predictor variable and hence correlates perfectly with it. When there is only a single predictor and we are interested merely in ranking the cases with respect to the probable criterion scores, the following have identical utility:

1. Scores as predicted from a regression equation;
2. Any linear transformation of predictor scores; and
3. The original predictor scores.

The value of the regression equation in this instance lies only in finding predicted scores that numerically deviate as little as possible from actual criterion values, using a procedure that makes the sum of the squares of the differences between actual and predicted scores as small as possible.

It is apparent that, as the correlation increases, errors in prediction decrease. This is shown by the formula for the standard deviation of the discrepancies between observed scores and predicted scores (Formula 6.8):

$$s_{0.1} = s_0 \sqrt{1 - r_{01}{}^2}$$

While $s_{0.1}$ can be called the *standard error of estimate*, or $s_{\text{est } 0}$, theoretically it requires correction before it can be applied to cases not yet observed. It can be shown that the appropriate correction requires division of the sum of the squares of the errors by the number of degrees of freedom (in this case, $N - 2$) instead of N. Accordingly, the formula for the standard error of estimate (Formula 6.8) becomes

$$s_{\text{est } 0} = s_0 \sqrt{\frac{N}{N - 2}} \sqrt{1 - r_{01}{}^2} \qquad (6.8a)$$

With 30 cases, $s_{\text{est } 0}$ by Formula 6.8a is about 3 percent larger than it is without the correction; whereas, with very large N, the correction is negligible. However, when N is small and it is necessary to make precise statements about the zone in which a criterion score is likely to be found, the use of the correction is essential.

PREDICTING A DICHOTOMIZED CRITERION

The factor $\sqrt{1 - r_{01}{}^2}$, sometimes called the *coefficient of alienation*, which appears in the formula for the standard error of estimate, $s_{\text{est } 0}$, is the basis for prevalent (but unnecessary) pessimism about the effectiveness of prediction in psychology and education.

It is true that only when r reaches .707 is the variance of the errors of prediction reduced to half of the original criterion variance. At that point, the standard deviation of the errors is .707 of the standard deviation of the criterion. Since in psychology very few correlations between even a team of predictors and a criterion reach .707, it might appear that prediction by psychological methods is ineffective. Such is not the case.

In a practical situation, such as selecting employees, the usefulness of a psychological instrument depends upon three independent factors:

1. The proportion of cases considered "satisfactory" without the use of psychological methods;
2. The selection ratio, or proportion of individuals selected for the job or for the training program; and
3. The validity of the instrument in the original range of talent.

Grading individuals as "satisfactory" or "unsatisfactory" means either a dichotomous criterion or dichotomizing a continuous criterion. Obviously, if only a small proportion of unselected individuals is satisfactory, selection techniques have more possibility of being helpful than if a large proportion is satisfactory. The principles now under discussion apply, whether the criterion is dichotomous or is graded in categories, but they are easier to demonstrate for a dichotomous criterion.

If all applicants must be selected, then of course psychological instruments cannot improve their quality. However, as the selection ratio decreases, provided the instrument has at least some validity, the quality of selected personnel improves.

The importance of the third factor, the validity (or correlation between the predictor and the criterion in the original group) is obvious, since without some degree of correlation, prediction is no better than a guess.

The artificial data of Example 10.1 may be considered as showing the relationship between a predictor, X_1, and job success, X_0, prior to the use of the predictor for selection. In the computations in Table 10.10, it will be noted, however, that the validity is high, .64, which is greater than that often found in real situations.

When an X score of 50 or more is taken as representing "satisfactory" individuals, the situation is summarized in the upper part of Table 10.6, which assumes that with greater selectivity, performance standards remain unchanged. It may be noted that when the proportion selected or "selection ratio" becomes .77 (386 chosen out of 500), the proportion of "satisfactory" individuals increases from .77 to .86. When the selection ratio decreases still further to .40 (201 out of 500 selected), there is a further increase in the proportion of satisfactory individuals to .97, while with a selection ratio of .11, one would expect all those chosen to be "satisfactory."

TABLE 10.6. NUMBERS AND PROPORTIONS "SATISFACTORY" AND "UNSATISFACTORY" WITH NO SELECTION AND WITH THREE CUT-OFF POINTS[a]

	CUT-OFF SCORES			
	NO SELECTION	$X_1 = 45$	$X_1 = 55$	$X_1 = 65$
Number "Satisfactory"[b]	387	331	194	53
Proportion "Satisfactory"	.77	.86	.97	1.00
Number "Unsatisfactory"	113	55	7	0
Proportion "Unsatisfactory"	.23	.14	.03	.00
TOTAL SELECTED	500	386	201	53
SELECTION RATIO	1.00	.77	.40	.11

	CUT-OFF SCORES			
	NO SELECTION	$X_1 = 45$	$X_1 = 55$	$X_1 = 65$
Number "Satisfactory"[c]	201	189	139	46
Proportion "Satisfactory"	.40	.49	.69	.87
Number "Unsatisfactory"	299	197	62	7
Proportion "Unsatisfactory"	.60	.51	.31	.13
TOTAL SELECTED	500	386	201	53
SELECTION RATIO	1.00	.77	.40	.11

[a] Data from Example 10.1.
[b] "Satisfactory" defined as X_0 score of 50 or more
[c] "Satisfactory" defined as X_0 score of 70 or more.

If performance standards are raised so that, without selection, less than half are considered satisfactory, expected results are shown in the lower half of Table 10.6. With successive decreases in the selection ratio, a dramatic increase may be noted in the likelihood that a selected individual will prove to be satisfactory. Without screening, and a criterion score of 70 being considered as satisfactory, the individual's likelihood of being regarded satisfactory is .40; but with a selection ratio of .11, his likelihood is more than twice as great, or .87.

THE TAYLOR-RUSSELL TABLES

Taylor and Russell (3) prepared tables, reproduced in part as Table 10.7 for nine different proportions of employees considered satisfactory, ranging from .10 to .90. Entry is by means of the validity coefficient before selection (from .05 to .95) and the selection ratio (from .10 to .90). The predicted proportion of employees considered satisfactory is thus obtained from three factors:

1. Proportion considered satisfactory without selection;
2. Correlation between predictor and criterion; and
3. Proportion chosen through the use of the selection device.

TABLE 10.7. PREDICTED PROPORTIONS OF SATISFACTORY EMPLOYEES[a] (P = Proportion considered satisfactory without selection)

VALIDITY	(P=.10)					(P=.20)					(P=.30)				
	.90	.70	.50	.30	.10	.90	.70	.50	.30	.10	.90	.70	.50	.30	.10
.95	.11	.14	.20	.33	.78	.22	.29	.40	.64	.97	.33	.43	.60	.85	1.00
.85	.11	.14	.20	.31	.62	.22	.28	.39	.56	.85	.33	.43	.56	.74	.94
.75	.11	.14	.19	.29	.51	.22	.28	.37	.50	.74	.33	.42	.52	.67	.86
.65	.11	.14	.18	.26	.43	.22	.27	.35	.45	.64	.33	.40	.49	.60	.78
.55	.11	.14	.17	.23	.36	.22	.27	.32	.41	.56	.33	.39	.46	.55	.69
.45	.11	.13	.16	.20	.29	.22	.26	.30	.36	.48	.32	.37	.43	.50	.61
.35	.11	.13	.15	.18	.24	.22	.24	.28	.32	.41	.32	.36	.40	.45	.54
.25	.11	.12	.15	.16	.19	.21	.23	.26	.29	.34	.32	.34	.37	.41	.47
.15	.10	.11	.13	.13	.15	.21	.22	.23	.25	.28	.31	.33	.34	.36	.40
.05	.10	.10	.11	.11	.12	.20	.21	.21	.22	.23	.30	.31	.31	.32	.33

VALIDITY	(P=.40)					(P=.50)					(P=.60)				
	.90	.70	.50	.30	.10	.90	.70	.50	.30	.10	.90	.70	.50	.30	.10
.95	.44	.57	.77	.96	1.00	.56	.71	.90	.99	1.00	.67	.84	.97	1.00	1.00
.85	.44	.56	.71	.86	1.00	.55	.69	.82	.94	.99	.66	.80	.91	.97	1.00
.75	.44	.54	.66	.79	1.00	.55	.66	.77	.87	.97	.66	.77	.86	.93	.99
.65	.44	.52	.62	.72	.98	.55	.64	.73	.82	.92	.65	.74	.82	.89	.96
.55	.44	.50	.58	.67	.96	.54	.61	.69	.77	.87	.64	.71	.78	.84	.92
.45	.43	.49	.54	.61	.93	.53	.59	.65	.71	.81	.64	.69	.74	.80	.87
.35	.42	.47	.51	.56	.89	.53	.57	.61	.66	.74	.63	.67	.71	.75	.82
.25	.42	.45	.48	.51	.84	.52	.55	.58	.62	.67	.62	.65	.68	.71	.76
.15	.41	.43	.45	.47	.79	.51	.53	.55	.57	.61	.61	.63	.65	.67	.70
.05	.40	.41	.42	.42	.73	.50	.51	.52	.52	.54	.60	.61	.62	.62	.63

VALIDITY	(P=.70)					(P=.80)					(P=.90)				
	.90	.70	.50	.30	.10	.90	.70	.50	.30	.10	.90	.70	.50	.30	.10
.95	.78	.94	.99	1.00	1.00	.89	.99	1.00	1.00	1.00	.98	1.00	1.00	1.00	1.00
.85	.77	.89	.96	.99	1.00	.87	.96	.99	1.00	1.00	.96	.99	1.00	1.00	1.00
.75	.76	.86	.92	.97	1.00	.86	.93	.97	.99	1.00	.95	.98	.99	1.00	1.00
.65	.75	.83	.89	.94	.98	.85	.91	.95	.97	.99	.94	.97	.98	.99	1.00
.55	.74	.81	.86	.91	.96	.84	.89	.92	.95	.98	.93	.96	.97	.99	1.00
.45	.73	.78	.83	.87	.93	.83	.87	.90	.93	.96	.92	.94	.96	.98	.99
.35	.73	.76	.80	.83	.89	.82	.85	.89	.90	.94	.92	.93	.95	.96	.98
.25	.72	.75	.77	.80	.84	.82	.84	.86	.88	.91	.91	.92	.93	.95	.96
.15	.71	.73	.74	.76	.79	.81	.82	.83	.85	.87	.91	.91	.92	.93	.94
.05	.70	.71	.71	.72	.73	.80	.81	.81	.82	.82	.90	.90	.91	.91	.91

[a] Abridged by permission from H. C. Taylor, and J. T. Russell, "The Relationship of Validity Coefficients to the Practical Effectiveness of Tests in Selection: Discussion and Tables," *J. Appl. Psychol.*, 1939, 23, 565–578.

Since Table 10.6 is designed to illustrate the principle behind the Taylor-Russell tables, it is of interest to compare results. In the lower part of Table 10.6 the proportion satisfactory without selection is .40 and the validity is approximately .65. When the cut-off score is 55, the selection ratio is .40. Under these circumstances we expect the proportion satisfactory to be .69.

Entering the Table 10.7 for "Proportion of Employees Considered Satisfactory = .40" with a validity of .65 and selection ratio of .40, we find that the expected proportion of satisfactory employees is .67. Thus, findings from the hypothetical scatter diagram and the Taylor-Russell tables are practically identical.

This is really not surprising, since the Taylor-Russell tables, like Example 10.1, are constructed from the proportion of cases expected in various regions of the scatter diagram under specified conditions, including a linear relationship between criterion and predictor.

PREDICTION IN TERMS OF COST AND UTILITY

Another way of looking at a scatter diagram representing the relationship between a criterion and a predictor is in terms of "cost," defined as the percentage of satisfactory individuals rejected at a given cut-off point, and "utility," defined as the percentage of unsatisfactory individuals rejected. The comparison of cost and utility in Table 10.8 summarizes the effectiveness of prediction under defined circumstances; namely, the validity, the proportion satisfactory without selection, and the selection ratio. Expectancy is shown in a format rather different from the Taylor-Russell tables, although the underlying phenomena are, of course, identical.

TABLE 10.8. EFFECTIVENESS OF SELECTION IN TERMS OF COST AND UTILITY[a]

CUT-OFF	TOTAL NO. RE- JECTED	% RE- JECTED	NO. SATIS- FACTORY REJECTED	% SATIS- FACTORY REJECTED: "COST"	NO. UNSATIS- FACTORY REJECTED	% UNSATIS- FACTORY REJECTED: "UTILITY"
75	496	99.2	195	97.0	299	100.0
70	480	96.0	183	91.0	297	99.3
65	447	89.4	155	77.1	292	97.7
60	386	77.2	117	58.2	269	90.0
55	299	59.8	62	30.8	237	79.3
50	201	40.2	26	12.9	175	58.5
45	114	22.8	12	6.0	102	34.1
40	53	10.6	2	1.0	51	17.1
35	20	4.0	1	0.5	19	6.4
30	6	1.2	0	0.0	6	2.0

[a] Data from Example 10.1. A score of 70 or better in X_0 is taken as satisfactory; $N=201$, satisfactory; $N=299$, unsatisfactory.

CUT-OFF POINTS AND CRITICAL POINTS

In the application of psychological techniques to personnel selection, the cut-off point on the predictor variable is often established administratively. Someone in authority makes a decision as to the number of position vacancies to be filled or the number of students to be accepted. After consideration of the number of applicants and the distribution of the predictive scores, a point is established above which candidates are to be accepted and below which they are to be rejected. When all information is available at the time the decision is made, a firm cut-off point can be established and those with highest predictive scores can be selected. Often, however, in a rapidly changing situation, cut-off points are raised or lowered according to the supply of candidates and the needs of the organization for new personnel, yielding a solution less than optimal.

As contrasted with "cut-off," the use of the term *critical point* implies an unvarying criterion. Sometimes a critical point can be established as the average predictive score corresponding to a criterion value defined as a certain standard of work. When the criterion is dichotomous, the critical score might be the point on the predictor variable at which the individual would have a specified probability of being "satisfactory" on the criterion.

If, with the data of Example 10.1, we take an X_0 score of 70 or more as being "satisfactory" and an X_0 score of 69 as "unsatisfactory," the predictor distributions for the two graphs would be as shown in Table 10.9.

With real data and with a correlation as high as .64, regular increases in "percent satisfactory" from step to step would be expected. The reason for certain irregularities and approximately equal percentages in three pairs of steps is that, in the example, regression departs slightly from linearity. However, the results show reasonably well how a critical point can be set up.

TABLE 10.9. NUMBERS OF SATISFACTORY AND UNSATISFACTORY CASES BY CATEGORIES[a]

X_1 SCORES	UNSATISFACTORY f	SATISFACTORY f	PERCENT SATISFACTORY
75–79	0	6	100
70–74	2	12	86
65–69	5	28	85
60–64	23	38	62
55–59	32	55	63
50–54	62	36	37
45–49	73	14	16
40–44	51	10	16
35–39	32	1	3
30–34	13	1	7
25–29	6	0	0

[a] Data from Example 10.1. Critical point, $X_0 = 70$.

The same data are presented graphically in Fig. 10.3. If the critical point is defined as the predictor score at which the probability of being satisfactory is .50, the point at which the two distributions cross locates the score. The histogram does not permit precise location of the point, but it is apparent that an X_1 value of 55 would be approximately correct.

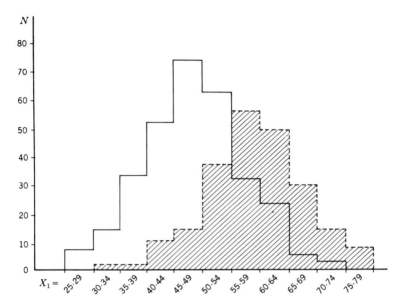

FIG. 10.3. ESTABLISHMENT OF A CRITICAL POINT GRAPHICALLY. (DATA FROM EXAMPLE 10.1.)

Shaded distribution (dotted line) is of "satisfactory" individuals ($X_0 = 70$ or more). Unshaded distribution (solid line) is of "unsatisfactory" individuals ($X_0 = 69$ or less). Critical point, at which probability of success goes from less than .50 to more than .50 is approximately 55.

There is, of course, no requirement that the critical score be established at the point at which the probability becomes .50. It could be taken at any value of p, such as .40, or .60, or .75. In an applied testing situation, other considerations might enter into the decision. A study might show that unless the probability of success of candidates was .75 or better, the firm would be likely to lose money by hiring them. Accordingly, a probability of .75 might be used in establishing the critical score.

CORRECTION FOR CHANGES IN RANGE

The accuracy of predicting X_0 from any particular X_1 score is not directly indicated by r_{01}, but rather by the variance of the array (X_1 column) in which the X_1 score appears.

The bivariate distribution in Example 10.1 has been constructed so that it is homoscedastic vertically, that is to say, the variances within the columns are almost precisely equal. Few bivariate distributions based on empirical psychological data are as homoscedastic vertically as this distribution. However, many are reasonably homoscedastic in two dimensions, as this one is not, since the variability in the horizontal arrays varies greatly.

E X A M P L E 10.1

PREDICTION WITHIN A BIVARIATE DISTRIBUTION

In Table 10.10 the regression for predicting x'_0 from x'_1 is approximately linear, and the line connecting the means would extend about from the cell identified with 0 in the column at the left to the cell similarly identified in the column at the right. In each column, which corresponds to a single x'_1 value, the most probable value x'_0 is at the column mean.

Variabilities in terms of coded scores are approximately equal.

The 0 cell in column ($x'_1 = 10$) is ten steps to the right and six steps above the 0 cell in column ($x'_1 = 0$). Since r has been shown to be the slope of the regression line when variabilities are equalized, we can estimate r as 6/10, or .60, which agrees quite well with the computed value of .64. Of course, only when variabilities are equal and regression is strictly linear can r be estimated in this fashion. In effect, the formulas for r convert original scores to z-scores, so that $\Sigma z_0 z_1/N$ is both the slope of the straight line of best fit and the correlation coefficient.

Estimation of r from the variability around the regression line. The artificial bivariate distribution in Table 10.10 was constructed so as to be homoscedastic within columns. (Definitely, it is not homoscedastic within rows.) The variability within two columns ($x'_1 = 4$ and $x'_1 = 6$) may be taken as typical. The variance around the mean in terms of coded scores is

$$V'_0 = \frac{\Sigma x'_0{}^2}{N} - \left(\frac{\Sigma x'_0}{N}\right)^2 = \frac{971}{87} - \left(\frac{261}{87}\right)^2 = 2.161$$

This may be taken as an estimate of the partial variance of the criterion after variance associated with the predictor has been removed, or (except for a correction involving the degrees of freedom, as explained in the text) as the square of the standard error of estimate.

The total variance of variable 0 in terms of coded scores is 3.808.

From the discussion in Chapter 6, it would be expected that

$$r_{01} = \sqrt{\frac{V_0 - V'_0}{V_0}} = \sqrt{\frac{3.808 - 2.161}{3.808}} = .66$$

This result again is close to the computed value of .64.

This is not a practical computation method, since it applies only when regression is linear and when the bivariate distribution is homoscedastic around the regression line.

Whenever we assume that the variance around the regression line (that is, the partial variance of the criterion after variance predictable from the independent variable has been removed) represents the error in prediction throughout the range, we assume homoscedasticity.

When the symbol $V_{0.1}$ is used to indicate the variance around the regression line, its numerical size depends upon the units in which the criterion is measured and is equal to $V_0(1 - r_{01}^2)$. If the criterion is in z scores with variance of unity, as in multiple correlation, $V_{0.1}$ becomes $(1 - r_{01}^2)$. Here, for convenience in computation, $V_{0.1}$ is used to mean the partial variance of the criterion in terms of coded scores. Exactly the same results can be obtained by using all variances either in raw-score form or in z form.

ASSUMPTION OF HOMOSCEDASTICITY

On the assumption of homoscedasticity, inferences can be made as to how changes in range will affect the correlation coefficient.

As pointed out in Chapter 6, the term *changes in range* does not refer to linear transformations of one variable or the other such that the range (as measured by the difference between highest and lowest scores) changes numerically. Linear changes in scale values have, of course, no effect on r. However, if at either end of a bivariate distribution, cases are added or taken away so that the range is increased or decreased, the magnitude of the r will change.

Consider a selection device that on experimental trial yields a correlation with the criterion of, say, .64. As the consequence of the discovery of a highly valid predictor, a decision is made henceforth to select only individuals with high scores. Provided criterion standards remain the same, it will be found that when the device is validated again, the correlation in the restricted range will be reduced from that observed in the original, or unrestricted, range. The amount of the reduction will be related to the degree of restriction.

When the swarm of points representing the scatterplot of two variables falls in a perfectly circular area (after variabilities are equalized), r is .00, whereas the closer the points are to the regression line, the higher the r. The scatterplot of Example 10.2 is the bivariate distribution of Example 10.1 less the first four columns. When compared with its original, it will be noticed that if the variabilities of the X_0 and X_1 distributions were equalized again, the scatterplot would be more nearly circular than originally. As expected, the correlation for the data of Example 10.2 is less than for Example 10.1. It is .55.

TABLE 10.10. PREDICTION OF A CONTINUOUS CRITERION (X_0) FROM A CONTINUOUS PREDICTOR (X_1)

Artificial Data ($r = .64$)

X_0	$x'_0 = d_0$	X_1 25–29	30–34	35–39	40–44	45–49	50–54	55–59	60–64	65–69	70–74	75–79	f_0	Cf_0	m	$C\Sigma d_1 f_{01}$
	$x'_1 = d_1$	0	1	2	3	4	5	6	7	8	9	10				
110–119	10									1	1	2	4	4	19	37
100–109	9							4	3	4	1	2	14	18	17	143
90–99	8						5	10	7	7	3	0	32	50	15	360
80–89	7				3	4	11	18	13	9	4	1	63	113	13	757
70–79	6		1	1	7	10	20	23	15	7	3	1	88	201	11	1257
60–69	5		1	4	13	18	26	18	13	4	1		98	299	9	1747
50–59	4	1	3	7	15	23	20	10	7	1	1		88	387	7	2127
40–49	3	1	4	9	13	18	11	4	3				63	450	5	2360
30–39	2	0	3	7	7	10	5						32	482	3	2463
20–29	1	2	1	4	3	4							14	496	1	2497
10–19	0	2	1	1									4	500		2500
f_1		6	14	33	61	87	98	87	61	33	14	6	500			
Cf_1		500	494	480	447	386	299	201	114	53	20	6				
m			1	3	5	7	9	11	13	15	17	19				
$C\Sigma d_0 f_{01}$		2500	2491	2449	2350	2106	1758	1268	746	380	149	51				

$\Sigma x'_0 = \Sigma Cf_0 = 2500$

$\Sigma x'^2_0 = \Sigma mCf_0 = 14{,}404$

$\sqrt{N\Sigma x'^2_0 - (\Sigma x'_0)^2} = 975.705$

$\Sigma x'_1 = \Sigma Cf_1 = 2500$

$\Sigma x'^2_1 = \Sigma mCf_1 = 14{,}504$

$\sqrt{N\Sigma x'^2_1 - (\Sigma x'_1)^2} = 1001.000$

$\Sigma x'_0 x'_1 = \Sigma C\Sigma d_0 f_{01} = \Sigma C\Sigma d_1 f_{01} = 13{,}748$

$r = \dfrac{N\Sigma x'_0 x'_1 - \Sigma x'_0 \Sigma x'_1}{\sqrt{N\Sigma x'^2_0 - (\Sigma x'_0)^2}\,\sqrt{N\Sigma x'^2_1 - (\Sigma x'_1)^2}}$

$\quad = \dfrac{(500 \times 13{,}748) - (2500 \times 2500)}{975.705 \times 1001.000} = .64$

Variances in terms of coded scores,

x'_0 and x'_1:

$V'_0 = \dfrac{14{,}404}{500} - \left(\dfrac{2500}{500}\right)^2 = 3.8080$

$V'_1 = \dfrac{14{,}504}{500} - \left(\dfrac{2500}{500}\right)^2 = 4.0080$

$M_0 = M'_0 + \dfrac{i\Sigma x_0}{N} = 14.5 + \dfrac{10 \times 2500}{500} = 64.50$

$s_0 = \dfrac{i}{N}\sqrt{\Sigma x'^2_0 - (\Sigma x'_0)^2} = \dfrac{10}{500} \times 975.705 = 19.51$

$M_1 = M'_1 + \dfrac{i\Sigma x'_1}{N} = 27 + \dfrac{5 \times 2500}{500} = 52.00$

$s_1 = \dfrac{i}{N}\sqrt{N\Sigma x'^2_1 - (\Sigma x'_1)^2} = \dfrac{5}{500} \times 1001.000 = 10.01$

Regression equation in z form:

$\tilde{z}_0 = r_{01} z_1$

$\tilde{z}_0 = .64 z_1$

Regression equation in raw-score form:

$\dfrac{\tilde{X}_0 - M_0}{s_0} = r_{01}\left(\dfrac{X_1 - M_1}{s_1}\right)$

$\left(\dfrac{\tilde{X}_0 - 64.50}{19.51}\right) = .64\left(\dfrac{X_1 - 52.00}{10.01}\right)$

$\tilde{X}_0 = 1.25 X_1 - .36$

EXAMPLE 10.2

COMPUTATIONS FOR CORRECTION FOR CHANGE IN RANGE

(Data are seven columns from Example 10.1.)

X_0	$x'_0 = d_0$	X_1 45–49 (0)	50–54 (1)	55–59 (2)	60–64 (3)	65–69 (4)	70–74 (5)	75–79 (6)	Cf_0	m	$C\Sigma d_1 f_{01}$
110–119	9					1	1	2	4	17	21
100–109	8			4	3	4	1	2	18	15	71
90–99	7		5	10	7	7	3		50	13	160
80–89	6	4	11	18	13	9	4	1	110	11	308
70–79	5	10	20	23	15	7	3	1	189	9	468
60–69	4	18	26	18	13	4	1		269	7	590
50–59	3	23	20	10	7	1	1		331	5	590
40–49	2	18	11	4	3				367	3	660
30–39	1	10	5						382	1	688
20–29	0	4							386		693
Cf_1		386	299	201	114	53	20	6			
m			1	3	5	7	9	11			
$C\Sigma d_0 f_{01}$		1720	1459	1067	632	327	129	45			

Computations

$$\Sigma x'_0 = \Sigma Cf_0 = 1720$$

$$\Sigma x'^2_0 = \Sigma mCf_0 = 8920$$

$$V_0 = \frac{\Sigma x'^2_0}{N} - \left(\frac{\Sigma x'_0}{N}\right)^2 = \frac{8920}{386} - \left(\frac{1720}{386}\right)^2 = 3.2532 \text{ (in terms of } x'_0)$$

$$\Sigma x'_1 = \Sigma Cf_1 = 693$$

$$\Sigma x'^2_1 = \Sigma mCf_1 = 2089$$

$$V_1 = \frac{2089}{368} - \left(\frac{693}{368}\right)^2 = 2.1887 \text{ (in terms of } x'_1)$$

$$\Sigma x'_0 x'_1 = \Sigma C\Sigma d_1 f_{01} = \Sigma C\Sigma d_0 f_{01} = 3659$$

$$r_{01} = \frac{N\Sigma x'_0 x'_1 - \Sigma x'_0 \Sigma x'_1}{\sqrt{N\Sigma x'^2_0 - (\Sigma x'_0)^2}\,\sqrt{N\Sigma x'^2_1 - (\Sigma x'_1)^2}} = .55$$

Computation of r. This example shows again a procedure for computing r from a scatter diagram, already demonstrated in Examples 6.3 and 10.1. Data are exactly the same as for Example 10.1, except that the first four columns have been omitted and both variables have been recoded.

Knowledge of the variances and the correlation of the truncated bivariate distribution permit an empirical study of correction for changes in range, as explained in the text.

CORRECTION ON THE INDEPENDENT VARIABLE WHEN CRITERION
VARIANCES ARE KNOWN

Usually, correction is for restriction rather than extension of range, but
the principle is identical. In the basic formulas there is merely a change in
which correlation is known and which is unknown.

The following notation is applicable:

v_i = variance of a variable in lesser range.

V_i = variance of the same variable in a greater range that includes
the lesser range.

r_{ij} = correlation in the lesser range.

R_{ij} = correlation in the greater range (in this case R does not refer to
multiple R).

It is assumed that the partial variance of the criterion after the portion
predictable from the independent variable has been partialed out is identical in both ranges. This assumption is that $v_{0.1} = V_{0.1}$. This is clearly true
when the vertical arrays have equal variances, as in Example 10.1, and may
be true under other circumstances. If $v_{0.1} = V_{0.1}$, then, expanding each,

$$v_0(1 - r_{01}{}^2) = V_0(1 - R_{01}{}^2)$$

When three of the four constants are known, this equation can be readily
solved for the fourth.

Solving for R_{01} yields

$$R_{01} = \sqrt{1 - \frac{v_0}{V_0}(1 - r_{01}{}^2)} \qquad (10.1)$$

This formula is not very useful in practice. When the independent variable is restricted, we are more likely to know its two variances than we are
to know the two variances of the criterion. Nevertheless, to test the approach, Formula 10.1 is applied to the data of Example 10.2. Then

$$R_{01} = \sqrt{1 - \frac{3.2532}{3.8080}[1 - (.55)^2]} = .64$$

a result identical with R_{01} as computed in Example 10.1.

CORRECTION FOR RESTRICTION WHEN PREDICTOR VARIANCES ARE KNOWN

When predictor instead of criterion variances are known, corrections must
be based on the partial variances of the predictor. However, it is clear that
even if the bivariate distribution were homoscedastic horizontally before
truncation, it would not be so subsequently. Hence, it cannot be assumed
that $V_{1.0} = v_{1.0}$. Actually, $V_{1.0}$ is necessarily greater than $v_{1.0}$.

A plausible assumption is that the change in the proportion of predictable variance ($r_{01}{}^2$ over $R_{01}{}^2$) will be directly related to the change in the

proportion of unpredicted variance around the regression line when variable 1 is predicted from variable 0. Thus

$$\frac{r_{01}^{2}}{R_{01}^{2}} = \frac{v_{1.0}}{V_{1.0}} = \frac{v_{1}(1 - r_{01}^{2})}{V_{1}(1 - R_{01}^{2})}$$

Again, the equation has four constants, and when three are known, the fourth can be determined. Solving for R_{01} yields

$$R_{01} = \sqrt{\frac{V_1 r_{01}^{2}}{v_1 - v_1 r_{01}^{2} + V_1 r_{01}^{2}}} \tag{10.2}$$

while solving for r_{01} gives

$$r_{01} = \sqrt{\frac{v_1 R_{01}^{2}}{V_1 - V_1 R_{01}^{2} + v_1 R_{01}^{2}}} \tag{10.3}$$

Applying Formula 10.2 to the data of Example 10.3,

$$R_{01} = \sqrt{\frac{4.0080(.55)^2}{2.1887 - 2.1887(.55)^2 + 4.0080(.55)^2}} = .67$$

The result is a little higher than the value of .64 computed in Example 10.1, but nevertheless appears to be good approximation. If the horizontal arrays had variances that were more nearly uniform, it is likely that the approximation would be closer.

There is an important implication of the discussion of the effects of changes in range. When psychological selection techniques are applied in real situations, criterion scores will no longer be available for poor performers eliminated because of low test scores, and the criterion in this restricted range will automatically yield lower validities. Nevertheless the devices may remain just as useful. Only if the decrease is greater than anticipated should there be concern that the selection technique may have lost some of its effectiveness.

PREDICTION WITH A TEAM OF VARIABLES

MULTIPLE REGRESSION EQUATION

The prediction of a criterion with a team of variables differs somewhat from prediction with a single variable. However, as long as prediction is by using a straight regression line[1] fitted by the principle of least squares, basic phenomena remain identical.

---

[1] Mathematically, the equation for predicting a criterion from a team of variables is that of a plane. However, the weighted sum of predictors has a correlation of R with the criterion, and if both the weighted sum and the criterion are in standard measure, R is the slope of the line of best fit.

The statistical method that is, explicitly or implicitly, behind most efforts to forecast a criterion from a group of predictors is multiple correlation, described in Chapter 7. There it was noted that multiple R is a product-moment correlation between the criterion on the one hand and a weighted sum of predictors on the other, each weighted so that (in the sample in which R is found) the correlation is as high as possible. It is found by a forward solution, which reduces step by step the variance of the criterion to a partial variance from which all variation predictable from the "independent" variables has been removed. From this partial variance, $V_{0.12...n}$, the multiple, $R_{0(12...n)}$, is easily determined.

A back solution (which actually solves a set of n simultaneous linear equations in n unknowns) yields the n betas. For each of the N cases, the betas can be used as multipliers of the z scores on n predictors, yielding a set of values of $\tilde{z}_0$, which have a correlation of $R_{0(12...n)}$ with the criterion z_0. Thus the regression equation in z form is

$$\tilde{z}_0 = \beta_{01.23...n}z_1 + \beta_{02.13...n}z_2 + \cdots + \beta_{0n.12...(n-1)}z_n \qquad (7.1a)$$

This equation is seldom useful in practical prediction because it is applicable only to predictors with equal standard deviations. However, to change the standard deviation of any variable to 1.00, all that is needed is to divide each value by the observed standard deviation. Thus the correlation between $\tilde{X}'_0$, a weighted sum of raw scores, and the criterion is the multiple if each raw score is divided by the standard deviation of the variable and multiplied by the appropriate beta. This yields the following method of summing raw scores so as to produce a composite with maximum correlation with a criterion:

$$\tilde{X}'_0 = \beta_{01.23...n}\frac{X_1}{s_1} + \beta_{02.13...n}\frac{X_2}{s_2} + \cdots + \beta_{0n.12...(n-1)}\frac{X_n}{s_n} \qquad (10.4)$$

The mean of $\tilde{X}'_0$ can be shown to be $\Sigma(\beta_i M_i/s_i)$ and the standard deviation $R_{0(12...n)}$. With this information, $\tilde{X}'_0$ can be transformed to a series of predictive scores in standard score form with assigned mean and assigned standard deviation.

RAW-SCORE REGRESSION EQUATION

Slightly less convenient to use and yielding exactly the same correlation with the criterion is the "raw-score form" of the regression equation. It can be conveniently derived from the z score form merely by substituting for each z its equivalent in raw-score terms, namely, $(X_i - M_i)/s_i$. Thus, substituting in (Formula 7.1a),

$$\frac{X_0 - M_0}{s_0} = \beta_{01.23\ldots n}\left(\frac{X_1 - M_1}{s_1}\right) + \beta_{02.13\ldots n}\left(\frac{X_2 - M_2}{s_2}\right)$$

$$+ \cdots + \beta_{0n.12\ldots(n-1)}\left(\frac{X_n - M_n}{s_n}\right) \tag{10.5}$$

We now multiply both sides by the standard deviation of the criterion s_0. Each beta is thus multiplied by s_0/s_i, s_i being the standard deviation of the predictor. The resultant weights are called b weights and are written with the same subscripts as the original betas.

At the same time we can:

1. Move $(-M_0)$ to the right-hand side of the equation with sign changed;
2. Collect from each term the constant portion, which is $(-\beta_i M_i s_0/s_i)$; and
3. Call the sum of all the constant terms K.

The equation then becomes

$$\tilde{X}_0 = b_{01.23\ldots n}X_1 + b_{02.13\ldots n}X_2 + \cdots + b_{0n.12\ldots(n-1)}X_n + K \tag{10.6}$$

In this equation, the value of K, which is $[M_0 - s_0\Sigma(\beta_i M_i/s_i)]$, serves to adjust the predicted scores so that their mean is M_0. The standard deviation of $\tilde{X}_0$ is $s_0 R_{0(12\ldots n)}$.

The raw-score regression equation yields predicted scores that are as close as possible to the original criterion scores. It is therefore of interest when the scale used for the criterion needs to be reflected in the predicted scores.

MODIFICATIONS OF THE MULTIPLE CORRELATION TECHNIQUE

For any sample there is a unique set of betas for a group of predictors, yielding a maximum value of the multiple R. However, there are various modifications of the regression weights that often yield a correlation between a weighted score and a criterion that is almost as high as R. Regression weights can often be modified considerably without lowering the correlation appreciably.

One convenient modification is to round the weights so that they become single-digit integers approximately proportional to the regression coefficients. If there is no need to equate the mean of the predictive scores to the criterion mean, the simplest procedure is to divide each beta by the standard deviation of the predictor to which the beta is to be applied, and then choose a set of integers that has a high relationship with these ratios. Since each beta has been divided by the standard deviation of the predictor, the new weights can be applied to raw scores.

Sometimes it is appropriate to eliminate from the predictive equation the variables with negative betas. In theory, a "suppressor" variable with a negative regression weight (already described in Chapter 7) can add considerably to the multiple. When a "suppressor" can logically be anticipated, there may be good reason for using it. However, the slight negative betas that occasionally appear in regression equations without logical explanation probably represent variance pretty well duplicated by other predictors, and these variables might well be eliminated. Also, there is probably more justification for using negative weights with biographical and personality variables than with aptitude tests on which all candidates are expected to perform to capacity.

Generally speaking, as discussed in Chapter 7, the larger the number of variables and the smaller the number of cases, the more "shrinkage" is to be expected. In establishing a regression equation on a particular sample, all errors implicit in the measurement are used in the calculation of the line of best fit. Consequently, the regression line fits better in the sample than would be expected in the population. With two or three predictors, all of which are highly reliable, the shrinkage may not be serious. The shrinkage becomes large when relatively unreliable data, such as item information, are used. In this case the error in the various intercorrelations is compounded.

IMPROVEMENT OF PREDICTION FROM A MULTIPLE REGRESSION EQUATION

In addition to developing predictors that measure more of the criterion variance, there are three ways to improve the validity of regression equations. The first is to improve the reliability of the predictor variables. As the reliability of these variables is increased, their intercorrelations tend to become stable, and stable intercorrelations improve the stability of the regression equation. The second principle is to use large samples in establishing the regression equation. Here again the direct effect is on the stability of zero-order r's. Reliability of constituent variables remaining the same, the reliability of a composite is increased as the number of observations grows larger. The third principle involves the number of predictor variables. As their number increases, there is more chance for the capitalization on chance error. Hence it is a good general plan to use as few variables as possible, consistent with reaching a multiple R somewhat close to the maximum validity. In the typical situation in applied psychology, little is generally gained from using more than five or six predictors. These may be selected by the modification of the Wherry-Doolittle technique described in Chapter 7.

While the amount of "shrinkage" in a multiple can be anticipated, personnel psychologists have generally found that there is no substitute for "cross-validation," that is, trying out in a completely new sample any multiple regression technique developed in an observed sample. Only when a technique involving maximization holds up repeatedly on new samples does it become worthy of confidence. With multiple R it is all too easy to maximize a relationship within a sample without being aware of the degree to which there has been capitalization of error.

MULTIPLE CUT-OFF

In prediction with a number of variables, the use of multiple cut-offs instead of multiple correlation is occasionally advocated. In practical situations, multiple cut-offs are often used, as when candidates for a police force are acceptable only when they fall within specified limits of age, height, and weight, and meet specified requirements as to physical condition and residence. A conviction for a felony or even a misdemeanor may be disqualifying for police work. Cut-offs such as these are generally established administratively rather than by validation. The theory of multiple cut-off is that deficiency in one characteristic cannot be compensated for by excellence in another.

Multiple correlation and a series of multiple cut-offs used to select the same number of individuals from the same parent sample would ordinarily select somewhat differently. However, if both procedures were based on empirical validities, the overlap would be great. In practice, a series of multiple cut-offs has seldom, if ever, been demonstrated to predict better than multiple R. The multiple cut-off procedure would probably work better than multiple R with a number of predictors related to the criterion in curvilinear fashion.

SUMMARY

Psychological prediction involves two steps:

1. Determination of a relationship within an observed sample; and
2. Application of knowledge of this relationship to new cases.

Obviously, unless the sample is representative of a wider population and unless the relationship is stable from sample to sample, prediction is ineffective.

A predictive system can be expressed as a graph ("expectancy chart"), as a scatter diagram, or as a mathematical function. In psychological statistics the function is most often a straight line, as in a regression equation.

Predictions of mean scores ("group predictions") are numerically more accurate than predictions of scores for individuals. The main difference, however, is in the way results are summarized.

When an investigator attempts to predict a continuous criterion exactly, psychological methods appear to involve a large proportion of error. In real-life situations, prediction of a criterion in broad categories is ordinarily sufficient. Here, even low correlations are useful.

The utility of a relationship is to be judged not only by the numerical size of the correlation, but also by the way the criterion is categorized and by the critical point used in selection.

The numerical size of the correlation coefficient changes greatly with variation in the "range of talent" without affecting the efficiency of the observed relationship in making predictions.

EXERCISES

1. Using the data of Table 6.4, develop an expectancy chart showing the prediction of reading rate from reading comprehension. One way of doing this would be to find the percentage of cases with reading rate scores of, say, 56 or more, for each of the following groups on the reading comprehension test: 70–99, 100–129, 130–159, 160–189, and 190–219.

2. Again using the data of Table 6.4, try out the usefulness of Formula 10.2 for correction for restriction of range. Using only cases with X scores of 140 or more, find r_{xy}, the correlation in the range restricted on the predictor variable. Using this correlation and the variance of X in both restricted and unrestricted range, compare R_{xy} as estimated with the computed r_{xy} of .63.

3. A dichotomous criterion is met by 40 percent of a group of 100 cases. The ϕ coefficient between a dichotomous predictor, with 60 percent in the upper category, and the criterion is .50.
   (a) Construct the diagram showing this relationship.
   (b) For another group of 100 cases with similar divisions into upper and lower categories, construct the diagram for $\phi = .00$.

4. Prior to the introduction of a systematic selection program in a certain company, the proportion of salesmen considered successul was .45. A testing battery with a validity of .25 was introduced, using a selection ratio of .35. From the Taylor-Russell tables (3) or from Table 10.7, estimate the proportion of selected individuals who would be successful if the criterion remains unchanged.

5. A criterion variable has a standard deviation of 12. The correlation between the predictor and the criterion is .60. What is the expected standard deviation of the differences between predicted scores and actual criterion values?

6. Given the following regression equation:

$$\tilde{z}_0 = .20z_1 + .39z_2 + .19z_3 + .04z_4$$

and means and standard deviations as follows:

VARIABLE	M	$S.D.$
X_0	3	1
X_1	8	2
X_2	50	8
X_3	550	120
X_4	500	100

develop the regression equation in raw-score form.

7. Prepare a diagram to illustrate the difference between selection by a single, weighted combination of two predictors (as in multiple correlation) and the use of two separate cutting scores for the same two predictors. On a hypothetical bivariate distribution indicate which cases selected by one technique would be rejected by the other, and vice versa, overall selection rate being the same for the two methods.

8. When the intercorrelations of three variables in a restricted range are known together with the variances of variable 2 in the restricted range (v_2) and the unrestricted range (V_2), a Pearson formula (2) for the correlation between variables 0 and 1 in the unrestricted range may be written as

$$R_{01} = \frac{v_2 r_{01} + r_{02} r_{12}(V_2 - v_2)}{\sqrt{v_2 + r_{02}{}^2 (V_2 - v_2)} \sqrt{v_2 + r_{12}{}^2(V_2 - v_2)}}$$

If the intercorrelations of the three variables in a restricted range are all .40 and if $v_2 = 100$ and $v_2 = 140$, what is the estimate of R_{01}?

REFERENCES

1. DUBOIS, P. H. (ED.), *The Classification Program.* Report No. 2, AAF Aviation Psychology Program Research Reports. Washington, D.C.: U.S. Government Printing Office, 1947.
2. PEARSON, K., "Mathematical contributions to the theory of evolution, XI. On the influence of natural selection on the variability and correlation of organs." London: *Philos. Trans. Roy. Soc.*, **200A**, 1903.
3. TAYLOR, H. C., AND RUSSELL, J. T., "The relationship of validity coefficients to the practical effectiveness of tests in selection: discussion and tables," *J. Appl. Psychol.*, 1939, **23**, 565–578.
4. WORCHEL, PHILIP, AND DALLENBACH, K. M., "Vestibular sensitivity in the deaf," *Am. J. Psychol.*, 1950, **63**, 161–175.

PROBABILITY
AND THE
NORMAL CURVE

11

THE NATURE OF THEORETICAL DISTRIBUTIONS

SIMPLE PROBABILITY

The chief function of a theoretical distribution is to evaluate an event (that is to say, a finding or an observation) in terms of its probable rarity, determined on the basis of a set of stated conditions.

Under a group of hypotheses or conditions, one may deduce a list of all possible events in a given domain, together with their relative frequency, on the basis of chance alone. It then becomes possible, for each actual event in the domain, to find its probable frequency (within a more or less arbitrary total number) or its probability, stated as a proportion of 1.000.

As a simple example, take a die. A die has six faces, with values from 1 to 6. An appropriate hypothetical condition would be that each face is equally likely to fall uppermost. We can then say with regard to an actual event, such as a 5 falling uppermost, that its probable frequency is 1 out of 6; or out of a large number of throws, one-sixth of them can be expected to be 5. The probability of throwing a 5 on any given cast can be stated as .1667.

Usually the probability of a single event in a series of discrete events is of little interest. In the case of the throw of a die, for example, we are more likely to be interested in the probability of throwing a 5 or higher than in the probability of throwing a 5. Accordingly, we should add to the probability of throwing a 5 (namely, .1667) the probability of throwing a 6, since 6 is the only higher value. The probability of throwing either a 5 or a 6 is 2/6 of all the possibilities, each of which is taken as equally likely to occur. Accordingly, the probability of throwing a 5 or higher, with one die and with a single throw, is .3333.

For a die with a different number on each face, the probability for each of the six faces is exactly the same. Consider a somewhat different situation: a die with one face with a value of 1; two faces, each with a value of 2; two faces, each with a value of 3; and one face with a value of 4. The probabilities on any single throw are now:

DIE FACE	PROBABILITY
1	.1667
2	.3333
3	.3333
4	.1667

Because of greater numbers of 2's and 3's than 1's or 4's, the distribution is no longer composed of equal theoretical frequencies, but is humped in the middle. With theoretical N's of 100 and 300, the following distributions are expected:

VALUE	THEORETICAL FREQUENCIES ($N = 100$)	THEORETICAL FREQUENCIES ($N = 300$)
4	17	50
3	33	100
2	33	100
1	17	50

The frequencies for $N = 100$ have been rounded to the nearest whole number but, except for the decimal point, these frequencies correspond to probabilities that add up to 1.0000. For convenience, theoretical frequencies usually add to 100, or to 1000, or to 10,000, while probabilities add to unity. It is readily seen that the basic principle is the same, even in the case of the column in which the theoretical frequencies sum to 300.

Probabilities provide numerical values that reflect the degree of truth of certain statements. When the probability of an event is .00, it is certainly untrue that the event will occur. When the probability of an event is 1.00, it is certainly true that the event will occur. Thus, with a single toss of a die with faces valued from 1 to 6, inclusive, the probability of throwing a 7 or greater is .00, and the probability of throwing some number greater than 0 and less than 7 is 1.00.

COMPOUND PROBABILITY

Consider two independent events such that the occurrence of one has no effect on the occurrence of the other. Let each event be such that either it occurs or does not occur. Let probability of one event occurring be p_1 and the probability of its nonoccurrence be q_1. Similarly, with the second event, let the probability of its occurrence be p_2 and the probability of its nonoccurrence be q_2. It is understood that in both cases $(p + q) = 1.00$, that is, each event is certain either to occur or not to occur. The probabilities of the first event occurring or not occurring can be represented as

$$p_1 + q_1 = 1.00 \qquad (11.1)$$

and of the second event

$$p_2 + q_2 = 1.00 \qquad (11.2)$$

The joint probabilities, as will shortly appear appropriate, may be found by multiplying Eq. 11.1 by Eq. 11.2. Thus,

$$(p_1 + q_1)(p_2 + q_2) = p_1 p_2 + p_1 q_2 + p_2 q_1 + q_1 q_2 \qquad (11.3)$$

It is now seen that, with two independent events, the probability of both occurring is the product of their separate probabilities, $p_1 p_2$. The probability of the first event occurring without the second is $p_1 q_2$ and of the second without the first is $p_2 q_1$. Finally, the simultaneous probability of neither occurring is $q_1 q_2$.

Suppose p_1, the probability of the first event, is .4, and p_2, the probability of the second event is .7. Accordingly, $q_1 = .6$ and $q_2 = .3$. Substitution of these values in Formula 11.3 yields a joint distribution, based on compound probability.

$$p_1 p_2 = .4 \times .7 = .28$$

$$p_1 q_2 = .4 \times .3 = .12$$

$$p_2 q_1 = .7 \times .6 = .42$$

$$q_1 q_2 = .6 \times .3 = .18$$

TOTAL 1.00

All probabilities of occurrence and nonoccurrence add to 1.00, and various fractions of 1.00 are allotted to the four different possibilities.

The same procedure can be applied to developing the theoretical distribution for a true-false test of two items. Let us state, as a basic condition under which the distribution is developed, that success on each item comes entirely by chance, and that for item 1, $p_1 = .5$ and $q_1 = .5$; and also for item 2, $p_2 = .5$ and $q_2 = .5$. Applying Formula 11.3 again, we have

$$p_1 p_2 = .5 \times .5 = .25$$

$$p_1 q_2 = .5 \times .5 = .25$$

$$p_2 q_1 = .5 \times .5 = .25$$

$$q_1 q_2 = .5 \times .5 = .25$$

It now appears that $p_1 p_2$ represents the probability of attaining a score of 2, entirely by chance. Similarly, $p_1 q_2$ and $p_2 q_1$ represent the probabilities of attaining a score of 1. Since, in scoring psychological tests, we generally do not preserve the information as to the specific items answered correctly, these two categories can be consolidated. The final term, $q_1 q_2$, is the probability of failure on both items. Accordingly, the probabilities are

SCORE	PROBABILITY
2	.25
1	.50
0	.25

This is a theoretical distribution. To be sure, it is of limited value for testing hypotheses, but an important principle has been demonstrated; namely, that by the principles of mathematical probability we can find a distribution expected when, within a certain framework, only chance is operating.

TESTING A HYPOTHESIS WITH A CHANCE DISTRIBUTION

We shall now develop a chance distribution and then use it to test a hypothesis.

Consider a psychological test of six items, each with five choices. If a large group of subjects answers the six items entirely by chance, with no knowledge whatever of the subject matter, with each choice of each item equally likely to be chosen but with only one answer recorded for each item, what would be the distribution of the scores?

This question can be answered by the use of $(p + q)$ raised to the sixth power, since there are six independent events: the six items. This is in contrast with the case just described with two independent events. Since there are five choices here, only one of which is correct, the probability of success on any one item is 1/5, or .20. Accordingly, on any item, the probability of failure (denoted as q) is .80. We could, if we wished, keep the p with their subscripts (such as p_1 and p_2) distinct as we multiplied repeatedly by $(p_i + q_i)$. But it is simpler to raise $(p + q)$ to the sixth power, using the exponent of p, which in successive terms is 6, 5, and so on down to zero, to indicate the number of coinciding successes. From each term the probability of the score corresponding to the exponent can then be calculated.

We can expand $(p + q)^6$ by the conventional binomial expansion. When $(p + q)$ is expanded to the nth power, there are $(n + 1)$ terms. In successive terms, exponents of p decrease from n to 0; and the exponents of q increase from 0 to n. (In elementary algebra it is noted that any quantity except 0 raised to the zero power is 1. When terms include p^0 or q^0, there is no need to write p^0 or q^0 explicitly. Accordingly, the first term is written as p^n and the last term as q^n.)

The $(n + 1)$ coefficients are the combinations of n things, 0, 1 $\cdots$ n at a time, a series that is identical and symmetrical with the combinations of n things n, $(n - 1)$ $\cdots$ 0 at a time. The combination of n things r at a time, which can be written $\binom{n}{r}$ is always $n(n - 1)(n - 2)$ to r terms, divided by $1 \cdot 2 \cdot 3$ to r terms. This product of r successive integers beginning with 1 is factorial r (written as $r!$), while $n(n - 1)(n - 2)$ to r terms is equal to $n!/(n - r)!$ Hence $\binom{n}{r}$ is $n!/(n - r)! \, r!$ Factorial 0 (or 0!) is 1 (as is factorial 1).

Accordingly, $\binom{n}{0}$ is $n!/n!$, or 1, as is $\binom{n}{n}$, so that the coefficient of the first term and the coefficient of the last term are both 1 (and need not be written explicitly).

By the above principles,

$$(p + q)^6 = p^6 + 6p^5q + 15p^4q^2 + 20p^3q^3 + 15p^2q^4 + 6pq^5 + q^6 \quad (11.4)$$

Formula 11.4 yields the probabilities for six independent conditions. Substitution of .20 for p and .80 for q results in the theoretical distribution of scores when there are six independent items with a likelihood of .20 of success on each item. The distribution is as follows:

SCORE	PROBABILITY	
6	$(.20)^6 =$	.000064
5	$6(.20)^5(.80) =$	.001536
4	$15(.20)^4(.80)^2 =$	.015360
3	$20(.20)^3(.80)^3 =$	.081920
2	$15(.20)^2(.80)^4 =$	.245760
1	$6(.20)(.80)^5 =$	.393216
0	$(.80)^6 =$	.262144
	TOTAL	1.000000

Again the probabilities sum to unity. The most common chance scores are 0, 1, and 2, with 1 having the greatest frequency. Chance scores of 3 occur about 8 percent of the time, while chance scores of 4, 5, and 6 are relatively rare.

Suppose a classroom test consists of six items, all of the five-choice type. Suppose also that a member of the class has a score of 5. We assume that the test has been so well constructed that anyone who knew nothing of the subject matter would obtain a chance score. From the table it can be noted that the probability of attaining a score of 5 is .001536 and of attaining a score of 6 is .000064.

The hypothesis set up is, "The score of this student is the result of chance, not knowledge." In testing the hypothesis, it seems appropriate to lump together the probabilities of the attained score and any higher score or scores. It thus appears that there are only 16 chances in 10,000 of a score of 5 or 6 occurring purely by chance ($p = .0016$). Accordingly, it is reasonable to conclude that the student's score of 5 is not a chance happening.

By multiplying by N, probabilities can be translated into expected frequencies. If the probabilities of the preceding distribution are multiplied by 1000 and rounded to the nearest whole number, the following theoretical frequencies (f_e) are obtained:

SCORE	f_e
6	0
5	2
4	15
3	82
2	246
1	393
0	262
TOTAL	$1000 = N$

The sum of the expected frequencies is supposed to be N. However, because of rounding error, integral expected frequencies may not sum precisely to N. For example, if N in the preceding example were 500 instead of 1000, Σf_e would be 501. Also, the expected frequency of 0 for a score of 6 is not precisely 0, but rather a very small number.

THE NORMAL PROBABILITY CURVE

The binomial expansion, as exemplified in raising $(p + q)$ to the nth power, is related to the normal probability curve, which has widespread applications in statistics and which is useful in that in many (but not all) types of psychological measurement the following characteristics are observed:

1. Scores or measurements tend to cluster close to the mean, with small deviations more numerous than large deviations.

2. The distribution of measurements tends to be symmetrical.

3. The greater the distance from the mean, the rarer the score. Beyond certain limits above and below the mean, scores almost never occur.

To facilitate deductions from a collection of observed data, a mathematical model of such a distribution is needed. When the observations are such that the mathematical model is applicable, then properties of the mathematical curve can be taken as properties of the parent population represented by the observed sample.

If a phenomenon is caused by a large number of factors, each of them equally influential and each equally likely to be present or absent, the distribution of the resultant variable can be represented by the binomial expansion $(p + q)^n$ when $p = q$. However, if n is large, the successive terms of $[n!/(n - r!)r!]p^{n-r}q^r$, representing frequencies of successive values, become burdensome to evaluate. Tables for this "point binomial" distribution curve would also be too extensive to publish.

The normal curve is a close approximation to the binomial. In effect, it is generated by taking p equal to q, expanding without limit, and evaluating the formula for any term through the use of an approximation for factorials developed by Stirling in the eighteenth century. In this expansion of $(p + q)^n$, both p and q are .5 and n approaches infinity. The curve was originally discovered by DeMoivre, rediscovered by Gauss and by Laplace, and applied to anthropometric variables by Quetelet and Galton. The formula for the curve gives its height or ordinate at any point on the base line, or abscissa, representing the values of the variable.

FORMULAS FOR THE NORMAL PROBABILITY FUNCTION

The formula, the development of which is beyond the scope of this text, can be written[1] as

$$y = \frac{Ne^{-\frac{(X - \mu_x)^2}{2\sigma_x^2}}}{\sigma_x\sqrt{2\pi}} \tag{11.5}$$

The variable is denoted as X, with mean represented by μ_x, and standard deviation by σ_x. The total number of cases is N. Two mathematical constants appear in the formula, π (the ratio of the diameter of a circle to its circumference, approximately 3.14159) and e, important in calculus and the base of the natural system of logarithms, approximately 2.71828.

The formula can be simplified by the following steps:

1. N can be taken as 1. Thus, areas under the curve will be in proportions of N and will be more convenient with which to work.

---

[1] The standard deviation in Formula 11.5 is a parameter and is written as σ_x rather than s_x. Similarly, the mean is indicated by μ rather than by M.

2. The variable can be measured in z scores with mean of zero and standard deviation of unity. Thus σ_x will drop out in front of the radical and the exponent of e will become $-z^2/2$.
3. $\sqrt{2\pi}$ can be evaluated numerically as approximately 2.50662. When divided into unity, this yields .39894 as the numerator of the formula.
4. The negative exponent of e can be eliminated by moving the expression involving e to the denominator.

The formula now becomes

$$y = \frac{.39894}{e^{z^2/2}} \qquad (11.5a)$$

in which y is the height of the normal curve when the frequencies are expressed in proportions of N and when values of the variable are in z scores.

PROPERTIES OF THE NORMAL CURVE

By examining Formula 11.5a, certain properties of the normal curve can be deduced:

1. The ordinate of the curve at the mean of the distribution is .39894. This follows from the fact that any number (other than 0) raised to the zero power is 1. At the mean, z is 0, and the denominator is e^0 or $(2.71828)^0$, which is 1. Accordingly, y, the height of the curve, is .39894.
2. The highest part of the curve is at the mean, where z equals zero. As z increases from its minimum, $e^{z^2/2}$ also increases and y decreases.
3. The curve is symmetrical. Since z is squared, the ordinate will be exactly the same for positive and negative values of z.
4. Since the highest part of the curve is at the mean, the mode and the mean coincide. Since the curve is symmetrical, the median and the mean coincide. Hence, three measures of central tendency are identical.
5. With large values of z, y approaches zero. Mathematically, y never reaches zero; however, y becomes so small that, for practical purposes, it is negligible. As will be shown later, only a small proportion of the cases fall outside the limits of ± 3.00 standard deviations; that is, below a z of -3.00 and above a z of $+3.00$.

By the methods of the calculus (equating the second derivative of the formula to zero), it can be ascertained that the inflection of the curve changes at points exactly one standard deviation above the mean and exactly one standard deviation below it.

As indicated by this statement and as shown explicitly in Formula 11.5 (and implicitly in Formula 11.5a), the standard deviation helps to "define the normal curve." The converse is not true. The normal curve is not needed in the definition of the standard deviation. Irrespective of the shape of the distribution, the standard deviation is a meaningful concept. However, when one knows that a distribution is normal, or approximately so, knowledge of its mean and standard deviation permits numerous deductions about specific parts of the distribution. The closer an obtained curve approximates the normal distribution, the more valid the deductions.

DEVELOPMENT OF A TABLE OF THE NORMAL CURVE

Since the probability functions of greatest interest in statistics are awkward to evaluate, they are most conveniently used in the form of tables. Example 11.1 illustrates the development of tables of the normal curve by reasonably effective (but not necessarily the most accurate nor the most elegant) methods.

The first part of the example shows how values of the ordinate are found from Formula 11.5a and a table of natural logarithms, similar to Table E (Appendix) but more detailed.

EXAMPLE 11.1

Development of Tables of the Normal Curve. In this example, the development of tables of the normal curve is shown in four steps:

1. The computation of values of the ordinate from $z = .00$ to $z = 3.00$ by the use of Formula 11.5a. The work is shown in Table 11.1, and the values are those of Table O in the appendix.
2. Plotting these values as Figure 11.1, which shows one-half of a normal curve.

TABLE 11.1. COMPUTATION OF VALUES OF y FROM $z = .00$ TO $z = 3.00$.

z	$z^2/2$	ANTILOG$_e$ OF $z^2/2$	ORDINATE (y)
.00	.00	1.00000	.39894
.20	.02	1.02020	.39104
.40	.08	1.08329	.36827
.60	.18	1.19722	.33322
.80	.32	1.37713	.28969
1.00	.50	1.64872	.24197
1.20	.72	2.05443	.19419
1.40	.98	2.66446	.14973
1.60	1.28	3.59664	.11092
1.80	1.62	5.05309	.07895
2.00	2.00	7.38906	.05399
2.20	2.42	11.24586	.03547
2.40	2.88	17.81427	.02239
2.60	3.38	29.37077	.01358
2.80	3.92	50.40044	.00792
3.00	4.50	90.01713	.00443

3. Counting the units between successive pairs of z values, and cumulating these counts.
4. Determining the proportions of the total area of the curve which lie between the mean and the particular z value. These proportions, shown in the final column of Table 11.2, are, in effect, the values of Table A in the Appendix.

In Table 11.1 the first column gives z, the deviation on either side of the mean in standard deviation units. Ordinates are computed at intervals of a fifth of a standard deviation (whereas in Table O, in the Appendix, ordinates are given at intervals of $.01\sigma$). The second column gives values of the exponent of e in Formula 11.5a, corresponding to the z values. For example, at 1.00 standard deviation from the mean ($z = 1.00$), $z^2/2$ is .50. The numerical value of the denominator is found by using a table of natural logarithms, similar to, but more extensive than, Table E in the Appendix. These logarithms have a base of e, or 2.71828, instead of common logarithms with a base of 10. Since any exponent of e is the natural logarithm of some number, $e^{z^2/2}$ is evaluated by finding the antilogarithm corresponding to $z^2/2$ These numbers are displayed in the third column. It has already been noted how .39894 can be found as the ordinate at the mean. To find other ordinates, .39894 is divided by the appropriate anti-logarithm, yielding the ordinates as shown in the fourth column.

TABLE 11.2. COMPUTATION OF PROPORTIONS OF NORMAL CURVE BETWEEN μ_x AND z (THAT IS, x/σ_x)

LIMITS OF INTERVAL (z VALUES)	UNITS (SQUARES) IN INTERVAL FIG. 11.1	CUMULATIVE NUMBER OF UNITS BETWEEN MEAN AND z	PARTITIONING z VALUE (x/σ_x)	PROPORTION OF TOTAL AREA OF CURVE BETWEEN MEAN AND z
0.00–0.20	159.0	159.0	.20	.080
0.20–0.40	151.5	310.5	.40	.156
0.40–0.60	140.5	451.0	.60	.226
0.60–0.80	124.5	575.5	.80	.289
0.80–1.00	105.5	681.0	1.00	.342
1.00–1.20	86.5	767.5	1.20	.385
1.20–1.40	68.5	836.0	1.40	.420
1.40–1.60	50.5	886.5	1.60	.445
1.60–1.80	38.5	925.0	1.80	.464
1.80–2.00	27.0	952.0	2.00	.478
2.00–2.20	17.5	969.5	2.20	.487
2.20–2.40	11.5	981.0	2.40	.492
2.40–2.60	6.5	987.5	2.60	.496
2.60–2.80	3.5	991.0	2.80	.497
2.80–3.00	2.0	993.0	3.00	.498
Beyond 3.00	3.0	996.0		

In Fig. 11.1 these ordinates are plotted on graph paper. Computations to find the proportions are shown in Table 11.2. First of all on the graph, between pairs of z values, the number of squares is counted or, rather, estimated. Squares that are not intersected by the curve are easy enough to count. In each section, however, there are also several partial squares, which can be summed only approximately. In Table 11.2 the limits of each interval are given in the first column. The approximate number of units (squares) within that interval are shown in the second column. The units are, of course, completely arbitrary, since their number would vary with the type of graph paper and with how the curves were laid out on that particular type of paper. In the third column the units have been cumulated away from the mean. The total number of units, including an estimated three beyond 3.00σ is 996. Since only half of the curve is included, these 996 arbitrary units correspond to one-half of the total N. In order to work with proportions, N is taken as 1; hence, the proportion of the curve above the mean is .500.

By dividing each cumulative number of units by 1992 (twice the number of arbitrary units), the entries for the last column are obtained. These indicate the proportion of total area of the curve between the mean and the partitioning z value shown in the preceding column, and correspond to the entries in Table A in the Appendix.

AREAS UNDER THE NORMAL CURVE

Tables of areas (corresponding to frequencies or proportions of cases) under the normal curve are developed by the use of approximation formulas that, in effect, integrate or sum up proportions between specified partitioning z values. The logic of developing such a table is illustrated by the graphical integration summarized in Table 11.2.

In Fig. 11.1 a series of points has been plotted on cross-section paper, the location of each point in two-dimensional space being determined by its y value (plotted on the ordinate) and its z value (plotted on the abscissa). Corresponding y and z values have been taken from Table 11.1. The points

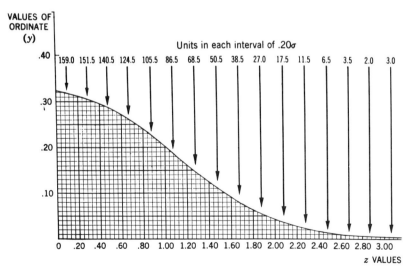

FIG. 11.1. GRAPHICAL INTEGRATION OF THE NORMAL CURVE

have been connected with a smooth curve, constituting nearly one-half of the normal curve, since it extends from the mean to 3.00σ above the mean.

Certain properties of the normal curve, previously noted from its mathematical equation, may be observed from the graph. The maximum height is at the mean where the z value is .00. The curve drops away from the mean with increasing acceleration until the distance of 1.00σ from the mean is reached. Thereafter, in successive units along the base line, the decrease in y value is progressively less. At 3.00 standard deviations from the mean, the curve is very close to the base line, but there is no indication that it will reach it.

There are various tables of the area under the curve, but one useful version is in terms of the proportion of cases falling between the mean and a distance, defined in standard deviation units, away from the mean. An example is Table A in the Appendix. In Figure 11.1 this proportion can be ascertained from the area, measured in squares, under the curve and between two vertical lines, one erected at the mean, the other at the appropriate distance, and divided by the total number of squares under the curve. Computations are shown in Table 11.2.

READING A TABLE OF THE NORMAL CURVE

Although the normal distribution curve can be described as a mathematical function (such as Formula 11.5) or presented in graphical form (as in Fig. 11.1), it is used most frequently in the form of a table.

Tables of the normal curve come in two principal forms: tables of the area (such as Table A, Appendix) and tables of the ordinate or height (such as Table O, Appendix). Details of presentation differ widely,[2] but frequently (as in both Table A and Table O, Appendix) entry is through x/σ_x, the distance in standard deviation units from the mean.

From a table of the area, the proportion of a normally distributed variable between any two limits may be readily found. In Table A the total area of the curve is taken as 1.0000, and for each value of x/σ_x, or z, the table shows the proportion of cases between that value and the mean. Thus, the proportion of cases lying between the point one standard deviation above the mean ($x/\sigma_x = 1.00$) and the mean is .3413.

Table A gives values for only one-half the curve, but since the curve is symmetrical, any area can be easily found. If one limit is below the mean and the other is above, the areas between each limit and the mean are summed. Thus the area between -1.00σ and $+1.00\sigma$ is (.3413 + .3413), or .6826. Any proportion can be converted into a percentage. Accordingly

---

[2] While both Tables A and O (Appendix) have five places of decimals, their use in this chapter and in subsequent chapters assumes that they have been read correct to four places of decimals.

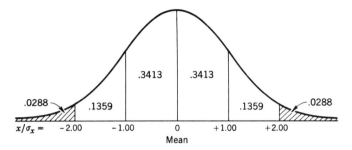

FIG. 11.2. SCHEMATIC REPRESENTATION OF THE AREA OF THE NORMAL CURVE

In this diagram, values of the variable in z form (that is, x/σ) are shown on the x axis, while the y axis represents proportional frequencies. Proportions of N, the total number of cases sum to 1.0000, which is taken as the total area.

it can be found from Table A that if a distribution is normal, 68.26 percent of the cases will fall between the limits of 1σ above and below the mean.

To find the area between two limits on the same side of the mean, it is necessary to find the difference between two proportions. From the proportion of cases between the mean and the limit farther away, we subtract the proportion of cases between the mean and the nearer limit. Thus, to find the area between -2.00σ and -1.00σ, we subtract the area between -1.00σ and the mean (.3413) from the area between the mean and -2.00σ (.4772). In this way it is ascertained that in a normal distribution, the proportion of cases between -1.00σ and -2.00σ is .1359. This finding agrees very well with a similar deduction from Table 11.1A, where the last column yields in abbreviated fashion the same type of information that Table A (Appendix) gives more precisely. For the partitioning z value of 2.00, the proportion of the total area of the curve between the mean and z is given as .478, while for the partitioning z value of 1.00, the proportion is .342. By subtraction, the area between the limits of 1.00σ and 2.00σ (or -1.00σ and -2.00σ) is .136.

SOME APPLICATIONS OF THE NORMAL CURVE

One application of a table of the area of the normal curve is to find the limits of a stated proportion of the normal distribution, either in reference to the mean or to one or both ends of the distribution. Below are some questions, with answers as deduced from Table A (Appendix).

LIMITS ENCLOSING MIDDLE 50 PERCENT OF A NORMAL DISTRIBUTION

One question is: Between what standard deviation limits will be found the middle 50 percent of a normal distribution?

The first step in answering this question from a table that gives only one-half the normal distribution is to find the partitioning value that, with the mean, encloses one-quarter the distribution. From Table A it is seen that .2486 of the distribution lies between the mean and a z value of .67, while .2517 is the proportion between the mean and a z value of .68. By interpolation, a z value can be found that, with the mean, encloses a proportion of .2500 of the distribution. In this instance the difference between the two areas (.0031) corresponds to an increment of $.01\sigma$. The difference between the smaller area .2486 and .2500 is .0014. Accordingly, the more precise partitioning value that, with the mean, encloses a quarter of the distribution is the lower of the two limits, $.67\sigma$, plus $(.0014)/(.0031)$ of $.01\sigma$, which is the difference in the limits. Thus

$$.67\sigma + \frac{.0014}{.0031}(.01\sigma) = .6745\sigma$$

LIMIT BETWEEN 5 AND 95 PERCENT OF A NORMAL DISTRIBUTION

Another question is: In standard deviation units, what is the partitioning value between the lower 95 percent of a normal distribution and the upper 5 percent?

Since the normal distribution is symmetrical, the limit that divides the lower 95 per cent from the upper 5 percent will, with sign reversed, also divide the lower 5 percent from the upper 95 percent. Figure 11.3 illustrates these divisions graphically. These limits are important in the "one-tailed" tests of significance to be described in Chapter 13.

With Table A (Appendix) giving the areas between the mean and the partitioning values (in σ units), it is first of all necessary to find the partitioning value that separates 45 percent of the cases from the upper 5 percent. The other 50 percent of the cases are, of course, below the mean. From Table A it is seen that the proportion of cases between a partitioning value of 1.64σ and the mean is .4495, while the proportion of cases between 1.65σ and the mean is .4505. It is apparent, therefore, that the desired value is between 1.64σ and 1.65σ. A reasonably precise value can be found by interpolation. To 1.64σ is added $.0005/.0010$ of the distance between 1.64σ and the next partitioning value, 1.65σ, or .005. Accordingly, in a normal distribution, 5 percent of the cases lie above $+1.645\sigma$, and 5 percent lie below -1.645σ.

LIMIT BETWEEN 1 AND 99 PERCENT OF A NORMAL DISTRIBUTION

Exactly analogously, the partitioning value between the lower 99 percent and the upper 1 percent of a normal distribution can be found. From Table A it is seen that .4898 of the cases are between the mean and 2.32σ, while .4901 of the cases are between the mean and 2.33σ. The desired value, .4900, is accordingly $.0002/.0003$, or two-thirds the distance between the tabled values of 2.32σ and 2.33σ. Therefore $2.32\sigma + (2/3).01\sigma$, or 2.327σ, can be taken as the dividing line between the lower 99 percent and the

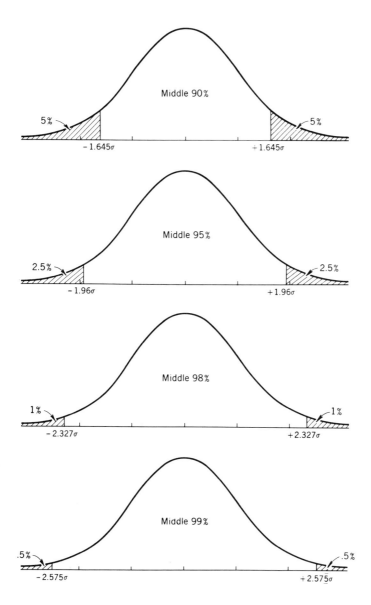

FIG. 11.3. SELECTED DIVISIONS OF THE NORMAL CURVE

upper 1 percent. It also follows that 1 percent of the cases fall below -2.327σ.

LIMITS ENCLOSING MIDDLE 99 PERCENT OF A NORMAL DISTRIBUTION

A pair of symmetrical limits often useful in testing hypotheses are the partitioning values that include the middle 99 percent of a normal distribution. One of these limits will, of course, be above the mean and will be positive in sign; the other will be of the same absolute size, but will have a negative sign. Each of the desired limits will be at a point that, with the mean, includes .495 of the cases.

Table A (Appendix) gives .4949 as the proportion between the mean and 2.57σ, and .4951 as the proportion between the mean and 2.58σ. The desired value is $2.57\sigma + (.0001/.0002).01\sigma$, or 2.575σ. Accordingly, 1 percent of the cases in a normal distribution can be expected to fall outside the limits of -2.575σ and $+2.575\sigma$.

LIMITS ENCLOSING THE MIDDLE 95 PERCENT

The value that encloses the middle 95 percent of a normal distribution can be read directly from Table A without interpolation. Since .0250 of the cases will be above this limit, .4750 will lie between the limit and the mean. Table A gives this partitioning value as 1.96σ. Accordingly, 95 percent of the cases are between -1.96σ and $+1.96\sigma$.

Later it will be noted that certain important statistical functions are normally distributed, and in Chapter 13 it will be seen how specified partitioning values in z form, dividing the normal curve into two segments, can be used in testing hypotheses.

USE OF A TABLE OF ORDINATES

Table O (Appendix) of the height of the ordinate at stated x/σ_x or z values is not as useful in educational and psychological research as Table A. It could be used to find y in Formula 9.22 for biserial r. However, the information in Table P is arranged more conveniently for this purpose.

INFERENCES ABOUT DISTRIBUTIONS WHEN NORMALITY IS ASSUMED

If a distribution is normal, knowledge of three constants—N (the total number of cases), the mean, and the standard deviation—permits inference as to the number of cases between any two values or between a single value and either end of the distribution. If N is unknown, similar inferences can be made, but only in terms of proportions or percentages.

If a proportion of the total distribution is stated, together with one limit (which may be one end of the distribution), the other limit may be found.

No observed distribution is ever perfectly normal, but in many cases an empirical distribution can be taken as representing a normal population. If a distribution departs considerably from normality, inferences on the basis of normal curve properties may still be useful, but of course the greater the departure from normality, the less valid the inferences are likely to be.

Another limitation in applying the mathematically continuous normal curve to psychological data is that many observed psychological variables are effectively discrete. An I.Q., for example, may be either 117 or 118; it is never recorded at an intermediate value. This results in slightly less valid inferences than might be the case with truly continuous variables.

The problems below can all be solved with information in Table A.

PREDICTION OF NUMBER OF CASES BELOW A STATED CUT-OFF POINT

On a certain mechanical aptitude test, the mean is 15.4 and the standard deviation is 4.6. On the assumptions that the variable is normally distributed and that future applicants for employment will show the same M and s, below what cut-off point can 85 percent of the applicants be expected to fall?

Solution: The first requirement is to find the value of x/σ_x that is the partitioning value between the lower 85 percent and the upper 15 percent of a normal distribution. It will be the point that separates .3500 of the cases from the mean. From Table A, we have:

PARTITIONING VALUE	AREA TO MEAN
1.03σ	.3485
1.04σ	.3508

By interpolation, the partitioning value corresponding to an area of .3500 is $1.03\sigma + (.0015/.0023)(.010\sigma) = 1.037\sigma$. In the empirical distribution, the point $1.037s$ above the mean would be expected to be $15.4 + (1.037)(4.6)$, or 20.2. Accordingly, one would expect approximately 85 percent of the scores to be 20 or less and 15 percent of the scores to be 21 or more.

PREDICTION OF NUMBER OF CASES BETWEEN STATED LIMITS

If intelligence is normally distributed and if an intelligence test is standardized so that the mean I.Q. is 100, with a standard deviation of 14.83, how many children in 1000 would be expected to have I.Q.'s of 130 to 134, inclusive?

Solution: With integral I.Q.'s, the appropriate partitioning values are 129.5 and 134.5. In σ units these partitioning values are $(129.5 - 100)/14.83$ and $(134.5 - 100)/14.83$, or 1.99σ and 2.33σ. These values are found by applying the usual formula for a z score, $z = (X - M_x)/s_x$. From Table A it is seen that .4767 of a normal distribution lies between the mean and 1.99σ and .4901 between the mean and 2.33σ. Subtracting .4767 from .4901 yields .0134 as the proportion between the stated limits. Accordingly, 13 children in 1000 could be expected to have I.Q.'s of 130 through 134.

STANDARD SCORES WITH PREDETERMINED CHARACTERISTICS

In reporting the results of a civil service examination, a system of standard scores is to be used. A mean and standard deviation (M' and s') are to be assigned such that, on the assumption of normality, 10 percent of the converted scores will be 70 or below and 2 percent will be 98 or above. Find M' and s'.

Solution: Information about an observed mean and standard deviation is not required, since the problem relates to the normal curve generally. By interpolating in Table A it is inferred that .4800 of a normal curve lies between the mean and the partitioning value of $+2.0540\sigma$, while .4000 lies between the mean and -1.2817σ. Accordingly, 2 percent of the cases can be expected to be above $+2.0540\sigma$ and 10 percent below -1.2817σ. The 28 specified standard-score units (70 to 98) correspond to a range of $(2.0540 + 1.2817)\sigma$, or 3.3357σ. Dividing 28 by 3.3357 yields 8.39 as the s' to be assigned as the standard deviation of the standard scores. Since M' is to be 1.2817σ above 70, M' is $70 + (1.2817 \times 8.39)$, or 80.75.

DETERMINATION OF SCALE VALUES OF ITEMS

On an attitude test, percentages of subjects agree with statements A through G as follows: A, 87; B, 68; C, 45; D, 55; E, 30; F, 5; and G, 15. What are plausible scale values of these statements?

Solution: On the assumption that each item is a measure of a normally distributed characteristic for which only dichotomous information (agree-disagree) is available the s distance from the mean to the point of dichotomy may be taken as the working scale value. Such values may be adjusted by changing the reference point from the mean to an arbitrary origin. Computations are shown as a table below.

STATE-MENT	PERCENT AGREEING	AREA BETWEEN POINT OF DICHOTOMY AND MEAN	DIRECTION OF POINT OF DICHOTOMY FROM MEAN	s VALUE	ADJUSTED s VALUE
A	87	.3700	Above	1.13	2.83
B	68	.1800	Above	.47	2.17
C	45	.0500	Below	−.13	1.57
D	55	.0500	Above	.13	1.83
E	30	.2000	Below	−.52	1.18
F	5	.4500	Below	−1.64	.06
G	15	.3500	Below	−1.04	.66

The area between the point of dichotomy and the mean is found by converting the percent agreeing with the statement to a proportion and subtracting .5000. A negative value indicates that the dichotomy is below the mean. From Table A (Appendix), values in standard deviation units are then read directly.

To make all scale values positive, any convenient constant may be added to the obtained s values. In the last column of the table here, 1.70 has been added to the s values of the preceding column. These final values probably represent relative popularity (or difficulty in the case of test items) somewhat more adequately than do the original percentages, although, of course, there is no change in order.

THE PROBABLE ERROR AND THE STANDARD DEVIATION

One of the major applications of the normal curve is in connection with errors of observation or measurement, which are often found to be normally distributed. Accordingly, it is appropriate that when Q (half the distance between the 75th percentile and the 25th percentile, as described in Chapter 4) is applied to a normal distribution, it is called the *probable error*.[3] It has already been found that 25 percent of the cases lie between the mean and $.6745\sigma$. Accordingly, in a normal curve, P_{25} (or -1P.E.) is at $-.6745\sigma$ and P_{75} (or $+1$P.E.) is at $+.6745\sigma$. From Table A the relationships in the following table can be worked out:

PARTITIONING VALUES		PROPORTION OF TOTAL AREA ENCLOSED
P.E. UNITS	σ UNITS	
± 1.0000P.E.	$\pm\ .6745\sigma$	.5000
± 2.0000P.E.	$\pm 1.3490\sigma$	.8226
± 3.0000P.E.	$\pm 2.0235\sigma$	.9570
± 4.0000P.E.	$\pm 2.6980\sigma$	.9930
± 1.4826P.E.	$\pm 1.0000\sigma$	.6826
± 2.9652P.E.	$\pm 2.0000\sigma$	.9544
± 4.4478P.E.	$\pm 3.0000\sigma$	.9973

NONNORMALITY IN DISTRIBUTIONS: ASYMMETRY, OR SKEWNESS

Many obtained distributions of psychological and educational variables deviate from the normal; very frequently by being skew, or asymmetrical, as shown in Fig. 11.4. If the items of a test are very easy, high total scores will be more numerous than low scores, and the distribution will be negatively skewed and the tail at the low end of the distribution will be elongated. On the other hand, if the test is composed of very difficult items, low scores will be common, high scores will be relatively rare, and the

---

[3] Abbreviated either P.E. or PE.

distribution will show positive skewness, that is, the long, thin tail will extend toward the high side of the distribution.

There are other reasons for skewness. In some cases, the true distribution of a human characteristic, such as weight, may be skewed rather than symmetrical. In other cases, units of measurement that yield equal numerical differences may not represent equal differences in the character-istic. If the units at one end of the scale are systematically larger or smaller than the units at the other, the resultant distribution will be skewed, even if the underlying trait is normally distributed.

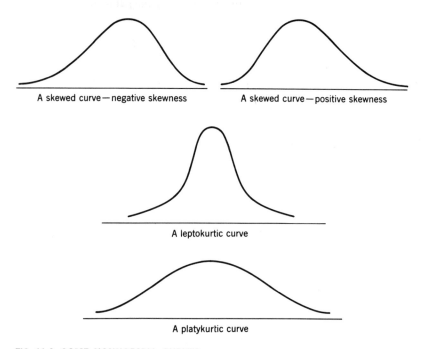

A skewed curve — negative skewness   A skewed curve — positive skewness

A leptokurtic curve

A platykurtic curve

FIG. 11.4. SOME NONNORMAL CURVES

Another cause of skewness is selection of a sample on the basis of a correlated variable. Suppose, for example, all 10-year old children in a school system with I.Q.'s of 115 or more were given a reading test. The intelligence distribution would certainly be asymmetrical because it would be the upper portion of a more or less normal distribution. It is virtually certain that the scores on a well-made reading test administered to this group would also be positively skewed, although not as much as the I.Q.'s. On the other hand, a variable uncorrelated with intelligence, such as pitch discrimination, might show a normal distribution even in this highly selected group.

FORMULAS REFLECTING SKEWNESS

The simplest procedure for the detection of skewness is direct inspection of the tabulated frequencies. However, several formulas exist for obtaining a coefficient reflecting the degree of skewness. The common feature of these formulas is that negative coefficients indicate prolongation of the distribution toward the low values and concentration of scores at the high end of the scale, while coefficients carrying the plus sign indicate the reverse. The coefficients computed by the different formulas are not comparable, and with one exception, they are difficult or impossible to evaluate statistically. The logical bases of the formulas, however, help to clarify the concept of skewness.

In a normal distribution, mean, median, and mode coincide. An abundance of extreme scores at one end of the distribution lowers or raises the mean, but in general does not affect the other two measures. Therefore, if the mean is less than the median (or mode), the distribution is negatively skewed, whereas if it is greater, the skew is positive. One of the earliest measures was developed by Karl Pearson:

$$Sk = \frac{\text{mean} - \text{mode}}{s} \qquad (11.6)$$

which is simply the difference between the two measures in standard deviation units. However, the mode envisaged by the formula is not the familiar crude mode (the score of greatest frequency, or some function of the step with largest numbers of cases), but rather a statistic estimated as three times the median less twice the mean. The following formula involves the median (or 50th percentile) and is merely Formula 11.6 revised in accordance with the procedure for estimating the mode.

$$Sk = \frac{3(\text{mean} - P_{50})}{s} \qquad (11.6a)$$

The next measure also capitalizes on the difference between a measure that tends not to be affected by skew (again the median) and a measure likely to be affected, the mean of two percentiles, P_{10} and P_{90}. Although $(P_{10} + P_{90})/2$ is a "point measure," its behavior resembles that of the mean in that it may change when a substantial proportion of the values at one end of the distribution are not symmetrical with a similar proportion at the other end. The formula is

$$Sk = \frac{(P_{10} + P_{90})}{2} - P_{50} \qquad (11.7)$$

The next statistic takes into account all the values in the distribution. It is generally noted as g_1, and is simply the mean of the cubes of all the values in z form:

$$g_1 = \frac{\Sigma z^3}{N} \tag{11.8}$$

MOMENTS ABOUT THE MEAN IN TESTING SKEWNESS

Formula 11.8 sometimes is written in terms of the moments about the mean, which may be denoted as m_1, m_2, m_3, m_4, and so on. The first moment is the mean of the deviations from the mean and is, of course, always 0:

$$m_1 = \frac{\Sigma x}{N} = 0$$

The second moment is the mean of the squares of the deviations from the mean, and is the sample variance:

$$m_2 = \frac{\Sigma x^2}{N} = V_x = s_x{}^2$$

Similarly, the third moment about the mean is the mean of the cubes of the deviations; the fourth moment, the mean of the fourth powers; the fifth moment, the mean of the fifth powers; and so on.

It is readily seen that in a perfectly symmetrical distribution (including a normal distribution), all odd-numbered moments are zero. The first moment is not affected by the shape of the distribution, and for statistical purposes, moments beyond the fourth are seldom used. Consequently, a measure of skewness is built on the third moment, $\Sigma x^3/N$.

Because of the "weight" of the values in a long tail, any distribution with positive skewness will have a positive third moment, while a distribution skewed toward the lower limit will have a negative third moment. However, the absolute magnitude of the third moment, as is the absolute magnitude of a variance, is a function of the units of measurement. By dividing the third moment by the cube of the standard deviation, a statistic, g_1, is obtained that is independent of these units; it is, in fact, the mean of the cubes of the z scores.

A computing formula in terms of the sum of deviations, the sum of squares of deviations, and the sum of third powers of deviations, all in terms of step intervals from an arbitrary origin, is given as:

$$g_1 = \frac{m_3}{m_2\sqrt{m_2}} = \frac{\Sigma z^3}{N} = \frac{N^2\Sigma x'^3 - 3N\Sigma x'^2\Sigma x' + 2(\Sigma x')^3}{[N\Sigma x'^2 - (\Sigma x')^2]^{3/2}} \tag{11.8a}$$

As are the measures of skewness involving percentiles, obtained values of this coefficient are difficult to evaluate because the expected distribution of the statistic based on successive samples of N cases each, drawn at random from an unlimited normal population, is unknown. To remedy this difficulty, Fisher has suggested a modified g_1, with known sampling distribution, as follows:

$$g'_1 = \frac{\Sigma z^3}{N} \sqrt{\frac{N(N-1)}{(N-2)^2}} \tag{11.8b}$$

Standard errors and their applications are to be treated in Chapter 13. The standard error of the g'_1 of Formula 11.8b is

$$\sigma_{g'_1} = \sqrt{\frac{6N(N-1)}{(N-2)(N+1)(N+3)}} \tag{11.9}$$

This is the expected standard deviation of a large distribution of g'_1, each computed from a random sample of N cases drawn from a normal population.

The use of Formulas 11.8a and 11.8b in testing skewness is illustrated in Example 11.2.

EXAMPLE 11.2

USE OF HIGHER MOMENTS IN TESTING FOR SKEWNESS AND KURTOSIS

Inspection of the distribution of the scores of 1016 high school seniors on a test shows that it is reasonably symmetrical, with neither skewness nor kurtosis apparent. Nevertheless, tests for these characteristics may be applied.

Skewness. For finding g_1 (defined as $m_3/m_2^{3/2} = m_3/s_x^3 = \Sigma z^3/N$), the first, second, and third moments around the mean or around an arbitrary origin are necessary. Formula 11.8a is written in terms of x', but either x or X can be substituted without other change, since the formula applies to:

1. Sums of powers of x, the deviations in original units from the mean (in which case all terms involving Σx would be zero);
2. Sums of powers of x', the deviations in step-interval units from an arbitrary origin; and
3. Sums of powers of X, or raw scores (that is, deviations in original units from zero).

In the numerical example (Table 11.3), frequencies are multiplied by corresponding d (deviations in terms of step intervals) or powers of d to form $\Sigma x'$, $\Sigma x'^2$ and $\Sigma x'^3$. These values, together with N, are then substituted in Formula 11.8a to find g_1, which is $+.056$, showing a very slight tendency to positive skewness.

To find Fisher's g'_1, the value of $\Sigma z^3/N$ (which happens to be $+.056$) is multiplied by $\sqrt{N(N-1)/(N-2)^2}$, which in this case is 1.0015. The N is so large that the correction is negligible and g_1 is unchanged. By Formula 11.9, the standard error of g'_1 is .077.

TABLE 11.3. TESTING FOR SKEWNESS AND KURTOSIS

(Scores of 1016 High School Seniors on a Reading Test)

STEPS	f	d	d^2	d^3	d^4
33–35	3	5	25	125	625
30–32	14	4	16	64	256
27–29	38	3	9	27	81
24–26	129	2	4	8	16
21–23	191	1	1	1	1
18–20	233	0	0	0	0
15–17	215	−1	1	−1	1
12–14	128	−2	4	−8	16
9–11	52	−3	9	−27	81
6–8	10	−4	16	--64	256
3–5	3	−5	25	−125	625

$N = 1016$

Computations

$$\Sigma x' = \Sigma df = -48$$
$$\Sigma x'^2 = \Sigma d^2 f = 2778$$
$$\Sigma x'^3 = \Sigma d^3 f = -138$$
$$\Sigma x'^4 = \Sigma d^4 f = 21{,}702$$

By Formula 11.8a,

$$g_1 = \frac{\Sigma z^3}{N} = \frac{N^2 \Sigma x'^3 - 3N \Sigma x'^2 \Sigma x' + 2(\Sigma x')^3}{[N \Sigma x'^2 - (\Sigma x')^2]^{3/2}}$$

$$= \frac{(1016)^2(-138) - 3(1016)(2778)(-48) + 2(-48)^3}{[(1016)(2778) - (-48)^2]^{3/2}}$$

$$= \frac{263{,}760{,}000}{(2{,}820{,}144)(1679.328)} = +.056$$

By Formulas 11.10 and 11.11,

$$g_2 = \frac{\Sigma z^4}{N} - 3 = \frac{N^3 \Sigma x'^4 - 4N^2 \Sigma x'^3 \Sigma x' + 6N \Sigma x'^2 (\Sigma x')^2 - 3(\Sigma x')^4}{[N \Sigma x'^2 - (\Sigma x')^2]^2} - 3$$

$$= \frac{22{,}772{,}102{,}968{,}320}{7{,}953{,}212{,}180{,}736} - 3 = 2.863 - 3.000 = -.137$$

It has already been noted that the middle 95 percent of the cases of a normal distribution lie between the limits of -1.96σ and $+1.96\sigma$. The standard error of g'_1 can be taken as an estimate of the standard deviation of an indefinitely large number of g'_1, each computed from a sample of 1016 cases drawn randomly from an indefinitely large, normally distributed population. Therefore, 5 percent of these g'_1 could be expected to exceed $\pm 1.96 \times .077$; that is, they would be outside the limits of $-.151$ and $+.151$. Since the obtained g'_1 ($+.056$) is well inside these limits, the value is such that it would ordinarily be accepted as deviating from .000 only by chance. Hence the distribution can be regarded as showing no significant degree of skewness.

Kurtosis. To test the peakedness, or *kurtosis*, of a distribution, we first find the sum of the fourth powers of the z scores by means of Formula 11.11 which, like the formula for $\Sigma z^3/N$, is applicable to sums of powers of deviations from the mean, or to deviations in step-interval units from an arbitrary origin, or to raw scores. The numerical example yields: $\Sigma x'$, $\Sigma x'^2$, $\Sigma x'^3$, and $\Sigma x'^4$.

In a perfectly normal distribution, $\Sigma z^4/N$ has a value of 3.00. Accordingly, 3.00 is subtracted from $\Sigma z^4/N$ to find g_2, a measure of kurtosis. In the example, $g_2 = \Sigma z^4/N - 3.00 = 2.863 - 3.000 = -.137$, indicating a very slight tendency for the distribution to be flat-topped. However, by Fisher's method of testing the significance of g_2 (as computed by a formula for which the standard error is known), $-.137$ is not significantly different from zero, and as far as this test is concerned, the distribution is normal.

NONNORMALITY IN DISTRIBUTIONS: PEAKEDNESS, OR KURTOSIS

Two symmetrical distributions with identical standard deviations may nevertheless differ considerably in contour. If the distribution has a high peak, with long tails going out in either direction, it is called *leptokurtic*, but if the distribution is relatively flat-topped, with stubby tails, it is called *platykurtic*. Examples are shown graphically in Fig. 11.4. Intermediate between the leptokurtic and the platykurtic distribution is the *mesokurtic*, exemplified by the normal curve.

The use of adjectives to describe the relative shapes of obtained symmetrical distributions is undoubtedly helpful, although the common terms *peaked* and *flat-topped* are probably just as useful as the fancier words derived from the Greek. Nonsymmetrical distributions also differ in peakedness, and some method of measuring this characteristic is desirable.

It can be demonstrated mathematically that the mean of the fourth powers of the z scores of a perfectly normal distribution is 3.00. It is also generally true that distributions with considerable peakedness tend to have values of $\Sigma z^4/N$ greater than 3.00 (because of the high values of the fourth powers of the values out in the long tails), and that distributions of the same variance, but flatter than normal, tend to have values of $\Sigma z^4/N$ less than 3.00. Accordingly, g_2, as an indication of peakedness, may be defined as

$$g_2 = \frac{m_4}{m_2^2} - 3 = \frac{\Sigma z^4}{N} - 3 \qquad (11.10)$$

With notation identical to that used in Formula 11.8a and with $\Sigma x'^4$ indicating the sum of the fourth powers of deviations in terms of step intervals from an arbitrary origin, a computing formula for $\Sigma z^4/N$ is

$$\frac{\Sigma z^4}{N} = \frac{N^3 \Sigma x'^4 - 4N^2 \Sigma x'^3 \Sigma x' + 6N\Sigma x'^2(\Sigma x')^2 - 3(\Sigma x')^4}{[N\Sigma x'^2 - (\Sigma x')^2]^2} \qquad (11.11)$$

In Formula 11.10 the fourth moment, m_4, has been divided by the square of the second moment, m_2, to eliminate the effect of the units of measurement. It can be shown that m_4/m_2^2 is precisely the mean of the fourth powers of the z scores.

Fisher (1) has proposed a modification of g_2, a modification with a known sampling distribution, to which the interested reader is referred. There is also a "measure of kurtosis" based on percentiles. However, the utility of all these coefficients as measures of the degree of one type of departure from normality has been questioned by mathematical statisticians. However, the use of adjectives to describe "peakedness," with Formula 11.10 to indicate the direction of the variation from normality, may be useful occasionally. Such a use is demonstrated in Example 11.2.

TESTING A DISTRIBUTION FOR NORMALITY WITH CHI SQUARE

When frequencies are distributed in categories, it is possible to generate a set of theoretical frequencies, with identical total N, distributed in the same categories in accordance with some principle. Whether or not the difference between the two sets of frequencies can be accounted for by sampling variation can be tested by chi square, already described in Chapter 3.

Chi square affords a method of testing the agreement between any observed grouping of frequencies and the way the same total number of frequencies would be distributed in accordance with some hypothesis (in the present instance, the normal curve).

Actually, the curve with which the observed distribution is compared is not precisely the continuous normal curve as generated mathematically, but rather is a distribution in discrete steps (much like a histogram) that closely approximates the normal curve. This theoretical distribution has the same N, mean, and standard deviation as the observed distribution, and in practice, the difference between this theoretical distribution and the true normal curve is of no importance.

Computational details are shown in Example 11.3. Briefly the method involves:

1. Determining the mean and standard deviation of the observed frequency distribution.

2. Developing the theoretical distribution, the one that would obtain if the hypothesis of a normal curve were true. The theoretical distribution must have N, M, and s identical with the observed distribution, and the step frequencies must be such that they yield the closest possible approximation to the normal curve.

3. There is a further requirement that no f_e (the frequency expected in a category) be less than 5. When one or more f_e as computed are less than 5, categories in the theoretical distribution must be consolidated to obtain f_e of 5 or more. Corresponding categories in the obtained distribution are also consolidated. This requirement is sometimes relaxed when the number of categories (and hence the number of df) is large.

4. Chi square is computed by finding the differences between frequencies in corresponding categories (one from each distribution), squaring these differences, dividing each square by its f_e, and summing the quotients. This is Formula 3.1, $\chi^2 = \Sigma(f_0 - f_e)^2/f_e$. In Example 11.3 an algebraic variant of this formula is employed, but the value of χ^2 is exactly the same.

5. As is always the case, the evaluation of a computed value of χ^2 requires knowledge of the degrees of freedom (df), since a chi square table is in effect a series of curves, one for $1df$, another for $2df$, a third for $3df$, and so on, until df becomes large. By entering a chi square table (Table C, Appendix) by means of df and the numerical value of χ^2, P may be determined. P is the probability of obtaining a χ^2 as large as the one observed simply by chance.

EXAMPLE 11.3

TESTING A DISTRIBUTION FOR NORMALITY WITH CHI SQUARE

In the numerical example in Table 11.4 the first column gives the working step limits, with the true lower limit or partition value one-half unit below the stated lower limit of each step. Thus the true lower limit of the top step is 32.5.

TABLE 11.4 CALCULATION OF THE CHI–SQUARE TEST OF "GOODNESS OF FIT"

(Scores of 1016 High School Seniors on a Reading Test)

(1)	(2)	(3)	(4) AREA TO	(5)	(6)	(7)	(8)
STEPS	f_0	x/s_x	MEAN	p_e	f_e	$f_0{}^2$	$f_0{}^2/f_e$
33–35	3 ⎫ 17	2.75	.497	.003	3.05 ⎫ 16.26	289	17.77
30–32	14 ⎭	2.15	.484	.013	13.21 ⎭		
27–29	38	1.54	.438	.046	46.74	1,444	30.89
24–26	129	.94	.326	.112	113.79	16,641	146.24
21–23	191	.33	.129	.197	200.15	36,481	182.27
18–20	233	−.27	−.106	.235	238.76	54,289	227.38
15–17	215	−.88	−.311	.205	208.28	46,225	221.96
12–14	128	−1.48	−.431	.120	121.92	16,384	134.38
9–11	52	−2.09	−.482	.051	51.82	2,704	52.18
6–8	10 ⎫ 13	−2.69	−.496	.014	14.22 ⎫ 18.28	169	9.25
3–5	3 ⎭	−3.30	−.500	.004	4.06 ⎭		

$$\Sigma f_e = 1016.00 \qquad \Sigma(f_0{}^2/f_e) = 1022.12$$

Computations

$N = 1016$

$M_x = 18.86 \qquad \chi^2 = \Sigma\frac{(f_0 - f_e)^2}{f_e} = \Sigma\frac{f_0{}^2}{f_e} - N = 1022.12 - 1016 = 6.12$

$s_x = 4.96 \qquad df = n' - 3 = 6$

$\qquad\qquad .50 > P > .30$

The second column gives the observed frequency (f_o) of each step.

The third column shows the true lower limit as a deviation from the mean, divided by the standard deviation of the distribution; that is, $(X_1 - M_x)/s_x = x_1/s_x$. Using this information with a table of area of the normal curve, such as Table A (Appendix), the entries of column 4 are found: the proportion of a normal curve between the lower step limit and the mean. For example, when Table A is entered with x/s_x of 2.75, it is found that .497 of a normal distribution lies between this limit and the mean. It follows that $.500 - .497$, or a p_e (expected proportion) of .003 would be anticipated in the top step; $(.497 - .484)$, or a p_e of .013 in the second step; $(.484 - .438)$, or .046 in the third step, and so on. For steps for which x/s_x is negative, the area has been denoted with a minus sign to show that the determination of the expected proportion of cases on any step is algebraic; that is, for the step that includes the mean, $p_e = .129 - (-.106) = .235$, and for the step below, $p_e = -.106 - (-.311) = .205$.

Entry in the sixth column, (f_e), the frequency expected in the step on the hypothesis of a normal distribution, is determined by multiplying the corresponding p_e by N; in this case, 1016.

In this example, two f_e's are less than 5. Accordingly, f_e's in the steps at the end are combined with f_e's in adjacent steps; and f_o's in corresponding steps in column 2 are similarly combined.

Chi square may be readily found by the following formula:

$$\chi^2 = \sum \frac{(f_o - f_e)^2}{f_e} \qquad (3.1)$$

This requires that the difference be found between each f_o and corresponding f_e, that this difference be squared, and then divided by the f_e. The sum of all these quotients is χ^2.

A slightly more convenient way to find chi square is by the formula

$$\chi^2 = \sum \frac{f_o^2}{f_e} - N \qquad (3.3)$$

In column 7 of Table 11.4 are the squares of the observed frequencies. When each square is divided by the corresponding f_e, the result is the quotient in column 8. The sum of these quotients less N is χ^2.

Instructions booklets for most desk calculators give a procedure for summing quotients when a series of divisions is performed.

In developing the normal distribution in column 6, it was made so that the number of cases, the mean, and the standard deviation would be identical with those of the observed distribution. This reduced the df for the chi-square test from 9 (n', or the number of categories) by 3 (the number of imposed restrictions) to 6.

For six degrees of freedom, the P value of a χ^2 of 6.12, is between .50 and .30. (A more exact P may be found, if desired, by interpolation.) Since with $6df$, a χ^2 of 6.12 is expected by chance between 30 and 50 percent of the time, the hypothesis of a normally distributed population remains tenable.

INTERPRETATION OF CHI SQUARE

If the population is distributed according to some hypothesis (in this case the hypothesis of normality), then a long series of samples might include one or more samples yielding a χ^2 of .00 (indicating no difference at all between the sample and the theoretical distribution). In general, however, the χ^2 will be greater than zero, and the chi-square distribution for the given degrees of freedom can be used to infer the theoretical rarity of any obtained chi square.

When P is .05 or less, the hypothesis of no difference between the obtained distribution and a normal distribution is disproved at the 5 percent level of confidence. In this case, there is only 1 chance in 20 (or less) that a chi square as large as the one obtained could have been found if the sample were drawn at random from a normally distributed population.

In Example 11.3, P is between .30 and .50; hence, by conventional standards, normality has not been disproved. The distribution can be said to be compatible with the hypothesis that the characteristic is distributed normally in the population that the sample represents.

NORMALIZING A DISTRIBUTION

When an empirical distribution is normalized, a conversion system is developed such that the distribution of converted scores is as close as possible to a normal distribution. Since no linear conversion will change the shape of a distribution, the usual procedure is to establish partitioning values in the form of percentiles, such that the frequencies in the categories so formed will approximate a normal curve.

As an example, consider the problem of assigning five letter grades, A, B, C, D, and E, so that a distribution approximately normal results. One possibility would be to have one standard deviation as the width of each of the five intervals, since from Table A (Appendix) it is seen that the limits $\pm 2.5\sigma$ include 98.76 percent of a normal distribution. The few cases lying outside these limits can be placed in the A and E categories without much distortion from approximate normality.

From Table A it is found that the mean and the limit of $.5\sigma$ enclose .1915 of the area of a normal curve, while the mean and 1.5σ enclose .4332 of the area. From these figures the desired proportion of the total distribution for each letter grade category is readily found, as shown in the accompanying table.

CATEGORY	LIMITS	PROPORTION	HOW OBTAINED
A	$+1.5\sigma$ and above	.0668	.5000 − .4332
B	$+.5\sigma$ to $+1.5\sigma$	.2417	.4332 − .1915
C	$-.5\sigma$ to $+.5\sigma$	.3830	.1915 + .1915
D	-1.5σ to $-.5\sigma$	.2417	.4332 − .1915
E	Below -1.5σ	.0668	.5000 − .4332

By cumulating the proportions upward and changing decimal points, the following percentiles (rounded to whole numbers) are found as partitioning values:

	PARTITIONING PERCENTILE
Between A and B . . .	P_{93}
Between B and C . . .	P_{69}
Between C and D . . .	P_{31}
Between D and E . . .	P_{7}

When a continuous or nearly continuous variable is divided into five groups by means of these partitioning percentiles, the resultant five-category variable is reasonably close to normal.

THE C SCALE AND THE STANINE SCALE

Example 11.4 demonstrates a procedure to divide an obtained distribution into 11 categories yielding a close approximation to the normal curve, the so-called C scale. Here the original distribution appears to be somewhat skewed negatively, whereas the converted distribution seems definitely closer to normal. However, when N is low, when values are discontinuous and limited in range, and when the frequencies are fitted into relatively few categories, the resultant distribution can be expected to be only approximately normal.

A variant of the C scale is the stanine scale ("standard nine") originally used by Army Air Force psychologists in World War II. In Example 11.5 the C distribution is converted into a stanine distribution by consolidating the frequencies in steps 9 and 10 as 9's and the frequencies in steps 0 and 1 as 1's.

Stanines deviate from the normal a little more than do C scores, since the tails of the stanine distribution are blunt. As single-digit scores, however, they are easy to handle, both in routine reporting and in statistical analyses. Because a single digit is often sufficient to indicate individual differences, stanines are often used as test norms.

EXAMPLE 11.4

NORMALIZING AN OBTAINED DISTRIBUTION

To convert an observed distribution into something approximating a normal distribution, it is first necessary to choose a basis for the normalization. This example is chiefly concerned with the C scale—a distribution of 11 steps extending from 0 to 10, with a mean of 5. With the exception of the step at either end of the distribution, each step has a width of $.5\sigma$.

Table 11.5 shows the development of the partitioning percentiles, which are general and applicable to any distribution for which C-score equivalents are desired. Only the pN in the final column are specific to the distribution normalized in Table 11.6.

TABLE 11.5. DEVELOPMENT OF A C SCALE ($N=256$)

(1)	(2)	(3)	(4)	(5)	(6)	(7)	(8)
LOWER LIMIT x/σ_x	AREA FROM x/σ_x TO MEAN	C SCORE	COMPUTATION OF PROPOR- TION IN STEP	PROPOR- TION IN STEP	CUMU- LATIVE PROPOR- TION IN STEP	PARTI- TIONING PERCEN- TILE (LOWER LIMIT)	pN AT PERCEN- TILE
2.25	.4878	10	.5000 — .4878	.0122	1.0000	$P_{98.78}$	252.88
1.75	.4599	9	.4878 — .4599	.0279	.9878	$P_{95.99}$	245.73
1.25	.3944	8	.4599 — .3944	.0655	.9599	$P_{89.44}$	228.97
.75	.2734	7	.3944 — .2734	.1210	.8944	$P_{77.34}$	197.99
.25	.0987	6	.2734 — .0987	.1747	.7734	$P_{59.87}$	153.27
— .25	.0987	5	.0987 + .0987	.1974	.5987	$P_{40.13}$	102.73
— .75	.2734	4	.2734 — .0987	.1747	.4013	$P_{22.66}$	58.01
—1.25	.3944	3	.3944 — .2734	.1210	.2266	$P_{10.56}$	27.03
—1.75	.4599	2	.4599 — .3944	.0655	.1056	$P_{4.01}$	10.27
—2.25	.4878	1	.4878 — .4599	.0279	.0401	$P_{1.22}$	3.12
		0	.5000 — .4878	.0122	.0122		

TABLE 11.6. COMPUTATION OF PARTITIONING PERCENTILES AND REDISTRIBUTION
(Scores of 256 applicants on a police aptitude test)

OBTAINED DISTRIBUTION		PARTITIONING	NORMALIZED SCORES				
				C SCORE DISTRIBUTION		STANINE DISTRIBUTION	
STEPS	f	PERCENTILES	STEPS	C SCORE	f	STANINE	f
76–79	2		75 or more	10	2		
72–75	8	$P_{98.78} = 74.9$	72–74	9	8	9	10
68–71	11	$P_{95.99} = 71.4$	67–71	8	20	8	20
64–67	25	$P_{89.44} = 66.5$	62–66	7	28	7	28
60–63	30	$P_{77.34} = 61.9$	56–61	6	45	6	45
56–59	27	$P_{59.87} = 55.5$	50–55	5	47	5	47
52–55	33		44–49	4	47	4	47
48–51	34	$P_{40.13} = 49.4$	35–43	3	30	3	30
44–47	27		27–34	2	20	2	20
40–43	15	$P_{22.66} = 43.2$	21–26	1	5	1	9
36–39	12		20 or below	0	4		
32–35	18	$P_{10.56} = 34.4$					
28–31	3						
24–27	3	$P_{4.01} = 26.5$					
20–23	6	$P_{1.22} = 20.3$					
16–19	1						
12–15	1						

Examples of Computation of Percentiles

$(pN = 3.12)$: $P_{1.22} = 19.5 + \dfrac{1.12}{6} \times 4 = 20.3$

$(pN = 10.27)$: $P_{4.01} = 23.5 + \dfrac{2.27}{3} \times 4 = 26.5$

Column 1 of Table 11.5 gives the partitioning z scores (x/σ_x) at the lower limit of each step. Corresponding areas of the normal curve to the mean (from Table A, Appendix) are shown in column 2. C scores are given in column 3. The proportion of the distribution to be allotted to each step is indicated in column 5, and the computations to obtain the required proportions are shown in column 4. Except for the C score of 5, where the areas on either side of the mean are added, the proportion in each step involves subtraction of one area from another. In the case of the two end steps, .5000 represents the area in one-half the curve.

In column 6 the proportion of cases in each step has been cumulated. These figures, each multiplied by 100, give the required partitioning percentiles at the top of the step. In column 7 are shown the partitioning percentiles at the lower limit of the step. The pN of column 8 are found by multiplying the cumulative proportion at the bottom of the step by N, which is 256. These figures are useful in finding the ten needed percentiles by the method described in Chapter 4.

In Table 11.6 two examples of finding numerical values for partitioning percentiles are given. In each case the required percentile is the lower limit of the step containing the percentile plus a fraction of the step interval, which in this case is 4. The fraction is pN less the number of scores below the step, divided by the step frequency.

The frequencies in the C score distribution cannot be found from the distribution at the left of Table 11.6 because the frequencies there are grouped in categories. They were obtained by distributing the original scores in the C steps, which vary considerably in interval. As examples, scores of 72, 73, and 74 are converted to 9; scores of 35 through 43, inclusive, are converted to 3. Thus it is seen that the transformation is not accomplished by a linear equation, but rather by sorting the original scores into categories that yield a modified distribution.

The C-score distribution is not perfectly normal, since it lacks complete symmetry and tends to be flat-topped. Deviations from normality can, however, be explained as resulting from chance.

The stanine distribution is obtained from the C-score distribution by combining the two categories at either end of the C scale.

THE CENTRAL LIMIT THEOREM

An important principle for inferring characteristics of the population from properties of samples is the *central limit theorem*. As sample size increases, many statistics, including the mean, the standard deviation, and the variance, have a distribution that becomes more and more normal, and this may be true even though the underlying variable is not normally distributed in the population. A requirement for the theorem is that the underlying variable have finite mean and variance, but this is generally true of variables of interest in psychology.

The distribution of a statistic is, of course, the tabulation that would be expected if the statistic were repeatedly computed on a long series of random samples of identical size, each representing the same population. When such a distribution is normal, it is adequately described by its standard deviation, and knowledge of such standard deviation (that is, the "standard error" of the statistic) facilitates deductions about the population, as will be discussed further in Chapter 13.

Here, in connection with chance error, are the most important implications of the normal curve. The fact that the error in the estimation of a parameter may be distributed normally and with known variance facilitates the use of statistical methods as tools in the development of dependable knowledge.

SUMMARY

Of the theoretical distributions developed from probability theory and of interest in statistics, the so-called normal distribution has the widest range of applications. This distribution curve is symmetrical about its mean, with cases becoming rarer as departure from the mean becomes greater. It has points of inflection one S.D. above and below the mean and varies in either direction without limit.

Many empirical variables appear to be distributed normally. Procedures exist to determine whether an observed distribution differs from the normal in skewness and kurtosis. By means of the chi-square test of goodness of fit, it is possible to decide whether an obtained distribution differs significantly from normality or whether the hypothesis of a normal distribution remains tenable. When a variable can be regarded as normally distributed, the use of a table of the normal distribution makes various deductions possible.

The fact that many statistics are normally distributed is of great importance in inferring characteristics of the population from observations of specific samples.

EXERCISES

1. Using Formula 11.5a and a table of logarithms to the base e, find y, the ordinate of the normal curve at $z = .50$, $z = 1.50$, and $z = 2.50$. Compare results with values found in Table O (Appendix).

2. In an experiment on generalization, the subjects' task is to arrange four objects in a certain order. What is the probability of a subject's doing the task correctly completely by chance?

3. By interpolation in Table O, determine the height of the ordinate of the normal curve at the following percentiles: P_1, P_5, P_{10}, P_{20}, P_{30}, P_{40}, P_{50}, P_{60}, P_{70},

P_{80}, P_{90}, P_{95}, and P_{99}. Plot the resultant y values on coordinates with appropriate z values on the base line. Does the curve appear to be normal?

4. For the distribution in Example 5.4 compute g'_1, Fisher's measure of skewness, and determine how many standard errors g'_1 is from the value of .00 expected for a sample representing a normal population.

5. Find the partitioning percentiles by which the distribution of Example 5.3 might be converted to stanines.

6. Apply the chi square test of goodness of fit to the distribution of Example 5.4 to determine whether the hypothesis of normal distribution is tenable.

7. Find the partitioning percentiles needed to convert a continuous variable to a seven-category "normal" scale, high values ranging from 1 to 7, centered at 4, and with a band width of $.8\sigma$.

8. A professional school uses as a selection device an aptitude test with $M = 500$ and S.D. $= 100$. It has a quota of 175 entering students and, in the interest of good public relations, wishes to accept any fully qualified student as soon as his aptitude score becomes available.
    Make the following assumptions:
    1. The number of applicants who meet other qualifications and who are permitted to take the aptitude test will be 800;
    2. Any student accepted will enter;
    3. The mean and standard deviation will continue to be 500 and 100, respectively; and
    4. The aptitude test is normally distributed.
    What cutting score can be expected to yield approximately 175 entering students?

REFERENCE

1. FISHER, R. A., *Statistical Methods for Research Workers.* Edinburgh and London: Oliver and Boyd, 1936, p. 339.

FAMILIES
OF CHANCE
DISTRIBUTIONS

12

Of the theoretical frequency curves applicable to statistical problems, the normal distribution has the widest range of applications. Not only do many observed variables appear to be normally distributed, but also, as has already been mentioned, the normal curve is frequently useful in estimating how much variation would be anticipated if a given statistic were to be computed from a number of different samples. Often it appears as the limiting case in a family of closely related theoretical frequency distributions.

The number of theoretical distributions that have been or could be developed on the basis of probability theory is exceedingly large. It is beyond the scope of this text to treat any of them with mathematical rigor. Nevertheless, workers in the fields of psychology, education, and the social sciences frequently need to appreciate certain families of curves and their applications.

The rarity of a particular observation or of a statistic based upon a number of operations can be estimated by finding the place of the empirical information in a model distribution of all the values of the observation or of the statistic possible under a stated hypothesis. If the observed finding appears to be highly unlikely under the model, the hypothesis may require revision or replacement. On the other hand, if observations appear to be in accordance with the hypothesis, it may be allowed to stand, pending further evidence. This chapter is concerned with the description of certain distributions rather than with their use to substantiate or, to some degree, to refute a stated generalization. The matter of testing hypotheses will be considered in Chapter 13.

In a real sense, there is only one normal distribution. Its shape is constant despite variation in the number of cases, in the mean, and in the standard deviation. It is always symmetrical about the mean. It extends in either direction indefinitely, and the points of inflection are exactly one standard deviation above and below the mean.

In contrast, each of the mathematical models described in this chapter yields a family of distribution curves, members of which may differ widely in contour, but which nevertheless are based on a single underlying mathematical function based on probability theory. Because of this underlying function, it is mathematically quite appropriate to speak of the binomial, or the Poisson, or χ^2, or the t or the F distribution. However, one must be aware that each of these distributions takes different forms under different conditions. In the case of the binomial, the shape varies with p (the probability of an event) and n (the number of independent events); and in other cases the shape of the distribution varies with v, the number of degrees of freedom,[1] which is akin to the number of independent events. Since the normal curve can be developed as a special case of the binomial when $p = q$ and when the number of independent events is indefinitely great, it may be no surprise that there are other curves that also approach normality when the number of degrees of freedom become large.

While any distribution function could be utilized in the form of an equation or a graph, the most convenient medium is generally a table. In the case of the normal curve, it will be remembered that entry into a table is usually in terms of the distance in standard deviation units above or below the mean, and the table yields information as to an area or an ordinate of the curve. In the case of a table representing a family of curves, a convenient format provides for entry by means of the degrees of freedom and the value of the statistic. The table then yields information as to the rarity of the observation under defined conditions.

THE BINOMIAL DISTRIBUTION

In connection with the discussion of probability, certain aspects of the binomial expansion were noted in Chapter 11, together with the use of the binomial (when $p = q$) in the development of the normal distribution.

---

[1] The symbol v is the lower case Greek letter "nu," corresponding to n. In this text, v always refers to the number of degrees of freedom.

Here the binomial will be treated somewhat more generally and as the basis for a family of distribution curves. The binomial is a useful model when events are discrete and p (the probability of a single event) can be considered to be a constant for all events.

The $(n + 1)$ terms of the expansion $(p + q)^n$ are the proportions of the $(n + 1)$ possible values of a function, X, which ranges in value from n down to 0, each value being the number of coinciding events. Thus the distribution is discontinuous in that it consists of discrete values.

The proportion of cases within a value of X is given by the formula for any term of the expansion of $(p + q)^n$:

$$p_x = \binom{n}{X} p^X q^{n-X} = \frac{n!}{X!(n-X)!} p^X q^{n-X} \qquad [X = n, (n-1)\cdots 0] \qquad (12.1)$$

This formula may be readily applied to a simple problem. If an albino rat has one chance in five of making a correct discrimination entirely by chance ($p = .20$), what is the probability of exactly four correct discriminations in seven trials? Formula 12.1 becomes

$$p_4 = \binom{7}{4} p^4 q^3 = \frac{7 \times 6 \times 5 \times 4(3 \times 2 \times 1)}{1 \times 2 \times 3 \times 4(1 \times 2 \times 3)} (.2^4)(.8^3) = .028672$$

It should be noted that .029 is the probability of exactly four correct discriminations, not the probability of four or more, which would ordinarily be required for testing a hypothesis about the rat's behavior. The probability of a score of four or more would be the sum of the probabilities of scores of 4, 5, 6, and 7; that is

$$\sum_{X=4}^{X=7} p_x$$

The sum of probabilities of all the values of X from n down to and including 0 is, of course, 1.00. The mean of the values of X is

$$\mu_x = np \qquad (12.2)$$

and the standard deviation is

$$\sigma_x = \sqrt{npq} \qquad (12.3)$$

The variable X can be converted to z form, with mean of 0 and variance of 1, by the usual procedure:

$$z = \frac{X - \mu_x}{\sigma_x} = \frac{X - np}{\sqrt{npq}} \qquad (12.4)$$

Skewness can be tested by a variant of Formula 11.8:

$$g_1 = \frac{\Sigma z^3}{N} = \frac{q - p}{\sqrt{npq}} \tag{12.5}$$

If $q > p$, the distribution is positively skewed, while if $p > q$, the skew is negative. The value of g_1 becomes precisely 0 only in the special case when $p = q$; however, when n is large and p and q not too greatly different, it can be seen that g_1 becomes very small.

Kurtosis can be tested by a variant of Formula 11.10:

$$g_2 = \frac{1 - 6pq}{npq} \tag{12.6}$$

When n is large and neither p or q is very small, g_2 is close to zero, and hence the distribution meets another criterion of normality.

Actually, p and q can differ considerably and still yield a distribution that is essentially normal. If $p < .5$ and $np > 5$, or if $q < .5$ and $nq > 5$, the binomial may be considered normal. Thus the curve produced by the binomial under very different conditions tends to approach normality. However, many of the uses of the binomial in psychological experiments involve cases where the chance distribution is markedly skewed.

Binomial distributions for n of 6, 12, and 24 are shown in Figs. 12.1, 12.1A, 12.1B. On each graph, two distributions are shown: one for $p = .25$ and $q = .75$; the other, for $p = q = .50$. The latter is always symmetrical, whereas the former is markedly skewed for $n = 6$, less so for $n = 12$, and almost symmetrical for $n = 24$. Since $p = .25$ (which is less than .50) and $np = 6$ (which is greater than 5), this last distribution can be considered essentially normal.

APPLICATION OF THE BINOMIAL

An example of the use of the binomial follows: On an achievement test of 100 five-choice items, how high a score would a student have to attain before it could be said that his performance was not "just chance?"

In the use of the binomial in this problem, it is assumed that with a five-choice format, a p of .2 is constant for each item, and that the items are independent in that success on one item has no effect on success on any other.

Actually, any total score from 100 down to 0 could happen "by chance" (that is, without the student having any knowledge of the subject matter), but high scores would be exceedingly improbable. By Formula 12.1 the probability of answering all 100 questions correctly by chance is $(.2)^{100}$, a proportion that is almost infinitesimally small, but which is still not precisely zero. (The probability of a score of zero is mathematically greater, $(.8)^{100}$, but still is practically zero.) In this problem, however, only the high end of the distribution is of concern. A score below what would be expected by chance has little, if any, psychological meaning.

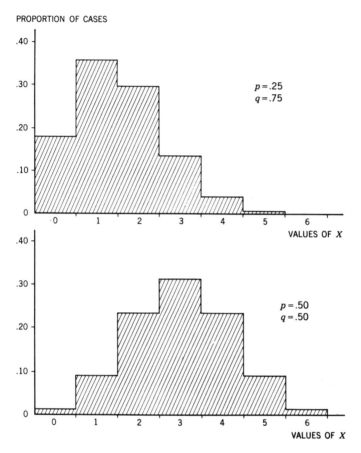

FIG. 12.1. BINOMIAL DISTRIBUTIONS FOR $n = 6$

It is apparent that since any score can occur by chance, some standard must be established for regarding an event as something not happening at hazard. Conventionally, two levels of probability-improbability have been most frequently used, depending on the choice of the investigator: the .01, or 1 percent level; and the .05, or 5 percent level. In this example we arbitrarily choose to regard a score as deviating significantly above chance performance if by hazard it could happen only once in 100 times; that is, it attains the .01 or 1 percent level of significance.

The defined distribution of chance scores, as generated by the binomial, can be taken as normal. With p less than .5, np is 20, which is considerably

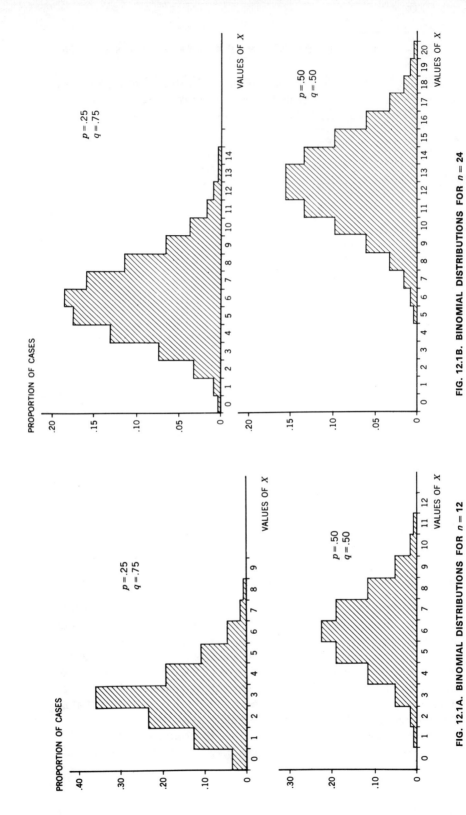

PROPORTION OF CASES

p = .25
q = .75

VALUES OF X

p = .25
q = .75

PROPORTION OF CASES

p = .50
q = .50

VALUES OF X

FIG. 12.1A. BINOMIAL DISTRIBUTIONS FOR n = 12

p = .50
q = .50

VALUES OF X

FIG. 12.1B. BINOMIAL DISTRIBUTIONS FOR n = 24

greater than the 5 that experience has shown as the figure above which the fit of the normal distribution to the binomial is good.

From Table A (Appendix), it is deduced that 1 percent of the scores of a normal distribution lie above 2.323σ above the mean. On the hypothesis of chance performance, μ_x, by Formula 12.2, is 20, and σ_x, by Formula 12.3, is $\sqrt{100 \times .2 \times .8}$, or 4. The value of 2.323σ is therefore 9.3, and the point above which 1 percent of the scores would be expected to fall by chance is $(20 + 9.3)$, or 29.3. Accordingly, a score of 30 would be attained by chance less than once in 100 times.

Of course the mere improbability of a score on the chance hypothesis does not demonstrate that the performance is the result of knowledge of the subject matter. The explanation of the performance must come from sources other than statistical analysis. Also, the description of the proba- bility-improbability of a score does not in itself indicate anything of the degree of any characteristic that the variable may reflect. How much knowledge is represented by a score of 30, or any other score, must be studied by test development methods.

THE POISSON DISTRIBUTION

A chance distribution for which values are relatively easy to find and which is often useful in psychological research is the Poisson, a function described by Poisson in 1837 (7). Although not difficult, its derivation is beyond the scope of this presentation. Like the binomial, the distribution is dis- continuous, comprising discrete variables. Relative frequencies of the variable X, from j down to 0, may be given as

X	f
j	$Ne^{-\alpha}\dfrac{\alpha^j}{j!}$
.	.
.	.
.	.
3	$Ne^{-\alpha}\dfrac{\alpha^3}{3!}$
2	$Ne^{-\alpha}\dfrac{\alpha^2}{2!}$
1	$Ne^{-\alpha}\dfrac{\alpha}{1!}$
0	$Ne^{-\alpha}$

In the preceding values, N is the total number of cases and e is $2.71828\cdots$, the base of the natural or Napierian system of logarithms, a constant of the curve. An important characteristic of the Poisson is that the mean and the variance are equal, and in the expressions for the frequencies given above, either the mean or the variance may be taken as α.

Indicating the mean as μ, the probability of any value of X is

$$p_x = e^{-\mu} \frac{\mu^X}{X!} \qquad (X = 0, 1, 2 \cdots) \tag{12.7}$$

To obtain the frequency, the probability is multiplied by N, as in the algebraic distribution on page 309. The sum of the probabilities is, as usual, 1.000.

From Formula 12.7 it can be noted that the successive terms of this exponential series, beginning with $X = 0$, are, as probabilities:

$$p = e^{-\mu}, \quad e^{-\mu}\mu, \quad e^{-\mu}\frac{\mu^2}{2!}, \quad e^{-\mu}\frac{\mu^3}{3!}, \quad \cdots \tag{12.8}$$

Any term corresponding to X, the value of the variable, can be obtained from its predecessor in the series by multiplying by μ/X. When the mean is known, any number of terms may be readily found. While there is no mathematical limit to the number of terms in the series, characteristically they soon become so small as to be negligible.

Formula 12.2 for the mean of a binomial series, $\mu = np$, applies to the Poisson. Actually, when n is very large and p approaches zero, the Poisson yields good approximations to binomial frequencies. The p_x obtained by Formula 12.7 can be used to estimate p_x by Formula 12.1. The advantage is in ease of computation.

Among other applications, the Poisson has been used in the study of accidents. If accidents are connected with individuals purely by chance, and if there are fewer accidents than people, then the distribution of the frequencies of accidents by individuals can be expected to follow the Poisson. In this case the Poisson can be regarded as a convenient substitute for the binomial, $(p + q)^n$, with n, the number of independent events, considered to be large, and with p, the probability of an accident during any single event (or "exposure"), as very small.

The goodness of fit of an empirical distribution to the Poisson can be tested with χ^2, exactly the way the fit of a set of observed frequencies to the normal distribution is tested. The one difference is in the number of degrees of freedom. As noted in connection with Example 11.3, df in fitting a normal curve is the number of categories less three, one df being lost for N, another for M, and a third for s. Since for a Poisson $\mu = \sigma^2$, only $2df$ are lost, one for N and another for M, which is taken to represent np. The usual restriction with χ^2 holds, namely, that no f_e be less than 5. Any category with an expected frequency less than 5 must be combined with one or more other categories to build up the f_e to 5 or more. Example

12.1 illustrates the process of fitting a Poisson to observed data and testing the goodness of fit by means of χ^2.

EXAMPLE 12.1

TESTING THE FIT OF A POISSON TO AN OBSERVED DISTRIBUTION

From N, ΣX and ΣX^2 of the observed distribution, the mean (.370 in this case) and the variance (.369) are found by regular procedures. The fact that the mean and the variance are practically identical leads one to believe that the Poisson may be taken as the underlying distribution.

TABLE 12.1. TESTING THE FIT OF A POISSON TO AN OBSERVED DISTRIBUTION
Data from O'Gorman and Kunkle (6)

NUMBER OF ACCIDENTS	f_o	p_e	Np_e or f_e	$(f_o - f_e)$	$\dfrac{(f_o - f_e)^2}{f_e}$
3	6	.006	6	0	.000
2	47	.047	45	2	.089
1	242	.256	245	−3	.037
0	662	.691	661	1	.002

$$\Sigma p_e = 1.000$$

Computations

$$N = 957 \qquad \chi^2 = \Sigma \frac{(f_o - f_e)^2}{f_e} = .128$$
$$\Sigma X = 354$$
$$\Sigma X^2 = 484 \qquad df = 2$$
$$M_x = .370$$
$$s_x^2 = .369 \qquad P > .50$$

From a table of e^{-M}, such as Table E (Appendix), the value of $e^{-.370}$ is found to be .691, which, in accordance with Formula 12.7, is the proportion of cases for which the expected value of X is 0. (The value of e^{-M} may also be found, but not quite so conveniently, from any table of natural logarithms. It is the reciprocal of the antilogarithm of M.)

Subsequent proportions are found by multiplying the proportion corresponding to the next lower value of the variable by μ/X, as indicated in Formula 12.8. Thus, p_1 is (.691)(.370), or .256; p_2 is (.256)(.370)/2, or .047; and p_3 is (.047)(.370)/3, or .006. The value of p_4 is (.006)(.370)/4, or less than .001, and subsequent terms in the series are clearly negligible.

Chi square can be computed either as $\Sigma(f_o^2/f_e) - N$ or as $\Sigma(f_o - f_e)^2/f_e$. With a χ^2 of .13 and two degrees of freedom, it is found from Table C (Appendix) that P is greater than .50. Hence the difference between the observed distribution and the Poisson can be regarded as a highly likely chance occurrence, and the Poisson can be considered as an excellent fit to the data.

Of course the fact that the data fit the Poisson does not prove that in this sample, the accidents were actually distributed among people by chance. Rather it shows that the hypothesis of chance distribution is not refuted by the facts.

In those instances in which χ^2 is significant and the Poisson does not fit the data, further investigation would be required to ascertain the cause of the difference, which might be factors within individuals ("accident proneness"), or differential exposure, or even a systematic difference within the criterion itself.

DISTRIBUTIONS OF STATISTICS: χ^2, t, AND F

As already noted, the binomial and Poisson distributions are mathematical models that may be applied to observed frequency data. Not only do some sets of observed measurements take normal form, but also, as will be discussed further in Chapter 13, the expected distributions of certain statistics are normal.

There are three important distributions that apply to statistics rather than to observed measurements: chi square, applicable to squared differences between frequencies; the t distribution, applying to differences between statistics (particularly means); and F, a family of distributions of ratios of variances.

Mathematically, these distributions are interrelated, both with one another and with other theoretical distributions, including the normal. Derivations and mathematical relationships are presented by numerous authors, including Fisher (2), Kendall and Stuart (4), Adams (1), and Lewis (5).

Applications of χ^2 have already been presented in Chapter 3 and in connection with testing the fit of the normal and Poisson distributions to observed data. After discussion of certain general aspects in this chapter, t will be encountered again in Chapter 13 and F in Chapter 14.

THEORETICAL AND EMPIRICAL DISTRIBUTIONS OF χ^2

Applications of χ^2 involve the comparison of frequencies actually obtained (observed frequencies, designated as f_o) with frequencies anticipated under some hypothesis (theoretical or expected frequencies, designated as f_e). As defined by Formula 3.1,

$$\chi^2 = \sum \frac{(f_o - f_e)^2}{f_e} = \sum \frac{f_o^2}{f_e} - N$$

The following characteristics of χ^2 may be noted:

1. For each f_o there is a corresponding f_e.
2. χ^2 is the sum of computations involving pairs of f_o and f_e.
3. Since frequencies are always positive, and since differences between f_o and f_e are squared, each contribution to χ^2 is zero or a positive quantity, and the χ^2 for any set of data is zero or positive.
4. When there is no difference between each f_o and its corresponding f_e, χ^2 is zero. It varies without upper limit.

5. χ^2 is a pure number rather than a number representing units of measurement. The magnitude of a value of χ^2 obtained under defined conditions can be interpreted only in terms of the probability of its occurrence.
6. As χ^2 increases from zero to infinity the probability P of its occurrence decreases from 1.00 to 0.

Actually, chi square is distributed as the sum of the squares of v independent values, in z form, v being the number of degrees of freedom. This would appear reasonable in that each component of χ^2 has a format $(f_o - f_e)^2/f_e$, which resembles the square of a z score with the format of $(X - M_x)^2/s_x^2$. Just as $(X - M_x)$ is the distance above or below the mean value (which might be considered the expected value and which is evaluated in relation to s_x), so $(f_o - f_e)$ is the difference between obtained and expected frequencies, and the square of this difference is evaluated in reference to f_e.

Theoretical tables of χ^2, such as Table C (Appendix), are based on a continuous mathematical function, the formula for which is given in advanced texts, including Lewis (5). The distribution of all possible values of χ^2 that could be found from, say, a 2×2 table with limited N and with fixed marginal frequencies is, of course, discrete, with many values not appearing at all in the distribution. Nevertheless, it is useful to use a theoretical, continuous distribution to evaluate the rarity of an obtained χ^2.

The general nature of the χ^2 family of curves may become clear through the development of a set of empirical curves, using the χ^2 basic principle, as illustrated in Example 12.2. The principle is that the variable defined as the sum of the squares of n uncorrelated z scores is distributed as χ^2 with n degrees of freedom.

For the required z-score values, samples of 100 lines each were selected from a table of the random normal deviate. An adequate sample of the squares of these values would be expected to approximate the χ^2 distribution with $1df$.

Since pairs of these values should be uncorrelated, sums of pairs of squares of these values should be distributed as χ^2 with $2df$. Sums of four squares would be expected to follow the distribution of χ^2 with $4df$, and so on. In Example 12.2 and Table 12.2 the curves derived from entries in a table of the random normal deviate yield good approximations to the corresponding χ^2 curves.

EXAMPLE 12.2

COMPARISON OF THEORETICAL AND OBTAINED χ^2 DISTRIBUTIONS

Using the Rand tables (8), empirical distributions for one, two, four, and six degrees of freedom were developed. In Tables 12.2 and 12.3 they are compared with corresponding distributions obtained from mathematical functions. The particular degrees of freedom were selected for ease in computation and as good examples of χ^2 curves.

TABLE 12.2. COMPARISON OF THEORETICAL AND OBTAINED χ^2 DISTRIBUTIONS FOR 1, 2, 4, AND 6 DEGREES OF FREEDOM

χ^2 Distributions for 1, 2, 4, and 6 Degrees of Freedom

χ^2	$df=1$ p_e	p_o	$df=2$ p_e	p_o	$df=4$ p_e	p_o	$df=6$ p_e	p_o
> 16	...	...	...	...	.001	...	.004	.010
15–15.999	...	...	...	...	.002	...	.007	.020
14–14.999	...	...	...	...	.003	...	.009	.010
13–13.999	...	...	.001	...	.004	...	.013	.020
12–12.999	...	...	.001	...	.006	.010	.019	.000
11–11.999	...	...	.002	...	.009	.010	.026	.000
10–10.999	...	...	.003	...	.014	.010	.036	.070
9–9.999	.001	...	.004	...	.021	.010	.049	.020
8–8.999	.002	.010	.007	.010	.030	.030	.065	.070
7–7.999	.003	.000	.011	.000	.044	.060	.083	.090
6–6.999	.006	.020	.020	.020	.063	.030	.102	.070
5–5.999	.011	.000	.032	.010	.088	.090	.121	.080
4–4.999	.020	.030	.053	.080	.119	.140	.133	.160
3–3.999	.038	.060	.088	.100	.152	.160	.132	.190
2–2.999	.074	.070	.145	.130	.178	.170	.111	.130
1–1.999	.160	.190	.239	.220	.174	.180	.066	.050
0– .999	.683	.620	.393	.420	.090	.100	.014	.010

TABLE 12.3. COMPARISON OF PROPORTIONS OF χ^2 EXPECTED TO EXCEED GIVEN VALUES (P_e) AND PROPORTIONS ACTUALLY OBSERVED TO EXCEED THOSE VALUES BY CHANCE (P_o) FOR 1, 2, 4, AND 6 DEGREES OF FREEDOM[a]

χ^2	$df=1$ P_e	P_o	$df=2$ P_e	P_o	$df=4$ P_e	P_o	$df=6$ P_e	P_o
1	.317	.380	.607	.580	.910	.900	.986	.990
2	.157	.190	.368	.360	.736	.720	.920	.940
3	.083	.120	.223	.230	.558	.550	.809	.810
4	.046	.060	.135	.130	.406	.390	.677	.620
5	.025	.030	.082	.050	.287	.250	.544	.460
6	.014	.030	.050	.040	.199	.160	.423	.380
7	.008	.010	.030	.020	.136	.130	.321	.310
8	.005	.010	.018	.010	.092	.070	.238	.220
9	.003	...	.011	...	.061	.040	.174	.150
10	.002	...	.007	...	.040	.030	.125	.130
11	...	...	.004	...	.027	.020	.088	.060
12	...	...	.002	...	.017	.010	.082	.060
13	...	...	.002	...	.011	...	.043	.060
14	...	...	.001	...	.007	...	.030	.040
15	...	...	.001	...	.005	...	.020	.030
16	...	...	.000	...	.003	...	.014	.010

[a] Data are the same as in Table 12.2.

To avoid bias, the table of random numbers was entered at hazard and the order of first encounter with the digits 1, 2, 4, and 6 were noted. This order was 2–6–4–1. Accordingly, the empirical χ^2 curve for $2df$ was computed first, followed by the curves for $6df$, $4df$, and $1df$.

The table of random digits was entered again and a second line of random digits selected at random. The first random digits of this line were 2–2–7–3, which was taken as the number of the line in the table of random normal deviates at which to begin computations. These "random normal deviates" are, of course, z scores with population mean of zero and population variance of unity. In any subsample drawn from the table, some variation from the theoretical mean and variances is to be expected. The plan called for four sets of synthetic χ^2 values, as follows:

INCLUSIVE ENTRY NUMBERS	z SCORES SQUARED AND SUMMED	χ^2 CURVE APPROXIMATED
2273–2372	First 2 columns	$2df$
2373–2472	First 6 columns	$6df$
2473–2572	First 4 columns	$4df$
2573–2672	First column	$1df$

Examples of the computation of the artificial χ^2's follow:

ENTRY NUMBER	"GAUSSIAN DEVIATES" = z SCORES						$\Sigma z^2 = \chi^2$	df
2273	.747	−.284					.64	2
2274	.491	.517					.51	2
⋮								
2373	.794	−.794	−.979	−.523	−1.906	1.317	7.86	6
2374	−.966	1.051	−.928	−3.293	.871	−.356	14.63	6
⋮								
2473	−.952	−.065	−1.214	−1.369			4.26	4
2474	.219	.486	1.064	−.071			1.42	4
⋮								
2573	−.128						.02	1
2574	.412						.17	1
⋮								

In Table 12.2 the hundred χ^2's for each df: 2, 6, 4 and 1, have been reduced to proportions (p_o) and compared with corresponding p_e found from published tables of complete χ^2 curves. The proportions are always values within indicated limits, so that corresponding graphs are histograms (Fig. 12.2) rather than continuous curves. It is to be noted that the fit of the observed to expected proportions is close.

In Table 12.3 both the p_e and p_o have been cumulated toward 0 to find proportions of χ^2 expected to exceed stated values of χ^2.

Table C in the Appendix, which gives the probability of exceeding tabulated values of χ^2 for specified df, is in effect modification and extension of the type of information presented in Table 12.3. By interpolation, fair approximations of the χ^2 values in the body of Table C can be found. For example, for $6df$, what value of χ^2 is exceeded by 5 percent of obtained χ^2 entirely by chance; that is, what is χ^2 value corresponding to $P = .05$?

From the P_e column for $6df$ in Table 12.3, it is apparent that the required value is between 12 and 13. By interpolation, χ^2 for $P = .05$ is $13 - (.007)/(.039) = 12.82$. The .007 is what must be added to .043 to obtain .050, while .039 is the proportion of the chance χ^2 in the step 12 to 13. In Table C the value of χ^2 for $6df$ and P of .05 is 12.59, which is reasonably close to the value of 12.82 found from Table 12.3. Both values are, of course, derived from the same mathematical function, and identity is to be expected.

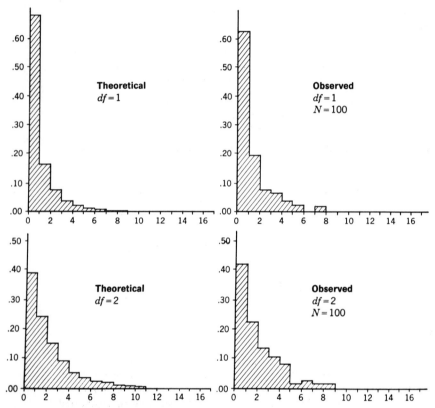

FIG. 12.2(a). THEORETICAL AND OBSERVED χ^2 DISTRIBUTIONS (HISTOGRAM FORM)
(Data are the same as in Example 12.2)

From Figure 12.2, based on the data of Example 12.2, it can be seen that the χ^2 distributions for $df = 1$ are highly skewed. (The theoretical distribution is plotted as a histogram to make it comparable to the obtained distribution. Had the theoretical distribution been plotted as a continuous mathematical function, it would have been higher at the left and more elongated at the right, and hence even more skewed.) For $df = 2$, the theoretical curve is still highly skewed, but less so than for $df = 1$. For $4df$, the mode of the theoretical curve is in the interval between 2.00 and 3.00, and skew is still further reduced. While the curve for $df = 6$ is not symmetrical, it appears that as the degrees of freedom continue to increase, normality might be reached.

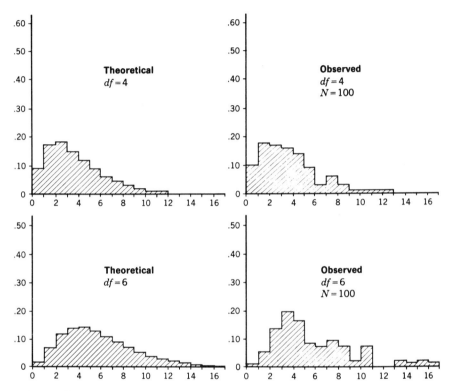

FIG. 12.2(b). THEORETICAL AND OBSERVED χ^2 DISTRIBUTIONS (HISTOGRAM FORM)

Actually the central limit theorem does apply, and any χ^2 curve for more than $30df$ is regarded as essentially normal. However, when $df = 30$, χ^2 itself is not tested to find its place in the normal distribution. Rather, a function of χ^2 is used, a function for which the normal curve is a better approximation than it is for χ^2 itself. Generally, this function is $\sqrt{2\chi^2}$, which has a mean of $\sqrt{2v - 1}$ and unit variance. A still more accurate approximation is the function $\sqrt[3]{\chi^2/v}$, with a mean of $1 - (2/9v)$ and variance of $2/9v$, v in all cases being the degrees of freedom.

As far as χ^2 itself is concerned, the mean is always v, (the number of df), the variance is $2v$, and the mode (except for the curve for $1df$) is $v - 2$.

RELATIONSHIP BETWEEN χ^2 AND THE NORMAL CURVE

Certain relationships between χ^2 and the normal curve may now be summarized. Since the χ^2 curve for $1df$ can be reproduced by squaring a normally distributed variable in z form, $\sqrt{\chi^2}$ for $1df$ is distributed as the positive half of a normal distribution.

A relationship already noted is that as degrees of freedom increase, the resultant distribution becomes a better and better approximation of the complete normal curve, centered around a mean of v.

Since the mathematical derivation of χ^2 involves the squares of normally distributed z scores, it is also clear why f_e must not become too small. If an f_e were permitted to become, say, 1, then the contribution to χ^2 could be expected to be skewed. Another way of stating this is: χ^2 assumes that the sampling of differences between the f_o and f_e follows the normal curve. On the other hand, no assumptions are made about the shape of the distribution of the f_o themselves.

OTHER CONSIDERATIONS IN THE USE OF χ^2

χ^2 is a statistic that corresponds to no parameter in the population. It is a pure number, evaluated only in reference to v (the number of df) and not to N (the number of cases). As the degrees of freedom increase, possible values of χ^2 increase, and the size of the χ^2 required for a fixed value of P also increases.

In Table 12.3 are shown theoretical P's derived from the mathematical χ^2 curves, together with P_o's obtained by cumulating the proportions of Table 12.2 toward zero. The relationship between the theoretical P's and those derived empirically is close.

For $1df$ through $30df$, χ^2 can be evaluated directly, and often with sufficient accuracy, from Fig. 3.4, which shows lines representing $P = .10$, $P = .05$, $P = .01$, and $P = .001$. The graph shows df as a continuous function; however, df is always integral, since fractional v's never occur.

As an example of the use of Fig. 3.4, take a χ^2 of 20, with $10df$. The intersection of the horizontal line for $10df$ and the vertical line for a χ^2 value of 20 is between the curves for $P = .05$ and $P = .01$. Accordingly, $.05 > P > .01$, and the hypothesis that provided the f_e's in the computation of χ^2 is disproved at the .05 level but not at the .01 level.

More frequently, tabled values of χ^2 are used instead of charts. It will be noted, however, that when Table C (Appendix) is entered for $10df$ and χ^2 of 30, the conclusion is exactly the same as when Fig. 3.4 is used.

The use of χ^2 always assumes that the events or measures or observations that form the basis of the frequencies are independent. Thus, the frequencies must not represent the same group of subjects over and over again or even two or more observations on the same person.

χ^2 has an important additive property. With all frequencies independent, two or more sets of observations in their respective categories may be regarded as a combined set of categories, with *df* equal to the sum of the *df* of the categories as originally grouped. Conversely, a χ^2 over a number of categories may be partitioned into two or more χ^2's over subsets of categories. This flexibility is an appropriate deduction from the way theoretical χ^2 curves are established as sums of squares of v normally distributed variables, v being the number of *df*.

RELATIONSHIP BETWEEN χ^2 AND ϕ

In the special case of a 2 by 2 diagram, there is a fixed relationship between χ^2 and ϕ. Let interval and marginal frequencies be represented as follows:

VARIABLE X

	a	b	$(a+b)$
VARIABLE Y	c	d	$(c+d)$
	$(a+c)$	$(b+d)$	N

By formula 3.6, $\chi^2 = N[\Sigma(f_o^2/f_r f_c) - 1]$. Thus, in terms of frequencies,

$$\chi^2 = N\left[\frac{a^2}{(a+b)(a+c)} + \frac{b^2}{(a+b)(b+d)} + \frac{c^2}{(a+c)(c+d)}\right.$$

$$\left. + \frac{d^2}{(c+d)(b+d)} - 1\right]$$

This simplifies to

$$\chi^2 = N\left[\frac{(bc-ad)^2}{(a+b)(a+c)(b+d)(c+d)}\right]$$

which in turn, by Formula 9.16a for ϕ, simplifies to

$$\chi^2 = N\phi^2 \tag{12.9}$$

or

$$\phi = \sqrt{\frac{\chi^2}{N}} \tag{12.9a}$$

THE *t* DISTRIBUTION

Of considerable utility in psychological research is the *t* distribution, published in 1908 by William S. Gossett, who wrote under the pseudonym "Student" (9). Gossett's discovery is often considered as the beginning of the modern era in mathematical statistics, with its emphasis on the use of exact sampling distributions and on making the best possible use of observed data for inferring parameters.

As with χ^2, there is a separate t distribution for each value of v, the degrees of freedom, and also as does χ^2 (and some other theoretical distributions), the t distribution approaches normality as a limit as v becomes indefinitely large.

Each of the t distributions is conceived as the distribution of the ratio of:

1. A numerator variable distributed normally with mean of zero; and
2. A denominator variable distributed independently of the numerator and as the square root of χ^2 divided by v.

If z is a normally distributed random variable with mean of zero and unit variance, then the t distribution can be described as

$$t = \frac{z}{\sqrt{\chi^2/v}} \tag{12.10}$$

If $z_i, z_j, z_k, z_l, z_m \cdots$ are random normal variables in z form, the following distributions for t may be envisaged:

For $1df$, $t_1 = \dfrac{z_i}{z_j}$

For $2df$, $t_2 = \dfrac{z_i}{\sqrt{\dfrac{z_j^2 + z_k^2}{2}}}$

For $3df$, $t_3 = \dfrac{z_i}{\sqrt{\dfrac{z_j^2 + z_k^2 + z_l^2}{3}}}$

and for $4df$, $t_4 = \dfrac{z_i}{\sqrt{\dfrac{z_j^2 + z_k^2 + z_l^2 + z_m^2}{4}}}$

Inspection of these formulas makes it apparent why there is a separate t distribution for each value of v_i. Since z_i is symmetrical around 0, and since the denominator is always positive, t is also symmetrical around 0. Both, of course, vary from $-\infty$ to $+\infty$, and it can be shown that the inflection points are at values $\pm\sqrt{v/(v + 2)}$, while the variance is $v/(v + 2)$.

Although, for any value of t, the uncorrelated denominator z values do not necessarily sum to zero, it is apparent that the term $\sqrt{\chi^2/v}$ has a strong resemblance to a standard deviation. Intuitively, t might seem to be an appropriate model distribution for a normally distributed difference divided by the standard error of that difference.

COMPARISON OF THEORETICAL AND OBSERVED t

Table 12.4 gives the following information:

1. The expected proportion of values of t within stated limits, as determined from the table of t for $v = 1$;
2. Actual frequencies of 100 observed values of z_i/z_j found by drawing pairs of values from a table of the random normal deviate and computing the ratios;
3. The expected proportions of values of t within stated limits for $v = 6$, as found in a table; and
4. Actual frequencies of 100 observed values of $z_i/\sqrt{\chi^2/6}$. (Actually, the artificial χ^2's tabulated in Table 12.2 were used as the values for χ^2 with 6df.)

TABLE 12.4. EXPECTED AND OBSERVED VALUES OF t (1df and 6df)

	$v = 1$		$v = 6$	
VALUES OF t	EXPECTED PROPORTION	OBSERVED PROPORTION	EXPECTED PROPORTION	OBSERVED PROPORTION
Above 5.5	.057	.07	.001	.00
4.5 to 5.5	.012	.02	.001	.00
3.5 to 4.5	.019	.01	.004	.00
2.5 to 3.5	.033	.08	.017	.01
1.5 to 2.5	.066	.06	.069	.08
.5 to 1.5	.165	.17	.225	.28
−.5 to .5	.295	.34	.365	.32
−1.5 to − .5	.165	.12	.225	.22
−2.5 to −1.5	.066	.06	.069	.08
−3.5 to −2.5	.033	.01	.017	.00
−4.5 to −3.5	.019	.01	.004	.00
−5.5 to −4.5	.012	.02	.001	.01
Below −5.5	.057	.03	.001	.00

In both cases, the fit of the observations to the theoretical distributions seems reasonably good. Both empirical curves are symmetrical, and as expected, the curve for $v = 1$ is much flatter than for $v = 6$.

Both the curve for $v = 1$ and for $v = 6$ are too platykurtic to be considered normal. Actually, it can be shown that when $v = \infty$, t is normal, and it is practically so when $v = 25$.

The model provided by the t distribution is useful in evaluating the value of a normally distributed variable (such as the difference between a sample mean and the parameter) by dividing it by an unbiased estimate of its sampling error. The ratio can then be interpreted by reference to the appropriate t distribution. Specific applications are discussed in Chapter 13.

THE F DISTRIBUTION

Somewhat more general in its application than the t distribution is the distribution of F, so-named[2] in honor of its discoverer, Sir Ronald Fisher.

If random normal variates are $z_i, z_j \cdots z_v$ and $z_k, z_l \cdots z_{v'}$, then F may be defined as

$$F = \frac{\dfrac{z_i^2 + z_j^2 + \cdots + z_v^2}{v}}{\dfrac{z_k^2 + z_l^2 + \cdots + z_{v'}^2}{v'}} \qquad (12.11)$$

From Formula 12.11 it is seen that:

1. F is always positive, with the possibility of values up to ∞;
2. When and only when the numerator variable has a single degree of freedom, $t = \sqrt{F}$ and $F = t^2$;
3. For every pair of df there is a distinct distribution; and
4. The shape of the F distribution varies with the two values, v and v'.

From Formula 12.11 it is also reasonable to believe, as is actually the case, that when v and v' are both very large, the F distribution approaches normality.

Probably the most important use of F is that it can be taken as the distribution of the ratio of two independent variances, each with its own df. It was the discovery of the F distribution that made possible the development of the analysis of variance, described briefly in Chapter 14.

RELATIONSHIP OF F TO χ^2

Examination of Formula 12.11 shows that the numerator of F is distributed as χ^2 with v degrees of freedom (v being a constant divisor), while the denominator is distributed as χ^2 with v' df (v' being the constant divisor in the denominator term).

In terms of χ^2, Formula 12.11 becomes

$$F = \frac{\chi_v^2/v}{\chi_{v'}^2/v'} = \frac{\chi_v^2 v'}{\chi_{v'}^2 v} \qquad (12.11a)$$

which shows that F is the ratio of two values of χ^2, each divided by the appropriate number of degrees of freedom.

EMPIRICAL F DISTRIBUTION

To develop an empirical distribution of F, the 100 artificial χ^2's with $6df$, the distribution of which is in the last column of Table 12.2, were matched at random with the 100 artificial χ^2's with $4df$ in the same table. The distribution of the resultant ratios, appropriately weighted by $6df$ and $4df$, is shown in Table 12.5.

---

[2] By G. W. Snedecor, who prepared the first tables of F.

Tables of the F function usually show, for each pair of df, the values beyond which are found 5 and 1 percent of the F by chance.

TABLE 12.5. AN EMPIRICAL DISTRIBUTION OF F

$(v = 6; v' = 4)$

VALUES OF F	f
10 or more	2
9–9.999	0
8–8.999	1
7–7.999	2
6–6.999	1
5–5.999	2
4–4.999	2
3–3.999	6
2–2.999	7
1–1.999	30
0–0.999	47
	$N = 100$

For 6df and 4df,
   5 percent level: $F=6.16$.
   1 percent level: $F=15.21$.

From Table F (Appendix) it is seen that with 6df for the greater mean square and 4df for the lesser, 1 percent of the F by chance would be beyond 15.21 and 5 percent beyond 6.16. In the empirical chance distribution, 2 percent of the F are 10 or more, and 6 percent are 6 or more so that the empirical distribution is probably not greatly different from the one that would be developed mathematically for this particular pair of df.

SUMMARY

Among the theoretical distributions that observed distributions sometimes approximate are the normal (discussed in Chapter 11), the binomial, and the Poisson. The normal distribution may be developed as a continuous and limiting case of the binomial, and the binomial may be approximated very closely by another discontinuous distribution, the Poisson.

In the testing of statistical hypotheses, a general strategy is to evaluate the rarity of a specific empirical finding in terms of the distribution of the statistic developed on the basis of a probability model. Both the normal distribution, described in Chapter 11, and the binomial are often used for this purpose. Three other distributions, which vary with the degrees of freedom and which are applicable to statistics rather than to the observations on which statistics are based, are χ^2, t, and F.

χ^2 can be developed as the sum of v squares of random z scores; t can be developed as a random z score divided by the square root of χ_v^2/v;

and F, as the ratio of χ_ν^2/ν to $\chi_{\nu'}^2/\nu'$. Both χ^2 and F are always positive. With few degrees of freedom, χ^2 and F are highly skewed, but both approach normality as the degrees of freedom become larger. The distribution of t is symmetrical around zero. When $\nu = 1$, it is very platykurtic, but it becomes more peaked as the degrees of freedom increase, eventually becoming normal.

EXERCISES

1. A subject in a perceptual experiment is required to say whether two stimuli presented simultaneously are the same or different, and his responses are considered correct or incorrect. What is the chance expectation of five or six successes in six attempts?

2. A short classroom quiz consisted of 5 five-choice items. If 100 students were to take the test, and success on each item were completely at random, what would be the distribution of scores?

3. Prepare a table showing the mean, mode, and standard deviation of the chi-square curves from $df = 2$ to $df = 20$.

4. In a problem with $42df$, $\chi^2 = 112.5$. Is χ^2 significantly different from zero?

5. In a perceptual learning experiment, three of the five possible choices on each trial were considered correct. If a subject had 59 successes in a run of 96 trials, should his performance be considered as definitely better than could be expected by chance?

6. From Table 12.3 the data for expected and observed values of t for $6df$ may be consolidated as follows:

VALUE OF t	f_e	f_o
Above 1.5	9	9
.5 to 1.5	23	28
−.5 to .5	36	32
−1.5 to −.5	23	22
Below −1.5	9	9

By the χ^2 test of goodness of fit determine whether the observed values of the artificial t depart significantly from the expected distribution. (Assume $\nu = 4$.)

7. For $N = 50$, $\phi = .20$. By the χ^2 test, can the association between the two variables be considered significantly different from zero?

8. The following data from Jones (3) represent the frequency of aircraft accidents experienced by 2546 pilots during a four-year period.

NUMBER OF ACCIDENTS	f
5	1
4	3
3	13
2	71
1	422
0	2036

Fit a Poisson to this distribution and apply the χ^2 test of goodness of fit to test whether the hypothesis of the data following the Poisson is tenable.

REFERENCES

1. ADAMS, JOE KENNEDY, *Basic Statistical Concepts*. New York: McGraw-Hill Book Company, Inc., 1955.
2. FISHER, R. A., *Statistical Methods for Research Workers*. Edinburgh and London: Oliver and Boyd, 1936.
3. JONES, EDWARD R., *A Study of Accident Proneness*, Unpublished Ph.D. dissertation. St. Louis: Washington University, 1954.
4. KENDALL, MAURICE G., AND STUART, ALAN, *The Advanced Theory of Statistics, Volume I: Distribution Theory*. London: Charles Griffin, 1958.
5. LEWIS, DON, *Quantitative Methods in Psychology*. New York: McGraw-Hill Book Company, Inc., 1960.
6. O'GORMAN, WILLIAM D., AND KUNKLE, E. CHARLES, "Study of the inventory scores and 'pilot error' in aircraft accidents," *J. Aviat. Med.*, 1947, **18**, 31–38.
7. POISSON, S. D., *Recherches sur la Probabilité des Jugements*. Paris: 1837.
8. Rand Corporation, *A Million Random Digits with 100,000 Normal Deviates*. Glencoe, Illinois: The Free Press, 1955.
9. Student, "The probable error of a mean," *Biometrika*, 1908, **6**, 1–25.

INFERENCES
ABOUT THE
POPULATION

13

ROLE OF DESCRIPTIVE STATISTICS IN GENERALIZATION

Descriptive statistics, computed from particular samples, provide a basis for making inferences about the populations the samples are taken to represent. The scientific psychologist has as his primary interest the establishment of sound generalizations, that is, the discovery of principles that apply not only to the sample that he has investigated but also to the population, from which, theoretically at least, samples not yet observed can be selected. If the generalization is correct, it will apply to new samples not used in its development. This chapter is concerned with statistical procedures used in making valid inferences about the population even though direct knowledge is always limited to samples.

It will be seen that knowledge of the population is, in general, not certain, but rather probable. Some collections of observations are worthless for making generalizations because of inappropriate techniques for establishing the sample or inadequate numbers of cases, or faulty observations, or improper statistical manipulations. On the other hand, by stating assumptions and procedures very carefully, by refining the means of making the observations, and by extending the number of properly selected cases, it is often possible to make statements about the population with a high degree of probability, sometimes amounting to virtual certainty.

DEVELOPMENT OF REPRESENTATIVE SAMPLES

Occasionally, as in certain aspects of the U.S. Census, sample and population coincide. More commonly a relatively small group is used to represent all cases of interest, and statistics computed within the group are used to infer characteristics of the population. Three methods used to develop representative groups are:

1. Random sampling;
2. Stratified sampling; and
3. Area sampling.

In random sampling, every case in the population must have equal probability of being selected at each step in developing the sample. Procedures designed to accomplish this vary with whether the population is finite and knowable or whether it is considered unlimited or even infinite. With a finite population all members may be numbered and then some sort of mechanical device or table of random numbers used to select the sample. If individuals are already arranged in an order that can be considered random and a subsample of N' cases is needed from the total sample of N cases, then each (N/N')th case may be used, provided bias is avoided in selecting the initial case.

When there is a relatively unlimited pool of cases from which to draw, more elaborate procedures may be required, such as using a table of random numbers to decide the interval between each successive case drawn from an unending and naturally occurring sequence.

In stratified sampling, the population is divided in categories on one or more variables of interest, and then random samples are taken from each of these categories in such a way that the sample has the same proportions by categories as the population has as a whole. Stratified sampling is often used in conducting polls to forecast voting behavior, and the categories selected are those believed to have some correlation with voting tendencies. These may be how individuals voted in a previous election, occupation, economic status, urban-rural classification, and the like.

A variant of stratified sampling is called *quota* sampling, in which the subsamples are not randomly determined, but sampling is continued until a certain number of cases in each category is obtained.

In area sampling, the total population is broken down into smaller units and a random sample of the units is chosen. Thus the census of a country might be taken by laying off the entire area in small sections and choosing a random sample of these areas for a precise count. Undoubtedly, the sample would be improved by a mixture of stratified and area sampling in which areas were first classified by categories and then sections chosen within each of the categories.

Many different sampling plans, some of which cannot be classified too clearly, can be used to develop a group from which characteristics of the population can be inferred. Whatever the precise details of constructing the sample, it must meet three requirements:

1. The sample must represent the population, that is, it must be unbiased;
2. It must be large enough so that the statistics computed on it will be reliable; and
3. It must be small enough so that data collection and subsequent analysis will be efficient.

Size is no guarantee of the quality of the sample. If a small sample is representative, it may be more efficient than a large one.

ESTIMATING PARAMETERS FROM STATISTICS

A statistic computed from a sample is frequently used to estimate a *parameter*, the corresponding value in the population.

In theoretical distributions, parameters are often known, but parameters corresponding to statistics in observed psychological data can only be estimated and have no exact numerical values. The fact that a statistic is used to estimate a parameter can be indicated by the symbol $\doteq$ ("equals approximately"). Thus, if $\sigma_x \doteq 12.5$, we know that the value of 12.5, obtained from s_x in a sample, is taken as an estimate of a parameter.

BIASED AND UNBIASED ESTIMATES OF PARAMETERS

Some of the statistics computed from samples are the best available estimates of the corresponding parameters. Examples are p, the proportion of cases falling in one of two categories, and M, the mean. These statistics may be incorrect estimates for various reasons, such as poor sampling techniques, inadequate numbers of cases, or faulty measurement procedures, but they exhibit no bias or systematic distortion.

In the case of the mean, it is readily seen that in a truly random sample of cases drawn from a normally distributed population, observed scores X units above the parameter μ_x and observed scores X units below μ_x are equally likely to be selected. Hence, there is no tendency for M_x to have a predetermined relationship to μ_x, and M_x can be taken as an unbiased estimate of μ_x. Actually, M_x is an unbiased estimate of μ_x whether or not the variable is normally distributed in the population.

As contrasted with p and the mean, the standard deviation and the variance in the sample are biased in that they are underestimates of corresponding parameter values. By mathematical methods, it can be shown that, on the average, an appropriate allowance can be made for the bias by using $(N - 1)$ as the divisor instead of N. When N is large (say, greater than 30), the correction is inconsequential, but with small numbers of cases the correction is essential for making an unbiased estimate of the parameter. It is to be noted that $(N - 1)$ is actually the number of degrees of freedom in a frequency distribution with a fixed mean. (In effect, the mean must be determined from the sample data before it is possible to find the variance.) The formulas for unbiased estimates of parameter values of the variance and standard deviations are

$$\hat{V}_x = \sigma_x{}^2 \doteq \frac{\Sigma x^2}{N - 1} \qquad (13.1)$$

and

$$\sigma_x \doteq \sqrt{\frac{\Sigma x^2}{N - 1}} \qquad (13.2)$$

DISTRIBUTION OF A STATISTIC

As indicated in Chapter 11, every statistic theoretically has its "distribution," defined as the array of values that would be found if the statistic were computed for each one of a series of samples of the same size drawn completely at random from an unlimited population. A primary endeavour of modern mathematical statistics has been the discovery of these "sampling distributions" or of satisfactory approximations to them. In any given instance there is no way of knowing whether the obtained statistic is above or below the parameter value. However, if it can be assumed that the sampling procedure has been correct, a knowledge of the statistic and its distribution often permits valid and useful inferences about the parameter.

In this connection a set of values of a statistic, each computed from a properly developed sample, is thought of as varying around the parameter. The theoretical relative frequencies of this fluctuation constitute the "distribution of the statistic," a mathematical construct by means of which a statistic obtained from a particular sample may often be evaluated.

The most important distributions of statistics are the normal, χ^2, the t distribution, and F, all of which have been discussed. This chapter is concerned with statistics distributed normally, such as means based on samples drawn from a normal population, and with those that follow the t distribution, such as the difference between two means divided by s. Certain applications of the F distribution are presented in Chapter 14.

These distributions, as pointed out in Chapter 12, are interrelated and also have relationships with other theoretical distributions, including χ^2. Before using one as the distribution of a statistic, it is always necessary to examine the conditions under which the statistic was obtained, to determine whether the proposed mathematical model is actually applicable. The form of the distribution is not necessarily a fixed characteristic of a statistic, since it may vary with the distribution of the variable or variables in the parent population, with the magnitude of the parameter value, with N, and with v (the number of the degrees of freedom). The central limit theorem is often crucial in this connection, since as numbers of cases or numbers of summed variables increase, there is a tendency for a nonnormal sampling distribution to become normal.

CONCEPT OF THE STANDARD ERROR

The distributions in common use are always based on mathematical functions that are chosen either because of theoretical considerations or because the function has repeatedly been found to give a good fit to observed data, or for both reasons. With the exception of the binomial (when n is small) and the Poisson, direct numerical methods for finding the relative frequency at various values or for a band of values of a theoretical distribution tend to be too complex for routine usage. This is a chief reason for the extensive use of tables in statistical analysis. Thus, when it is known that a statistic is distributed normally, tables of the normal curve can be used in evaluating an obtained value.

The true standard deviation of the distribution of a statistic is itself a parameter which, with empirical data, cannot be known. Nevertheless, an estimated standard deviation of the sampling distribution, called the *standard error*, can be found for a wide variety of statistics and is especially useful with those computed for large samples of cases. The standard error of the mean is a good illustration of the concept.

Consider a parent population in which the variable is highly skewed. If a series of samples of one case each were drawn at random from this population, we should expect to find the distribution of these samples to approximate the distribution of the variable in the parent population.

Now consider the distribution of sums of two cases, each drawn from the same population. Because any extreme case would be probably coupled with a case not so extreme, the shape of the distribution of these sums would be less skewed than that of the original variable. In fact, the only way in which the shape of the distribution of sums would repeat the shape of the original distribution would require that all pairs of cases be formed by coupling adjacent values. By random sampling, such a series of events is so highly improbable that it may be dismissed as impossible. The shape of the distribution of means would, of course, be exactly the same as the distribution of sums. (Division by a constant N would affect absolute numerical values, but not the shape. In this case the constant would be 2.)

With each subgroup forming the sum (or mean) selected completely at random from the parent population, the skew would become still less in samples of three cases each, and in general would continue to diminish as the number of values in each sample became larger, eventually becoming more or less normal. What is true for skewed populations is true also for populations departing in other ways from the normal. The point at which a set of means becomes "normal" depends, of course, on the criterion of normality, on how the variable is distributed in the parent population, and on N (the number of cases in each sample). It seems reasonable to regard the mean as distributed normally when either of the following conditions, or both, apply:

1. The variable is distributed normally in the population; or
2. The number of cases in the sample is large.

STANDARD ERROR OF THE MEAN

By methods of mathematical statistics it has been found that the standard deviation of an array of means derived under either of these conditions is

$$\sigma_M = \frac{\sigma_x}{\sqrt{N}} \tag{13.3}$$

in which σ_M is read as the "standard error of the mean," σ_x is the parameter standard deviation, and N is the number of cases in each sample. The formula appears appropriate. When $N = 1$, $\sigma_M = \sigma_x$, and as N increases, σ_M decreases. It is also reasonable that σ_M should vary directly with σ_x.

Since σ_x is an unknown parameter, it is conventionally estimated by Formula 13.2. Accordingly, the standard error of the mean, designated as s_M and estimated from the sample standard deviation, is

$$s_M = \frac{\sqrt{\dfrac{\Sigma x^2}{N-1}}}{\sqrt{N}} = \frac{s_x}{\sqrt{N-1}} \tag{13.3a}$$

It is to be noted that σ_M gives the variability of means around the parameter μ, not around the sample mean M. Consequently, we cannot say, since 95 percent of a normal distribution lies between the limits of $\pm 1.96\sigma$, that there are 95 chances in 100 that the true mean lies within $\pm 1.96s_M$ of an observed mean. In general, however, the smaller the s_M, the closer the observed mean will be to the parameter. In a later section a method involving M, s_M, and t will be given for establishing *fiducial*, or *confidence*, limits within which μ is very likely to be found.

OTHER EXAMPLES OF STANDARD ERRORS

Standard errors have been discovered for most of the descriptive statistics in common use. Just as a standard deviation can be meaningfully computed for a variable that is not normally distributed, so the existence of a formula for a standard error does not imply that the statistic itself is normally distributed. For the standard error to be useful in making inferences, knowledge of the shape of the distribution is essential. A nonzero correlation coefficient (which is not normally distributed) can be converted to a function that is more or less normally distributed and which has a known standard error, so that a table of the normal curve can be used in evaluating the observed statistic.

In reading reports of research, standard errors can always be interpreted as the expected standard deviation of the statistic if it were computed from a series of samples of the same size drawn from a population. Generally, this population is considered to be unlimited. If, however, the population is finite and consists only of N' cases, then the standard error is somewhat less than when the population is infinite. The correction factor, by which the usual formula is to be multiplied, is $(N' - N)/(N' - 1)$ in which N' is the number of cases in the population and N is the number of cases in the sample. When N' is large compared with N, the correction is negligible.

Descriptions of various standard errors are available in advanced texts. Here, only a few need be mentioned.

The standard error of the median is somewhat larger than that of the mean. Hence, it can be said that the mean is more "reliable" than the median. If the sample is large, the median is distributed approximately normally, and if the sample is from a normal population, the standard error is

$$\sigma_{\text{mdn.}} = 1.253 \frac{\sigma_x}{\sqrt{N}} \tag{13.4}$$

In estimating $\sigma_{\text{mdn.}}$, the parameter σ_x is replaced in practice with the estimated population value of the standard deviation, $\sqrt{\Sigma x^2/(N - 1)}$.

The standard error of a proportion is

$$\sigma_p = \sqrt{\frac{\hat{p}\hat{q}}{N}} \doteq \sqrt{\frac{pq}{N}} \tag{13.5}$$

which indicates that since the parameters $\hat{p}$ and $(1 - \hat{p})$ or $\hat{q}$ are unknown, the observed proportion p and its complement q may be used as estimates of $\hat{p}$ and $\hat{q}$.

STANDARD ERROR OF r

The standard error of a correlation coefficient is given by

$$\sigma_r = \frac{1 - \hat{r}^2}{\sqrt{N - 1}} \tag{13.6}$$

in which $\hat{r}$ is the parameter and N is the number of cases measured on the two variables. As $\hat{r}$ departs from .00, the distribution becomes more and more skewed, so that the normal curve becomes less and less applicable. Also, it is never appropriate to substitute the obtained r for $\hat{r}$, the unknown parameter.

A special case of Formula 13.6, however, is often very useful. For an $\hat{r}$ of .00, the formula becomes

$$\sigma_{r_0} = \frac{1}{\sqrt{N-1}} \tag{13.7}$$

When N is large, r's computed from samples drawn from a bivariate normal population, in which $\hat{r}$ is zero, tend to follow a normal distribution. Accordingly, multiplication of an obtained correlation by $\sqrt{N-1}$ yields the number of standard error units that it falls above or below an assumed parameter value of .00. The result can be readily evaluated from a table of the normal curve, such as Table A (Appendix).

As a numerical example, consider an r of .25 computed from 65 cases. The value of $\sqrt{N-1}$ is 8 and $1/\sqrt{N-1}$ is .125. When .25 is divided by .125, the result is 2.00, showing that the obtained r is 2.00 standard errors above a hypothetical parameter value of .00. (Since division by a reciprocal $[1/\sqrt{N-1}]$, is numerically the same as multiplying by the number $[\sqrt{N-1}]$, an identical result is found as $r\sqrt{N-1}$, or .25 × 8 = 2.00.)

From Table A it is seen that the proportion of cases in a normal distribution between the mean and 2.00σ is .477. Accordingly, the proportion of cases above $+2.00\sigma$ is .023. Hence, it can be said that there are 2.3 chances in 100 that an r of .25 or more could be found for a random sample of 65 drawn from a population in which $\hat{r} = .00$.

LEVELS OF SIGNIFICANCE OF r

A method of evaluating many obtained statistics, including correlations, is in reference to a *level of significance*, which is chosen arbitrarily, but which is helpful in determining whether or not a statistic computed from a sample should be considered a chance deviation from a posited parameter value. Since exceedingly improbable events can occur fortuitously, even a perfect correlation might conceivably be found in a sample, say, of 65 cases drawn at random from a population in which $\hat{r} = .00$.

The practice is to determine a point on the theoretical distribution of the statistic, beyond which is found a certain percentage of the distribution, usually 5 or 1 percent. This is then taken as the dividing point between statistics that are "significant" at that level and those that are not.

When a statistic is known to be normally distributed, any desired significance level can be established from a knowledge of the standard error and the use of a table of the area of the normal curve. Tests for normally distributed statistics are illustrated graphically in Fig. 13.1.

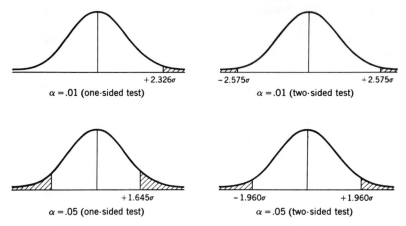

$\alpha = .01$ (one-sided test) $+2.326\sigma$

-2.575σ $\alpha = .01$ (two-sided test) $+2.575\sigma$

$+1.645\sigma$ $\alpha = .05$ (one-sided test)

-1.960σ $\alpha = .05$ (two-sided test) $+1.960\sigma$

FIG. 13.1. STATISTICAL TESTS FOR NORMALLY DISTRIBUTED STATISTICS. ($\alpha = .01$ AND $\alpha = .05$ FOR ONE-SIDED AND TWO-SIDED TESTS.)

When the observed statistic, in terms of standard errors, falls in the shaded area, the null hypothesis may be rejected at the stated level of confidence.

VALUES OF z SCORES FOR ONE-SIDED AND TWO-SIDED TESTS

	P VALUE	
z SCORE	ONE-SIDED TEST	TWO-SIDED TEST
2.575	.005	.010
2.326	.010	.020
1.960	.025	.050
1.645	.050	.100

In the particular instance, the standard error is .125 and the theoretical distribution is known to be approximately normal. From Table A it is seen that 49 percent of a normal distribution lies between the mean and $+2.326\sigma$. The value of 2.326 standard errors is 2.326 × .125, or .291, which can be taken as the division point between coefficients, based on a sample of 65 cases, that are "significant at the 1 percent level" and correlations that are not. Since the obtained coefficient in the example is .25, it is not significant at the 1 percent level. It is, however, significant at the 5 percent level. Since 45 percent of a normal distribution lies between the mean and $+1.645\sigma$, it follows that 5 percent of the cases in a chance distribution fall 1.645 standard errors above the mean. With mean of zero (the parameter value) and standard error of .125, it would be expected that 5 percent of the r would fall above .206. Hence, the obtained r can be considered to be significant at the 5 percent level.

In this example the hypothesis is to the effect that there is no association between the two variables in the population. This has been considered disproved only if the r in the sample is high and in a stated direction (in this case, positive). In psychological research, this is the usual way in which a hypothesis about a correlation is investigated, since there is generally some anticipation of the direction of association.

If the logic of the situation calls for disproof of the hypothesis, whether the correlation is positive or negative (provided, of course, its absolute value is sufficiently high), then the procedure involves a "two-tailed" test rather than the "one-tailed" test demonstrated above.

Reference to Table A again shows that 49.5 percent of a normal distribution lies between the mean and 2.575σ. Accordingly, 1 percent of the distribution lies outside the limits $\pm 2.575\sigma$. For the hypothesis of no association to be disproved at the 1 percent level of significance under a "two-tailed" test, an observed r (based on a sufficient number of cases so that the assumption of normal distribution of the $\hat{r}$ of .00 is plausible) must lie outside the limits of $+2.575$ standard errors and -2.575 standard errors.

From Table A it can also be seen that 2.5 percent of a normal distribution is above $+1.96\sigma$ (and a similar percentage below -1.96σ). These, then, are the limits for the 5 percent on the "two-tailed" basis. If r is more than 1.96 standard errors above or below .00, the hypothesis of no association in either direction is disproved at the 5 percent level of significance.

When N is not large (customarily considered as less than 30), the use of a table of a normal curve for evaluating whether or not an obtained r is significantly different from zero involves appreciable error. The reason is that the distribution of sample r's (when $\hat{r} = .00$) approaches normality only as N becomes large and is perfectly normal only when N is infinite.

THE t DISTRIBUTION APPLIED TO r

A joint function of r and N follows the t distribution with $(N - 2)$ degrees of freedom precisely, provided N is 3 or more. For r based on small samples, the use of this function is essential, and it is convenient to use when N is 30 or more. This is an application of the t distribution described in Chapter 12. The function is

$$t = \frac{r\sqrt{N - 2}}{\sqrt{1 - r^2}} \tag{13.8}$$

To evaluate an obtained r, t may be computed by Formula 13.8 and its significance found from any table of t, such as Table T (Appendix). More conveniently, however, a table of the significant points of the function, such as Table R, is entered directly with the degrees of freedom, which for zero-order r are $(N - 2)$.

For a partial r, the number of degrees of freedom is decreased from $(N - 2)$ by 1 for each variable partialled out. For a multiple R, $(N - 2)$ is reduced by 1 for each variable beyond the first used as a predictor to find v, the degrees of freedom. When Table R is used, only the line entered is changed; if t is computed, Formula 13.8 becomes

$$t = \frac{r\sqrt{v}}{\sqrt{1 - r^2}} \tag{13.8a}$$

in which v is the number of degrees of freedom.

Correlations significant at the 1 and 5 percent levels for various degrees of freedom are graphed in Fig. 13.2. This graph is usable for one-sided tests in which the correlation is to be tested for the presence of association

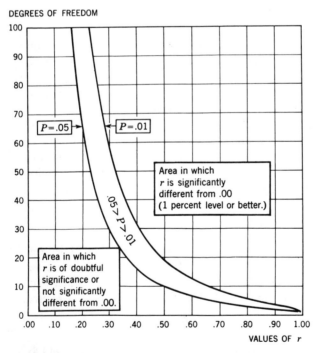

FIG. 13.2. CORRELATIONS SIGNIFICANT AT THE 1 PERCENT AND 5 PERCENT LEVELS FOR VARIOUS df

in one direction only. The information is exactly the same as in two columns of Table R. For routine usage the table is probably to be preferred, since r's close to the significance levels are easier to evaluate.

Using Table T and Fig. 13.2, the r of .25 based on 65 cases, which was previously tested by the formula for the standard error of an $\hat{r}$ of zero, may be readily retested for significance.

Using $63df$,

$$t = \frac{r\sqrt{v}}{\sqrt{1 - r^2}} = \frac{.25\sqrt{63}}{\sqrt{1 - (.25)^2}} = 2.05$$

FISHER'S z_r TRANSFORMATION OF r

As described above, r may be regarded as normally distributed when N is large and $\hat{r} = .00$; when $\hat{r} = .00$ and N is not specified, a function of r and v follows the distribution of t corresponding to v. Appropriate procedures have been described for testing whether or not an observed r can be regarded as a chance deviation from a parameter $\hat{r}$ of zero at a fixed level of significance. These procedures are not useful, however, for testing whether an observed r differs significantly from a posited nonzero parameter value, nor for testing the significance of the differences between two skewed r's.

The difficulty is that only when $\hat{r} = .00$ are sample r's distributed symmetrically, and only when $\hat{r} = .00$ and N is large are they distributed normally. The higher the absolute value of $\hat{r}$, the more skewed the distribution of sample r's becomes. To remedy this situation, Fisher (1) developed the z_r transformation of r, which, for all practical purposes, is normally distributed. While the value of z_r varies, of course, directly with r, the shape of the distribution of z_r is independent of the magnitude of r. The formula is

$$z_r = \frac{1}{2} \log_e \frac{1 + r}{1 - r} = 1.1503 \log_{10} \frac{1 + r}{1 - r} \tag{13.9}$$

Values of r and z_r are presented in Table Z (Appendix), which permits conversion from r to z_r and from z_r to r more readily than does the use of Formula 13.9. As will be noted from Table Z, r and z_r up to .25 do not vary more than .005. When $r = .50$, z_r is .55, and thereafter the divergence continues to become progressively greater. For negative values of r, the sign of z_r also becomes negative.

STANDARD ERROR OF z_r

The standard error of z_r is

$$s_{z_r} = \frac{1}{\sqrt{N - 3}} \tag{13.10}$$

It is to be noted that there is no advantage in converting an r to z_r in order to test whether its divergence from a posited $\hat{r}$ of .00 can be attributed to chance fluctuation at a given level of confidence. The t test is always applicable, and it is often permissible to divide the obtained r by the standard error of a zero $r(s_{r_0})$ to find the number of standard errors the observed correlation is above or below the posited parameter value of .00.

The previous example of an r of .25 based on 65 cases can, however, be readily tested through the use of z_r. The z_r value is .255 and s_{z_r} is 1/7.874, both slightly greater than the corresponding r and s_{r_0}. Multiplication of .255 by 7.874 (numerically equivalent to dividing .255 by 1/7.874) yields 2.01 standard errors, which, by a one-sided test, is significant at the 5 percent level but not at the 1 percent level.

A more exacting comparison of the z_r technique is with a large r based on only a few cases and evaluated through the use of both t and s_{z_r}. From Table R it may be noted that an r of .75 with $7df$ ($N = 9$) is significantly different from .00 at the .01 level of confidence. Table Z shows that the z_r value corresponding to an r of .75 is .973, while by Formula 13.10, 3_{z_r} is $1/\sqrt{9 - 3} = 1/2.4495$. Multiplication of .973 by 2.4495 yields the fact that the obtained z_r is 2.38 standard errors above zero. Table A indicates that the proportion of cases in a normal distribution above 2.38σ is .0087, which would show that the r of .75 is significant at the 1 percent level. (There is a slight discrepancy between the two techniques, since in the normal curve, the dividing point between the lower 99 percent and the upper 1 percent is approximately 2.33. However, the agreement should be considered excellent.) Other illustrations of testing the significance of a correlation are given in Example 13.1.

EXAMPLE 13.1

TESTING THE SIGNIFICANCE OF AN OBTAINED r

In Table 6.3 a correlation of .56 is reported for a sample of 20 cases. If the parameter value were .00, what would be the expectation of a positive r of .56 or more, merely by sampling?

This can be evaluated by Formula 13.8a and Table T as follows:

$$t = r\sqrt{v}/\sqrt{1 - r^2} = .56\sqrt{18}/\sqrt{1 - (.56)^2} = 2.38/.83 = 2.87$$

If Table T is entered with $18df$, it is seen that the expected proportion of t's occurring by chance beyond the limits of ± 2.552 is .02. A one-sided test is appropriate because in analyzing the relationship between variables, the investigator typically has information as to its direction. Accordingly, since .01 of chance t's are greater than $+2.552$, the t of 2.87 indicates that the r is significantly different from .00 at better than the .01 level.

The same conclusion can be readily reached by inspection of Fig. 13.2.

Another method of testing whether the divergence from .00 is greater than can reasonably be attributed to chance is through the z_r transformation. By Table Z, the obtained r of .56 is converted to a z_r of .633. The standard error of z_r is independent of its size, and by Formula 13.10, is $1/\sqrt{N-3}$ or .24. The obtained z_r is .63/.24, or 2.63, standard errors above a z_r of .00. From Table A it is seen that in a normal distribution, the proportion of cases between the mean and 2.63σ is .495. Since the .5000 cases are above the mean, the expected proportion of cases above $+2.63\sigma$ is .0043, and again r can be taken as significantly different from .00 at better than the .01 level.

When N is large (say, 50 or more), an r may be tested for divergence from zero by Formula 13.7. Consider an r of .20 based upon $N = 50$. Here $s_{r_0} = 1/\sqrt{49}$, and $rs_{r_0} = .20 \div 1/7 = .20 \times 7 = 1.40$. Reference to Table A shows that in a normal distribution, the proportion of cases above 1.40σ is $(.5000 - .4192)$, or .0808. Accordingly, r is not high enough to reach the .05 level of significance. (To reach the .05 level in a one-direction test, the r would have to be $1.645s_{r_0}$; and for the .01 level, $2.326s_{r_0}$.)

APPLICATIONS OF THE z_r TRANSFORMATION

While the z_r transformation is not needed for testing the departure of an observed r from an $\hat{r}$ of .00, it has three important uses:

1. In setting limits, on the basis of an observed r, within which $\hat{r}$ is likely to be found;
2. In testing differences between r's; and
3. In averaging r's from different samples so as to obtain a single value representative of several coefficients.

The first two applications will be discussed in later sections.

When considered as covariances of z scores (standard scores with mean of zero and variance of unity), r's may be added to find a covariance involving a sum variable. However, r's as such cannot be added or averaged.

When two or more r's involving the same variables have been obtained from different samples, the most rigorous technique for finding the average of these r's involves the following steps:

1. Convert each r to the corresponding z_r (Table Z).
2. Correct each z_r by subtracting a correction term, $r/[2(N-1)]$. Strictly speaking, this should be $\hat{r}/[2(N-1)]$, but $\hat{r}$ is unknown.
3. Multiply each corrected z_r by the number of its degrees of freedom, $(N-3)$.
4. Obtain the sum of these results.
5. Divide this sum by the sum of all the degrees of freedom. This results in a mean corrected z_r value.
6. By the use of Table Z, convert this z_r to an r, which may then be considered the mean r over all the samples.

The use of corrected z_r is important when N's are small, and weighting by df is important when N's vary widely from sample to sample.

If N's are large and do not vary greatly from sample to sample, a simple mean of the z_r's is ordinarily sufficient.

Somewhat more approximate, but reasonably accurate, is the procedure of taking the quadratic mean of the correlations as the representative r. Thus

$$M_r \doteq \sqrt{\frac{\Sigma r^2}{n}} \qquad (13.11)$$

in which n is the number of r's. If all r's are low (say, .30 or less) little violence will be done if they are averaged directly, since in that case all r's are almost identical with corresponding z_r's.

THE NULL HYPOTHESIS AND TESTS OF SIGNIFICANCE

The testing through the use of s_{r_0} or t or s_{z_r} of whether an obtained coefficient of correlation varies from a posited parameter value of zero more than could be expected by chance is a concrete example of the use of what is called, in Fisher's terminology, a *null hypothesis*.

A null hypothesis need not be simply that $\hat{r}$ is zero, nor that there is a difference of zero between two parameters (such as means), although frequently it is either of these. A null hypothesis is far more general. It is a statement about one or more parameters (or characteristics of the population) cast in such form that probabilities of divergence from the hypothesis in defined and randomly selected samples can be precisely stated. This, of course, requires knowledge of the applicable distribution function, which most generally is the normal distribution, or t, or F, but which could be some other chance distribution, such as the binomial.

In all cases a null hypothesis assumes that in specific samples there are no differences from the posited parameter value, except those differences resulting purely from chance.

A null hypothesis can never be proved because, if no differences are found in one or more experiments, the possibility will always remain of discovering a difference in a subsequent study. However, a null hypothesis can be disproved, not absolutely, but at a certain level of significance, often denoted as α, the Greek letter alpha, which is written as a proportion. In the earlier discussion of the detection of association between two variables, two levels of significance are used, the 5 percent level ($\alpha = .05$) and the 1 percent level ($\alpha = .01$).

STEPS IN TESTING A HYPOTHESIS

The use of the null hypothesis permits a logical sequence in the development of inferences about a population parameter. The steps are:

1. Development of a hypothesis that if disproved would help to establish the research hypothesis;
2. Selection of an acceptable level of significance in the study;
3. Collection of measurements or other observations on a sample considered a representative of the population;
4. Decision, based on the known sampling distribution of the statistic employed, as to whether the observations (summarized as a statistic) are in accordance with the null hypothesis or whether, at the level of significance already selected, it has been disproved;
5. If the null hypothesis can no longer be accepted, evidence has been found for an alternate view, which eventually may come to be regarded as established.

The null hypothesis, then, is an integral part of the design of the study. It may or may not assume an experimental effect. It must, however, be exact and specific, and it must provide a basis by which all possible outcomes can be evaluated, usually by a table showing critical points of the sampling distribution of the statistic. The choice of α (the level of significance required for the hypothesis to be regarded as disproved) depends on the risk involved in an erroneous decision.

The place of the observed statistic in the sampling distribution is denoted as P, its probability. Figure 13.1 shows graphically the difference between one-sided and two-sided tests. If a two-sided test is required by the logic of the study, the function has to be cumulative so as to include both ends of the chance distribution.

The probability (or P) that a given statistic can occur only by chance if the null hypothesis is true is, of course, between .00 and 1.00. If it happens that an observed statistic has a very small P, there are two alternatives, either that the hypothesis is false or that a rare event has transpired. In general, if there is little likelihood that the specified statistic could have occurred by chance, the hypothesis is rejected. If P is large, the null hypothesis is accepted, pending further evidence.

ALTERNATIVES IN STATISTICAL TESTS

Figure 13.3 shows diagrammatically the four possibilities in statistical tests. The hypothesis is either correct or incorrect; the decision of the investigator is to accept it or reject it.

In two of the four cells of the figure, the decision is correct.

The situation when the hypothesis is correct but is rejected is known as *Type I error*, or "error of the first kind." A Type I error is a calculated risk because, for those cases in which the hypothesis is correct, its probability varies directly with and is actually α, the selected level of significance. In the instances in which the hypothesis is correct, and in which α is, say,

.05, 5 percent of the statistics computed on comparable samples would be expected, on the basis of chance also, to meet the criterion for rejection. Accordingly, 5 percent of the decisions for the instances in which the null hypothesis is correct would be in error.

FIG. 13.3. ALTERNATIVES IN STATISTICAL TESTS

ALTERNATIVES AS TO HYPOTHESIS	ALTERNATIVES AS TO DECISION	
	REJECT	ACCEPT
Hypothesis is correct	Type I Error	Decision is correct
Hypothesis is incorrect	Decision is correct	Type II Error

When the null hypothesis is in fact incorrect, the probability of making the correct decision (that is, to reject the hypothesis) is known as the *power* of the test. The acceptance of the null hypothesis when it is incorrect is known as *Type II error*, or "error of the second kind."

In the conduct of research, major attention is often given to increasing the power of the test applied to the statistics summarizing the observations. If α is increased, power is increased; but this step also increases the Type I error. In general, the methods of reducing Type II error are to use a more homogeneous population, to increase sample size, to decrease random errors of all kinds, and to seek to increase the experimental effect.

EVALUATION OF DIFFERENCES BETWEEN MEANS

The goal of a social science research study is often the discovery of a difference between the means of two groups measured on the same variable, or between the means of the same group on the same variable under different conditions.

With hardly an exception, pairs of observed means do differ, some fractionally, some by a considerable number of points on the scale that is being used. The fact that two sample means are not identical is never, in itself, of scientific interest. The question is always whether the two underlying parameters differ. In addition, there is often a question as to the size of the difference or of its practical importance. These questions would require analyses beyond those described here and might be answered in terms of a correlation or the proportion of a variance (both evaluated as to reliability) or in reference to a null hypothesis that a difference in the population was not more than a certain amount.

Here the null hypothesis is that the observed difference is no greater than could be expected by chance. The level of significance, α, is selected with reference to the consequences of erroneous decisions. Routinely, precautions are taken to reduce errors, whether of observations or induced by variation extraneous to the problem of concern. Methods of sampling, of experimental control, and of measurement all need to be considered in the design of any study. Here the discussion is limited to procedures for evaluating the reliability of a difference, that is, for determining whether at a stated level of significance (α) the observed difference between two sample means reflects a difference between two parameters. It is always assumed that proper controls have been imposed on outside sources of variance.

UNCORRELATED AND CORRELATED MEANS

The statistical test of the reliability of a difference varies according to whether the samples are small or large, and according to whether the means are uncorrelated or correlated.

Two sample means cannot be "correlated" in the sense that a correlation coefficient can be computed between them. The variables on which the means are based may, however, be correlated if each value in one set is coupled with a value in the other set. This, of course, requires that the N for the two means be identical, either through the use of the same subjects or by some pertinent linkage, such as father-son or mother-daughter. Two sets of means representing variables correlated in the population would of themselves have a correlation in that in successive pairs of samples they would tend to vary together. This is the meaning of the concept of *correlated means*, or of other correlated statistics such as variances or correlation coefficients.

DIFFERENCES BETWEEN UNCORRELATED MEANS

Since M_x is normally distributed if the sample is drawn from a normal population or if N is large, it is reasonable to believe (what is actually the case) that the difference between two means $(M_1 - M_2)$ is normally distributed around the parameter, $(\mu_1 - \mu_2)$. To evaluate such an obtained difference, the sampling distribution of an unlimited series of differences based upon samples drawn at random from two unlimited populations must be known. The theoretical standard deviation of such a series of differences is the standard error of the difference of the means, which may be indicated as $s_{\text{diff.}M}$ or $s_{M_1-M_2}$. There are two forms of this standard error: one when the means are uncorrelated and another when they are correlated.

For uncorrelated means,

$$s_{M_1-M_1} = \sqrt{s_{M_1}{}^2 + s_{M_2}{}^2} \tag{13.12}$$

in which $s_M{}^2$ is the square of the standard error of the mean by Formula 13.3a and the two groups are designated as 1 and 2.

When two means are drawn from normally distributed populations (or are based on large numbers of cases), the difference $(M_1 - M_2)$ is normally distributed. If the population variances, $\sigma_1{}^2$ and $\sigma_2{}^2$, are known, then $(M_1 - M_2)/s_{M_1-M_2}$ is normally distributed with unit variance. On the hypothesis that there is no difference between the two means, this ratio of the difference divided by the standard error of the difference can be evaluated directly from a table of the normal curve (Table A, Appendix) either as a one-sided or a two-sided test, depending on the logic of the situation.

The reason why $(M_1 - M_2)/s_{M_1-M_2}$ has unit variance is, of course, because $s_{M_1-M_2}$ is the standard deviation of the distribution of the differences between means. If the parameter difference is zero, then any obtained difference is in z score form.

An important fact is that when $s_{M_1-M_2}$ is estimated from the variances of small samples rather than found from population variances, the ratio $(M_1 - M_2)/s_{M_1-M_2}$ is no longer distributed normally but follows the t distribution with an appropriate number of degrees of freedom. If the population variances can be assumed to be equal, as is ordinarily plausible, then the number of degrees of freedom can be taken as $(N_1 + N_2 - 2)$, and $s_{M_1-M_2}$ is computed as follows:

$$s_{M_1-M_2} \doteq \sqrt{\left(\frac{N_1V_1 + N_2V_2}{N_1 + N_2 - 2}\right)\left(\frac{N_1 + N_2}{N_1N_2}\right)} \tag{13.12a}$$

As stated in Chapter 12, the t distribution becomes a closer and closer approximation to the normal as the number of degrees of freedom becomes large. Accordingly, with large samples (say, 30 or more in each group) $s_{M_1-M_2}$ can be estimated as

$$s_{M_1-M_2} = \sqrt{s_{M_1}{}^2 + s_{M_2}{}^2} \doteq \sqrt{\frac{N_1\Sigma X_1{}^2 - (\Sigma X_1)^2}{N_1{}^2(N_1 - 1)} + \frac{N_2\Sigma X_2{}^2 - (\Sigma X_2)^2}{N_2{}^2(N_2 - 1)}} \tag{13.12b}$$

In this situation the difference between the means divided by $s_{M_1-M_2}$ as found from Formula 13.12b can be taken as normally distributed, and the hypothesis that the parameter difference is zero can be tested through the use of the normal distribution.

The testing of differences between uncorrelated means is illustrated in Example 13.2.

EXAMPLE 13.2

TESTING THE SIGNIFICANCE BETWEEN TWO UNCORRELATED MEANS

Definition. Two means are "uncorrelated" if the two sets of observations involve cases that can in no way be matched. Ordinarily, the two means are based on the same variable.

Small Sample Method. An obtained difference between two means ($M_1 - M_2$) divided by $s_{M_1 - M_2}$, as found by Formula 13.12a can be tested by the t distribution. When samples are small ($30 > N$), the use of t is considered essential. An arithmetical example is given below:

$$N_1 = 8 \qquad M_1 = 7.5 \qquad V_1 = \Sigma x_1^2 / N_1 = 7.0$$
$$N_2 = 10 \qquad M_2 = 9.4 \qquad V_2 = \Sigma x_2^2 / N_2 = 6.5$$

$$t = \frac{M_1 - M_2}{s_{M_1} - M_2} = \frac{M_1 - M_2}{\sqrt{\left(\dfrac{N_1 V_1 + N_2 V_2}{N_1 + N_2 - 2}\right)\left(\dfrac{N_1 + N_2}{N_1 N_2}\right)}}$$

$$= \frac{9.4 - 7.5}{\sqrt{\left(\dfrac{(8 \times 7.0) + (10 \times 6.5)}{8 + 10 - 2}\right)\left(\dfrac{8 + 10}{8 \times 10}\right)}} = 1.46$$

Evaluating the Obtained t by Table T. In testing the significance of the difference between two means, a hypothesis as to their relative direction generally exists. If a conventional teaching method has been used in group 1 and a novel technique has been tried out in group 2, the introduction of the new procedure implies the expectation that it may be better than, rather than merely different from, the old. Hence the "one-tailed" test of the null hypothesis is appropriate.

Table T (Appendix) includes instruction as to how it is to be entered for "one-tailed" and "two-tailed" tests. In the example given above, $v = N_1 + N_2 - 2$; that is, there are $18 df$ for which the critical points from Table T are

TEST	.05 LEVEL	.01 LEVEL
One-tailed	1.73	2.55
Two-tailed	2.10	2.88

Since $t = 1.46$, it clearly does not meet the requirement of significance at, say, the .05 level (which, of course, would be established prior to the statistical analysis).

"Significance" is greatly affected by the number of cases. When N's are large, a relatively small difference may serve to disprove the null hypothesis.

With large N's the standard error of the difference of Formula 13.12 can be written

$$s_{M_1 - M_2} = \sqrt{s_{M_1}^2 + s_{M_2}^2} \doteq \sqrt{\frac{V_1}{N_1 - 1} + \frac{V_2}{N_2 - 1}}$$

Consider the numerical example above, with $N_1 = 80$ and $N_2 = 100$, but with means and variance remaining unchanged. The difference divided by the standard error of the difference (a statistic sometimes called the *critical ratio*) may be written as

$$\frac{M_1 - M_2}{s_{M_1} - _{M_2}} = \frac{9.4 - 7.5}{\sqrt{\dfrac{7.0}{79} + \dfrac{6.5}{99}}} = \frac{1.9}{.393} = 4.83$$

Both Table A and Fig. 13.1 show that a value of 4.83σ is so far above a parameter mean difference of zero that the null hypothesis is refuted at better than the .01 level of confidence.

DIFFERENCES BETWEEN CORRELATED MEANS

A frequent problem in educational and psychological research is the evaluation of a series of differences of pairs of scores, using the hypothesis of no difference between the means as the hypothesis to be tested. In this case the means are correlated and Formulas 13.12, 13.12a, and 13.12b for $s_{M_1-M_2}$ do not apply.

The simplest procedure is to find the difference (D) between the two scores for each case, summing these differences with regard to algebraic sign to find ΣD, and summing the squares of the differences to find ΣD^2.

Then, for small samples,

$$t = \frac{M_1 - M_2}{s_{M_1-M_2}} \doteq \frac{\Sigma D \sqrt{N-1}}{\sqrt{N \Sigma D^2 - (\Sigma D)^2}} \tag{13.13}$$

in which N is the number of differences, which may be evaluated as t with $(N-1)$ degrees of freedom.

When N is large, t may be taken as z and evaluated from a table of the normal curve.

The standard error of the difference between correlated means may be obtained from a modification of Formula 13.12, which includes a correlation term for samples that are not independent:

$$s_{M_1-M_2} = \sqrt{s_{M_1}{}^2 - 2r_{12}s_{M_1}s_{M_2} + s_{M_2}{}^2} \tag{13.14}$$

This formula is sometimes useful, as when pairs of scores are not immediately available. The use of both formulas is illustrated in Example 13.3.

EXAMPLE 13.3

TESTING THE DIFFERENCE BETWEEN CORRELATED MEANS

Sanford (7) reports the following recognition distances in centimeters for lower case letters for two observers H and J. Differences, D, and squares of differences, D^2, are also shown.

LETTER	OBSERVED VALUES		DIFFERENCES		LETTER	OBSERVED VALUES		DIFFERENCES	
	H	J	D	D^2		H	J	D	D^2
a	13	12	1	1	n	15	14	1	1
b	16	16	0	0	o	13	13	0	0
c	13	11	2	4	p	16	16	0	0
d	16	14	2	4	q	16	16	0	0
e	12	8	4	16	r	15	15	0	0
f	15	17	−2	4	s	13	12	1	1
g	14	16	−2	4	t	14	14	0	0
h	16	14	2	4	u	15	13	2	4
i	13	13	0	0	v	16	17	−1	1
j	16	17	−1	1	w	17	17	0	0
k	16	14	2	4	x	16	15	1	1
l	15	13	2	4	y	16	19	−3	9
m	18	18	0	0	z	13	13	0	0

The two sets of values are matched by letter and are correlated. Accordingly, tests for correlated means are appropriate. For the t test by Formula 13.13, the following constants are needed:

$$N = 26 \qquad \Sigma D = 11 \qquad \Sigma D^2 = 63$$

The algebraic sign of the differences is arbitrary. Interpretation of the result would be unchanged if signs were reversed and ΣD became -11. Taking ΣD as positive,

$$t = \frac{\Sigma D \sqrt{N-1}}{\sqrt{N \Sigma D^2 - (\Sigma D)^2}} = \frac{55}{\sqrt{1517}} = 1.41$$

If ΣD were taken as negative, t would be -1.41. A two-tailed test is required, since the appropriate null hypothesis is that there is no difference in either direction in the two population means. Here the "population" is regarded as one of letters. Let us establish in advance the 5 percent level as the arbitrary level of significance that we shall accept as indicating a real difference in the means of the two observers. To evaluate the obtained difference (in this case, 11/26), we need to estimate what proportion of t's would fall outside the limits of $+1.41$ and -1.41 in an unlimited series of samples, if there were no difference between means. The expected proportion of such t is taken as the P value, or probability.

The number of degrees of freedom is 1 less than N, the number of pairs of observations, and in this case is 25. From Table T it is seen that for $25df$, a t greater than 1.41 or less than -1.41 would be expected more than 10 percent of the time; that is, $P > .10$. Accordingly, a difference between the means cannot be considered to have been demonstrated.

Formula 13.14 yields a similar interpretation, but requires computations as follows:

$$\Sigma X_H = 388 \qquad \Sigma X_J = 377 \qquad \Sigma X_H X_J = 5699$$
$$\Sigma X_H^2 = 5848 \qquad \Sigma X_J^2 = 5613 \qquad r = .79$$

By Formula 5.1,

$$M_H = \frac{388}{26} = 14.92$$

$$M_J = \frac{377}{26} = 14.50$$

By Formula 5.8a,

$$s_H = \tfrac{1}{26} \sqrt{26 \times 5848 - (388)^2} = 1.49$$

$$s_J = \tfrac{1}{26} \sqrt{26 \times 5613 - (377)^2} = 2.37$$

To estimate the standard error of the mean, Formula 13.3 may be written as

$$s_M \doteq \frac{s_x}{\sqrt{N-1}}$$

in which s_x is the sample standard deviation rather than the parameter as estimated by Formula 13.2 Accordingly, $s_{M_H} \doteq .30$, and $s_{M_J} \doteq .47$.

By Formula 13.14 the standard error of the difference between the two means is

$$s_{M_H - M_J} = \sqrt{s_{M_H}^2 - 2r_{HJ}s_{M_H}s_{M_J} + s_{M_J}^2}$$

$$= \sqrt{(.30)^2 - 2(.79)(.30)(.47) + (.47)^2} = .30$$

An obtained difference divided by its standard error is sometimes called a *critical ratio*. When *df* is less than 30, as in this case, it must be interpreted as a *t*. Hence,

$$t = \frac{14.92 - 14.50}{.30} = \frac{.42}{.30} = 1.40$$

which is approximately the same as that obtained more simply by the direct method demonstrated above. In practice, the formula involving r is used when means, standard deviations, and the correlation are known, but when original observations are no longer available.

TESTING DIFFERENCES BETWEEN CORRELATIONS

If the correlation between two variables is computed in two independent samples, the question as to whether the obtained difference between the r can be attributed to chance can be tested through the use of the z_r transformation (Table Z) and the normal distribution. Since the difference between any two normally distributed variables is itself distributed normally, and since the distribution of z_r is approximately normal with a standard error of $\sqrt{1/(N-3)}$, it is necessary only to:

1. Convert both the r to z_r.
2. Find the difference between the z_r.
3. Divide this difference by $s_{z_1 - z_2}$.

4. Evaluate the ratio by means of a table of the normal curve. On the condition that both samples have been randomly selected from the same population, the ratio $(z_{r_1} - z_{r_2})/s_{z_1 - z_2}$ has a mean of zero and unit variance.

The formula for the standard error of the difference between two such correlations may be written as

$$s_{z_1 - z_2} = \sqrt{s_{z_1}{}^2 + s_{z_2}{}^2} = \left[\frac{1}{N_1 - 3} + \frac{1}{N_2 - 3}\right] = \left[\frac{N_1 + N_2 - 6}{(N_1 - 3)(N_2 - 3)}\right] \quad (13.15)$$

A very different situation is the testing of the difference between two correlations obtained on the same sample, and with one variable in common. In Formula 13.16, this common variable is denoted as variable 3. By the procedure about to be described, it is possible to test whether, for example, the obtained correlation of a vocabulary test with measured scholastic achievement differs significantly from the obtained correlation of a verbal analogies test with the same criterion.

Here the t test applies, t being found from

$$t = (r_{13} - r_{23})\sqrt{\frac{N - 3}{2(1 - r_{12})(1 - R^2_{3(12)})}} \quad (13.16)$$

in which the correlations among the three variables are r_{12}, r_{13}, and r_{23}, and where $R^2_{3(12)}$ is the square of the multiple correlation between the common variable and the weighted sum of the other two.

The t found from Formula 13.16 is evaluated with a table of t (such as Table T), with $(N - 3)$ being the number of degrees of freedom.

The use of these procedures for evaluating differences between r's is illustrated in Example 13.4.

EXAMPLE 13.4

TESTING DIFFERENCES BETWEEN CORRELATIONS

The Difference Between the r in Two Samples. The following correlations between the Stanford Binet and the Army Beta were reported for two samples of World War I recruits (8). Conversions to z_r by Table Z (Appendix) are shown below:

SAMPLE	N	r	z_r
Camp Dix	93	.744	.9594
Camp Jackson	102	.649	.7738

Since z_r is regarded as normally distributed, a difference between z_r's is divided by the standard error of the difference (as given by Formula 13.15) and the resultant ratio is evaluated in terms of the normal frequency distribution. The null hypothesis would be that there is no difference in either direction between parameters represented by observed r's. Accordingly, a two-tailed test of significance is appropriate. This requires a $D/s_{z_r-z_r}$ of 1.96 or more for significance at the 5 percent level and of 2.58 or more for significance at the 1 percent level.

By Formula 13.15,

$$s_{z_r-z_r} = \sqrt{\frac{N_1 + N_2 - 6}{(N_1 - 3)(N_2 - 3)}} = \sqrt{\frac{93 + 102 - 6}{90 \times 99}} = .146$$

Accordingly,

$$\frac{D}{s_{z_r-z_r}} = \frac{(.9594 - .7736)}{.146} = 1.27$$

which is less than the 1.96 required for significance at the 5 percent level. (It can also be seen from Table A that 1.27σ falls within the middle 80 percent of a normal distribution.) The conclusion is that an r of .744 based on 93 cases and an r of .649 for 102 cases cannot be regarded as significantly different.

The Difference Between Two r in the Same Sample. As reported in the same source (8), E. K. Strong secured ratings by superiors for the intelligence of 313 men in three national guard companies. Intercorrelations of three variables, the oral directions and memory span subtests of Group Examination *a* (a forerunner of the Army Alpha) and the ratings, are as follows ($N = 313$):

	2.	3.
1. Oral directions	.53	.47
2. Memory span		.34
3. Rating		

In advance of computations, let us decide that a difference significant at the 5 percent level will lead us to reject the null hypothesis of no real difference between the r. Also, it is to be noted that a two-tailed test would be called for in the absence of a hypothesis as to the direction of a difference between the r.

In Formula 13.16 for t, the quantity $(1 - R^2_{3(12)})$ is $V_{3.12}$, a second-order partial variance that can be found by the method for finding multiple R demonstrated in Chapter 7 as follows:

	1	2	3
1	1.0000	.5300	.4700
2	.5300	1.0000	.3400
3	.4700		1.0000
		.7191	.0909
		.1264	.7791

$$V_{3.12} = .7676$$

Then,

$$t = (r_{13} - r_{23}) \sqrt{\frac{N-3}{2(1-r_{12})(1-R^2_{3(12)})}}$$

$$= (.47 - .34) \sqrt{\frac{310}{2 \times .47 \times .768}} = 2.69$$

By Table T, a value of 2.69 for 310 df is significant at slightly better than the 1 percent level. Since a t of 1.97 would have been sufficient to cause us to reject the null hypothesis, a difference in the r's may be considered to be demonstrated.

Of course, as with significance tests in general, a statistically significant difference in r's may or may not have important practical consequences. However, if either the oral directions test or memory span test is to be used as a predictor, the former is the better choice in this case.

DEPARTURE OF A STATISTIC FROM A HYPOTHETICAL VALUE

When used for research, which aims at the discovery of general principles applicable to populations, obtained statistics are estimates of corresponding parameters. As discussed earlier, some statistics, such as the mean, are "unbiased" in the sense that they exhibit no systematic warping in either direction, the descriptive statistic being the best possible approximation of the parameter obtainable from the particular sample. Other statistics, such as the variance, require a correction when used as estimates of population values. In all cases, however, the statistic, as computed or as slightly modified, is a single value that constitutes a "point estimate" of the corresponding parameter.

When the distribution of a statistic is known, the probability that an obtained statistic departs from any fixed value can be determined. Previous discussions in this chapter have exhibited several cases in which the fixed value was taken as zero. Thus, the reliability of a correlation coefficient was discussed in terms of the likelihood of an observed r departing from an $\hat{r}$ of zero. Also, the reliability of the difference between two means or between two r was discussed in terms of the probability of the parameter value of the difference being greater than zero.

The likelihood of the departure of an observed statistic from any hypothetical value can be tested, provided the sampling distribution of the statistic around that value is known. The situation is simplest when the statistic (or its transformation) divided by the appropriate standard error is normally distributed.

Consider the case in which it is wished to discover whether an obtained r of .80 (based on 67 cases) differs significantly at the 5 percent level from an $\hat{r}$ of .70. Since Fisher's z_r transformation of r can be regarded as normally distributed with standard error of $1/\sqrt{N-3}$, z_r equivalents for both r and the hypothetical $\hat{r}$ are found from Table Z, and the difference is tested by dividing by s_{z_r}. For an r of .80, $z_r = 1.099$, and for an $\hat{r}$ of .70, $z_r = .867$. Since a one-sided test is appropriate, it may be deduced from Table A that for significance at the 5 percent level, the ratio $(z_r - z_{\hat{r}})/s_{z_r}$ must be 1.645 or more. Since the obtained ratio (.232/.125) is 1.86, r may be regarded as significantly different from .70 at the 5 percent level.

It may be noted that if the decision at the appropriate time (namely, in advance of computation) had been to use the 1 percent level of significance, a difference of 2.327 standard errors would have been required. Accordingly, the obtained r of .80 would not have been regarded as significantly different from a hypothetical population value of .70.

CONFIDENCE INTERVALS

Another way of utilizing statistical information from a sample is to develop limits within which a given parameter is likely to be found. While for any sample the inference that the parameter is within these limits is either correct or incorrect, an α of, say, .05 indicates confidence that the parameters will fall within the established limits in 96 out of 100 similar samples drawn from the same population. In this way, two statistics of unequal value provide a joint estimate of an interval that is likely to include the parameter.

The first step is to choose a "confidence coefficient" (which may be denoted as "conf.") such as .95 or .99. "Conf." is the complement of α, the probability that the parameter is outside the limits. Since two limits are involved, the procedure resembles a "two-sided" test of significance, and probability tables are entered accordingly. Let μ be the parameter corresponding to any normally distributed statistic and let U and L be the upper and lower confidence limits for the confidence coefficient of $(1 - \alpha)$. Then

$$\text{Conf. } (U > \mu > L) = 1 - \alpha \tag{13.17}$$

which is a formal statement of the situation described above. Strictly speaking, the inequality sign $>$ in Formula 13.17 should be written $\geqslant$, indicating "equal to or greater than," but it is assumed here for purposes of simplifying the discussion that no parameter falls precisely at a limit.

In a normal distribution, .025 of the cases are above $+1.96\sigma$ and .025 are below -1.96σ. Arbitrarily designating any normally distributed statistic as $\dot{X}$ and its standard error as $s_{\dot{x}}$, two equations must be solved to establish a confidence interval of .95:

$$\frac{\dot{X} - L}{s_{\dot{x}}} = 1.96 \quad \text{and} \quad \frac{U - \dot{X}}{s_{\dot{x}}} = -1.96 \tag{13.18}$$

Similarly, .005 of the cases of a normally distributed variable are above 2.58σ and .005 below -2.58σ. Thus the equations to be solved to establish U and L for a confidence coefficient of .99 are

$$\frac{U - \dot{X}}{s_{\dot{x}}} = -2.58 \quad \text{and} \quad \frac{\dot{X} - L}{s_{\dot{x}}} = +2.58 \qquad (13.18a)$$

This procedure applies to establishing confidence limits for statistics such as the mean for large samples, r (through the z_r transformation), and p, the proportion of cases falling in one of two categories.

When the statistic, divided by its estimated standard error, follows the t distribution, the procedure is modified so as to employ values of $\pm t$ corresponding to the chosen α and the appropriate number of degrees of freedom.

Example 13.5 gives numerical examples of establishing confidence limits for normally distributed statistics, and Example 13.6 illustrates the determination of confidence intervals for a mean based on a small number of cases.

EXAMPLE 13.5

CONFIDENCE LIMITS FOR A NORMALLY DISTRIBUTED STATISTIC

As noted in the text, if a parameter is normally distributed and known, the standard error is the standard deviation of the statistic as computed in successive random samples with constant N. Generally, however, the parameter is unavailable and the center of the distribution remains unknown. If the statistic is known to be normally distributed and a good estimate of the standard error is available, it is possible to establish confidence (or fiduciary) limits within which the parameter (which has a unique value) is, at a stated level of probability, likely to be found.

For an observed mean of 28.0 with an estimated s_M of 2.1, what are the confidence limits within which the parameter is likely to be found, with a probability of .95? In Formula 13.18, upper and lower limits are designated as U and L. Then,

$$\frac{28.0 - L}{2.1} = 1.96 \quad \text{and} \quad \frac{U - 28.0}{2.1} = 1.96$$

Solving, $L = 23.9$ and $U = 32.1$

For the same date, what are the confidence limits within which the probability is .99 that the parameter will fall? By Formula 13.18a,

$$\frac{28.0 - L}{2.1} = 2.58 \quad \text{and} \quad \frac{U - 28.0}{2.1} = 2.58$$

Solving, $L = 22.6$ and $U = 33.4$

A higher probability, of course, requires a wider confidence interval than would a lower probability, and this is reflected in the changes in the upper and lower limits.

EXAMPLE 13.6

CONFIDENCE LIMITS FOR A MEAN WHEN N IS SMALL

If N is small, conventionally 30 or less, the ratio $(M - \mu)/s_M$ is not normally distributed, but rather follows the t distribution with $(N - 1)df$. Accordingly, Formulas 13.18 and 13.18a must be modified by finding from a table of the t function (such as Table T) the appropriate constants for the right-hand side of each equation.

As in Example 13.5, let us consider an observed mean of 28.0 with estimated s_M of 2.1. However, instead of M being based on a large number of observations, as was implied in Example 13.5, let $N = 12$. What now are the confidence limits for confidence coefficients of .95 and .99?

In Table T we use the line for $(N - 1)$ as $11 df$. A confidence coefficient of .95 requires the points beyond which .05 of the distribution is likely to fall. In other words, we need the value of t for a two-sided test when $P = .05$. In this case $t = 2.201$.

Formula 13.18 now becomes

$$\frac{28.0 - L}{2.1} = 2.201 \quad \text{and} \quad \frac{U - 28.0}{2.1} = 2.201$$

Solving, $L = 23.4 \quad \text{and} \quad U = 32.6$

Similarly, when $df = 11$ and $P = .01$, $t = 3.106$. By Formula 13.18a we have

$$\frac{28.0 - L}{2.1} = 3.106 \quad \text{and} \quad \frac{U - 28.0}{2.1} = 3.106$$

which give the lower confidence limits for a confidence coefficient of .99 as 21.5 and the upper limit of 34.5.

By the methods demonstrated in this example and in Example 13.5, it becomes possible to specify with stated probability the band of values within which the unique value that is the parameter is likely to be found.

It can be seen that confidence limits include the range of possible parameter values such that the hypothesis of no difference between each one of these values and $\dot{X}$, the observed statistic, is not violated at level α. For any given confidence coefficient, the range becomes narrower as N is increased. Should the sample become coextensive with the population, the confidence interval would, of course, be reduced to a single point.

SUMMARY

Modern mathematical statistics centers on the development of valid inferences about the population or inferences based on investigations in particular samples.

When samples are representative, probability theory provides a basis for the exact sampling distributions of various statistics, the development of the best possible estimates of parameters, and the use of testable hypotheses in utilizing specific observations as the basis for sound generalizations.

EXERCISES

1. Below are ΣX and ΣX^2 for 50 samples of 25 cases, each of single-digit scores on a college level reading test.

ΣX	ΣX^2	ΣX	ΣX^2	ΣX	ΣX^2	ΣX	ΣX^2	ΣX	ΣX^2
133	873	123	689	122	786	106	552	118	642
125	693	133	785	110	626	118	660	123	691
121	657	127	733	133	843	138	876	127	781
133	819	124	706	104	536	100	522	117	641
103	517	101	499	133	803	110	580	121	733
122	716	112	548	105	501	121	649	110	622
130	748	120	688	125	751	115	635	114	640
114	610	103	543	118	682	112	572	128	736
131	835	125	727	146	944	115	681	110	554
139	877	132	844	136	802	125	711	115	603

$$N = 1250 \qquad \Sigma X = 6026 \qquad \Sigma X^2 = 34{,}462$$

Choose at random one of the samples as the "observed sample," and from ΣX and ΣX^2 estimate s_M. Compare s_M so estimated with the actual standard deviation of the 50 observed means.

2. Studying 32 octopus vulgaris lamarck, Muntz (5) reported that there were more attacks on a vertical rectangle than on a horizontal rectangle. With $31 df$, $t = 4.21$. Evaluate the significance of the difference.

3. In a study by Kates, Yudin, and Tiffany (3) total times in seconds for solving certain problems were as follows:

	N	M	s
Older hearing group	30	11.83	6.58
Deaf group	30	12.85	6.28
Younger hearing group	30	10.32	7.13

Test the hypothesis that the older hearing group and the deaf group do not differ significantly.

4. In an appropriately selected random sample of 145 cases, the correlation between two variables is observed to be .15. Test whether it is reasonable to believe that the parameter r is positive rather than zero or negative.

5. Panton (6) gives the following data on the Pd (psychopathic deviate) scale of the Minnesota multiphasic personality inventory for nonhabitual and habitual criminals:

	NONHABITUAL CRIMINALS	HABITUAL CRIMINALS
Mean	65.9	75.7
s	9.7	10.3
N	50	50

Test whether the difference in means is significantly different from zero.

6. In one sample of 25 cases, the observed correlation between two variables was .40; in a second sample of 40 cases, it was .30. Can the difference in the *r*'s be attributed to chance?

7. For 37 cases at age 9, Goodenough (2) found a correlation of .728 between the Stanford Binet mental age and the Draw-a-Man mental age. What are the limits for this *r* for a confidence coefficient of .99?

8. For 255 student pilots, Melton (4) reports that the validity of a practice trial on a complex coordination test was .24 compared with a validity on the first regular trial of .31. The correlation between the two predictors, practice trial and first regular trial, was .66. Is there a difference between the two *r*'s?

REFERENCES

1. FISHER, R. A., *Statistical Methods for Research Workers*. Edinburgh and London: Oliver and Boyd, 1936.

2. GOODENOUGH, FLORENCE L., *Measurement of Intelligence by Drawings*. New York: Harcourt, Brace and World, 1926.

3. KATES, S. L., YUDIN, L., AND TIFFANY, R. K., "Concept attainment by deaf and hearing adolescents," *J. Educ. Psychol.*, 1962, **53**, 119–126.

4. MELTON, ARTHUR W. (ED.), *Apparatus Tests*. Report No. 4, AAF Aviation Psychology Program Research Reports. Washington, D.C.: U.S. Government Printing Office, 1947.

5. MUNTZ, W. R. A., "Stimulus generalization following monocular training in octopus," *J. Comp. Physiol. Psychol.*, 1962, **55**, 535–540.

6. PANTON, J. H., "The identification of habitual criminalism with the MMPI," *J. Clin. Psychol.*, 1962, **18**, 133–136.

7. SANFORD, E. C., "The relative legibility of the small letters," *Am. J. Psychol.*, 1887–1888, **1**, 402–435.

8. YERKES, ROBERT M. (ED.), *Memoirs of the National Academy of Sciences* Washington, D.C.: U.S. Government Printing Office, 1921, XV.

ANALYSIS
OF VARIANCE

14

Many of the results of educational and psychological experiments (as of experiments in other fields, such as agriculture, where the method was first applied) are reported in terms of *analysis of variance*. The term covers a large body of statistical knowledge and practice, originally organized by Fisher, and in recent years extended by other mathematical statisticians. The scope of this text permits only a short introduction to the topic.

In all its ramifications, analysis of variance involves logical application and extension of techniques already described. It employs means, deviations from means, variances, estimates of error, and in advanced work that includes the "analysis of covariance," various reflections of correlation. From the point of view of the types of variables considered, this method is far more flexible than correlational analysis, since only the dependent variable need be scaled in units. Theoretically, any number of independent variables may be used, although, in practice, few studies use more than two or three and many use only one. Often the independent variables are nominal scales or two or three degrees of some scaled variate. As the number of independent variables and the number of their categories or degrees increase, the arithmetic of the analysis of variance tends to become somewhat difficult to follow. Here, only the simplest cases are considered.

F DISTRIBUTION IN ANALYSIS OF VARIANCE

The most distinctive characteristic of the analysis of variance is its use of the F distribution, discovered by Fisher in the early 1920s. As described in Chapter 12, each F distribution is a chance distribution of the ratio of two variances, each with its stated degrees of freedom and each based on values drawn at random from the same normally distributed population. There is a separate F distribution for each pair of v's, and the published tables, such as Tables F_1 and F_5 (Appendix), generally give only two points for each distribution: the point exceeded by 5 percent of the ratios purely by chance and the point exceeded by 1 percent.

The test of significance that is the core of analysis of variance is the "F test." It involves finding the ratio of two variances which, if a stated null hypothesis were true, would fall inside a specified point of the appropriate F distribution. If this variance ratio falls beyond the 5 percent (or 1 percent) point of the particular F distribution, determined by the degrees of freedom of the two variances concerned, then the null hypothesis is rejected at the 5 percent (or 1 percent) level of significance. Thus, in the analysis of variance, testing of hypotheses follows the same basic procedures as those discussed in Chapter 13, except for the use of a novel statistic (the variance ratio) and F, its distribution.

NEW EMPHASES IN THE ANALYSIS OF VARIANCE

In addition to the distinctive feature of the variance ratio, certain important emphases are found in discussions of analysis of variance, most of which have been discussed in preceding chapters. These include:

1. The insistence that the primary objective of statistical analysis is to make inferences about the population—inferences that have general validity—rather than merely the description of a particular sample.

2. The use of a precise mathematical model in the form of the exact distribution of a key statistic that would be expected by random sampling if a given null hypothesis were true. This involves careful attention to the degrees of freedom, since with the small samples that are characteristic of much experimental work, the shapes of certain chance distributions (notably t and F) change markedly with variations in the degrees of freedom.

3. The development of precise hypotheses that can be tested by collecting observations. The null hypothesis can be developed in a wide variety of forms, but it is always exact, and potentially it can always be refuted (not absolutely, but at a given level of significance). Among its more useful forms are "no experimental effect" or "no difference among means," but forms that include posited parameters other than zero can be readily established.

4. The use of fixed levels in judging significance. With the normal distribution, it is mechanically simple to evaluate the rarity of an event without regard to a fixed level, such as the 5 percent level or the 1 percent level. With F (as with t), complete tables would be cumbersome, since each change in the degrees of freedom involves a new distribution. The advantage of fixed levels, however, is not merely mechanical. By deciding on a fixed level of significance in advance, standards for rejecting null hypotheses become objective for the course of the experiment, and interpretations of outcomes are less likely to be influenced by subjective considerations.

5. The use of methods to control extraneous variation that might obscure results. These include eliminating variables and sources of variation, matching subjects to form equivalent samples, and using chance procedures, particularly tables of random numbers, to make assignments to groups.

6. Systematic designing of the experiment in advance, so that the maximum amount of useful information can be extracted from the observations.

STUDY OF DIFFERENCES AMONG MEANS

In the analysis of variance the question that is always asked is whether the differences among a set of sample means of scores on the criterion or dependent variable are greater than what would be expected if the samples were drawn from the same population. The samples, except for differences on the dependent variable (or variables) must be equivalent at the beginning of the study. If no differences are found among the means (at the chosen level of significance), the null hypothesis is accepted; if the differences are statistically significant, the null hypothesis is rejected.

Analysis of variance used only as a test of a null hypothesis results neither in the estimation of the magnitude of parameters nor in statements as to the degree of relationship between variables, and it is often a preliminary type of analysis. A study indicating an experimental effect of some sort on a dependent variable might lead to a further study that would aim to obtain more precise information as to the effect of variation in the independent variable.

In the sense that it tests differences among any number of means simultaneously, analysis of variance represents a generalization of the t test described in Chapter 13 for the difference between two means.

As will be seen later, analysis of variance provides a convenient format for the arithmetic of one or more tests of significance from a set of data. Through its use, a mass of statistical data can be summarized in a format in which the presence of influences and trends may be readily appreciated.

TERMINOLOGY AND NOTATION

SOME SPECIAL TERMS

With the development of the analysis of variance as a statistical method, certain special terms and symbols have been introduced. Some will be noted here; more will be presented later. Since analysis of variance originally developed in the context of agricultural research, it includes terms from that source, notably "plots" and "treatments." Other words and phrases have been modified from earlier statistical terminology.

The phrase "sum of squares" always refers to the sum of squares of deviations, either from the grand mean of all the values or from submeans. A "sum of squares" divided by the appropriate number of degrees of freedom (the number of values less one) becomes a "mean square," or an estimate of population variance, here denoted at V. Thus $\Sigma x^2/(N - 1) = V_x$.

If the sum of squares or mean square is derived by finding (in effect, not necessarily directly) the deviation of each value from the mean of all values, it may be distinguished by the subscript t (for total). Similar values for "between groups" (or treatments) or for "within groups" (or treatments) may be designated with the subscripts b and w, respectively.

ARRANGEMENT OF DATA

Very often it is pertinent to analyze the values used in an analysis of variance in a rectangular, two-way classification, as shown in Table 14.1. In such an arrangement the number of rows may be denoted as r, the number of columns c, and these same letters may be used as subscripts wherever needed. At the intersection of any row and any column is a "cell."

A double subscript notation is convenient in identifying entries within a row and within a column. If the rows are designated as $i = 1, 2 \cdots r$ and the columns $j = 1, 2 \cdots c$, then any single cell value X may be identified with a first subscript indicating row and a second subscript indicating column. (The order is universal, and comes from a convention in matrix algebra.) Thus X_{32} refers to the entry in the third row and second column.

This rectangular arrangement has various applications, some of which will be encountered only in advanced work in analysis of variance. In Table 14.1, columns represent treatments, and the rows represent subjects or observations. Table 14.1 shows four "treatments," or "levels," in the independent variable and ten observations within each treatment. While the term *level* may seem to imply some sort of ordering of the independent variable, such a connotation is not necessarily present. "Levels" may refer merely to the several categories of a nominal variable.

The number of "treatments," or "levels," within an independent variable may be denoted as k; the number of observations (or subjects) within each treatment, as n. For a simple analysis of variance design, with a single independent variable (or "factor") and the same number of observations for each "treatment," or "level," the total number of observations is kn, or N. Such is the case in Table 14.1, which shows k of 4, n of 10 and N of 40.

TABLE 14.1. REPRESENTATION OF ORIGINAL DATA IN THE ANALYSIS OF VARIANCE

In this table there are $c = k = 4$ columns, each representing a group or "treatment" (that is, four "levels" or "categories") of the independent variable. Within each group there are ten cases. (Equal-sized groups are not essential in analysis, but by considering only equal-sized groups, the proofs presented in the text are simplified.)

The number of rows is $r = n = 10$. However, in this particular design, the rows have no special significance because the N observations are independent and the order within the column is arbitrary.

Values of the dependent variable are given as X. The first subscript denotes the row; the second, the column.

CASE WITHIN GROUP	GROUP			
	1	2	3	4
1	X_{11}	X_{12}	X_{13}	X_{14}
2	X_{21}	X_{22}	X_{23}	X_{24}
3	X_{31}	X_{32}	X_{33}	X_{34}
4	X_{41}	X_{42}	X_{43}	X_{44}
5	X_{51}	X_{52}	X_{53}	X_{54}
6	X_{61}	X_{62}	X_{63}	X_{64}
7	X_{71}	X_{72}	X_{73}	X_{74}
8	X_{81}	X_{82}	X_{83}	X_{84}
9	X_{91}	X_{92}	X_{93}	X_{94}
10	$X_{10,1}$	$X_{10,2}$	$X_{10,3}$	$X_{10,4}$

A set of observations, one for each treatment (or combinations of treatments when there are two or more independent variables) may be called a *replication*. Since in Table 14.1 there are ten observations for each "treatment," the number of replications is ten. Occasionally, a complex study with several "factors" or independent variables includes but a single replication; in general, however, the number of replications is considerably greater than one.

A "factorial" study is one with two or more "factors" or independent variables. The number of levels or categories within each is indicated separately. Thus, a $4 \times 3 \times 3$ factorial experiment is one with three factors or independent variables; the first has four levels or categories and the others have three each. In describing a factorial study, the degree of replications is stated. A $4 \times 3 \times 3$ experiment with five replications would require a total of 180 observations.

THE VARIANCE RATIO

The analysis of variance is based on the following principles:

1. The ratio of two variances, each calculated from independent samples from the same normally distributed population, follows the particular F distribution for the degrees of freedom of the numerator variance and the degrees of freedom of the denominator variance.
2. When a sample is divided into groups of some sort, two uncorrelated estimates of the population variance can be obtained; the first is estimated from the variability of the means of the groups and the second from the variability within the several groups.
3. If the division of the sample into groups is merely at random, then the expected distribution of the variance ratio is F, with the appropriate pair of df. This follows from the fact that F, for any pair of df, is the expected distribution of an indefinitely large aggregation of ratios of independent variances obtained by random sampling from the same population.
4. The null hypothesis is that the division of the sample into groups is at random (more precisely, the null hypothesis is that there is no difference in the populations from which the two variances have been formed).
5. When a variance ratio exceeds the chosen significance point (5 or 1 percent), the null hypothesis is rejected. It now seems likely that the division of the sample into groups was not at random.
6. In setting up a study, grouping can be by the categories of an independent variable, which may be any type of a scale (nominal, ordinal, interval, or ratio). The quantitative variable from which two estimates of the population variance are obtained is the dependent variable.
7. If the null hypothesis is rejected, the presence of a relationship between the variable represented by the grouping and the dependent variable becomes plausible.

DIVISION OF A SUM OF SQUARES INTO TWO COMPONENTS

To demonstrate that, when a total group consists of subgroups, the total sum of squares may be considered to have two sources, one may start with simple numerical examples.

Consider a total distribution of nine values, ranging from 3 to 5, with three cases at each step. Then:

X	f	x	fx^2
5	3	+1	3
4	3	0	0
3	3	−1	3

$N = 9$; $M_x = 4$; $\Sigma x_t^2 = 6$.

Now consider the same cases divided into three groups: A, B, and C:

X	GROUP A f	GROUP B f	GROUP C f
5	1	1	1
4	1	1	1
3	1	1	1

For each group it is readily seen that $\Sigma x^2 = 2$, and the sum of these Σx^2's for three groups is 6, just as for the total sum of squares. However, this is a very unusual case in that $M_A = M_B = M_C = M_t = 4$. Because the three group means are identical, the "between groups sum of squares" is zero. Therefore V_b, the "between groups variance," is zero. V_w, the "within groups variance," is obviously a positive number, while the F ratio, V_b/V_w, is .00.

Now consider a different division of the cases into three groups:

X	GROUP A f	GROUP B f	GROUP C f
5	0	0	3
4	0	3	0
3	3	0	0

Here it is apparent that there is no variability at all within any group and that the "within group sum of squares" is zero. Therefore V_w is zero.

The means, however, are 3, 4, and 5, respectively. They exhibit variability, and a variance of some magnitude could be computed for them.

Again, this is a special and atypical situation, but with V_b positive and V_w zero, the F ratio V_b/V_w is infinitely large.

In the discussion of the F distribution in Chapter 12, it was noted that the F ratio varies from 0 to ∞. Examples of the two extremes have been given. With real data, an F intermediate between 0 and ∞ can be anticipated.

ALGEBRAIC SOLUTION

It will now be shown algebraically how, when data are arranged in groups, the total sum of squares can be uniquely and precisely divided into two components, the "between groups sum of squares" and the "within groups sum of squares." From these two sums of squares, a variance ratio may be constructed and compared with the appropriate F distribution.

Let the subscript t identify statistics of the total sample; w, statistics within groups; and b, statistics of the means (that is, "between groups"). There are k groups, each with n cases. When groups are of the same size, the total number of cases is kn or N.

With any deviation, that is, any $(X - M_x)$ designated as x, its square is

$$x^2 = X^2 - 2M_x X + M_x^2 = X^2 - \frac{2(\Sigma X)}{N} X + \frac{(\Sigma X)^2}{N^2}$$

Summing and writing equivalents,

$$\Sigma x^2 = \Sigma X^2 - \frac{2(\Sigma X)^2}{N} + \frac{(\Sigma X)^2}{N} = \Sigma X^2 - \frac{1}{N}(\Sigma X)^2 = \frac{N\Sigma X^2 - (\Sigma X)^2}{N}$$

Specifically, the total sum of squares is

$$\sum_1^N x_t^2 = \sum_1^N X_t^2 - \frac{1}{N}\left(\sum_1^N X_t\right)^2 = \frac{N\Sigma X_t^2 - (\Sigma X_t)^2}{N} \tag{14.1}$$

Similarly, within any group the sum of squares is

$$\sum_1^n x_w^2 = \sum_1^n X_w^2 - \frac{1}{n}\left(\sum_1^n X_w\right)^2 = \frac{n\Sigma X_w^2 - (\Sigma X_w)^2}{n} \tag{14.2}$$

Summing Formula 14.2 over the k groups and using double summation signs to indicate that the sums have been summed,

$$\sum_1^k \sum_1^n x_w^2 = \sum_1^N x_w^2 = \sum_1^k \sum_1^n X_w^2 - \frac{1}{n}\sum_1^k\left(\sum_1^n X_w\right)^2 = \sum_1^N X_t^2 - \frac{1}{n}\sum_1^k\left(\sum_1^n X_w\right)^2 \tag{14.3}$$

The expression $\sum_1^k \sum_1^n X_w^2$ is precisely $\sum_1^N X_t^2$, the sum of the squares of the original values.

Substitution in Formula 14.3 of the equivalent for $\sum_1^N X_t^2$,

$$\sum_1^N x_t^2 + \frac{\left(\sum_1^N X_t\right)^2}{N}$$

found by rearranging terms in Formula 14.1, yields

$$\sum_1^N x_w^2 = \sum_1^N x_t^2 + \frac{1}{N}\left(\sum_1^N X_t\right)^2 - \frac{1}{n}\sum_1^k\left(\sum_1^n X_w\right)^2 \tag{14.4}$$

It will now be shown that the last two terms in Formula 14.4 are precisely equal to $-\Sigma x_b^2$, the "between groups sum of squares," or "treatment sum of squares," which is n times the sum of the squares of the deviations of the k group means from the total mean. Indicating the difference between any group mean $\left(\dfrac{1}{n}\sum\limits_{1}^{n} X_w\right)$ and the total mean $\left(\dfrac{1}{N}\sum\limits_{1}^{N} X_t\right)$ as d,

$$d = \frac{1}{n}\sum_{1}^{n} X_w - \frac{1}{N}\sum_{1}^{N} X_t$$

Squaring,

$$d^2 = \frac{1}{n^2}\left(\sum_{1}^{n} X_w\right)^2 - \frac{2}{nN}\left(\sum_{1}^{n} X_w\right)\left(\sum_{1}^{N} X_t\right) + \frac{1}{N^2}\left(\sum_{1}^{N} X_t\right)^2$$

Summing over the k cases,

$$\sum_{1}^{k} d^2 = \frac{1}{n^2}\sum_{1}^{k}\left(\sum_{1}^{n} X_w\right)^2 - \frac{2}{nN}\sum_{1}^{N} X_t\left(\sum_{1}^{k}\sum_{1}^{n} X_w\right) + \frac{k}{nkN}\left(\sum_{1}^{N} X_t\right)^2 \qquad (14.5)$$

Canceling k out of the final term, substituting the equivalent $\sum\limits_{1}^{N} X_t$ for $\sum\limits_{1}^{k}\sum\limits_{1}^{n} X_w$, consolidating the last two terms, and multiplying both sides of Formula 14.5 by n,

$$n\sum_{1}^{k} d^2 = \Sigma x_b{}^2 = \frac{1}{n}\sum_{1}^{k}\left(\sum_{1}^{n} X_w\right)^2 - \frac{1}{N}\left(\sum_{1}^{N} X_t\right)^2 \qquad (14.6)$$

Substituting Formula 14.6 in Formula 14.4 yields the fundamental equation:

$$\Sigma x_w{}^2 = \Sigma x_t{}^2 - \Sigma x_b{}^2 \qquad (14.7)$$

or

$$\Sigma x_b{}^2 = \Sigma x_t{}^2 - \Sigma x_w{}^2 \qquad (14.7a)$$

or

$$\Sigma x_t{}^2 = \Sigma x_w{}^2 + \Sigma x_b{}^2 \qquad (14.7b)$$

That is to say, the total sum of squares is equal to the within-groups sum of squares plus the between-groups sum of squares.

By methods beyond the scope of this text, these two sums of squares, $\Sigma x_b{}^2$ and $\Sigma x_w{}^2$, can be shown to be independent.

When a sum of squares is divided by the appropriate number of degrees of freedom, the result is a "mean square." By this procedure, $\Sigma x_b{}^2$ and $\Sigma x_w{}^2$ will yield two independent estimates of the population variance.

If the variation among the group means is no more than would be expected by random sampling, then a long series of variance ratios, V_b/V_w, would be expected to follow the appropriate F distribution. However, if an observed variance ratio V_b/V_w is so large that it is significant at the predetermined level (5 or 1 percent), then the null hypothesis is rejected and the conclusion is reached that the differences among the means are greater than could be expected by chance (always provided the assumptions underlying the F test have been met).

This use of F provides a way of detecting nonchance differences when a number of means are concerned, as contrasted with the t test, which is applicable to only two means at a time.

In a simple analysis of variance, with a single independent (or treatment) variable distinguishing groups $1, 2 \cdots k$, the null hypothesis is that $\mu_1 = \mu_2 = \cdots = \mu_k = \mu_t$. A significant variance ratio does not in itself indicate whether the means are generally different one from another or whether only one or two of the means differ from the others. Such a finding would require further investigation. Neither does a significant F indicate what type of relationship (such as linear, or nonlinear) might exist between the independent variable, on which the groups were formed, and the dependent variable. Nor does a highly significant F necessarily reflect a stronger degree of relationship between the independent and dependent variable than would a ratio less highly significant. Description of the type of relationship and measurement of its degree would require fitting a function (such as a straight line, as in correlation analysis, or some sort of a curve) and measuring the fit, as by the magnitude of the sum of the squares of the errors. In a sense, analysis of variance is often a preliminary technique aimed at detecting evidence for any type of relationship other than that expected by sampling variation.

DEGREES OF FREEDOM IN ANALYSIS OF VARIANCE

Like the sums of squares, the degrees of freedom in analysis of variance are additive. For the simplest design of k groups of n cases each and a single independent variable, the total number of df is $(N - 1)$, N being the total number of cases. For the "between groups" sum of squares there are $(k - 1)$ degrees of freedom, one less than the number of groups. For the "within groups" sum of squares, the df are $(N - 1) - (k - 1) = N - k$.

After the "between groups" sum of squares has been divided by $(k - 1)$ to form V_b and the "within groups" sum of squares has been divided by $(N - k)$ to form V_w, the variance ratio F is found by dividing V_b by V_w.

The degrees of freedom have their usual meaning. In forming any sum of squares, $1df$ is lost for each different constraint imposed. The number of df is always the number of varying values from which the sum of the squares of deviations is formed, less the number of means used in forming the deviations. For the total sum of squares, there are N values and a single mean; hence $(N - 1)df$. For the "between groups" sum of squares, there are k varying means and a total mean from which the deviations are taken; hence $(k - 1)df$. For the "within groups" sum of squares, there are N values, each used in reference to the mean of the group in which it appears. Since there are k such means, there are $(N - k)df$. The "between groups" df, $(k - 1)$, and the "within groups" df, $(N - k)$, sum to the total df, $(N - 1)$.

In the more complicated analysis of variance designs, with two or more independent variables and with terms representing single and combined effects of such variables, the determination of df for the several sums of squares may seem more complicated, but the basic principle is always the same. The first step is to count the number of deviations that have, in effect, been squared; the second step is to subtract the number of means used in forming them. The result is the number of df to be used in computing the "mean square" or variance estimate.

In complex designs, the df for the total sum of squares may be subdivided in alternate fashions so that the various sums of squares indicated in the analysis have more than $(N - 1)df$. However, in all cases, the total df equals the sum of the df of one subset of independent sums of squares.

ANALYSIS WITH A SINGLE INDEPENDENT VARIABLE

The simplest analysis-of-variance designs involve a single independent variable. Example 14.1 supposes that the subjects of a psychological study have been assigned at random to treatment groups and that the variances within each of the treatment groups may be taken as equal (within the limits of sampling error).

The investigator is interested in determining whether the independent variable, which in this case might, for example, be teaching methods, can be considered to have a relationship to the outcome of teaching (achievement in the subject matter), the dependent variable. It is to be noted that if a study involves several qualitatively different treatments, the independent variable necessarily consists simply of nominal categories.

The hypothesis to be tested, the null hypothesis, is that, within sampling error, $\mu_1 = \mu_2 = \mu_3 = \mu_4$; that is to say, the differences between pairs of means can be accounted for by sampling rather than by an experimental effect resulting from differential treatment of the groups. Unless the groups can be considered at the beginning of the study to be at the same level of the dependent variable, and equally susceptible to the treatment, results of the experiment will be ambiguous or even misleading. In this study, it is assumed that controls of extraneous variation that may affect the outcome have been adequate.

The arithmetic is simple. To adapt Formula 14.6 for computing purposes so that the n's of the groups need not be equal, it may be written as

$$\Sigma x_b{}^2 = \sum_1^k \frac{\left(\sum_1^n X_w\right)^2}{n} - \frac{1}{N}\left(\sum_1^N X_t\right)^2 \qquad (14.6a)$$

which requires that each group be summed on the dependent variable and that the square of this sum be divided by the number of cases in the group. From the sum of these quotients a correction term, $(\Sigma X)^2/N$, is subtracted, in which ΣX is the total sum of the dependent variable and N is the total number of cases.

The total sum of squares is found by Formula 14.1 and the within-groups sum of squares by Formula 14.3. The three sums of squares may be checked by Formula 14.7.

Provided the same step interval and arbitrary origin are used for the total group and for all the subgroups, Formulas 14.1, 14.3, and 14.6a can be used with only minor modifications for computations from frequency distributions. In this case, each X would be read as x' and each X^2 as x'^2, or as deviations and squares in terms of step intervals from an arbitrary origin. To form approximately true values for the sums of squares, final results would have to be multiplied by i^2, the square of the step interval. However, this correction would cancel out in the variance ratio.

The three sums of squares, corresponding degrees of freedom, mean squares or variances, and the F ratio may be tabulated as shown in the accompanying table.

MODEL FOR A SIMPLE ANALYSIS OF VARIANCE

SUM OF SQUARES	df	MEAN SQUARE, OR V	F
Between samples (or treatments)	$k-1$	V_b	V_b/V_w
Within samples (or treatments)	$N-k$	V_w	
TOTAL	$N-1$		

The tabulation may also show the size of F required for significance at the preselected level ($\alpha = .05$) or ($\alpha = .01$).

The use of this format is illustrated in Example 14.1, which, having a "randomized group design," illustrates the simplest form of the analysis of variance. Here, the total sum of squares and the related degrees of freedom are divided so that two independent mean squares are found. Since there are only two independent mean squares, the between-groups variance and the within-groups variance, only a single F test is possible.

EXAMPLE 14.1

SIMPLE ANALYSIS OF VARIANCE

Purpose. The simplest type of analysis of variance (sometimes called the *randomized group design*) aims to test the hypothesis that there are no differences among the group means; that is, that each differs from the others no more than would be anticipated on the basis of chance (at a stated level of confidence) if each sample were drawn at random from the same normally distributed population. In effect, the method of the t test is generalized to take care of more than two means.

In the present instance, we wish to test whether the four group means in Table 14.2 differ significantly among themselves. Arbitrarily we decide to reject the null hypothesis if the F test is significant at the .05 level.

TABLE 14.2. DATA FOR SIMPLE ANALYSIS OF VARIANCE

(Four groups, ten cases in each group; $k = 4$, $n = 10$, $N = 40$. Samples represent population known to be normally distributed.)

GROUP 1	GROUP 2	GROUP 3	GROUP 4
7	43	24	27
37	39	30	20
44	21	17	25
28	32	34	13
42	21	32	32
23	14	35	4
45	24	19	3
32	24	6	36
37	26	30	28
45	26	19	21

Computation of the Between-Groups Sum of Squares

Means:	34.0	27.0	24.6	20.9
$M_t - M_i$:	+7.375	+.375	−2.025	−5.725

$M_t = 26.625$ $\Sigma(M_t - M_i)^2 = 91.4075$ $n\Sigma(M_t - M_i)^2 = 914.075 = \Sigma x_b^2$

By Formula 14.6a,

$$\Sigma x_b{}^2 = \sum_1^k \frac{(\Sigma X_w)^2}{n} - \frac{(\Sigma X)^2}{N} = \frac{(340)^2}{10} + \frac{(270)^2}{10} + \frac{(246)^2}{10} + \frac{(209)^2}{10} - \frac{(1065)^2}{40} = 914.075$$

Method. Numerical computations are straightforward.

1. For each group find n_i, $\sum_1^n X$ and $\sum_1^n X^2$. For the data of Table 14.2, these values (together with the totals) are:

GROUP	n	$\sum_1^n X$	$\sum_1^n X^2$
1	10	340	12,874
2	10	270	7,976
3	10	246	6,828
4	10	209	5,493
TOTAL	$N = 40$	$\sum_1^N X = 1,065$	$\sum_1^N X^2 = 33,171$

2. For each group find $\sum_1^n x^2$, that is, the sum of the squares of the deviations from the group mean. A convenient computing formula, applicable to sums of squares generally, is

$$\Sigma x^2 = \frac{N\Sigma X^2 - (\Sigma X)^2}{N}$$

For the four groups of Table 14.2, these sums are

$$\Sigma x_1^2 = 1314$$
$$\Sigma x_2^2 = 686$$
$$\Sigma x_3^2 = 776.4$$
$$\Sigma x_4^2 = 1124.9$$

3. Sum these sums of squares to find the within-groups sum of squares; that is,

$$\sum_1^k \sum_1^n x_i^2 = \Sigma x_w^2 = 1314 + 686 + 776.4 + 1124.9 = 3901.3$$

4. For all groups, sum the n_i to find N, the total number of cases; that is,

$$\sum_1^k n_i = N$$

If all n_i are identical, $kn = N$.

For all groups, sum the $\sum_1^n X$ to find the grand sum of all the values; that is,

$$\sum_1^k \sum_1^n X_i = \sum_1^N X$$

For all groups, sum the $\sum_1^n X^2$ to find the grand sum of the X^2; that is,

$$\sum_1^k \sum_1^n X^2 = \sum_1^N X^2.$$

These values, N, ΣX, and ΣX^2, are the totals shown in step 1.

5. Compute Σx_t^2 as follows:

$$\Sigma x_t^2 = \frac{N\Sigma X^2 - (\Sigma X)^2}{N} = \frac{40 \times 33{,}171 - (1065)^2}{40} = 4815.375$$

6. Find the between-groups sum of squares by subtracting the within-groups sum of squares from the total sum of squares, as indicated by Formula 14.7a.

$$\Sigma x_b^2 = \Sigma x_t^2 - \Sigma x_w^2 = 4815.375 - 3901.3 = 914.075$$

7. Divide Σx_b^2 by the appropriate degrees of freedom $(k-1)$, in this case, $3df$, to form the between-groups variance; divide Σx_w^2 by $(N-k)$ or, in this case, $36df$, to form the within-groups variance. F is the ratio of these two variance estimates.

Final computations are shown in the table.

	SUM OF SQUARES	df	MEAN SQUARE, OR VARIANCE	F
Between groups	914.1	3	304.7	2.81
Within groups	3901.3	36	108.4	
TOTAL	4815.4	39		

Reference to Table F_5 indicates that with $3df$ in the numerator, $36df$ for the denominator, an F of 2.81 is very nearly significant at the 5 percent level.

Actually, the result is slightly surprising. As the source of the data, four samples of ten values each were drawn at random from the Rand table of random normal deviates (6) and converted linearly to two-digit positive numbers. These are the four groups analyzed. Only in 5 percent of such samplings can F be expected to be significant at the .05 level.

Formation of the variances is actually an optional step, since the F ratio can be readily found from the sums of squares and the two values of v, the degrees of freedom. In this case,

$$F = \frac{v_w \Sigma x_b{}^2}{v_b \Sigma x_w{}^2} = \frac{36 \times 914.1}{3 \times 3901.3} = 2.81$$

in which v_w is the number of df associated with the within-groups sum of squares and v_b is the number of df for the between-groups sums of squares.

Check on Between-Groups Sum of Squares. At the bottom of Table 14.2, the between-groups sum of squares is checked by working with the group means and the total mean. The difference between each group mean and the total mean is squared. These deviations are summed and multiplied by n, the number of cases within each group. The result, 914.075, is $\Sigma x_b{}^2$. If the groups were of unequal size, it would be necessary to multiply each squared difference by the n_i of the group, and then sum these. An even simpler method of finding $\Sigma x_b{}^2$ is by Formula 14.6a. Its use is shown at the bottom of Table 14.2.

An F test always tests whether two variances differ significantly. The numerator mean square always relates directly to the one hypothesis under consideration; the denominator variance reflects sampling variation. Terms applied to a denominator variance include *within-treatments mean square, residual mean square,* and *remainder mean square,* or simply, the *error term.*

A significant F is one that shows that the variance related to some hypothesis is greater than could be expected simply by sampling. Typically in analysis of variance, one or more sources of extraneous variation are controlled or eliminated. If group means are identical within sampling error, then there is no variability that can be considered to be related to the hypothesis under study.

The more advanced designs, which for the most part are beyond the scope of this text, involve dividing the total sum of squares (and related degrees of freedom) into more than two components, and applying the F test to one or more pairs of mean squares. Always the denominator variance is an "error term," but in some designs two error terms may be found from the same set of observations. Also, as the number of independent variables increases, the number of possible F tests increases, both for the effect of each independent variable with variation in the other independent variable eliminated and for combinations of independent variables. "Factorial design" involves the sorting out of effects of two or more independent variables in the same study.

Certain relationships of the sums of squares used in the analysis of variance to r, the product-moment coefficient of correlation, and η, the correlation ratio, are demonstrated in Example 14.2.

EXAMPLE 14.2

SOME   RELATIONSHIPS OF THE SUMS OF SQUARES TO r AND η

Purpose. The descriptive statistics, r and η, involve sums of squares of deviations, and it is pertinent to inquire as to relationships between them and certain sums of squares.

The Data. In Table 14.3 are exhibited six artificial scatter plots, constructed to bring out the relationships. In these diagrams, the independent variable X_1, is scaled, which is a requirement for r, but not for the analysis of variance. While analysis of variance is sometimes performed on scatter plots, it would ordinarily involve fewer categories in the independent variable or much greater numbers of cases than 27.

The Dependent Variable. In each of the six diagrams, the distribution of the dependent variable X_0 is exactly the same. It is for this variable that the sum of the squares of the deviations from the mean (Σx_t^2) is separated, in a simple analysis of variance, into two portions: the between-groups sum of squares, Σx_b^2, and the within-groups sum of squares, Σx_w^2. It can be readily ascertained that $N = 27$, $\Sigma X_0 = 54$, and $\Sigma X_0^2 = 144$. Accordingly, $\Sigma x_t^2 = 36$, while $V_0 = 36/27$, or 1.33 (Formulas 14.1 and 5.3b).

Computation of r. Arithmetical methods demonstrated in Chapter 6 were used to find the correlation coefficient reported at the upper left of each diagram.

Computation of η. In Chapter 9, η^2, the square of the correlation ratio, was defined as the ratio of the variance of the means of the arrays to the total variance. The two η's are thus $\eta_{yx} = s_{m_y}/s_y$ and $\eta_{xy} = s_{m_x}/s_x$. In this example, X_0 is always the dependent variable. Accordingly, $\eta_{01}^2 = V_{m_0}/V_0$. However, if both numerator and denominator are multiplied by N, η_{01}^2 becomes, with changes in notation, $\Sigma x_b^2/\Sigma x_t^2$; that is, the ratio of the between-groups sum of squares to the total sum of squares.

The F test is based on the same information, namely, Σx_b^2 and Σx_w^2 (or $\Sigma x_t^2 - \Sigma x_b^2$) plus knowledge of the df associated with each of the sums of squares.

TABLE 14.3. SCATTER PLOTS WITH r^2, η^2, AND SUMS OF SQUARES

1. $r^2 = 1.00$; $\eta_{01}^2 = 1.00$

X_0	X_1 0	1	2	3	4	5	6
4					3		
3				6			
2			9				
1		6					
0	3						

$\sum_1^n X_0$ 0 6 18 18 12

n 3 6 9 6 3

$\sum x_b^2 = 36$; $\sum x_w^2 = 0$; $\sum x_t^2 = 36$

2. $r^2 = .52$; $\eta_{01}^2 = 1.00$

X_0	X_1 0	1	2	3	4	5	6
4				3			
3					6		
2		9					
1			6				
0	3						

$\sum_1^n X_0$ 0 18 6 12 18

n 3 9 6 3 6

$\sum x_b^2 = 36$; $\sum x_w^2 = 0$; $\sum x_t^2 = 36$

3. $r^2 = .67$; $\eta_{01}^2 = .67$

X_0	X_1 0	1	2	3	4	5	6
4					1	1	1
3				2	2	2	
2			3	3	3		
1		2	2	2			
0	1	1	1				

$\sum_1^n X_0$ 0 2 8 14 16 10 4

n 1 3 6 7 6 3 1

$\sum x_b^2 = 24$; $\sum x_w^2 = 12$; $\sum x_t^2 = 36$

4. $r^2 = .15$; $\eta_{01}^2 = .31$

X_0	X_1 0	1	2	3	4	5	6
4			1	1	1		
3				2	2	2	
2					3	3	3
1			2	2	2		
0	1	1	1				

$\sum_1^n X_0$ 0 0 6 12 18 12 6

n 1 1 4 5 8 5 3

$\sum x_b^2 = 11.1$; $\sum x_w^2 = 24.9$; $\sum x_t^2 = 36$

5. $r^2 = .00$; $\eta_{01}^2 = .00$

X_0	X_1 0	1	2	3	4	5	6
4	1	1	1				
3			2	2	2		
2				3	3	3	
1		2	2	2			
0	1	1	1				

$\sum_1^n X_0$ 4 4 12 8 14 6 6

n 2 2 6 4 7 3 3

$\sum x_b^2 = 0$; $\sum x_w^2 = 36$; $\sum x_t^2 = 36$

6. $r^2 = .00$; $\eta_{01}^2 = .00$

X_0	X_1 0	1	2	3	4	5	6
4			1	1	1		
3		1	1	2	1	1	
2	1	1	1	3	1	1	1
1		1	1	2	1	1	
0			1	1	1		

$\sum_1^n X_0$ 2 6 10 18 10 6 2

n 1 3 5 9 5 3 1

$\sum x_b^2 = 0$; $\sum x_w^2 = 36$; $\sum x_t^2 = 36$

Below each diagram the $\sum_{1}^{n} X_0$ of each of the arrays is shown. Each of these has been squared and divided by its n. From the sum of these quotients, $(\Sigma X_0)^2/N$ is subtracted to find Σx_b^2. In these diagrams $(\Sigma X_0)^2/N$ is always 108. Each η_{01}^2 is simply $\Sigma x_b^2/\Sigma x_t^2$.

It will be remembered that η fits no function and is not dependent on the structure of the independent variable. Because there is no within-groups variance in diagrams 1 and 2, both values of η_{01}^2 are 1.00 (as are the values of η_{10}^2, which are not shown).

In diagrams 5 and 6, both r^2 and η_{01}^2 are .00. However, it can be seen that in diagram 5, η_{10}^2 would be high, while in diagram 6, η_{10}^2 would be .00 because in neither direction do the means of the arrays have variability.

Relationship of r. By Formula 6.7a, in terms of original values,

$$V_0 = \tilde{V}_0 + V_{0.1}$$

That is, the total variance is divisible into the predicted and the unpredicted variance. The predicted variance $\tilde{V}_0$ is $r_{01}^2 V_0$, and the residual variance $V_{0.1}$ is $(1 - r_{01}^2)V_0$.

Using the data of diagram 3, it will be shown that $N\tilde{V}_0$ is Σx_b^2, the between-groups sum of squares, and that $NV_{0.1}$ is Σx_w^2, the within-groups sum of squares. If $N = 27$, $V_0 = 4/3$ (or 1.33), and $r^2 = 2/3$ (or .67), then

$$N\tilde{V}_0 = 27 \times \tfrac{2}{3} \times \tfrac{4}{3} = 24 = \Sigma x_b^2$$

and

$$NV_{0.1} = 27\,(1 - \tfrac{2}{3})\tfrac{4}{3} = 27 \times \tfrac{1}{3} \times \tfrac{4}{3} = 12 = \Sigma x_w^2$$

These relationships, however, do not hold in diagrams 2 and 4, where r's are nonzero, but the regression is not linear. It is only in the case that both independent and dependent variables are in units suitable for correlation and the regression is strictly linear that $r = \sqrt{\Sigma x_b^2/\Sigma x_t^2} = \eta$.

The result is not surprising in that r^2 can be expressed as $\tilde{V}_0/V_0$, in which $\tilde{V}_0$ is the variability of the points exactly on the regression line. In the special case of strictly linear regression, $N\tilde{V}_0$ would therefore equal Σx_b^2 precisely.

Note: In all diagrams, $\Sigma X_0 = 54$, $\Sigma X_0^2 = 144$, and $\Sigma x_0^2 = 36$. The following information, obtained from the diagrams, was used in finding values of r^2:

DIAGRAM	ΣX_1	ΣX_1^2	Σx_1^2	$\Sigma X_0 X_1$	$\Sigma x_0 x_1$
1	54	144	36	144	36
2	54	156	48	138	30
3	81	297	54	198	36
4	99	423	60	216	18
5	87	357	76.7	174	0
6	81	295	52	162	0

It must be remembered, however, that the questions posed in the analysis of variance and in statistics descriptive of relationships are quite different. In effect, the purpose of a simple analysis of variance is merely to determine whether, at a stated level of significance, an observed relationship between an independent and a dependent variable is greater than can be ascribed to chance. The degree of significance attained by an F ratio is a function of the differences among the means, of the number of the means, and of the total number of cases. On the other hand, η provides a measure of the fit of the data to some unspecified function, while the correlation coefficient reflects the degree to which the values of a structured independent variable fall along a straight line.

BARTLETT'S TEST OF HOMOGENEITY OF VARIANCE

In addition to the assumption that cases are drawn randomly and independently from a normally distributed population (or rather from k normally distributed populations if the k groups are considered to have differing origins), the assumption is made that the variances of the k populations are equal.

Actually, the F test is not greatly affected by departures from normality of the distribution of the dependent variable, and (particularly when n's are equal) it is not greatly affected by inequalities among the group variances. However, Bartlett's test of the homogeneity of variance provides a method of determining at a preselected level of significance whether variation of the group variances can be attributed to chance. Its use is shown in Example 14.3.

EXAMPLE 14.3

BARTLETT'S TEST OF HOMOGENEITY OF VARIANCE

Purpose. When analysis of variance is applied to testing the differences among k independent means, two assumptions are made:

1. That the n_i values of the dependent variable in each group have been drawn from a normally distributed population; and
2. That the k populations represented by the k samples have identical variances.

A test developed by Bartlett (1) uses as the null hypotheses: $V_1 = V_2 = V_3 = \ldots = V_k$. A quantity

$$\frac{2.3026}{C}[(N-k)\log_{10}V_w - \Sigma(n-1\,\log_{10}V_i)]$$

is evaluated as χ^2 with $(k-1)$ degrees of freedom and with a high value of χ^2

indicating lack of homogeneity. The value of C is found[1] from the formula

$$C = 1 + \frac{1}{3(k-1)} \left[\sum \frac{1}{n-1} - \frac{1}{N-k} \right]$$

Data. The data are from Example 14.1, where all values were drawn at random from a single normally distributed population. The F test for differences among the means was, however, significant at the .05 level.

Computation of C. In Example 14.1, $k = 4$, since there are four groups; n is 10 for all groups; and $N = 40$. Accordingly,

$$C = 1 + \frac{1}{3(4-1)} \left(\frac{4}{9} - \frac{1}{36} \right) = 1.046$$

Further Computations. Using the several sums of squares and corresponding degrees of freedom from Example 14.1, the following estimated variances have been found. Corresponding logarithms have been obtained from a common log table (that is, logarithms to the base 10, not to the base e).

SUM OF SQUARES	df	V	$\log_{10} V$	$(n-1) \log_{10} V_i$
$\Sigma x_1^2 = 1314$	9	146	2.16435	19.4792
$\Sigma x_2^2 = 686$	9	76.2	1.88195	16.9376
$\Sigma x_3^2 = 776.4$	9	86.3	1.93601	17.4241
$\Sigma x_4^2 = 1124.9$	9	125	2.09691	18.8722

$$\Sigma(n-1) \log_{10} V_i = 72.7131$$

$\Sigma x_w^2 = 3901.3$	36	108.4	2.0305	$(N-k) \log_{10} V_w = 36(2.0305)$
				$= 73.0980$

Accordingly, the quantity to be evaluated as χ^2 with $3df$ is

$$\frac{2.3026}{1.046} (73.0980 - 72.7131) = .85$$

From Table C it is found that a χ^2 of .85 with $3df$ is not significant at the .05 level. The null hypothesis is not disproved and the variance can be considered equal in the populations represented by the samples.

What to Do When Variances Are Heterogeneous. When variances as tested seem not to be homogeneous, the F test (if applied) needs to be interpreted more stringently, since the effect of heterogeneity is to raise the value of F. A more adequate procedure, which involves adjustment of the scales of measurement, is suggested in advanced texts in experimental design.

---

[1] Here C is just a term to simplify the expression yielding the value distributed as chi square. This C, of course, has no relationship either to C, the contingency coefficient, or C, the covariance

COMPLEX DESIGNS USING ANALYSIS OF VARIANCE

Discussion of the more complex analysis of variance patterns is beyond the scope of this text. Treatments of the logic as well as numerical examples showing computing routines applicable to psychological and educational data are given by Edwards (2), Lindquist (4), McNemar (5), Ray (7), Walker and Lev (8), and Winer (9). Topics include:

1. Methods of handling two or more independent variables;
2. Techniques of handling correlated observations;
3. Methods of control of sources of variance not germane to the problem of interest;
4. Techniques for reducing error; and
5. Techniques for increasing efficiency in the use of data.

Principles carried over from simple analysis of variance to the more complex designs include:

1. Splitting the total sum of squares of the dependent variable into components (but with the number of components increased to three or four or more);
2. Breaking up the total df into the df associated with each of the sums of squares;
3. Computation of variance ratios; and
4. Evaluation of each variance ratio by means of the appropriate F distribution. A significant F ratio is taken as indicative of nonchance variation among a set of means, which, in advanced designs, may not actually be computed.

Novel elements in advanced designs include:

1. The development of precisely described mathematical models of complex experiments;
2. Consideration of the joint effects of two or more independent variables; and
3. New uses of continuously scaled variables, as an independent variable in "trend analysis" or as a control variable in the "analysis of covariance."

Often the advanced designs have descriptive names and distinctive computing techniques, and have their justification in the particular constellation of observed variables from which an answer is sought. More importantly, however, consideration of the design prior to the experiment often leads to a happy choice of sampling procedures, methods of operation, and statistical treatment such that the results of the study are far more useful than would otherwise be the case.

A TWO-WAY ANALYSIS OF VARIANCE

Example 14.4 comprises a two-way analysis of variance, again using artificial data drawn from a normally distributed population. As in Example 14.1, any F ratio would be expected to be insignificant, and here in fact no F ratio attains significance at the .05 level.

EXAMPLE 14.4

A TWO-WAY ANALYSIS OF VARIANCE

Purpose. In investigations employing analysis of variance, it is possible to use two or more independent variables. Since the present example is based on 100 values drawn at random (but rounded to eliminate fractions and adjusted linearly so as to avoid negative values) from the Rand table of 100,000 normal deviates (6), nothing beyond chance variation should appear among the means of the arrays.

The Problem. The four rows in Table 14.4 can be considered to represent four "levels," or categories, of any "treatment" variable; say, four different methods of instruction. The five columns can be considered to represent five "levels," or categories, of any other "treatment" variable; say, five different tutors. We can suppose that all five tutors are skilled in using the four different teaching methods and that each used method with five randomly assigned students who had no initial knowledge of the subject matter. It can also be assumed that other sources of variation, such as intelligence, reading speed, and interest, have been adequately controlled.

In each of the cells or "plots" of Table 14.4 are five values of the dependent variable. These values may be considered final test scores representing knowledge of the subject matter for five individuals after a stated number of hours of training and study under the prescribed method of instruction, as directed by the assigned tutor.

Questions that may be asked of the data are:

1. At a stated level of significance (say, .05), are there reliable differences among tutors, as measured by the attainment of their students?
2. At a stated level of significance (say, .05), are there reliable differences among methods?
3. Is there significant "interaction" between tutors and methods; that is, do one or more tutors attain reliably better results with one or more methods than do other tutors with other methods?

Analysis of a Portion of the Data. In actual research, of course, one would attack the main problem, using all available data. However, to show certain relationships between simple analysis of variance and analysis with two independent variables, Table 14.5 is presented. As in Table 14.4, rows can be taken to represent "methods" and columns can represent "tutors." However, there is only a single entry in each cell, the total number of cases being 20. Actually, the first observation in each of the cells of Table 14.4 is given as the only observation in each of the cells of Table 14.5.

TABLE 14.4. DATA FOR A TWO-WAY ANALYSIS OF VARIANCE

(100 values, drawn at random from a normal population: simulating a study with four rows, five columns, five replications)

ROWS	COLUMNS 1	2	3	4	5	$\overset{r}{\Sigma}\overset{n}{\Sigma}X$
1	46	19	27	18	30	
	23	16	25	26	23	
	23	22	19	35	47	
	31	38	33	29	37	749
	43	48	22	40	29	
$\overset{n}{\Sigma}X$	166	143	126	148	166	
2	30	43	27	28	31	
	34	6	46	8	32	
	32	31	24	23	29	
	25	28	39	20	42	725
	32	24	33	24	34	
$\overset{n}{\Sigma}X$	153	132	169	103	168	
3	32	39	24	24	26	
	48	36	17	36	18	
	23	41	33	32	21	
	17	33	5	32	35	699
	11	40	21	34	21	
$\overset{n}{\Sigma}X$	131	189	100	158	121	
4	29	50	34	35	25	
	17	37	28	26	18	
	16	21	23	34	33	
	27	13	17	31	43	712
	28	47	28	33	19	
$\overset{n}{\Sigma}X$	117	168	130	159	138	
$\overset{c}{\Sigma}\overset{n}{\Sigma}X$	567	632	525	568	593	$N=100$ $\Sigma X=2{,}885$ $\Sigma X^2 = 92{,}241$

Computations

$$\Sigma x_b{}^2{}_{(\text{rows})} = \frac{r\Sigma\left(\overset{c}{\Sigma}\overset{n}{\Sigma}X\right)^2 - (\Sigma X)^2}{N} = \frac{(4 \times 2{,}082{,}171) - (2885)^2}{100} = 54.59$$

$$\Sigma x_b{}^2{}_{(\text{cols})} = \frac{c\Sigma\left(\overset{r}{\Sigma}\overset{n}{\Sigma}X\right)^2 - (\Sigma X)^2}{N} = \frac{(5 \times 1{,}670{,}811) - (2885)^2}{100} = 308.30$$

$$\Sigma x_t{}^2 - \Sigma x_b{}^2{}_{(\text{rows})} - \Sigma x_b{}^2{}_{(\text{cols})} - \overset{c}{\Sigma}\overset{r}{\Sigma}\overset{n}{\Sigma}x_w{}^2 = 9008.75 - 54.59 - 308.30 - 6802.40$$
$$= 1843.46$$

$$\Sigma\Sigma\Sigma x_w{}^2 = \frac{n\overset{N}{\Sigma}X^2 - \overset{r}{\Sigma}\overset{c}{\Sigma}(\overset{n}{\Sigma}X)^2}{n} = \frac{(5 \times 92{,}241) - (427{,}193)}{5} = 6802.40$$

$$\Sigma x_t{}^2 = \frac{N\Sigma X^2 - (\Sigma X)^2}{N} = \frac{(100 \times 92{,}241) - (2{,}885)^2}{100} = 9008.75$$

Notation. In the tables, r is the number of rows and c is the number of columns. When used as superscripts, r and c indicate that summation has been over rows or over columns. In Table 14.4, n refers to the number of cases within cells; that is, the number of replications. When used as a superscript, n indicates summation within cells. When rows or columns are summed, summation is over cell totals, so that the sum of any array is indicated with double summation sign, while summation over the entire matrix may be indicated with triple summation signs, as $\overset{r}{\Sigma}\overset{c}{\Sigma}\overset{n}{\Sigma}x_w^2$ (in which, as always, the order of summation is from right to left) or with a single summation sign if all cases can enter directly into the sum, as in ΣX, ΣX^2, and Σx_t^2.

TABLE 14.5. TWO-WAY ANALYSIS OF VARIANCE

(Data from Table 14.4.)

r	c 1	2	3	4	5	$\overset{r}{\Sigma}X$	$\overset{r}{\Sigma}X^2$	$\overset{r}{\Sigma}x_w^2$
1	46	19	27	18	30	140	4430	510.00
2	30	43	27	28	31	159	5223	166.80
3	32	39	24	24	26	145	4373	168.00
4	29	50	34	35	25	173	6347	361.20
$\overset{c}{\Sigma}X$	137	151	112	105	112			

$$\overset{N}{\underset{1}{\Sigma}}X = 617$$

$$\overset{n}{\Sigma}\overset{c}{\Sigma}X^2 = \overset{c}{\Sigma}\overset{r}{\Sigma}X^2 = \overset{N}{\Sigma}X^2 = 20{,}373$$

$\overset{c}{\Sigma}X^2$ 4881   6231   3190   2909   3162 Σx_w^2 (rows) $= 1206.00$

$\overset{c}{\Sigma}x_w^2$ 188.75 530.75   54.00 152.75   26.00 Σx_w^2 (cols) $= 952.25$

$$\Sigma x_b^2 \text{(cols)} = \Sigma \frac{(\overset{c}{\Sigma}X)^2}{c} - \frac{(\Sigma X)^2}{N} = \frac{(137)^2 + (151)^2 + (112)^2 + (105)^2 + (112)^2}{4} - \frac{(617)^2}{20}$$

$$= 386.30$$

$$\Sigma x_b^2 \text{(rows)} = \Sigma \frac{(\overset{r}{\Sigma}X)^2}{r} - \frac{(\Sigma X)^2}{N} = \frac{(140)^2 + (159)^2 + (145)^2 + (173)^2}{5} - \frac{(617)^2}{20}$$

$$= 132.55$$

$$\Sigma x_t^2 = \frac{N\Sigma X^2 - (\Sigma X)^2}{N} = \frac{20 \times 20373 - (617)^2}{20} = 1338.55$$

Check: By rows	*Check: By columns*
$\Sigma x_b^2 = 132.55$	$\Sigma x_b^2 = 386.30$
$\Sigma x_w^2 = 1206.00$	$\Sigma x_w^2 = 952.25$
$\Sigma x_t^2 = 1338.55$	$\Sigma x_t^2 = 1338.55$

Remainder sum of squares $= 1338.55 - 386.30 - 132.55 = 819.70$

SUMS OF SQUARES		df	V	F
Between rows (methods)	132.55	$(r-1)=$ 3	44.18	$F < 1$
Between columns (tutors)	386.30	$(c-1)=$ 4	96.58	1.41
Remainder	819.70	$(r-1)(c-1)=12$	68.31	
TOTAL	1338.55	$(N-1)=19$		

Computations. More computations are presented in Table 14.5 than would ordinarily be the case with a two-way analysis with a single replication. The computations show:

1. ΣX and ΣX^2 for both rows and columns, with the superscript r or c indicating whether the summation has been in rows or columns;

2. The sum of the squares within each array as found by Formula 14.2. These sums have been summed to find the within-groups sum of squares, Σx_w^2, for both rows and columns.

3. Sums of squares between rows and also sums of squares between columns, Σx_b^2, as found by Formula 14.6a. It is seen that for both rows and for columns, the between-arrays sum of squares plus the within-arrays sums of squares equals the total sum of squares. This information is presented as a check.

4. In this analysis, the total sum of squares is divided into three portions: $\Sigma x_b^2{}_{(\text{rows})}$, $\Sigma x_b^2{}_{(\text{columns})}$, and the "remainder" sum of squares, or the *error term*. In a simple analysis, Σx_w^2 is used as the denominator for a single F. In a two-way analysis of variance, the remainder sum of squares is used for two F tests, one to test whether variation between rows (that is, among methods) is significant and the other to test whether variation between columns (that is, among tutors) is significant.

5. The degrees of freedom for rows is $(r-1)$; for columns, $(c-1)$; and for the "remainder" term, $(r-1)(c-1)$. It is to be noted that $(r-1)+(c-1)+(r-1)(c-1)=(N-1)$, the total number of degrees of freedom.

Analysis of the Complete Set of Data. Computations leading to an analysis of the complete set of data are shown in Table 14.4. The new feature (as compared with Table 14.5) is a *remainder*, or *error*, or *residual* sum of squares computed within the cells. This is used to form the denominator variance for testing not only the significance of the variation among the two sets of means (which, as in Table 14.5, are not actually computed), but also the "interaction" of the two independent variables. This "interaction" sum of squares corresponds to the error, or remainder, sum of squares in Table 14.5, where there is no replication.

In both simple and complex analysis of variance, the denominator of the F test is based on the unexplained, or error, sum of squares; that is, that portion of the total sum of squares not ascribable to identifiable "sources" of variability. In Table 14.2, the "unexplained" variance is within groups; in Table 14.5, it is that portion not associated with either the row means or the column means; in Table 14.4, it is "within cells." This explains in part why the remainder sum of squares in Table 14.5 is analogous to the interaction sum of squares in Table 14.4.

The between-rows and between-columns sums of squares are found by modifying Formula 14.6a as follows:

$$\Sigma x_b{}^2{}_{(rows)} = \frac{r\overset{r}{\underset{}{\Sigma}}(\overset{c}{\underset{}{\Sigma}}\overset{n}{\underset{}{\Sigma}}X)^2 - (\Sigma X)^2}{N} \qquad (14.6b)$$

$$\Sigma x_b{}^2{}_{(cols)} = \frac{c\overset{c}{\underset{}{\Sigma}}(\overset{r}{\underset{}{\Sigma}}\overset{n}{\underset{}{\Sigma}}X)^2 - (\Sigma X)^2}{N} \qquad (14.6c)$$

Actually, the mode of computation is the same as in simple analysis of variance, the change in notation resulting from the fact that a column sum is now $\overset{r}{\underset{}{\Sigma}}\overset{n}{\underset{}{\Sigma}}X$ (instead of $\overset{n}{\underset{}{\Sigma}}X_w$) with $\overset{c}{\underset{}{\Sigma}}\overset{r}{\underset{}{\Sigma}}X$ for a row sum, and from the fact that the n of Formula 14.6 becomes nr. For ease in computation, the two terms of the formula have been placed over N, utilizing the fact that $N = rcn$.

The within-cells sums of squares, $\overset{r}{\underset{}{\Sigma}}\overset{c}{\underset{}{\Sigma}}\overset{n}{\underset{}{\Sigma}}x_w{}^2$, is analogous to the within-groups sum of squares of Example 14.1 except that it represents variation around cell means instead of around means of entire columns. It can, in fact, be found from Formula 14.2, summed over rows and columns as follows:

$$\overset{r}{\underset{}{\Sigma}}\overset{c}{\underset{}{\Sigma}}\overset{n}{\underset{}{\Sigma}}x_w{}^2 = \overset{r}{\underset{}{\Sigma}}\overset{c}{\underset{}{\Sigma}}\frac{n\overset{n}{\underset{}{\Sigma}}X^2 - (\overset{n}{\underset{}{\Sigma}}X)^2}{n} \qquad (14.2a)$$

in which the summation of X and X^2 is within each of the cells.

An alternate formula, more convenient in use because it involves only ΣX^2 for the entire problem and the squares of the cell sums $(\overset{n}{\underset{}{\Sigma}}X)$, is

$$\overset{r}{\underset{}{\Sigma}}\overset{c}{\underset{}{\Sigma}}\overset{n}{\underset{}{\Sigma}}x_w{}^2 = \frac{n\overset{N}{\underset{}{\Sigma}}X^2 - \overset{r}{\underset{}{\Sigma}}\overset{c}{\underset{}{\Sigma}}(\overset{n}{\underset{}{\Sigma}}X)^2}{n} \qquad (14.2b)$$

This formula is applied in Table 14.4

The "interaction" sum of squares may be found by subtracting from the total sum of squares those sums of squares between rows, between columns, and within cells.

The analysis for Table 14.4 now takes this form:

	SUMS OF SQUARES	df	V	F
Between rows	54.59	$r - 1 = 3$	18.20	$F < 1$
Between columns	308.30	$c - 1 = 4$	77.08	$F < 1$
Interaction	1843.46	$(r - 1)(c - 1) = 12$	153.62	1.81
Within cells	6802.40	$N - rc = 80$	85.03	
TOTAL	9008.75	$N - 1 = 99$		

The estimated variance based on the within-cells sum of squares is the denominator for all three F tests. For rows and columns, F's are less than 1.00 and are clearly insignificant. Hence, if rows represent methods of instruction and columns represent tutors, we may conclude that in this study neither had a demonstrable effect on outcome.

The value of F for interaction of methods and tutors is 1.81. Reference to Table F_5 (Appendix) indicates that for $12df$ in the numerator variance and $80df$ in the denominator, an F of 1.88 is required for significance at the .05 level. Hence we can conclude that interaction variance also is within sampling error and is statistically insignificant.

Two analyses are presented. One, with a single observation in each cell, demonstrates how two F ratios may be found when there are two independent variables. An F ratio is computed for each of the two sets of means,

The second analysis finds three F ratios, one for each of the sets of means, and a third for the *interaction* of the two independent variables. An *error term*, or *residual* term, for the denominator of the F ratio becomes available for testing interaction when there are a number of replications in each of the cells, in this case, five.

Example 14.4 thus extends the basic technique to the case of two independent variables and investigates not only the effect of each of them separately on the dependent variable but also their effect in combination.

SUMMARY

A group of techniques collectively called the *analysis of variance* has found wide application in psychological and educational research. Basically, the question investigated is whether or not the means of a dependent variable in groups and subgroups vary more than could be expected on the basis of chance sampling. If greater variation than could be expected is actually found, a nonzero relationship between independent and dependent variable is indicated. The use of the F distribution, the ratio of two independent estimates of the population variance, is the most distinctive characteristic of the analysis of variance.

Two simple cases are considered in this chapter:

1. The case of a single independent variable; and
2. The case of two independent variables.

In the two examples, adequate selection of cases and appropriate control of extraneous variation is assumed. More complicated cases are discussed in advanced books on experimental design.

EXERCISES

1. For the following six groups of five cases each, $k = 6$, $n = 5$, $N = 30$. By computing the total sum of squares, the between-groups sum of squares, and the within-groups sum of squares, show arithmetically that $\Sigma x_t^2 = \Sigma x_b^2 + \Sigma x_w^2$.

GROUP A	GROUP B	GROUP C	GROUP D	GROUP E	GROUP F
7	7	7	8	6	9
5	9	4	10	8	11
9	8	5	2	7	3
1	6	6	6	5	7
3	5	3	4	4	5

2. In a large psychological clinic, four psychologists were assigned cases at random until each had tested 20 patients. The following means and standard deviations for obtained I.Q.s were observed.

PSYCHOLOGIST	M	s
A	90.7	14.0
B	87.9	15.0
C	92.0	13.5
D	91.8	13.7

The standard deviations were found by the formula $s = \sqrt{\Sigma x^2 / n}$, in which n is the number of cases in the group. Accordingly,

$$\sum^{n} x_w^2 = ns^2$$

Test whether the means differ significantly at the .05 level.

3. By Bartlett's test for homogeneity of variance, test whether the variances in Exercise 2 can be considered homogeneous.

4. In a learning study, Hull (3) tested three patients in each of three diagnostic categories. The criterion was the number of minutes required to form associations between 12 Chinese characters and 12 spoken nonsense syllables. Test whether the group means differ significantly at the .05 level.

CONSTITUTIONAL INFERIORS	DEMENTIA PRAECOX	PARETICS
89	45	200
170	52	150
72	39	140

5. How many observations would be required in a 2×3 factorial experiment with 25 replications?

6. A simple analysis of variance study used 45 subjects divided randomly and equally in five groups. The total sum of squares was 2,319.6 and the between-groups sum of squares was 642.8. Compute and evaluate F.

7. For the following table, based on a two-way classification, determine which of the three F are significant at the .01 level or better.

SOURCE OF VARIATION	SUMS OF SQUARES	df
Rows	7,382.7	1
Columns	9,111.8	2
Interaction	672.3	2
Within cells	21,357.8	43
TOTAL		48

8. Data for the nine cells below were found as follows:

   1. At hazard, 90 values were drawn from the Rand table of 100,000 normal deviates (6) and assigned to the nine cells, ten cases in each cell.
   2. The scores in each cell were converted linearly to two-digit scores with no negative values.
   3. Systematic differences in both rows and columns were introduced by adding constants within cells as follows:

CONSTANTS ADDED
WITHIN CELLS

4	6	8
2	4	6
0	2	4

Accordingly, one might well expect to find significant F's. Make the appropriate tests for significant differences for rows, for columns, and for interaction.

ROWS	COLUMNS 1		2		3	
1	24	25	16	20	38	33
	34	14	21	29	25	44
	23	12	21	40	12	11
	4	11	38	24	44	16
	48	28	11	25	30	48
2	26	21	17	28	21	7
	31	30	14	11	26	37
	11	13	16	34	22	40
	18	11	32	26	28	29
	31	29	18	30	32	41
3	14	29	4	21	38	32
	21	22	30	32	19	46
	27	34	25	12	37	31
	24	16	4	23	20	34
	48	16	19	12	29	35

REFERENCES

1. BARTLETT, M. S., "Properties of sufficiency and statistical tests," Proc. Royal Society of London, 1937, Series A, **160**, 1–273.
2. EDWARDS, ALLEN L., *Experimental Design in Psychological Research.* New York: Holt, Rinehart and Winston, Inc., 1960.
3. HULL, CLARK L., "The formation and retention of associations among the insane," *Amer. J. Psychol.*, 1917, **28**, 419–435.
4. LINDQUIST, E. F., *Design and Analysis of Experiments in Psychology and Education.* New York: Houghton Mifflin Company, 1956.
5. MCNEMAR, QUINN, *Psychological Statistics.* New York: John Wiley & Sons, Inc., 1962, 3rd ed.
6. Rand Corporation, *A Million Random Digits with 100,000 Normal Deviates.* Glencoe, Illinois: The Free Press, 1955.
7. RAY, WILLIAM S., *An Introduction to Experimental Design,* New York: The Macmillan Company, 1960.
8. WALKER, HELEN M., AND LEV, JOSEPH, *Statistical Inference.* New York: Holt, Rinehart and Winston, Inc., 1953.
9. WINER, B. J., *Statistical Principles in Experimental Design.* New York: McGraw-Hill Book Company, Inc., 1962.

STATISTICS
IN TEST
CONSTRUCTION
AND INTERPRETATION

15

A psychological test is valid to the degree to which it measures an aspect of human behavior, and reliable to the degree it yields consistent results, either from time to time or through alternate measurements.

Some psychological tests yield only a global score, such as the number of seconds required to complete a task, or the number of pegs turned in a fixed amount of time. Such tests may be normed, correlated with a criterion to determine validity, and correlated with alternate forms or with retest data to estimate reliability. However, since they are not composed of separately scored items, they are not amenable to item analysis, one of the major topics of this chapter.

HOMOGENEOUS AND HETEROGENEOUS TESTS

Psychological tests are generally composed of discrete items, which may be considered as little variables entering into a sum variable, the total score. Some tests are homogeneous, that is, made up of items that tend to measure the same basic characteristic, as indicated by positive interrelationships. However, if the intercorrelations are too high, the test would be internally consistent, but it would not constitute a scale making a large number of useful discriminations among people.

Other psychological tests are heterogeneous, that is, composed of items having relatively low intercorrelations and measuring different aspects of behavior. If the items have relatively high relationships with a criterion and relatively low relationships with one another, the resulting test may be far more efficient for a practical purpose (such as selecting candidates for a position) than would a homogeneous test. However, heterogeneous tests are of limited scientific interest, since the characteristic measured can be stated only in terms of a criterion. Often they are single-purpose tests, useful only for prediction in a few specific situations. The homogeneous tests are more versatile. They can be used in a variety of ways because they are inherently meaningful and measure variables of psychological interest.

ITEM STATISTICS

When an item is considered a variable, it is most often dichotomous, taking values of either 0 or 1. As a dichotomous variable it has a mean of p, in which p is N_p/N, the proportion of individuals passing. It has a variance of pq, in which q is the proportion of individuals failing the item. The standard deviation is $\sqrt{pq}$.

For item intercorrelations the phi coefficient is appropriate, and if the covariance is needed, it is found by the formula

$$C_{ij} = \frac{P_{ij}}{N} - p_i p_j \tag{15.1}$$

in which P_{ij} is the number of cases passing both item i and item j and in which p_i and p_j are the item means. This covariance, divided by the product of the two item standard deviations, yields the phi coefficient, or product-moment correlation, between the two items (discussed in Chapter 9).

The correlation between a dichotomous item and a continuous variable, such as the total score in the test of which the item is a part, or an outside criterion, is generally the point biserial r, which, as was pointed out in Chapter 9, is also an algebraic variant of product-moment r. The correlation between an item and the total score to which it contributes may be denoted as r_{it}, and the correlation between an item and an outside criterion may be indicated as r_{ic}.

CONCEPT OF RANDOM ERROR

Much of the theory of psychological tests centers around the concept of random error. By definition, random error is completely uncorrelated with the true score in the test and with random error in any other set of measurements. This is a logical postulate, which can be used to examine test reliability and related concepts.

Let X, the total score on a test, be represented as the algebraic sum of a true score A and an uncorrelated error component E. Then,

$$X = A + E \tag{15.2}$$

from which, by summing and dividing by N, the relationship of the means is found:

$$M_x = M_a + M_e \tag{15.3}$$

Subtracting Eq. 15.3 from Eq. 15.2 yields the relationship of the deviations:

$$x = a + e \tag{15.4}$$

Squaring Eq. 15.4, summing, and dividing by N yield

$$\frac{\Sigma x^2}{N} = \frac{\Sigma a^2}{N} + \frac{2\Sigma ae}{N} + \frac{\Sigma e^2}{N}$$

However, $\Sigma ae/N$ is the covariance between the true score and the error score. Since the corresponding correlation, by definition, is zero, the covariance must be zero, and can be dropped. The other terms can be written as variances:

$$V_x = V_a + V_e \tag{15.5}$$

That is to say, the total variance is the sum of two component parts: the true variance and the error variance. If all terms in Formula 15.5 are divided by V_x, it is seen that the total variance, taken as 1.00, is divisible into a proportion that is true or reliable variance and a proportion that is the variance of the random error component.

Consider two tests that are theoretical equivalents in that the true parts of each test measure exactly the same function and are perfectly correlated, but which also contain a certain proportion of random error. By definition, the random error in one test is uncorrelated with the random error in the other.

A form cognate with Eq. 15.4, but distinguished by primes, can represent the equivalent test:

$$x' = a' + e' \tag{15.4a}$$

TEST RELIABILITY

The correlation between x and x' can be taken as the reliability, or consistency, or self-correlation of the test. To estimate it algebraically, we multiply Eq. 15.4 by Eq. 15.4a, sum, and divide by N. This gives

$$\frac{\Sigma xx'}{N} = \frac{\Sigma aa'}{N} + \frac{\Sigma a'e}{N} + \frac{\Sigma ae'}{N} + \frac{\Sigma ee'}{N} \tag{15.4b}$$

Since $\Sigma a'e/N$, $\Sigma ae'/N$, and $\Sigma ee'/N$ are covariances corresponding to zero correlations, they are all zero and drop out. $\Sigma aa'/N$ is, by definition, the numerator of a perfect correlation, and is therefore equal to the product of the two standard deviations, s_a and $s_{a'}$. However, by definition, $s_a = s_{a'}$. Accordingly, Formula 15.4b can be rewritten as

$$\frac{\Sigma xx'}{N} = V_a$$

Dividing both sides by $s_x s_{x'}$ or V_x, since the standard deviations of the equivalent tests are equal,

$$\frac{\Sigma xx'}{N s_x s_{x'}} = r_{xx'} = \frac{V_a}{V_x} = \frac{V_x - V_e}{V_x} = 1 - \frac{V_e}{V_x} \tag{15.6}$$

which can be read: "The reliability of a test, $r_{xx'}$, is V_a/V_x, the proportion of the total variance that is true variance, or $1 - V_e/V_x$, that is, 1 less the proportion of error variance."

As applied to a psychological measuring instrument, reliability may be defined as its consistency, or the degree to which it correlates with itself. While this correlation is unknown and unknowable, it can be estimated by four different methods: test-retest, alternate forms, "split-half," and rational equivalence. Lack of reliability is conceived as the result of the presence of random error. A test consisting exclusively of random error would have no correlation with its theoretical equivalent test and would have a reliability of .00, while a test that included only "true" variance would have a reliability of 1.00.

TEST-RETEST METHOD

In the test-retest method, a group of individuals is given the same test on two different occasions. The ordinary product-moment r is computed and is used as the estimate of the reliability.

For some tests, which have no alternate form and which consist of a total task rather than a set of separate subtests or items, test-retest is the only feasible method. It is a relatively poor method for tests in which there is a good deal of learning from one exposure to the next, and on which subjects vary considerably in how much they learn. However, a test-retest correlation, at least for a motor task, is probably a "lower bound" of the true reliability, which is likely to be higher than the obtained coefficient.

ALTERNATE FORMS

The method of estimating reliability by the use of alternate forms requires at least two forms of a test, which are considered to be equivalent. The forms are administered to the same group of subjects and results are correlated. As does test-retest, the method of alternate forms tends to underestimate rather than overestimate the reliability. The reason is that, with most material, it is difficult to build two forms of the same measuring device that are precisely equivalent both in assaying the same function and in including the same proportion of random error. However, when alternate forms exist, the correlation between them must be considered an essential reliability estimate to report.

"SPLIT-HALF" RELIABILITY

The estimation or reliability by either test-retest or alternate forms is applicable to most kinds of psychological tests. Both methods are applicable to "speed" tests, which are so timed that very few subjects complete all items and in which the difficulties of the items are relatively low. They are also applicable to "power" tests, consisting of difficult items, but generally with enough time allowed so that subjects can attempt all items.

The "split-half" method, now to be described, applies only to power tests. It is useful when no alternate form exists and when it is not feasible to administer the same test twice to the same group of subjects.

The test is divided into two halves, which are judged to be equivalent. Sometimes two groups of items are equated on the basis of their item difficulties; sometimes the score on the odd items $(1, 3, 5 \cdots)$ is considered the score on one-half of the test; the score on the even items $(2, 4, 6 \cdots)$, the score on the other half. This latter procedure is sometimes described as "odd-even" reliability.

The scores on the two halves are now correlated, yielding the estimated reliability of one half of the test.

To infer the reliability of the whole, it is necessary to assume that the two halves are truly equivalent and that the correlation between them is typical of the six correlations that would be obtained among four half-tests, if two more half-tests were available.

Let z_a, $z_{a'}$, z_b and $z_{b'}$ be z scores on four equivalent half tests, of which only a and a' (halves of X) actually exist. Both in raw-score form and in z form, all variances of the half tests are considered equal, and all inter-correlations are taken as $r_{aa'}$, the observed correlation between the halves of X. The problem is to infer the correlation between the complete, existing test X and its hypothetical equivalent, X' or $b + b'$. In a permissible deviation form,

$$x = z_a + z_{a'} \tag{15.7}$$

and

$$x' = z_b + z_{b'} \tag{15.7a}$$

Multiplying Eq. 15.7 by Eq. 15.7a, summing and dividing by N, yield

$$\frac{\Sigma xx'}{N} = \frac{\Sigma z_a z_b}{N} + \frac{\Sigma z_a z_{b'}}{N} + \frac{\Sigma z_{a'} z_b}{N} + \frac{\Sigma z_{a'} z_{b'}}{N} = 4r_{aa'} \tag{15.8}$$

Squaring Eq. 15.7, summing, dividing by N, and replacing z score variances with unity give

$$\frac{\Sigma x^2}{N} = V_x = 2 + 2r_{aa'} \tag{15.9}$$

which is also $V_{x'}$.

The correlation is found by dividing Formula 15.8 by Formula 15.9. Thus,

$$\frac{\Sigma xx'}{Ns_x s_{x'}} = r_{xx'} = \frac{C_{xx'}}{V_x} = \frac{4r_{aa'}}{2 + 2r_{aa'}} = \frac{2r_{aa'}}{1 + r_{aa'}} \tag{15.10}$$

which indicates that the reliability of a variable when doubled in length may be estimated as twice the reliability of the half $(r_{aa'})$ divided by $(1 + r_{aa'})$.

SPEARMAN-BROWN "PROPHECY" FORMULA

If Eqs. 15.7 and 15.7a are extended to the general case, they may be written as

$$x = z_a + z_{a'} + \cdots + z_{a''} \tag{15.7b}$$

$$x' = z_b + z_{b'} + \cdots + z_{b''} \tag{15.7c}$$

On the premise that all n components are z scores with unit variance and that all $(n^2 - n)$ intercorrelations are equal to $r_{aa'}$, the variance of either variable is

$$V_x = V_{x'} = n + (n^2 - n)r_{aa'} \tag{15.11}$$

By multiplying Eq. 15.7b by Eq. 15.7c, summing, dividing by N, and taking each of the n^2 covariances as $r_{aa'}$, it is found that

$$C_{xx'} = n^2 r_{aa'} \tag{15.12}$$

Dividing Formula 15.12 by Formula 15.11 and simplifying yield the general Spearman-Brown "prophecy" formula for reliability:

$$\frac{C_{xx'}}{s_x s_{x'}} = \frac{C_{xx'}}{V_x} = r_{xx'} = \frac{n^2 r_{aa'}}{n + (n^2 - n)r_{aa'}} = \frac{nr_{aa'}}{1 + (n-1)r_{aa'}} \tag{15.13}$$

By substituting 2 for n, it can be seen that Formula 15.10 is a special case of Formula 15.13.

With the type of material that goes into conventional aptitude and achievement tests, it has been found that Formula 15.13 works reasonably well, provided (1) the additional material is similar to the old, (2) the revised test is not very long, and (3) the extra material does not materially change the task for the subjects. A very long test can become boring, and loss of interest can affect reliability adversely.

INFLUENCE OF TEST LENGTH ON RELIABILITY

The development of a reliability formula in terms of true variances and error variances may be helpful. To the original test as indicated in Formula 15.4, $x_1 = a_1 + e_1$, let there be added any amount of new material, each unit of the new material having the same proportion of true and error variance as the original test. In deviation form the expanded test can be represented as

$$x = a_1 + e_1 + a_2 + e_2 + \cdots + a_n + e_n$$

This expression is squared, summed, and divided by N. All covariances involving error are zero and disappear. All n true variances are equal, as are all n error variances. All $(n^2 - n)$ covariances of two a terms approach V_a as a limit and are considered equal to V_a.

By making these substitutions,

$$V_x = n^2 V_a + n V_e$$

It is obvious that the true variance in V_x is $n^2 V_a$ and that the proportion of true variance to the total variance, or the reliability coefficient, $r_{xx'}$, is

$$r_{xx'} = \frac{n^2 V_a}{n^2 V_a + n V_e} = \frac{n V_a}{n V_a + V_e} \tag{15.14}$$

If, for example, a test consists of ten items, each of which is .7 error and .3 true variance, the reliability is

$$r_{xx'} = \frac{10(.3)}{10(.3) + .7} = \frac{3}{3.7} = .81$$

Actually, Formula 15.14 is merely an algebraic variant of Formula 15.13, as can be readily seen by substituting the unit reliability $r_{aa'}$ for V_a and $(1 - r_{aa'})$ for V_e.

RELIABILITY BY KR FORMULA 20 (RATIONAL EQUIVALENCE)

A procedure that has similarities to correlating two halves of the same test and correcting the obtained correlation to estimate the reliability of the whole is the method of rational equivalence, using Kuder-Richardson[1] Formula 20. As is the method of alternate forms, it is based on the consistency of different measurements of the same general function. However, instead of reflecting the consistency of different forms, it is based on the consistency of items within a single form of the test.

---

[1] Originally derived by Kuder and Richardson (2), using somewhat different assumptions.

EXAMPLE 15.1

TEST RELIABILITY BY THE METHOD OF RATIONAL EQUIVALENCE

Purpose. The method of rational equivalence (using KR Formula 20) estimates the correlation of a test with its hypothetical equivalent. It assumes that the variance of the existing test is identical with the variance of the hypothetical test, and that the sum of the item covariances within the existing test is proportional to the sum of the between-test item covariances.

Data. In Table 15.1 are shown the correct and incorrect responses of 25 college students on the 15 items of a mathematics test. Correct responses are indicated by 1, incorrect by 0. Total scores are shown under X, while the number passing each item (N_p) is shown under each column of item responses. The p values (not shown) would be found by dividing each N_p by N, the total number of cases.

Item variances are shown in the row designated as pq. It may be noted that 2 of the 15 items make no discriminations at all (since their variances are .00) and 4 others have variances less than .08. Dropping items 4 and 5 would have no effect on test characteristics other than the mean, while the elimination of items 2, 3, 6, and 7 should not greatly change test reliability and validity.

The following computations summarize the information in Table 15.1:

$$N = 25 \quad \Sigma X = \Sigma N_p = 301 \quad \Sigma N_p^2 = 6255$$
$$n = 15 \quad \Sigma X^2 = 3729 \quad \Sigma pq = \Sigma V_i = 2.032$$

$$V_x = \frac{25 \times 3729 - (301)^2}{(25)^2} = 4.20$$

By Formula 15.20,

$$r_{xx'} = \frac{n}{n-1}\left(1 - \frac{\Sigma V_i}{V_x}\right) = \frac{15}{14}\left(1 - \frac{2.032}{4.20}\right) = .55$$

By Formula 15.20a,

$$r_{xx'} = \frac{n}{n-1}\left(1 - \frac{N\Sigma X - \Sigma N_p^2}{N\Sigma X^2 - (\Sigma X)^2}\right) = \frac{15}{14}\left(1 - \frac{25 \times 301 - 6255}{25 \times 3729 - (301)^2}\right) = .55$$

As estimated by KR Formula 20, in this small sample the reliability is .55. This low reliability partly reflects the short length of the instrument, since in effect it has only nine items.

In finding $r_{xx'}$ by KR Formula 20, the complete item matrix, as in Table 15.1, is seldom displayed. Various mechanical devices (scoring machines, tabulating machines, and electronic computers) can produce item counts (N_p values) more or less automatically. In the absence of such a mechanical device, a hand method can be readily designed. From the N_p it is necessary to find either ΣV_i or ΣN_p^2. The variance is computed from N, ΣX, and ΣX^2, or from a frequency distribution of total scores.

Like the split-half method, it is not applicable to speeded tests, since it would give results spuriously high. While test-retest and alternate forms

TABLE 15.1. ITEM SCORE MATRIX FOR 25 STUDENTS ON A 15-ITEM TEST

STUDENTS	1	2	3	4	5	6	7	8	9	10	11	12	13	14	15	X
A	1	1	1	1	1	1	1	0	1	0	1	0	1	0	1	12
B	0	1	1	1	1	1	0	1	0	0	1	0	0	0	0	8
C	1	1	1	1	1	1	1	1	1	0	1	0	0	1	0	11
D	1	1	1	1	1	1	1	1	0	1	1	0	0	0	0	10
E	1	1	1	1	1	1	1	1	1	0	1	0	0	1	0	11
F	1	1	1	1	1	1	1	1	1	1	1	1	0	1	1	14
G	1	1	1	1	1	1	1	1	1	0	0	1	1	1	1	13
H	1	1	1	1	1	1	1	1	1	1	1	1	1	1	1	15
I	0	1	1	1	1	1	1	1	1	0	0	1	1	1	1	12
J	1	1	1	1	1	1	1	1	0	1	1	0	0	0	0	10
K	1	1	1	1	1	1	1	1	1	1	1	1	1	1	0	14
L	1	1	1	1	1	1	0	0	1	1	1	1	1	1	1	13
M	1	1	1	1	1	1	1	1	1	1	1	1	1	1	1	15
N	1	1	0	1	1	1	1	1	1	0	0	0	1	1	0	10
O	1	1	0	1	1	1	1	1	0	1	1	0	0	0	0	9
P	0	1	1	1	1	1	1	1	0	1	1	0	0	0	1	9
Q	0	1	1	1	1	1	1	0	1	1	1	0	1	0	1	11
R	1	1	1	1	1	1	1	1	1	0	0	1	1	1	1	13
S	1	1	1	1	1	1	1	1	1	0	0	1	1	1	1	13
T	1	1	1	1	1	1	1	1	1	0	1	1	1	1	1	14
U	0	1	1	1	1	1	1	0	1	0	1	1	1	0	1	11
V	1	1	1	1	1	0	1	1	1	1	1	1	1	1	1	14
W	1	0	1	1	1	1	1	0	1	1	1	0	1	0	0	10
X	1	1	1	1	1	1	1	1	1	1	1	0	1	1	1	14
Y	1	1	1	1	1	1	1	1	1	1	1	1	1	1	1	15
N_p	20	24	23	25	25	24	23	20	20	16	20	13	17	16	15	
pq	.1600	.0384	.0736	.0000	.0000	.0384	.0736	.1600	.1600	.2304	.1600	.2496	.2176	.2304	.2400	

are applicable to both homogeneous and heterogeneous tests, the method of correlation with a theoretical equivalent can be used only with homogeneous tests that have internally consistent items. If applied to a heterogeneous test, developed to predict an external criterion, the resultant coefficient would be an underestimation of the true reliability.

The method is based on two assumptions:

1. That the total variance of the hypothetical test, $V_{x'}$, is equal to the variance of the existing test, V_x.

2. The covariances of the items within the existing test are representative of the covariances between the items of the existing test and the items of the theoretical test.

The second assumption may be so interpreted that the mean item covariance within the existing test can be taken as the mean covariance between items, one of each pair coming from the existing test and the other from the hypothetical test.

The item scores (in deviation form) of the existing test can be represented as

$$x = i + j + \cdots + n \tag{15.15}$$

and of the hypothetical test,

$$x' = i' + j' + \cdots + n' \tag{15.16}$$

Multiplying Eq. 15.15 by Eq. 15.16, summing, dividing by N, and writing resultant terms as covariances, we have

$$C_{xx'} = C_{i'i} + C_{i'j} + \cdots + C_{n'n}$$

With n items in each of the two tests, there are n^2 covariance terms. Denoting their mean as $\bar{C}_{ij'}$, we have

$$C_{xx'} = n^2 \bar{C}_{ij} \tag{15.17}$$

The correlation between x and x' is found by dividing both sides of Formula 15.17 by $s_x s'_x$. However, since $V_x = V_{x'}$, $s_x s_{x'} = V_x$. Then

$$\frac{C_{xx'}}{V_x} = r_{xx'} = \frac{n^2 \bar{C}_{ij'}}{V_x} \tag{15.18}$$

The next step is to estimate $\bar{C}_{ij'}$ from the internal characteristics of the existing test, since the average item covariance within x (that is, $\bar{C}_{ij}$) is taken as the average covariance between items in x and items in x' (that is $\bar{C}_{ij'}$).

Returning to Eq. 15.15, we square the expression, sum, divide by N, and obtain

$$\frac{\Sigma x^2}{N} = \frac{\Sigma i^2}{N} + \frac{\Sigma ij}{N} + \cdots + \frac{\Sigma in}{N}$$

$$+ \frac{\Sigma ji}{N} + \frac{\Sigma j^2}{N} + \cdots + \frac{\Sigma jn}{N}$$

$$\vdots \qquad \vdots \qquad \qquad \vdots$$

$$+ \frac{\Sigma in}{N} + \frac{\Sigma jn}{N} + \cdots + \frac{\Sigma n^2}{N}$$

It can be seen that on the right-hand side there are n variance terms, V_i, $V_j \cdots V_n$. Their sum can be written ΣV_i (or Σs_i^2). There are also $(n^2 - n)$ covariance terms, such as C_{ij}. Only their mean, $\bar{C}_{ij}$, is of interest, and their sum is $(n^2 - n)\bar{C}_{ij}$.

Accordingly,

$$V_x = \Sigma V_i + (n^2 - n)\bar{C}_{ij}$$

Solving for $\bar{C}_{ij}$,

$$\bar{C}_{ij} = \frac{V_x - \Sigma V_i}{n^2 - n} \tag{15.19}$$

Substituting Formula 15.19 in Formula 15.18 yields

$$r_{xx'} = \frac{\dfrac{n^2(V_x - \Sigma V_i)}{n^2 - n}}{V_x} = \frac{n^2}{n^2 - n}\left(\frac{V_x - \Sigma V_i}{V_x}\right) = \frac{n}{n - 1}\left(1 - \frac{\Sigma V_i}{V_x}\right) \tag{15.20}$$

This is Kuder-Richardson Formula 20, which requires three bits of information about a test in order to estimate its reliability: n, the number of items; ΣV_i, the sum of the item variances; and V_x, the total variance. Its use is not restricted to tests composed of dichotomous items; rather, the scoring system applied to the items may have any range as long as the total score is the simple sum of the item scores.

If items are, in fact, dichotomous, and the score is either 1 or 0, then Formula 15.18 can be simplified for easier computation. It will be remembered that for dichotomous items, the sum of the scores equals the sum of the squares of the scores, both with value of N_p. Accordingly,

$$V_i = \frac{N_p}{N} - \frac{N_p^2}{N^2} \tag{15.21}$$

Summing Formula 15.21 and noting that $\Sigma N_p = \Sigma X$, the sum of the total scores, we have

$$\Sigma V_i = \frac{1}{N} \Sigma N_p - \frac{1}{N^2} \Sigma N_p{}^2 = \frac{N}{N^2} \Sigma X - \frac{1}{N^2} \Sigma N_p{}^2 \qquad (15.22)$$

Dividing Formula 15.22 by V_x, or rather by its raw-score equivalent $(1/N^2)[N\Sigma X^2 - (\Sigma X)^2]$, and substituting the resulting quotient in Formula 15.20 yield

$$r_{xx'} = \frac{n}{n-1}\left(1 - \frac{N\Sigma X - \Sigma N_p{}^2}{N\Sigma X^2 - (\Sigma X)^2}\right) \qquad (15.20a)$$

The use of this formula is shown in Example 15.1.

EFFECT OF CHANGES IN RELIABILITY ON r

Two principles already demonstrated can be used in estimating the effect of changes in the reliability of either (or both) of the variables entering into a correlation. These are:

1. The fact that any variable can be considered the sum of two components, the true score and the random error. Thus, by Eq. 15.4, $x = a + e$.
2. The fact that the ratio of the true variance to the total variance equals the self-correlation, or reliability, of the test. By Formula 15.6, $r_{xx'} = V_a/V_x$.

Let x'' be a variable that includes a, the true score in x, but which, instead of e, has an alternate random component e''. Similarly, let y'' be a variable that includes b, the true score in y, but which, instead of e', has a different random component e'''. The covariance between these variables is found by multiplying $(x'' = a + e'')$ by $(y'' = b + e''')$, summing, dividing by N, and dropping out covariances involving random error. Thus

$$C_{x''y''} = \frac{\Sigma x''y''}{N} = \frac{\Sigma ab}{N} + \frac{\Sigma be''}{N} + \frac{\Sigma ae'''}{N} + \frac{\Sigma e''e'''}{N} = C_{ab}$$

By a similar development involving $(x = a + e)$ and $(y = b + e')$, it can be seen that the covariance of the original values, C_{xy}, is also C_{ab}. Hence,

$$C_{x''y''} = C_{xy} \qquad (15.23)$$

By analogy with Formula 15.6, the reliabilities of x'' and y'' are in each case the ratio of the true variance to the total variance; that is, $r_{xx''} = V_a/V_{x''}$, and

$$V_{x''} = \frac{V_a}{r_{xx''}} \qquad (15.24)$$

From Formula 15.6 it is seen that $V_a = V_x r_{xx'}$. Substitution of $V_x r_{xx'}$ for V_a in Formula 15.24 yields

$$V_{x''} = \frac{V_x r_{xx'}}{r_{xx''}}$$ (15.24a)

Similarly, the variance of y'' is

$$V_{y''} = \frac{V_y r_{yy'}}{r_{yy''}}$$ (15.24b)

in which $r_{yy'}$ is the original reliability and $r_{yy''}$ is the modified reliability. To estimate $\tilde{r}_{xy}$, the correlation between x'' and y'', Formula 15.23 is divided by the square roots of Formulas 15.24a and 15.24b. Then

$$\frac{C_{x''y''}}{s_{x''} s_{y''}} = \tilde{r}_{xy} = \frac{C_{xy}}{\sqrt{\dfrac{V_x r_{xx'}}{r_{xx''}}} \sqrt{\dfrac{V_y r_{yy'}}{r_{yy''}}}} = \frac{C_{xy}}{\sqrt{V_x} \sqrt{V_y}} \sqrt{\frac{r_{xx''} r_{yy''}}{r_{xx'} r_{yy'}}} = r_{xy} \sqrt{\frac{r_{xx''} r_{yy''}}{r_{xx'} r_{yy'}}}$$ (15.25)

in which $r_{xx'}$ and $r_{yy'}$ are obtained reliabilities and $r_{xx''}$ and $r_{yy''}$ are new or hypothetical reliabilities. With the restriction that values over 1.00 are conventionally taken as 1.00, Formula 15.25 gives a satisfactory indication of the effect of changes in the reliability of one of (or both) the variables. If the reliability of only one, say x, is changed, then $r_{yy'} = r_{yy''}$ and the formula becomes

$$\tilde{r}_{xy} = r_{xy} \sqrt{\frac{r_{xx''}}{r_{xx'}}}$$ (15.25a)

which estimates the change in the correlation between x and y brought about by changes in the reliability of x.

A special case of Formula 15.25 is the *correction for attenuation*, used to estimate the correlation between two variables when both become perfectly reliable; that is, when $r_{xx''} = r_{yy''} = 1.00$. In that case, Formula 15.25 becomes

$$\tilde{r}_{xy} = \frac{r_{xy}}{\sqrt{r_{xx'}} \sqrt{r_{yy'}}}$$ (15.25b)

The use of these formulas is shown in Example 15.2.

EXAMPLE 15.2

ESTIMATING THE EFFECT OF CHANGES IN RELIABILITY ON r

Purpose. The Spearman-Brown procedure (Formula 15.13) estimates the effect of changes in length on the reliability of a test. Reliability, of course, may also be modified by changes in item content or structure, but the effect of such alterations cannot be clearly predicted. The Spearman-Brown formula assumes item homogeneity.

Formulas 15.25 and its variants can be used to predict changes in the correlation between two variables as the result of changes in the reliability of one of them or of both.

Effects of Modifying Both Variables. Consider a variable X with $r_{xx'}$ of .80 and variable Y with $r_{yy'}$ of .70. If r_{xy} is .25, what correlation would be anticipated if both tests were made half as long? What would be the correlation if both tests were doubled in length?

In Formula 15.13, n can take fractional as well as integral values. If $n = .5$, then

$$r_{xx''} = \frac{.5 \times .80}{1 + (.5 - 1).80} = .667 \quad \text{and} \quad r_{yy''} = \frac{.5 \times .70}{1 + (.5 - 1).70} = .538$$

Substituting in Formula 15.25,

$$\tilde{r}_{xy} = r_{xy} \sqrt{\frac{r_{xx''} r_{yy''}}{r_{xx'} r_{yy'}}} = .25 \sqrt{\frac{.667 \times .538}{.80 \times .70}} = .20$$

Similarly, if $n = 2$,

$$r_{xx''} = \frac{2 \times .80}{1 + (2 - 1).80} = .889 \quad \text{and} \quad r_{yy''} = \frac{2 \times .70}{1 + (2 - 1).70} = .824$$

Then, by Formula 15.25,

$$\tilde{r}_{xy} = .25 \sqrt{\frac{.889 \times .824}{.80 \times .70}} = .25 \times 1.31 = .33$$

Effect of Changing the Reliability of a Single Variable. Consider a predictor variable X, with reliability of .81 and validity of .45, for predicting a defined criterion. If the test were shortened so that the reliability became .64, what would be the expected validity?

$$r_{xy} = r_{xy} \sqrt{\frac{r_{xx''}}{r_{xx'}}} = .45 \sqrt{\frac{.64}{.81}} = .40$$

Estimating the Maximum Possible Effect of Changes in Reliability (Correction for Attenuation). Formula 15.25b, Spearman's correction for attenuation, estimates what a correlation would be between two variables that were made perfectly reliable. If r_{xy} is .25, $r_{xx'}$, is .80, and $r_{yy'}$, is .70, what is the limit of $\tilde{r}_{xy}$ if all error variance is removed from X and Y?

By Formula 15.25b,

$$\tilde{r}_{xy} = \frac{r_{xy}}{\sqrt{r_{xx'}} \sqrt{r_{yy'}}} = \frac{.25}{\sqrt{.80 \times .70}} = .334$$

It is seen that, in this instance, the maximum possible correlation is not much greater than that anticipated from doubling the length of both variables.

Correction for attenuation is actually a special case of partial correlation, as described in Chapter 8. It can be demonstrated that the correlation between the random error component of variable X, e_x, and X itself is $\sqrt{1 - r_{xx'}}$. By definition, the random error component of Y, e_y, is uncorrelated with e_x and with X. The matrix of correlations of e_x, e_y, X, and Y, with all variances taken as 1.00, is as follows:

	e_x	e_y	X	Y
e_x	1.00	.00	$\sqrt{1 - r_{xx'}}$	.00
e_y		1.00	.00	$\sqrt{1 - r_{yy'}}$
X			1.00	r_{xy}
Y				1.00

If the matrix operations described in Chapter 8 are carried out,

$$r_{xy \cdot e_x e_y} = \frac{r_{xy}}{\sqrt{r_{xx'}}\sqrt{r_{yy'}}}$$

which, of course, is r_{xy} with e_x and e_y partialed out.

STANDARD ERROR OF MEASUREMENT

A practical interpretation of the consistency of a test is in terms of the standard error of measurement. Essentially, the standard error of measurement is the likely standard deviation of the errors made in predicting true scores when we have knowledge only of the obtained scores. True scores are, of course, forever unknowable, but if we know the standard deviation of the discrepancies in estimating them, we also know the degree to which we can trust the scores obtained from our tests.

Such a formula can be readily found by solving Formula 15.6 ($r_{xx'} = 1 - V_e/V_x$) for V_e. Then

$$V_e = V_x - V_x r_{xx'}$$

By taking the square root of both sides, we have

$$s_e = s_{\text{meas.}} = s_x\sqrt{1 - r_{xx'}} \tag{15.26}$$

The expression $s_x\sqrt{1 - r_{xx'}}$, gives the standard deviation of the discrepancies between true and observed scores. For example, for the I.Q., the standard deviation is approximately 15 and the reliability is of the order of .95. Accordingly,

$$s_{\text{meas.}} = 15\sqrt{1 - .95} = 15\sqrt{.05} = 3.35$$

This means that about two-thirds of the discrepancies between observed I.Q.s and true I.Q.s would be less than 3.35 I.Q. points.

The use of the standard error of measurement often assumes that the error in estimating the true score is the same in all parts of the range of the observed score. This by no means is necessarily true. In fact, the bivariate distribution of the two alternate forms of the 1937 Stanford Binet showed that the error of estimate was smaller for low I.Q.s than for high I.Q.s.

This is evidence that the standard error of measurement in either form followed the same pattern. Accordingly, in using the standard error of measurement to estimate the limits within which a true score might be found, we must temper our interpretation with the knowledge that $s_{meas.}$ is a kind of average throughout the range and may not represent the situation in the part of the range in which we may be particularly interested.

CHANGES IN RELIABILITY RESULTING FROM CHANGES IN RANGE

When there is reason to believe that $s_{meas.}$ is in fact constant throughout the range, there is a way of estimating the effect of changes of range on reliability. Let $s_x\sqrt{1 - r_{xx'}}$ be $s_{meas.}$ in the range in which the reliability of the test is known; and let $s'\sqrt{1 - r'}$ be $s_{meas.}$ in a different range, estimated from a different standard deviation, s', and different reliability, r'. Then, since the two variances of measurement are equal,

$$V_x(1 - r_{xx'}) = V'(1 - r')$$

Solving for r' yields

$$r' = 1 - \frac{V_x(1 - r_{xx'})}{V'} \tag{15.27}$$

Consider a test with reliability of .84, in a range in which the standard deviation is 10 (and variance 100). What would be the reliability in a range in which the standard deviation is reduced to 8, and variance to 64? By Formula 15.27,

$$r' = 1 - \frac{100(1 - .84)}{64} = .75$$

What would be expected to happen if the variance were increased to 128?

$$r' = 1 - \frac{100(1 - .84)}{128} = .875$$

It is understood, of course, that the "changes in range" come from adding or subtracting cases to a distribution. Changes in scale brought about by linear transformations of the original variable have no effect at all on the reliability of a variable or, except for rounding error, on its correlation with other variables.

CORRELATION BETWEEN TRUE AND OBTAINED SCORES

To develop a formula for the correlation between true scores, a, and obtained scores, x, both sides of Eq. 15.4, $(x = a + e)$, are multiplied by a, yielding

$$ax = a^2 + ae$$

When this is summed and divided by N, C_{ae} drops out as the covariance representing a zero correlation. Accordingly,

$$C_{ax} = V_a$$

By dividing both sides by $s_a s_x$ and remembering that V_a/V_x is $r_{xx'}$, the reliability coefficient, we have

$$\frac{C_{ax}}{s_a s_x} = r_{ax} = \frac{V_a}{s_a s_x} = \frac{s_a}{s_x} = \sqrt{r_{xx'}}$$

which shows that the correlation between observed and true scores is the square root of the reliability coefficient.

TEST VALIDITY

The criteria as to whether a test actually measures what it is supposed to measure are logical rather than statistical. While psychological test theory recognizes other types of validity, the only type of validity considered here is that involving the correlation of the instrument with one or more outside criteria.

If a test has an outside criterion, measured along an interval scale, then the validity coefficient is merely the product-moment correlation between the test and the criterion. Such a coefficient is, of course, subject to the same considerations in its interpretation as is any other product-moment r, such as the question of linearity of regression if r is to be taken as an indication of the closeness of fit between the two variables; the question of homoscedasticity, if the standard deviation of the residuals is to be used as the standard error of estimate; and the usual questions regarding the adequacy of sampling and possible curtailment or expansion of the range, if the sample r is to be taken as a valid estimate of the parameter value.

If the criterion is dichotomous, such as success or failure in a course of training, or whether or not a man receives a promotion in a certain length of time, it may be preferable to use a biserial r rather than a point biserial in computing validity coefficients. This will be true if we are trying to estimate what the relationship would be if the criterion information were on a continuous scale instead of in two categories. However, if we are using the validities in computing a multiple regression equation for forecasting the success of individuals for whom criterion information is not yet available, the point biserial is preferred to the regular biserial.

EFFECT OF CHANGES IN LENGTH ON VALIDITY

By changing notation somewhat, Formula 15.13 for the reliability of a test when lengthened n times can be written as

$$r_{xx''} = \frac{n r_{xx'}}{1 + (n-1)r_{xx'}} \tag{15.13a}$$

Dividing both sides by $r_{xx'}$ yields

$$\frac{r_{xx''}}{r_{xx'}} = \frac{n}{1 + (n-1)r_{xx'}} \tag{15.28}$$

which can be substituted in Formula 15.25a to estimate the correlation between x, when it is lengthened n times, and y, an outside criterion. The formula requires knowledge of $r_{xx'}$, the reliability of x in its unit length. Then

$$\tilde{r}_{xy} = r_{xy}\sqrt{\frac{n}{1 + (n-1)r_{xx'}}} \tag{15.25c}$$

Theoretically, n can take any positive value, including fractional values, but because of nonstatistical considerations, the formula may not yield a good estimate if n is very small or very large. It assumes, of course, that the proportion of random error in each equal subdivision of a test is identical.

Consider a test with a validity of .30 and a reliability of .70. What would be its validity if (1) it were doubled in length; and (2) if it were reduced to .4 of its present length?

By Formula 15.25b, when $n = 2$,

$$\tilde{r}_{xy} = .30\sqrt{\frac{2}{1 + .70}} = (.30)(1.08) = .32$$

and when $n = .4$,

$$\tilde{r}_{xy} = .30\sqrt{\frac{.4}{1 - (.6)(.7)}} = (.30)(.83) = .25$$

If the two reliabilities are known and x is lengthened n times and y is lengthened n' times, substitution of Formula 15.28 in Formula 15.25 yields a formula for estimating the changed correlation between x and y:

$$\tilde{r}_{xy} = r_{xy}\sqrt{\frac{nn'}{[1 + (n-1)r_{xx'}][1 + (n'-1)r_{yy'}]}} \tag{15.25d}$$

SCORING FORMULAS

The simplest, and one of the best, methods for scoring a test made up of separate items is to use merely the number of items correct. If omitted items, as well as items incorrectly marked, are counted wrong, then any weighted combination of rights and wrongs correlates perfectly with the number of rights. (The inconsequential and exceptional case is when rights and wrongs are added together, so that each score represents the number of questions, which would destroy the test as an instrument capable of making discriminations.)

The result of any effective scoring formula is to put items into three categories: rights, wrongs, and omits, with each category contributing differentially to the total score. Since the number of items is a constant, only two of the three bits of information are needed (rights, denoted as R; wrongs, denoted as W; or omits, denoted as O) with which to enter the formula. Generally, scoring formulas are in terms of R and W.

SCORING FORMULAS: CORRECTION FOR GUESSING

If the n items of a true-false or multiple-choice psychological test were answered at random by someone entirely lacking the characteristic measured by the instrument, the expected number of items answered correctly would be n/n', in which n' is the number of choices. Thus, in a true-false test (which has two choices), half the items should be answered correctly by chance; with three-choice items, a third; with four-choice items, 25 percent; and so on. Obviously, the larger the number of choices in each item (provided each is equally likely to be chosen), the less sheer chance is likely to influence the result.

It has been shown that the effect of guessing can be minimized by utilizing the following formula:

$$X = R - \frac{W}{n' - 1} \tag{15.29}$$

a formula that is useful when there is a large number of omissions and when it is desired to treat omissions differently from the responses that that are definitely wrong. For true-false tests, Formula 15.29 becomes

$$X = R - W \tag{15.29a}$$

and for five-choice multiple-choice tests,

$$X = R - \frac{W}{4} \tag{15.29b}$$

EMPIRICAL SCORING FORMULAS

In some types of tests it has been found that the psychological function measured by R has a high negative correlation with the function measured by W. In such cases a scoring formula is of little value, since by giving a negative weight to W, the score merely includes more of the same kind of variance already measured by R.

In other instances, W has little variance compared with the variance of R, and here again there is usually little to be gained by using a scoring formula. However, one occasionally finds a situation in which W has considerable variance, has a relatively low relationship with R, and has definite negative validity with a criterion.

If there are several such tests in a battery, and the battery has an outside criterion, the solution is clear: The rights and wrongs in each test are treated as separate variables and all variables are validated against the criterion. Raw-score regression coefficients applied to R and W in each test, then, constitute the scoring formula.

A similar procedure can be applied to a single test used to predict a single criterion. Let O be the criterion. The regression equation may be written

$$\tilde{X}_o = \frac{s_O}{s_R} \beta_{OR.W} X_R + \frac{s_O}{s_W} \beta_{OW.R} X_W + K$$

Since the constant K has no effect on the correlations of the summed variable, it can be dropped. Since it is convenient to apply the scoring formula only to the wrongs, the regression coefficients can be divided by the regression coefficient for the rights, and the weights to be applied to the rights can be made unity. If a is the weight to be applied to the wrongs,

$$a = \frac{s_O s_R \beta_{OW.R}}{s_W s_O \beta_{OR.W}} = \frac{s_R \beta_{OW.R}}{s_W \beta_{OR.W}} = \frac{s_R(r_{OW} - r_{OR} r_{RW})}{s_W(r_{OR} - r_{OW} r_{RW})} \qquad (15.30)$$

There is no need to use such a formula unless:

1. A substantial proportion of the items have been omitted, as in a speeded test; and
2. The intercorrelations of the three variables, R, W, and the criterion, are such that the multiple correlation of R and W with the criterion is appreciably higher than the validity of the rights alone.

As with any multiple R, shrinkage is to be anticipated in applying an empirical scoring formula in a new sample of cases. Any such formula should be cross-validated on a new sample in order to determine whether the gain in validity in the original sample holds up.

ITEM ANALYSIS

DIFFICULTY OR POPULARITY ANALYSIS

Item analysis refers to the computation of statistics describing individual items. Such statistics are frequently used in developing a useful test from a collection of experimental items; or in revising an existing test. The most common, the simplest, and possibly the most useful type of item analysis involves the measurement of the difficulty or popularity of particular responses.

In an aptitude or achievement test, item difficulty is measured in terms of p, the proportion of subjects choosing the correct answer. If each item is scored 1 or 0, then p is the mean score on the item. Sometimes the entire group of subjects taking the test is used in the formula

$$p = \frac{N_p}{N}$$

while in other cases, N refers to the number actually attempting the item. The choice depends on which base will make p the best reflection of item difficulty.

An important use of p is in determining the order of the items in the test as a whole or in a subtest. It is considered good practice to begin a power test with one or two items that all subjects are extremely likely to pass and end with a few items on which not many subjects are likely to succeed. The easy items are thought to help engender confidence. In a power test, items passed or failed by all subjects add nothing to the ability of the test to make discriminations among subjects. In such a test, items should be arranged more or less in inverse order of difficulty, from $p = 1.00$ toward $p = .00$.

A second use of the p values of items is in the development of speeded tests. Speed in a function may be measured by a collection of items of uniform difficulty, of which p is an accepted measure. The number of items answered in a set amount of time can then be taken as a measure of speed.

With items on structured interest and personality tests, p is a measure of popularity rather than difficulty. Again, however, items with p values of .00 or 1.00 do not make discriminations among the respondents, and items with very low or very high p values make relatively few discriminations.

As noted in Chapter 9 with respect to a dichotomous variable, knowledge of p leads directly to knowledge of the variance and the standard deviation, since $V = pq$, in which $q = 1 - p$. The variance (and the standard deviation) are at a maximum when $p = q = .50$, but at first the variance drops rather slowly as p changes. When p is .40 or .60, the variance is .24, as compared with a maximum of .25, and only at approximately .15 or .85 has half of the variance disappeared. What each item adds to the total variance of a test is a function of the item variance and the covariances of the item with all other items. However, if the covariances are too high, the item will add to the numerical value of the total variance without adding appreciably to the usefulness of the instrument in making discriminations among people.

POPULARITY OF DISTRACTORS

In a structured psychological test, each question has n' alternate answers. The p value reflects the proportion who choose the correct alternative. As a preparation for revising the items, the proportions of subjects choosing the several wrong responses (the "distractors" or "decoys") are useful. If p is the proportion choosing the right answer among n' choices, then the ideal distribution of those choosing wrong answers is $(1 - p)/(n' - 1)$ of the cases for each wrong response. This would indicate that the distractors are equally attractive.

If a decoy is not used at all, the item no longer has n' choices, but in effect has only $(n' - 1)$ choices. For the distractors to be maximally effective, they should all have a probability of being chosen by one who does not possess the characteristic measured by the item. While few items have the ideal distribution of wrong responses, tests can be greatly improved by using distractor analysis to indicate which decoys need to be replaced or edited.

ITEM ANALYSIS: INTERNAL CONSISTENCY

To develop a test that measures a single function, it is necessary to select a group of items with relatively high (but not too high) intercorrelations. If the intercorrelations are too high, each will measure the identical small aspect of the trait over and over again; and the test will not make the proper differentiations in the characteristic measured. The simplest method of choosing items with relatively high intercorrelations is to develop first a pool that is judged to measure aspects of the same general trait. A total score is obtained and each item is correlated with this total, designated as t. It is readily seen that the covariance between each item and the total of which it is a part is a function of the item variance and the covariances between the item and the other items in the pool.

Let $t = a + b + \cdots + i$, in which t is the total score and a, $b \cdots i$ are the item scores, all in deviation form. By multiplying the expression by i, summing, dividing by N, and writing the covariances and the single variance, we have

$$C_{it} = C_{ia} + C_{ib} + \cdots + V_i \qquad (15.31)$$

We can divide Formula 15.31 by $s_i s_t$, multiply each covariance such as C_{ia} by a term such as s_a/s_a, and write the correlation

$$r_{it} = \frac{1}{s_t}(r_{ic}s_a + r_{ib}s_b + \cdots + s_i) \qquad (15.32)$$

Although Formula 15.32 reflects high item intercorrelations, items can be selected on the basis of other approximations, such as Formula 15.31. Another possibility would be to correct Formula 15.31 by removing the item variance. Thus we could compute for each item:

$$C_{it} - V_i = C_{ia} + C_{ib} + \cdots \qquad (15.31a)$$

Items with high values of this function would have high covariances with other items.

It must be remembered, however, that t changes as items are added or subtracted. Consequently, if a function of the correlation or covariance between an item and the total score is used as a guide to the selection of internally consistent items, the process must be carried through several cycles, using a series of pools of items, each more consistent internally than its predecessor.

Another technique is to select items in which some measure of internal consistency is maximized, such as Kuder-Richardson Formula 20; that is

$$\left[\frac{n}{n-1}\left(1 - \frac{\Sigma s_i^2}{V_t}\right)\right]$$

or the ratio of the sum of the covariances to the total test variance. This can be done by maximizing a part of Kuder-Richardson Formula 20, namely, $\Sigma C_{ij}/V_t$. This technique tends to pick a group of items measuring the same general function, and hence constituting a homogeneous test.

ITEM ANALYSIS: EXTERNAL VALIDITY

With heterogeneous tests, the characteristic to be maximized is the correlation with an outside criterion. Selecting items in the order of their correlation with the criterion will tend to accomplish this objective. An item-criterion correlation may be expressed as r_{ic}, in which i represents the item and c the criterion. A solution somewhat better theoretically is to attempt to maximize the correlation between the total test and the criterion by choosing items with the highest item-criterion covariances.

By a development parallel to that of Formula 15.32,

$$\frac{C_{tc}}{s_t s_c} = r_{tc} = \frac{1}{s_t s_c}(C_{ac} + C_{bc} + \cdots + C_{ic}) \tag{15.33}$$

Inspection of this equation shows that selection of items with high covariances with the criterion c will result in a high numerator of the formula for r_{tc}. However, such selection does not guarantee the maximum r_{tc}, since the item intercorrelations are concealed within s_t, and their pattern has a marked effect on the validity of t.

ITEM SELECTION BY APPROXIMATIONS TO MULTIPLE R

Theoretically, r_{tc} can be improved by some approximation to multiple correlation, which would select items on the basis of high correlations with the criterion and low intercorrelations within the constituted test.

Multiple correlation itself would be time-consuming to use as an item selection technique, but its chief drawback is that its use would require fractional weights to be applied to the items in scoring the developed test. While it provides the best theoretical answer to the problem of developing an instrument to predict a single external criterion, it is seldom used.

Various approximations to the multiple correlation technique have been attempted, usually with the restriction that the permissible weights be either 1 or 0. An item with a weight of 1 is selected; an item with a weight of 0 is discarded.

One such procedure is to select items according to the value of the ratio r_{ic}/r_{it}; that is, directly according to their validities and inversely according to their correlations with the total score. A first group of items so selected can be used for a new cycle of selection procedures, using a new t.

Actually, procedures involving the use of item intercorrelations for maximizing external validity have not been very successful. While it is relatively easy to maximize (or maximize approximately) the validity in a specific sample, the validity in subsequent samples tends to be little more than what might be attained simply by choosing the most valid items. Item correlations tend to be somewhat unstable from sample to sample, and a solution that is theoretically perfect may not be particularly useful in a practical situation.

From time to time, proposals have been made to weight items differentially, with a rather wide range of weights. In theory the correlation between a group of items and a criterion is at a maximum when each item is weighted in accordance with its regression weight. Empirical attempts to do this have generally resulted in some increase in validity within the particular sample in which the key is developed, but little increase over simpler scoring procedures has been realized when the key is cross-validated in a new sample.

TEST VARIANCE AND ITEM STATISTICS

As are the variances and covariances of continuous variables, item variances and covariances are directly additive. The sum of the item covariances between a given item and all other items in a test plus the variance of that item is precisely equal to the covariance between the item and the total score. Similarly, the sum of the covariances between items and the total score equals precisely the total variance. If all item variances and covariances are arranged in a matrix of n rows and n columns, with n being the total number of items, we have a convenient form for determining the characteristics of a test at any stage. By eliminating from the matrix those statistics referring to any item or group of items, statistics of the test with such items eliminated can be readily found, since all the statements regarding additive properties continue to hold.

NORMING PSYCHOLOGICAL TESTS

As pointed out earlier, psychological data are gathered in units such as number of seconds required to complete a task, number of errors, or in psychological tests, raw scores, which may or may not involve a scoring formula.

In much laboratory work, raw data are graphed and otherwise analyzed without transformation. In most theoretical statistical work, however, variables are treated as though they were actually z scores, which are described in Chapter 5.

Few raw scores on psychological tests have inherent meaning. They must be interpreted by means of a transformation, which serves two purposes:

1. It permits direct interpretation of the score; and
2. Scores from different tests or different parts of the same test are made comparable.

Two general classes of norms resulting from such transformations are reference norms and statistical norms. Reference norms are those in which the raw scores are translated into terms directly significant. These include work norms, age norms, and grade norms. Statistical norms, which include percentiles, standard scores, and normalized scores, are mathematical transformations that are especially useful in test-to-test comparisons, but which in and of themselves have no direct meaning in terms of real life situations.

REFERENCE NORMS

Work norms have been used very little, probably because meaningful work standards closely related to psychological tests are seldom found. However, performance tests in stenography and typing are often reported in number of words per minute. Sometimes the scoring system involves penalties for errors, so that the final score involves a statistical adjustment. Another example is the grading of the oral trade tests, designed as instruments to estimate the knowledge of individuals about a particular trade or occupation. Raw scores on these tests are interpreted in three categories: novice, apprentice, and journeyman.

In age norms, often used with tests for children, the average performance for each age is determined and the raw scores are converted to age equivalents. In computing the mental age on the Stanford-Binet, the child is given a certain number of months credit based on his "basal mental age," the highest level at which he passes all the tests. He is given additional credit toward his mental age for each additional item passed, each item having a value in terms of months. When a test is carefully standardized, this procedure yields a score that is directly interpretable. Some group intelligence tests use a slightly different system, in which a raw score is first obtained and is then converted, by means of a table of norms, to a mental age equivalent. This same method is sometimes used with school achievement tests of reading and arithmetic.

For tests depending primarily upon learning in the elementary school situation, grade norms may be used in preference to age norms. Here the raw score is converted into a grade equivalent, defined as the average performance of a particular grade level. Fractional grades are used for norming purposes, even though in the real school situation all grades are generally at least half a year apart.

The use of reference norms implies that enough individuals have been measured so that stable and representative standards of performance are available. Unless the tests are reliable and the norms are stable, the possibilities of misclassification are high. The estimate of reliability is best made in terms of the standard error of measurement, that is, the variability to be anticipated between obtained and true scores.

STATISTICAL NORMS

In previous chapters, three transformations usable for norming psychological tests have been discussed. The following computational examples have been given: percentiles, Example 4.2; percentile ranks, Example 4.3; standard scores, Example 5.2; and normalized scores, Example 11.4.

The three types of statistical norms differ chiefly in their distributions. If a large number of raw scores, representing fine gradations of ability, are converted to percentiles, the distribution is theoretically rectangular. Between each percentile point, if the number of cases were very large and the gradations very fine, 1 percent of the distribution would be expected.

If obtained scores are converted into standard scores and then distributed, the result is a distribution similar in shape to the distribution of the original raw scores. The transformation of raw scores into standard scores is strictly linear, and the correlation of standard scores with the original raw scores is exactly 1.00, except for the effect of rounding error.

Normalized scores resemble standard scores and are theoretically identical with them when the original distribution of raw scores is normal. However, there is a correction for any departure from normality in the original raw scores. Accordingly, the distribution of the normalized scores is more or less normal, irrespective of the shape of the original distribution.

PERCENTILES AND PERCENTILE RANKS

As described in Chapter 4, the two types of percentile transformations are percentiles proper and percentile ranks. With distributions of extremely large N and fine score gradations, percentiles and percentile ranks theoretically coincide. In computing a percentile, we find the theoretical score below which lies a certain percentage of the distribution. This theoretical score is often fractional, even though the test is scored in discrete units. In computing percentile ranks, we start with integral scores and determine the theoretical percentage of the distribution that lies below that score. The formula for any particular percentile rank requires that the number of cases below the score, plus half the number of cases at the score, be divided by the total number of cases in the distribution.

Percentile ranks are readily computed from a frequency distribution, as in Example 4.3.

Occasionally, test norms are reported in terms of score equivalents for selected percentiles. Often the percentiles shown are P_1, P_5, P_{10}, and so on, at intervals of five percentile points up to P_{95} and P_{99}. An example of this type of norming is shown in Example 4.2 together with the computational steps.

STANDARD SCORES

The simplest type of standard score is the familiar z score, which is merely the number of standard deviations a score is above or below the mean of all the scores in its series. As presented in Formula 5.9, the z score is

$$z_x = \frac{x}{s_x} = \frac{X - M_x}{s_x}$$

and the general formula with any assigned mean (M') and any assigned standard deviation (s') is (Formula 5.10)

$$\text{S.S.} = \left(\frac{X - M_x}{s_x}\right)s' + M'$$

For norming tests, the most popular standard score system uses an arbitrary mean of 50 and arbitrary standard deviation of 10. When used with a carefully defined base population, such as 12-year olds, this becomes the T score; when used for achievement tests with a population who have completed a year's study of a subject, it becomes a scaled score.

Hull (1) advocated a standard score with M' of 50 and s' of 14 so as to attain as wide a spread as possible ($\pm 3.5s$) and still have two-digit scores. Wechsler (3) uses an M' of 10 and an s' of 3 for intelligence test subscores.

An unlimited variety of standard score systems is possible. Irrespective of the arbitrary mean and standard deviation:

1. Scores in different variables are reduced to a common metric;
2. Scores are easily interpreted by reference to the assigned mean and standard deviation; and
3. All differences in standard scores are directly proportional to differences in the original raw-score units.

Since with most psychological tests, the obtained mean and standard deviation are functions of the particular testing material that happens to be employed, the assigned mean and standard deviation are generally just as appropriate as the original values. Standard score norming is shown in Example 5.2.

The percentile system also reduces scores to a common metric, but differences in percentiles are not proportional to differences in original scores. Individuals who use tests in personnel selection, in counseling, and in clinical work find the percentile easy to interpret to others. The rectangular distribution of the percentile is probably less desirable than the distribution of standard scores, which is essentially unmodified from the distribution of the original observations. However, both systems seem likely to continue side by side.

NORMALIZED SCORES

Normalized scores are much like standard scores in that the mean and standard deviation are predetermined. However, conversion is effected in such a way that the normalized scores for the group used in establishing the norms yield a distribution that is approximately normal. The method has been treated in Chapter 11, where Example 11.4 demonstrates required computations.

SUMMARY

One of the principal areas for the application of psychological statistics is with measures of intelligence, aptitudes, achievement, interests, and personality traits. In a homogeneous test, items measure overlapping aspects of the same general characteristic; in a heterogeneous test, the items have relatively low intercorrelations, but normally have positive relationships with an outside criterion. Statistical concepts pertinent to total variables, including the mean, variance, and correlation, are applicable to items.

Much of the theory of psychological tests centers around the concept of random error, which contributes to the total variance, but which by definition is unrelated to true variance and to the random error in other tests. The reliability of a test is the proportion of true variance and may be estimated by test-retest; by the correlation of alternate forms; by correlating one half of a test against the other half and then deducing the reliability of the whole; and by the method of rational equivalence, which correlates an existing test with its theoretical equivalent. The correlation of a test with an outside variable is systematically affected by changes in reliability, changes which may be caused by variation in length. The standard error of measurement, the estimated standard deviation of errors made in predicting true scores when we have knowledge only of the obtained scores, affords a practical interpretation of reliability.

In building and revising a test, item analysis is an important tool. Difficulty or popularity analysis indicates which items may be dropped or modified because they contribute inadequately to the total variance. Various forms of internal consistency analysis are used in building a homogeneous test, while item analysis against an external criterion may yield an instrument with high predictive validity.

Another application of statistics is in establishing norms in terms of percentiles, standard scores, or normalized scores, permitting the comparison of the standing of the same individual on different tests or the comparison of an individual with a group of his peers.

EXERCISES

1. Using the item score matrix of Example 15.1, correlate the score on the odd-numbered items with the score on the even numbered items and apply the Spearman-Brown prophecy formula to estimate the reliability of the test as a whole. Compare with $r_{xx'}$, as estimated by KR Formula 20.

2. Below are the scores, 1 or 0, of 25 individuals on the 20 items of a mechanical comprehension test. Find $r_{xx'}$ by the "split-half" technique and by KR Formula 20.

ITEM

INDIVIDUAL	1	2	3	4	5	6	7	8	9	10	11	12	13	14	15	16	17	18	19	20
A	1	1	1	1	1	1	1	1	0	1	0	0	1	1	0	1	1	1	0	0
B	0	1	1	1	0	0	0	0	0	1	0	1	1	1	1	0	0	0	0	0
C	1	1	1	0	1	1	1	1	1	1	1	1	0	1	0	0	1	1	1	1
D	0	0	1	1	1	0	1	1	1	0	1	1	1	1	1	1	0	0	0	1
E	1	1	1	1	1	1	1	0	0	1	1	1	1	1	0	0	1	0	0	1
F	1	1	1	1	1	1	1	1	1	1	0	1	1	1	1	1	1	1	0	0
G	1	1	0	1	0	0	1	0	1	1	0	0	0	0	1	0	1	0	1	1
H	0	1	1	0	1	1	1	1	0	1	1	1	1	1	0	1	1	1	0	1
I	1	1	1	1	1	1	1	0	1	1	0	1	1	1	1	1	1	1	1	1
J	1	1	1	1	1	1	1	0	1	0	1	1	1	1	0	1	1	1	1	1
K	1	1	1	1	1	1	1	0	0	1	0	0	1	0	1	0	1	1	1	1
L	0	1	1	1	1	1	1	0	1	1	1	1	1	0	0	1	1	1	1	0
M	1	1	1	1	1	0	1	0	0	0	1	0	1	0	1	0	0	1	1	1
N	0	1	0	0	0	1	1	0	1	1	0	0	0	0	0	0	0	0	0	0
O	1	1	1	1	1	0	1	0	1	0	0	1	1	1	1	1	1	1	1	1
P	1	1	0	0	0	1	1	0	1	1	1	0	0	0	0	0	0	0	0	0
Q	1	1	1	1	1	1	1	0	1	1	0	0	1	0	0	1	1	1	0	1
R	1	1	1	1	1	1	1	0	1	1	0	0	0	0	1	1	1	1	0	0
S	0	1	1	1	1	1	1	0	1	1	1	1	1	1	1	0	1	0	1	1
T	1	1	1	0	1	1	1	1	1	0	0	1	1	1	1	1	1	1	0	0
U	1	1	1	1	1	1	1	1	1	1	1	1	1	0	1	1	1	1	0	0
V	1	1	1	1	1	1	1	1	1	1	0	1	1	0	1	1	1	0	0	1
W	1	1	1	1	1	1	1	1	1	1	1	1	1	1	1	1	1	1	1	1
X	1	1	1	1	1	1	1	1	1	0	1	1	1	1	0	1	1	1	1	1
Y	0	1	1	1	1	1	1	1	1	0	1	0	0	0	0	1	1	1	1	1

3. Below is the variance-covariance matrix of ten items on a test of aircraft information ($N = 1000$). Find $r_{xx'}$ by KR Formula 20. (A method for finding V_x is given in Chapter 9.)

ITEM	1	2	3	4	5	6	7	8	9	10
1	.217	.057	.023	.029	.047	.004	.014	.005	.058	.035
2		.246	.039	.048	.069	.004	.014	.015	.074	.054
3			.155	.040	.042	.007	.021	.018	.045	.029
4				.164	.052	.007	.017	.015	.061	.034
5					.236	.005	.016	.021	.088	.041
6						.040	.007	.004	.012	.006
7							.069	.009	.024	.009
8								.069	.018	.007
9									.232	.055
10										.165

4. A test, X, with a reliability of .85, is doubled in length to become X', while Y, with a reliability of .75, is tripled in length to become Y'. If $r_{xy} = .40$, what is the best estimate of $r_{x'y'}$ on the assumption that the new material in each test is homogeneous with the old?

5. The reliability of X, with S.D. of 5, is estimated to be .56. If the test is doubled in length (by adding new material with S.D. of 5, and with a correlation of .56 with the original material) what would be the new $s_{meas.}$?

6. If the reliability of a test is .70 in a group in which the S.D. is 9, what would be the expected reliability of the test in a group in which the S.D. is 10?

7. Prove that the correlation between a total score, X, and its error component, e_x, is $\sqrt{1 - r_{xx'}}$.

8. Demonstrate that if the p values of all items are identical, KR Formula 20 can be written as

$$r_{xx'} = \frac{n(V_x - M_x) + M_x^2}{(n-1)V_x}$$

REFERENCES

1. HULL, C. L., "The conversion of test scores into series which shall have any assigned mean and degree of dispersion," *J. Appl. Psychol.*, 1922, **6**, 298–300.

2. KUDER, G. F., AND RICHARDSON, M. W., "The theory of the estimation of test reliability," *Psychometrika*, 1937, **2**, 151–160.

3. WECHSLER, DAVID, *Manual for Wechsler Adult Intelligence Scale*. New York: The Psychological Corporation, 1955.

Suggested Readings in Text Construction

GHISELLI, EDWIN E., *Theory of Psychological Measurement.* New York: McGraw-Hill Book Co., 1964.

GULLIKSEN, HAROLD, *Theory of Mental Tests.* New York: John Wiley & Sons, Inc., 1950.

HELMSTADTER, G. C., *Principles of Psychological Measurement.* New York: Appleton-Century-Crofts, 1964.

THORNDIKE, ROBERT L., *Personnel Selection.* New York: John Wiley & Sons, Inc., 1949.

WOOD, DOROTHY ADKINS, *Test Construction.* Columbus, Ohio: Charles E. Merrill Books, Inc., 1960.

MATRICES AND
DETERMINANTS
IN PSYCHOLOGICAL
STATISTICS

16

NATURE OF MATRICES

In describing correlations involving many variables, the notation of matrices and determinants is concise and informative. Extensive groupings of data may be indicated by single letters, and processes requiring hundreds or thousands of multiplications and additions may be denoted by two or three letters and a few symbols. Matrix formulas and equations can be used to describe conventional statistical operations, and in some cases they point the way to advanced methods of analysis.

Actually, all the calculations of descriptive statistics can be described in words as series of numerical operations. More economically, however, these computations may be summarized in the notation of conventional scalar algebra, as in earlier chapters. When three or more variables are concerned, these same operations can generally be represented still more succinctly in matrix algebra, which is a further development of the scalar notation.

MATRIX CONCEPTS

Among the concepts often encountered in discussions of psychological data are types of matrices, the transpose of a matrix (an alternate way of writing a matrix in which columns take the place of rows, and vice versa), matrix addition and multiplication, and the inverse of a matrix, which corresponds in a general way to the reciprocal of conventional notation.

Certain matrices can be evaluated as determinants, which have further interesting properties. The numerical procedures used to find the partial variances and covariances pertinent to multivariate correlation may be conveniently expressed in determinantal terms.

ROWS AND COLUMNS OF A MATRIX

While any rectangular arrangement of numbers may be called a matrix, in psychological statistics a matrix is generally a systematic arrangement of numerical information in which rows and columns have assigned meanings. For example, Table 16.1 is a roster or matrix of test scores in which the rows represent individuals and the columns represent tests or variables.

TABLE 16.1. A HYPOTHETICAL ROSTER OF SCORES

	(1) GENERAL INTELLIGENCE	(2) MECHANICAL COMPREHENSION	(3) ARITHMETIC REASONING	(4) SPATIAL RELATIONS
Arthur	121	46	26	50
Benjamin	114	49	20	58
Charles	114	40	24	58
David	107	34	22	62
Eugene	100	43	24	42
Frederick	93	46	16	54
George	86	37	18	42
Henry	86	34	14	38
Irving	79	31	16	46

Full identification of the rows and columns can be omitted if the assigned meanings are well understood. In all work with matrices it is conventional to refer first to the row or rows and secondly to the column or columns. In Table 16.1, each separate number can be considered an element of the matrix, denoted by a letter such as a, and with subscripts to indicate the row and column in which the element belongs. If the rows are denoted as $a, b \cdots i$ and the columns as $1, 2 \cdots 4$, then the score of David on the arithmetic reasoning test is a_{d3}, or 22. In general terms, a_{ij} refers to the element in the ith row and jth column of matrix **A**.

Matrices are often considered to be divided by horizontal and vertical lines into sections of one element each. These sections may be thought of as cells and the elements within them as cell entries.

ORDER OF A MATRIX

The order of a matrix is merely the number of its rows and the number of its columns, connected by a multiplication sign. The order of the matrix in Table 16.1 is 9 × 4, 9 being the number of rows and 4 being the number of columns. In general terms, it is conventional to use m for the number of rows and n for the number of columns. If the matrix is square, with the same number of rows and columns, $m = n$, and the order is designated merely as n.

Elements within a matrix may also have "order" in a sense different from "order" as applied to the matrix as a whole. In a matrix of partial variances and covariances, for example, the "order" of the coefficients refers to the number of variables that have been partialed out in forming them. In a single matrix, then, the term *order* may be used with two entirely different meanings; in one sense, order refers to the number of rows and columns; and in the other sense, order refers to a characteristic of the elements.

VECTORS

The generic name for a row or column (without specifying which) is *vector*. More specifically, a vector is conceived to be a $1 \times n$ or an $n \times 1$ matrix, existing independently or as a part (or submatrix) of a larger matrix.

Vectors are often designated by lower-case letters in heavy type, and the elements of a row vector are generally enclosed in parentheses. Thus the row vector of Charles' scores (four elements) from Table 16.1 would be written

$$c = (114, 40, 24, 58)$$

Column vectors may be written vertically with the marks (yet to be described) used to distinguish matrices or, for convenience, they may be written horizontally and enclosed in brackets. Thus the column vector or the scores on the mechanical comprehension test in Table 16.1 consists of nine elements, one for each of the nine individuals. If it is designated x_2, the subscript indicating that it is the column assigned to the second variable, it may be written

$$x_2 = \{46, 49, 40, 34, 43, 46, 37, 34, 31\}$$

SCALARS

When the logic of matrices is carried down to the limiting case, we have a matrix with a single row and a single column. Such a 1×1 matrix is called a *scalar* and it may be considered as a chief connecting link between matrix algebra and conventional, or scalar, algebra. A scalar in matrix algebra has identical properties in all operations, as does any quantity (in literal or numeric form) in conventional algebra.

DESIGNATION OF COMPLETE MATRICES

A complete matrix is indicated by a capital letter in heavy type, such as **A**, **S**, or **X**, or by the typical element in conventional lower case enclosed in parentheses, such as (a_{ij}) or (x_{ij}). When the numbers or letters of a matrix are written out in full, they are enclosed in double lines, or brackets, or large parentheses, or single lines curved at the ends. All are recognized as good usage. Here we elect to use double lines, which contrast neatly with the single lines used to designate the determinants to be described later.

The scores of Table 16.1 can be converted to deviations by subtracting from each value the mean of the variable. (Later this familiar procedure will be stated as a series of matrix operations.)

Thus, from each value in vector 1, the general intelligence test, we subtract its mean, 100, and from each value in vector 2, we subtract the mean, 40, and so on. The resultant matrix is designated as **X** and is shown in Table 16.2.

TABLE 16.2. SCORES OF TABLE 16.1 AS DEVIATIONS FROM THEIR RESPECTIVE MEANS

$$
X = \begin{Vmatrix}
21 & 6 & 6 & 0 \\
14 & 9 & 0 & 8 \\
14 & 0 & 4 & 8 \\
7 & -6 & 2 & 12 \\
0 & 3 & 4 & -8 \\
-7 & 6 & -4 & 4 \\
-14 & -3 & -2 & -8 \\
-14 & -6 & -6 & -12 \\
-21 & -9 & -4 & -4
\end{Vmatrix}
$$

All the information of Table 16.1 is represented in **X**, provided we remember the meanings of the rows and columns and the means of the four variables.

The standard deviations of the four variables in **X** are respectively 14, 6, 4, and 8. If each deviation is divided by the standard deviation of the variable, the result is **Z**, the matrix of the four variables in z form, shown in Table 16.3.

TABLE 16.3. INFORMATION OF TABLE 16.1 AND TABLE 16.2 IN z FORM

$$
Z = \begin{Vmatrix}
1.50 & 1.00 & 1.50 & .00 \\
1.00 & 1.50 & .00 & 1.00 \\
1.00 & .00 & 1.00 & 1.00 \\
.50 & -1.00 & .50 & 1.50 \\
.00 & .50 & 1.00 & -1.00 \\
-.50 & 1.00 & -1.00 & .50 \\
-1.00 & -.50 & -.50 & -1.00 \\
-1.00 & -1.00 & -1.50 & -1.50 \\
-1.50 & -1.50 & -1.00 & -.50
\end{Vmatrix}
$$

SOME TYPES OF MATRICES

Terms useful in describing special types of matrices of interest in statistical operations include the zero, the symmetric, the triangular, the diagonal, and the identity matrices. In general, these matrix formats do not fit original data or even the results of statistical analyses; rather they are useful forms in connection with matrix computations and manipulations later to be described. All the terms describe regularities of internal matrix structure, as contrasted with the matrix in Table 16.1 where the internal structure is completely free, since no element is necessarily identical with any other element.

If a matrix is composed of elements all of which have the value of zero, it is a zero (or null) matrix. A zero matrix may be rectangular or square; whereas the symmetric, triangular, diagonal, and identity matrices are necessarily square.

In a symmetric matrix every element below the main diagonal (the cells that constitute a chain from the upper left to the lower right) has an element of exactly the same value in a predetermined position above the main diagonal. That is to say that a_{ij} (the element in the ith row and jth column) is identical with a_{ji} (the element in the jth row and ith column). If i does not equal j, a_{ij} is a general expression for off-diagonal elements, all of which appear in the matrix as pairs. Examples of symmetric matrices are complete matrices of variances and covariances and complete matrices of correlation coefficients.

If all elements below or above the main diagonal are zeros, it is a triangular matrix. If all elements both below and above the diagonal are zeros, but the elements in the diagonal have value, it is a diagonal matrix. A matrix with the same number in all the cells of the main diagonal but with 0 in all other cells is a scalar matrix. A scalar matrix with 1's in the diagonal is an identity or unity matrix. Numerical examples of these matrices are given in Table 16.4.

TABLE 16.4. EXAMPLES OF SPECIAL TYPES OF MATRICES USED IN
MATRIX OPERATIONS

0	0		1.00	.48	.32	.16		1.00	.50	.40	
0	0		.48	1.00	.24	.12		.00	.75	.30	
0	0		.32	.24	1.00	.08		.00	.00	.72	
			.16	.12	.08	1.00					

Zero Matrix   Symmetric Matrix   Triangular Matrix

.0714	.0000	.0000	.0000		5	0	0	0		1	0	0	0
.0000	.1667	.0000	.0000		0	5	0	0		0	1	0	0
.0000	.0000	.2500	.0000		0	0	5	0		0	0	1	0
.0000	.0000	.0000	.1250		0	0	0	5		0	0	0	1

Diagonal Matrix   Scalar Matrix   Identity Matrix

MATRIX TRANSPOSITION

Any matrix can be rewritten so that the elements of the rows of the original matrix become the elements of the columns of a new matrix, called the *transpose*. A transpose is indicated by a prime, or accent mark, or by a superscript T. Thus A' or A^T is the transpose of A. If S is the score matrix of Table 16.1, then the transpose is

$$S^T = \begin{Vmatrix} 121 & 114 & 114 & 107 & 100 & 93 & 86 & 86 & 79 \\ 46 & 49 & 40 & 34 & 43 & 46 & 37 & 34 & 31 \\ 26 & 20 & 24 & 22 & 24 & 16 & 18 & 14 & 16 \\ 50 & 58 & 58 & 62 & 42 & 54 & 42 & 38 & 46 \end{Vmatrix}$$

By transposition the rows of A become the columns of A^T, and vice versa. Another way of describing transposition is to say that element a_{ij} of the original becomes element a_{ji} of the transpose.

The transpose of the transpose is, of course, the original matrix, that is, $(A^T)^T$ is A. If a matrix is rectangular, we often think of the form with the smaller number of columns as the original and the form with the larger number of columns as the transpose; but actually, the designation as to which is which is more or less arbitrary. Any nonsymmetric matrix can be written in two forms, one of which is the transpose of the other; and in many matrix operations, transposition is vitally important. When rows and columns are interchanged, properties of the matrix may be changed. However, if a matrix is symmetrical, it is identical with its transpose.

MATRIX EQUATIONS

Table 16.1 may appear to be simply a display of information, but matrices in general are not inert. They enter into equations; they may be modified by other matrices, including scalars and vectors; and they may act upon or modify still other matrices. When a matrix equation is solved, values for a number of unknowns may be obtained more or less simultaneously, since in some cases a matrix equation is actually a set of n simultaneous linear equations in n unknowns, $n \times n$ and $n \times 1$ being the order of the matrices involved.

A matrix equation as a whole is handled analogously to an equation in ordinary algebra. An expression on one side may be simplified or otherwise modified by operations internal to that side, without affecting the other side of the equation. However, if the expression on one side of the equation is changed by adding, subtracting, or multiplying by an outside factor, then both sides must be treated in the same fashion. An advantage of matrix equations is that relationships which may be obscure when all ideas are expressed in conventional algebra may become conspicuous in matrix notation. To know how to handle matrix equations, it is necessary to understand fundamental operations, some of which are exactly parallel to those of scalar algebra. Other operations, however, involve new principles.

SOME OPERATIONS IN MATRIX ALGEBRA

EQUALITY OF MATRICES

Two matrices are equal if and only if they are of the same order and if each element in one matrix equals precisely the corresponding element in the other. If a_{ij} is the typical element in **A** and b_{ij} is the typical element in **B**, then a_{ij} must equal b_{ij} for all values of i and j. This principle permits a matrix equation involving simple simultaneous linear equations to be reduced to a vector of letters on one side of the equation and a vector of numerical values on the other.

ADDITION AND SUBTRACTION

Matrices can be added together if and only if they are of exactly the same order. Corresponding elements are merely summed. The order in which the matrices to be summed appear in an equation is immaterial; and if several matrices are summed, the order in which they are added is of no consequence. Exactly the same principles apply to matrix subtraction. An algebraic example, involving both subtraction and addition, is given below:

$$\begin{Vmatrix} a_{11} & a_{12} \\ a_{21} & a_{22} \\ a_{31} & a_{32} \\ a_{41} & a_{42} \end{Vmatrix} - \begin{Vmatrix} b_{11} & b_{12} \\ b_{21} & b_{22} \\ b_{31} & b_{32} \\ b_{41} & b_{42} \end{Vmatrix} + \begin{Vmatrix} c_{11} & c_{12} \\ c_{21} & c_{22} \\ c_{31} & c_{32} \\ c_{41} & c_{42} \end{Vmatrix} = \begin{Vmatrix} a_{11} - b_{11} + c_{11} & a_{12} - b_{12} + c_{12} \\ a_{21} - b_{21} + c_{21} & a_{22} - b_{22} + c_{22} \\ a_{31} - b_{31} + c_{31} & a_{32} - b_{32} + c_{32} \\ a_{41} - b_{41} + c_{41} & a_{42} - b_{42} + c_{42} \end{Vmatrix}$$

MATRIX MULTIPLICATION

Two matrices may be multiplied together, provided they can be arranged in an order such that the number of elements in the rows of the first matrix equals the number of elements in the columns of the second. This statement implies two important restrictions on matrix multiplication:

1. Only certain matrices may be multiplied together; and
2. The sequence in which the two matrices appear may affect the results of multiplication. In general, in terms of matrices, **AB** does not equal **BA**.

The computation of a variance affords a simple example of matrix multiplication. In scalar notation,

$$V_x = \frac{\Sigma x^2}{N} \tag{5.3}$$

that is, the variance is the mean of the squares of the deviations from the arithmetic mean. These deviations may be written as a vector $\mathbf{X}$, that is,

$$\mathbf{X} = \begin{Vmatrix} x_1 \\ x_2 \\ x_3 \\ \cdot \\ \cdot \\ x_n \end{Vmatrix}$$

of which the transpose (obtained by reversing rows and the single column) is

$$\mathbf{X}^T = \begin{Vmatrix} x_1 & x_2 & x_3 & \cdots & x_n \end{Vmatrix}$$

We now arrange the two matrices in the order $\mathbf{X}^T\mathbf{X}$ and multiply:

$$\mathbf{X}^T\mathbf{X} = \begin{Vmatrix} x_1 & x_2 & x_3 & \cdots & x_n \end{Vmatrix} \cdot \begin{Vmatrix} x_1 \\ x_2 \\ x_3 \\ \cdot \\ \cdot \\ x_n \end{Vmatrix} = x_1{}^2 + x_2{}^2 + x_3{}^2 + \cdots + x_n{}^2 = \Sigma x^2 \quad (16.1)$$

It is to be noted that the number of elements in the row vector $\mathbf{X}^T$ is N, exactly the same as the number of elements in the column vector $\mathbf{X}$. Each term in $\mathbf{X}^T$ is multiplied by the corresponding term in $\mathbf{X}$, and the products are summed as a scalar, Σx^2. It should be pointed out that $\mathbf{X}^T$ is post-multiplied by $\mathbf{X}$, that is, the matrices appear in the sequence $\mathbf{X}^T\mathbf{X}$. In this instance, as in instances to be pointed out later, a different sequence of the matrices (that is, $\mathbf{X}\mathbf{X}^T$, or $\mathbf{X}^T$ premultiplied by $\mathbf{X}$) would produce a radically different result.

The product of $\mathbf{X}^T\mathbf{X}$, Σx^2, now becomes the variance when divided by another scalar, N, but that is not a matrix operation. Instead of reverting to scalar algebra, two new principles are noted:

1. When a matrix is multiplied by a scalar, all the elements of that matrix are multiplied by the scalar (and in this case, there is no difference between premultiplication and post-multiplication); and
2. When three or more matrices are multiplied together, the temporal sequence in which the multiplications take place is completely immaterial.

In the general case, with matrices represented as $\mathbf{A}$, $\mathbf{B}$, and $\mathbf{C}$, and with parentheses indicating the two matrices first multiplied together, the second principle can be expressed as

$$\mathbf{ABC} = (\mathbf{AB})\mathbf{C} = \mathbf{A}(\mathbf{BC})$$

In the specific instance, with $1/N$ as a scalar, it can be said that

$$\left(\frac{1}{N}\mathbf{X}^T\right)\mathbf{X} = (\mathbf{X}^T\mathbf{X})\frac{1}{N} = \frac{\Sigma x^2}{N} = V_x$$

Choosing the $[(1/N)\mathbf{X}^T]\mathbf{X}$ route to the variance, we multiply $\mathbf{X}^T$ by $1/N$ and post-multiply the resultant row vector by the original column vector $\mathbf{X}$. Then

$$\left\Vert\frac{x_1}{N}\ \frac{x_2}{N}\ \frac{x_3}{N}\ \cdots\ \frac{x_n}{N}\right\Vert \cdot \left\Vert\begin{array}{c}x_1\\x_2\\x_3\\\vdots\\x_n\end{array}\right\Vert = \frac{\Sigma x^2}{N} = V_x \qquad (16.2)$$

Numerical operations as indicated in matrix notation are not necessarily the most efficient computationally. The operations indicated in Formula 5.3 are actually more efficient for finding the variance than the operations indicated in Eq. 16.2, while the conventional raw-score formula

$$V_x = \frac{\Sigma X^2}{N} - M_x{}^2 \qquad (5.3a)$$

is more efficient than either. We have used matrix notation in dealing with a single variable only to illustrate the notation itself. Concepts and procedures that seem slightly awkward in relatively simple instances become very appropriate when the same form of operation is extended to a large number of variables.

All operations in the multiplication of larger matrices follow precisely the model of Eq. 16.1; that is, the row elements of the first matrix are multiplied by the column elements of the second matrix, and the products are summed. For this reason, the number of elements in the rows of the first matrix must be identical with the number of elements in the columns of the second matrix.

In matrix multiplication, every row vector in the first matrix must be post-multiplied by every column vector in the second, and the resultant scalar (the sum of "inner products" of pairs of elements) becomes the element in the ith row and jth column of the product matrix. Thus each cell entry, a_{ij}, in the product matrix is formed by multiplying together two vectors, any row i in the first matrix and any column j in the second.

If the order of the first matrix is $m \times n$ and that of the second $n \times p$, the order of the product matrix will be $m \times p$. Since the sum of a series of multiplications is needed for each element in the product matrix, the total number of multiplications required is $n \times m \times p$.

A MATRIX OF r'S AS A PRODUCT OF TWO MATRICES

As an example of matrix multiplication, consider the development of **R**, a matrix of correlations with 1.00 in the diagonal (that is, a matrix of covariances and variances in z form).

If we transpose **Z** (the matrix shown in Table 16.3), multiply the transpose by the scalar $1/N$, and then post-multiply $(1/N)\mathbf{Z}^T$ by **Z**, the elements in the diagonal of the product matrix will be z-score covariances or correlation coefficients. The formula in matrix notation for a correlation matrix of any size is

$$\frac{1}{N} \mathbf{Z}^T \mathbf{Z} = \mathbf{R} \qquad (16.3)$$

In Table 16.5 the information of Table 16.3 is displayed algebraically and numerically in the format required by Formula 16.3. Letter subscripts indicate individuals; numerical subscripts indicate variables. In accordance with customary usage, the subscripts of the elements of the transpose retain their original sequence, and hence refer first to column and then to row.

The computation of two of the elements in the product matrix can be shown analytically. The first row of the first matrix is post-multiplied by the first column of the second matrix, yielding

$$\frac{z_{a1}}{N} z_{a1} + \frac{z_{b1}}{N} z_{b1} + \frac{z_{c1}}{N} z_{c1} + \frac{z_{d1}}{N} z_{d1} + \frac{z_{e1}}{N} z_{e1} + \frac{z_{f1}}{N} z_{f1}$$

$$+ \frac{z_{g1}}{N} z_{g1} + \frac{z_{h1}}{N} z_{h1} + \frac{z_{i1}}{N} z_{i1} = \frac{\Sigma z_1 z_1}{N} = \frac{\Sigma z_1{}^2}{N} = 1.00$$

A correlation coefficient, r_{12}, is formed by post-multiplying the first row of the first matrix by the second column of the second matrix:

$$\frac{z_{a1}}{N} z_{a2} + \frac{z_{b1}}{N} z_{b2} + \frac{z_{c1}}{N} z_{c2} + \frac{z_{d1}}{N} z_{d2} + \frac{z_{e1}}{N} z_{e2} + \frac{z_{f1}}{N} z_{f2}$$

$$+ \frac{z_{g1}}{N} z_{g2} + \frac{z_{h1}}{N} z_{h2} + \frac{z_{i1}}{N} z_{i2} = \frac{\Sigma z_1 z_2}{N} = {}_z C_{12} = r_{12}$$

From Table 16.5 it may be noted that, when the matrix is premultiplied by its transpose, the product matrix is symmetrical. (In this case the multiplication by the scalar is immaterial.) It is always true that the product matrix of any matrix and its transpose (either by pre- or post-multiplication) is symmetrical. Furthermore, a matrix and its transpose can always be multiplied together, since the number of elements in the rows of the first will equal the number of elements in the columns of the second.

TABLE 16.5. FORMATION OF CORRELATIONS BY MATRIX OPERATIONS

$$
\begin{bmatrix}
\frac{z_{a1}}{N} & \frac{z_{b1}}{N} & \frac{z_{c1}}{N} & \frac{z_{d1}}{N} & \frac{z_{e1}}{N} & \frac{z_{f1}}{N} & \frac{z_{g1}}{N} & \frac{z_{h1}}{N} & \frac{z_{i1}}{N} \\[4pt]
\frac{z_{a2}}{N} & \frac{z_{b2}}{N} & \frac{z_{c2}}{N} & \frac{z_{d2}}{N} & \frac{z_{e2}}{N} & \frac{z_{f2}}{N} & \frac{z_{g2}}{N} & \frac{z_{h2}}{N} & \frac{z_{i2}}{N} \\[4pt]
\frac{z_{a3}}{N} & \frac{z_{b3}}{N} & \frac{z_{c3}}{N} & \frac{z_{d3}}{N} & \frac{z_{e3}}{N} & \frac{z_{f3}}{N} & \frac{z_{g3}}{N} & \frac{z_{h3}}{N} & \frac{z_{i3}}{N} \\[4pt]
\frac{z_{a4}}{N} & \frac{z_{b4}}{N} & \frac{z_{c4}}{N} & \frac{z_{d4}}{N} & \frac{z_{e4}}{N} & \frac{z_{f4}}{N} & \frac{z_{g4}}{N} & \frac{z_{h4}}{N} & \frac{z_{i4}}{N}
\end{bmatrix}
\cdot
\begin{bmatrix}
z_{a1} & z_{a2} & z_{a3} & z_{a4} \\
z_{b1} & z_{b2} & z_{b3} & z_{b4} \\
z_{c1} & z_{c2} & z_{c3} & z_{c4} \\
z_{d1} & z_{d2} & z_{d3} & z_{d4} \\
z_{e1} & z_{e2} & z_{e3} & z_{e4} \\
z_{f1} & z_{f2} & z_{f3} & z_{f4} \\
z_{g1} & z_{g2} & z_{g3} & z_{g4} \\
z_{h1} & z_{h2} & z_{h3} & z_{h4} \\
z_{i1} & z_{i2} & z_{i3} & z_{i4}
\end{bmatrix}
=
\begin{bmatrix}
\frac{\Sigma z_1{}^2}{N} & \frac{\Sigma z_1 z_2}{N} & \frac{\Sigma z_1 z_3}{N} & \frac{\Sigma z_1 z_4}{N} \\[4pt]
\frac{\Sigma z_2 z_1}{N} & \frac{\Sigma z_2{}^2}{N} & \frac{\Sigma z_2 z_3}{N} & \frac{\Sigma z_2 z_4}{N} \\[4pt]
\frac{\Sigma z_3 z_1}{N} & \frac{\Sigma z_3 z_2}{N} & \frac{\Sigma z_3{}^2}{N} & \frac{\Sigma z_3 z_4}{N} \\[4pt]
\frac{\Sigma z_4 z_1}{N} & \frac{\Sigma z_4 z_2}{N} & \frac{\Sigma z_4 z_3}{N} & \frac{\Sigma z_4{}^2}{N}
\end{bmatrix}
$$

Numerical Solution

$$
\begin{bmatrix}
\frac{1.50}{9} & \frac{1.00}{9} & \frac{1.00}{9} & \frac{.50}{9} & 0 & -\frac{.50}{9} & -\frac{1.00}{9} & -\frac{1.00}{9} & -\frac{1.50}{9} \\[4pt]
\frac{1.00}{9} & \frac{1.50}{9} & 0 & -\frac{1.00}{9} & \frac{.50}{9} & \frac{1.00}{9} & -\frac{.50}{9} & -\frac{1.00}{9} & -\frac{1.00}{9} \\[4pt]
\frac{1.00}{9} & 0 & \frac{1.00}{9} & \frac{.50}{9} & \frac{1.00}{9} & -\frac{1.00}{9} & -\frac{.50}{9} & -\frac{1.50}{9} & -\frac{1.00}{9} \\[4pt]
0 & \frac{1.00}{9} & \frac{1.00}{9} & \frac{1.50}{9} & -\frac{1.00}{9} & \frac{.50}{9} & -\frac{1.00}{9} & -\frac{1.50}{9} & -\frac{.50}{9}
\end{bmatrix}
\cdot
\begin{bmatrix}
1.50 & 1.00 & 1.00 & .00 \\
1.00 & 1.50 & .00 & 1.00 \\
1.00 & .00 & 1.00 & 1.00 \\
.50 & -1.00 & .50 & 1.50 \\
.00 & .50 & 1.00 & -1.00 \\
-.50 & 1.00 & -1.00 & .50 \\
-1.00 & -.50 & -.50 & -1.00 \\
-1.00 & -1.00 & -1.50 & -1.50 \\
-1.50 & -1.00 & -1.00 & -.50
\end{bmatrix}
=
\begin{bmatrix}
1.00 & .64 & .83 & .64 \\
.64 & 1.00 & .42 & .31 \\
.83 & .42 & 1.00 & .39 \\
.64 & .31 & .39 & 1.00
\end{bmatrix}
$$

If A is a $m \times n$ matrix, A^T will be of order $n \times m$. The product AA^T will be of order m. On the other hand, the product A^TA will be of order n. In the case of the original matrix of psychological test scores, there are n columns representing tests. Consequently, when a transpose of one form of the score matrix is post-multiplied by the matrix, the result is a symmetrical matrix of order n, representing the intercorrelations.

Let C be a variance-covariance matrix of three variables in deviation form and let $\lambda_{1/s}$ be a diagonal matrix in which the elements are the reciprocals of the three standard deviations. Then, when $\lambda_{1/s}$ premultiplies C, the result will be

$$
\begin{Vmatrix} \dfrac{1}{s_1} & 0 & 0 \\ 0 & \dfrac{1}{s_2} & 0 \\ 0 & 0 & \dfrac{1}{s_3} \end{Vmatrix} \cdot \begin{Vmatrix} V_1 & C_{12} & C_{13} \\ C_{21} & V_2 & C_{23} \\ C_{31} & C_{32} & V_3 \end{Vmatrix} = \begin{Vmatrix} \dfrac{V_1}{s_1} & \dfrac{C_{12}}{s_1} & \dfrac{C_{13}}{s_1} \\ \dfrac{C_{21}}{s_2} & \dfrac{V_2}{s_2} & \dfrac{C_{23}}{s_2} \\ \dfrac{C_{31}}{s_3} & \dfrac{C_{32}}{s_3} & \dfrac{V_3}{s_3} \end{Vmatrix}
$$

When C is post-multiplied by $\lambda_{1/s}$, the elements in each column of C are multiplied by the corresponding nonzero column elements of $\lambda_{1/s}$, as follows:

$$
\begin{Vmatrix} V_1 & C_{12} & C_{13} \\ C_{21} & V_2 & C_{23} \\ C_{31} & C_{32} & V_3 \end{Vmatrix} \cdot \begin{Vmatrix} \dfrac{1}{s_1} & 0 & 0 \\ 0 & \dfrac{1}{s_2} & 0 \\ 0 & 0 & \dfrac{1}{s_3} \end{Vmatrix} = \begin{Vmatrix} \dfrac{V_1}{s_1} & \dfrac{C_{12}}{s_2} & \dfrac{C_{13}}{s_3} \\ \dfrac{C_{21}}{s_1} & \dfrac{V_2}{s_2} & \dfrac{C_{23}}{s_3} \\ \dfrac{C_{31}}{s_1} & \dfrac{C_{32}}{s_2} & \dfrac{V_3}{s_3} \end{Vmatrix}
$$

It follows that when a variance-covariance matrix obtained from deviation scores is premultiplied and post-multiplied by a diagonal matrix of reciprocals of standard deviations, the result is a variance-covariance matrix in z form; that is to say, a matrix of correlation coefficients with unity in the diagonal. In matrix notation,

$$\lambda_{1/s}C\lambda_{1/s} = R \tag{16.4}$$

Since the sequence in which matrix multiplications are performed is inconsequential, we can first premultiply C by $\lambda_{1/s}$, and then post-multiply the resulting product by $\lambda_{1/s}$; or we may start by post-multiplying C by $\lambda_{1/s}$ and then premultiplying the result by $\lambda_{1/s}$. In terms of scalars within the matrices:

$$\begin{Vmatrix} \dfrac{1}{s_1} & 0 & 0 \\[2mm] 0 & \dfrac{1}{s_2} & 0 \\[2mm] 0 & 0 & \dfrac{1}{s_3} \end{Vmatrix} \cdot \begin{Vmatrix} V_1 & C_{12} & C_{13} \\ C_{21} & V_2 & C_{23} \\ C_{31} & C_{32} & V_3 \end{Vmatrix} \cdot \begin{Vmatrix} \dfrac{1}{s_1} & 0 & 0 \\[2mm] 0 & \dfrac{1}{s_2} & 0 \\[2mm] 0 & 0 & \dfrac{1}{s_3} \end{Vmatrix} = \begin{Vmatrix} \dfrac{V_1}{s_1 s_1} & \dfrac{C_{12}}{s_1 s_2} & \dfrac{C_{13}}{s_1 s_3} \\[2mm] \dfrac{C_{21}}{s_2 s_1} & \dfrac{V_2}{s_2 s_2} & \dfrac{C_{23}}{s_2 s_3} \\[2mm] \dfrac{C_{31}}{s_3 s_1} & \dfrac{C_{32}}{s_3 s_2} & \dfrac{V_3}{s_3 s_3} \end{Vmatrix}$$

$$= \begin{Vmatrix} 1.00 & r_{12} & r_{13} \\ r_{21} & 1.00 & r_{23} \\ r_{31} & r_{32} & 1.00 \end{Vmatrix}$$

We now have a way of indicating how to find $\mathbf{R}$, the symmetrical matrix of correlation coefficients, from $\mathbf{X}$, the matrix of deviation scores displayed in Table 16.2. By analogy with Eq. 16.3, $\mathbf{C}$ can be found from $\mathbf{X}$ as follows:

$$\frac{1}{N} \mathbf{X}^T \mathbf{X} = \mathbf{C} \tag{16.3a}$$

Substituting $(1/N)\mathbf{X}^T\mathbf{X}$ for $\mathbf{C}$ in Eq. 16.4 and moving the scalar $1/N$ to the left yield

$$\frac{1}{N} \lambda_{1/s} \mathbf{X}^T \mathbf{X} \lambda_{1/s} = \mathbf{R} \tag{16.3b}$$

If we wish, we can work back to $\mathbf{S}$, the original matrix of raw scores displayed in Table 16.1. To find $\mathbf{X}$, the matrix of deviations from the respective means of the variables, we need to subtract $\mathbf{M}$ (a matrix of means) from $\mathbf{X}$. $\mathbf{M}$ can be found by premultiplying $\mathbf{S}$ by $\mathbf{U}$, an $m \times m$ matrix, all the elements of which are $1/N$. Thus,

$$\mathbf{S} \quad - \quad \mathbf{U} \quad \cdot \quad \mathbf{S} \quad = \quad \mathbf{S} \quad - \quad \mathbf{M} \quad = \quad \mathbf{X}$$

$$\begin{Vmatrix} X_{a1} & X_{a2} \\ X_{b1} & X_{b2} \\ X_{c1} & X_{c2} \end{Vmatrix} - \begin{Vmatrix} \dfrac{1}{N} & \dfrac{1}{N} & \dfrac{1}{N} \\[2mm] \dfrac{1}{N} & \dfrac{1}{N} & \dfrac{1}{N} \\[2mm] \dfrac{1}{N} & \dfrac{1}{N} & \dfrac{1}{N} \end{Vmatrix} \cdot \begin{Vmatrix} X_{a1} & X_{a2} \\ X_{b1} & X_{b2} \\ X_{c1} & X_{c2} \end{Vmatrix} = \begin{Vmatrix} X_{a1} & X_{a2} \\ X_{b1} & X_{b2} \\ X_{c1} & X_{c2} \end{Vmatrix} - \begin{Vmatrix} M_1 & M_2 \\ M_1 & M_2 \\ M_1 & M_2 \end{Vmatrix} = \begin{Vmatrix} x_{a1} & x_{a2} \\ x_{b1} & x_{b2} \\ x_{c1} & x_{c2} \end{Vmatrix}$$

It is now known that

$$X = S - US$$

Accordingly, the formula for **R** becomes

$$\frac{1}{N} \lambda_{1/s}(S - US)^T(S - US)\lambda_{1/s} = R \qquad (16.3c)$$

THE IDENTITY (OR UNIT) MATRIX IN MATRIX EQUATIONS

An important device for use in matrix equations is a square, symmetrical matrix consisting of ones in the main diagonal and zeros in all other cells. Generally, it is called the *identity matrix*, although *unit matrix* is an alternate designation. Its symbol is **I**, and its function resembles that of the number 1 in scalar algebra in that when any matrix **A** is premultiplied or post-multiplied by an identity matrix **I**, the product matrix is **A**. That is to say,

$$IA = AI = A \qquad (16.5)$$

If **A** is of order $m \times n$, a premultiplying identity matrix must be of order m, while an identity matrix used as a post-multiplier must be of order n.

When the usual rules for matrix multiplication are followed, it can be seen that Eq. 16.5 holds:

$$
\mathbf{I} \qquad \cdot \qquad \mathbf{A} \qquad = \qquad \mathbf{A}
$$

$$
\begin{Vmatrix} 1 & 0 & 0 \\ 0 & 1 & 0 \\ 0 & 0 & 1 \end{Vmatrix} \cdot
\begin{Vmatrix} a_{11} & a_{12} \\ a_{21} & a_{22} \\ a_{31} & a_{32} \end{Vmatrix} =
\begin{Vmatrix} a_{11} & a_{12} \\ a_{21} & a_{22} \\ a_{31} & a_{32} \end{Vmatrix}
$$

Similarly

$$
\mathbf{A} \qquad \cdot \qquad \mathbf{I} \qquad = \qquad \mathbf{A}
$$

$$
\begin{Vmatrix} a_{11} & a_{12} \\ a_{21} & a_{22} \\ a_{31} & a_{32} \end{Vmatrix} \cdot
\begin{Vmatrix} 1 & 0 \\ 0 & 1 \end{Vmatrix} =
\begin{Vmatrix} a_{11} & a_{12} \\ a_{21} & a_{22} \\ a_{31} & a_{32} \end{Vmatrix}
$$

In a matrix equation, an **I** may be introduced anywhere as a multiplier. Let one side of an equation begin with matrix **A** and let **I** of the same order be introduced as a premultiplier on the other side. Both **A** and **I** can be modified if both are premultiplied by a matrix of proper order and of a nature appropriate to our purpose. Such a matrix would have the effect of multiplying (or dividing) all the elements of one or more corresponding rows of **A** and **I** by a constant. Another type of permissible operation (because it can also be written as matrix premultiplication) is to add to, or subtract from, corresponding rows of $\mathbf{A}$ and $\mathbf{I}$ any multiple of a corresponding row of the matrix that is being modified.

Since both matrices are being modified by premultipliers, operations are limited to rows. (If $\mathbf{A}$ and $\mathbf{I}$ were established so that they were being modified by post-multiplication, operations would be entirely by columns.) Through a series of such operations on the two sides of the equation, both $\mathbf{A}$ and $\mathbf{I}$ can be radically modified. A procedure that is often useful is to modify $\mathbf{A}$ by operations described above until $\mathbf{A}$ becomes exactly equal to the original $\mathbf{I}$, and hence can be dropped out of the equation. By the same operations, what was the original $\mathbf{I}$ becomes a matrix of interesting properties: It is the inverse (or reciprocal matrix) of $\mathbf{A}$, denoted as $\mathbf{A}^{-1}$.

THE INVERSE

Only a square matrix can have an inverse, and not all square matrices qualify. If a square matrix has no inverse, it is called *singular*; if it has an inverse, it is called *regular*. Later, when determinants are considered, a procedure will be noted for discovering whether or not a matrix has an inverse.

Let $\mathbf{A}$ be a regular, square matrix. Then $\mathbf{A}^{-1}$, its inverse, may be defined as a matrix of the same order, which when used either as a premultiplier or post-multiplier of $\mathbf{A}$, yields the identity matrix $\mathbf{I}$ as the product. Thus, by definition,

$$\mathbf{A}^{-1}\mathbf{A} = \mathbf{A}\mathbf{A}^{-1} = \mathbf{I} \tag{16.5a}$$

The identity matrix is square and regular, and its inverse is the identity matrix itself; that is,

$$\mathbf{I} = \mathbf{I}^{-1}$$

as can be demonstrated by multiplying any $\mathbf{I}$ by itself, yielding $\mathbf{I}$.

By a few steps in matrix algebra it can be proved that if $\mathbf{A}$ has an inverse, then the inverse, $\mathbf{A}^{-1}$, is unique.

Let us assume for a moment that $\mathbf{B}$ is a matrix different from $\mathbf{A}^{-1}$ but also an inverse of $\mathbf{A}$, so that

$$\mathbf{B}\mathbf{A} = \mathbf{A}\mathbf{B} = \mathbf{I} \tag{16.6}$$

It follows from Eq. 16.5 that

$$\mathbf{B} = \mathbf{B}\mathbf{I} = \mathbf{B}(\mathbf{A}\mathbf{A}^{-1}) \tag{16.7}$$

This last multiplication can also be accomplished as $(\mathbf{B}\mathbf{A})\mathbf{A}^{-1}$. In Eq. 16.6, however, it has been stated that $\mathbf{B}\mathbf{A} = \mathbf{I}$; therefore, Eq. 16.7 becomes

$$\mathbf{B} = \mathbf{B}\mathbf{I} = \mathbf{B}(\mathbf{A}\mathbf{A}^{-1}) = \mathbf{I}\mathbf{A}^{-1} = \mathbf{A}^{-1}$$

and $\mathbf{B}$, supposedly an inverse different from $\mathbf{A}^{-1}$ is really $\mathbf{A}^{-1}$. Therefore it has been shown that the inverse of a regular matrix is unique.

An important property of the inverse has been hinted at in the operations on $\mathbf{A}$ and $\mathbf{I}$ on different sides of an equation, reducing $\mathbf{A}$ to $\mathbf{I}$ and modifying $\mathbf{I}$ to $\mathbf{A}^{-1}$.

Whenever a first premultiplying (or final post-multiplying) matrix is transferred from one side of a matrix equation to another, it appears as an inverse and as a first premultiplier (or final post-multiplier) on the second side.

Thus, if $\mathbf{AB} = \mathbf{C}$, then $\mathbf{B} = \mathbf{A}^{-1}\mathbf{C}$ or $\mathbf{A} = \mathbf{CB}^{-1}$. If two or more matrices in multiplicative arrangement making up the side of an equation are transferred to the other side, they appear as inverses, but in inverse order. Thus, if $\mathbf{ABC} = \mathbf{D}$, then $\mathbf{D}^{-1} = \mathbf{C}^{-1}\mathbf{B}^{-1}\mathbf{A}^{-1}$.

OTHER PRINCIPLES IN MATRIX EQUATIONS

As described earlier, the transpose consists of exactly the same elements as the original matrix, but the elements of the rows of the original are written as the elements of the columns of the transpose, and vice versa.

As applied to inverses, the transpose of an inverse is the inverse of the transpose. That is, $(\mathbf{A}^{-1})^T = (\mathbf{A}^T)^{-1}$.

A rule on transposes is often useful in manipulating matrix equations. The transpose of the product of any set of matrices is the product of their transposes, but in reverse order. Thus,

$$(\mathbf{AB})^T = \mathbf{B}^T\mathbf{A}^T \quad \text{and} \quad (\mathbf{ABC})^T = \mathbf{C}^T\mathbf{B}^T\mathbf{A}^T$$

Another principle is that the product of two matrices may be a zero matrix, $\mathbf{0}$, even if neither matrix is a zero matrix. Consider the matrix multiplication below, in which neither $\mathbf{A}$ nor $\mathbf{B}$ is a zero matrix:

$$\mathbf{A} \quad \cdot \quad \mathbf{B} \quad = \quad \mathbf{0}$$

$$\begin{Vmatrix} 1 & 0 \\ 1 & 0 \end{Vmatrix} \cdot \begin{Vmatrix} 0 & 0 \\ 1 & 1 \end{Vmatrix} = \begin{Vmatrix} 0 & 0 \\ 0 & 0 \end{Vmatrix}$$

However, if any matrix is multiplied by a zero matrix, the product is a zero matrix, which is cognate with the principle of multiplication by 0 in scalar algebra. Thus,

$$\mathbf{0} \cdot \mathbf{A} = \mathbf{A} \cdot \mathbf{0} = \mathbf{0}$$

FINDING BETAS FROM A MATRIX EQUATION

In Chapter 7 it was noted that the n final beta weights in multiple regression are found by solving n simultaneous linear equations. These are so-called *normal* equations. In a set of these equations, the correlations (or z score covariances) are known, while the betas are unknown.

With three predictors, these equations can be written as

$$V_3 \beta_{03.12} + C_{32} \beta_{02.13} + C_{31} \beta_{01.23} = C_{30} \qquad (16.8)$$

$$C_{23} \beta_{03.12} + V_2 \beta_{02.13} + C_{21} \beta_{01.23} = C_{20} \qquad (16.9)$$

$$C_{13} \beta_{03.12} + C_{12} \beta_{02.13} + V_1 \beta_{01.23} = C_{10} \qquad (16.10)$$

Each variance (equal to 1.00) is represented as V_i. The covariances, numerically equal to the r's, are symmetrical; that is, $C_{ij} = C_{ji}$.

ESTABLISHING A MATRIX EQUATION

A matrix often indicates an arrangement of coefficients detached from a set of equations. The known numerical coefficients can be detached from Eqs. 16.8, 16.9, and 16.10, and the resultant matrix is denoted as **R**. The vector of betas can be indicated as **β**, while the column vector of validities or z-score covariances between the three predictors and the criterion variable, 0, is $\mathbf{C}_v$. The matrix equation in expanded form and in concise matrix notation becomes

$$\begin{Vmatrix} V_3 & C_{32} & C_{31} \\ C_{23} & V_2 & C_{21} \\ C_{13} & C_{12} & V_1 \end{Vmatrix} \cdot \begin{Vmatrix} \beta_{03.12} \\ \beta_{02.13} \\ \beta_{01.23} \end{Vmatrix} = \begin{Vmatrix} C_{30} \\ C_{20} \\ C_{10} \end{Vmatrix}$$

or

$$\mathbf{R\beta} = \mathbf{C}_v \qquad (16.11)$$

Premultiplication of both sides of Eq. 16.11 by $\mathbf{R}^{-1}$ yields

$$\mathbf{R}^{-1}\mathbf{R\beta} = \mathbf{R}^{-1}\mathbf{C}_v \qquad (16.11a)$$

or

$$\mathbf{I\beta} = \mathbf{\beta} = \mathbf{R}^{-1}\mathbf{C}_v \qquad (16.11b)$$

In words, the column vector of beta coefficients can be found by premultiplying the column vector of validity coefficients by the inverse of the correlation matrix.

In more general notation, if

$$\mathbf{AB} = \mathbf{C} \qquad (16.12)$$

then, $\mathbf{A}^{-1}\mathbf{AB} = \mathbf{A}^{-1}\mathbf{C}$, and $\mathbf{B} = \mathbf{A}^{-1}\mathbf{C}$.

In Eq. 16.12, **A** might be a matrix of correlation coefficients, **B** a matrix of final order betas for predicting n different criteria, and **C** the matrix of covariances between all the predictors and the n criteria. Thus, if there are a number of criteria, the betas for predicting each criterion can be computed by premultiplying the matrix of validities by the inverse of the matrix of predictors.

Matrix methods provide a systematic guide to the solution of simultaneous equations, but any operation that can be performed with matrices can in general be performed analytically. Sometimes analytic and matrix procedures are parallel or even numerically identical, but often the variants of the analytic methods are the more numerous.

SOLUTION OF SIMULTANEOUS LINEAR EQUATIONS

The three equations below have correlation coefficients as the knowns and the three final betas for predicting variable 0 as the unknowns. They are solved below by a conventional procedure of eliminating one unknown at a time from the system, first $\beta_{03.12}$, and then $\beta_{02.13}$. After an equation has been established with $\beta_{01.23}$ as the single unknown, the betas that have been eliminated from the system ($\beta_{03.12}$ and $\beta_{02.13}$) are found from a "back solution."

With numerical values representing a set of correlation coefficients and with variances of unity, Eqs. 16.8 to 16.10 become

$$\beta_{03.12} + .60\beta_{02.13} + .50\beta_{01.23} = .30 \qquad (16.8a)$$

$$.60\beta_{03.12} + \beta_{02.13} + .70\beta_{01.23} = .50 \qquad (16.9a)$$

$$.50\beta_{03.12} + .70\beta_{02.13} + \beta_{01.23} = .60 \qquad (16.10a)$$

Multiplying Eq. 16.8a by .60:

$$.60\beta_{03.12} + .36\beta_{02.13} + .30\beta_{01.23} = .18 \qquad (16.8b)$$

Subtracting Eq. 16.8b from Eq. 16.9a:

$$.64\beta_{02.13} + .40\beta_{01.23} = .32 \qquad (16.13)$$

Multiplying Eq. 16.8a by .50:

$$.50\beta_{03.12} + .30\beta_{02.13} + .25\beta_{01.23} = .15 \qquad (16.8c)$$

Subtracting Eq. 16.8c from Eq. 16.10a:

$$.40\beta_{02.13} + .75\beta_{01.23} = .45 \qquad (16.14)$$

Multiplying Eq. 16.13 by .625:

$$.40\beta_{02.13} + .25\beta_{01.23} = .20 \qquad (16.13a)$$

Subtracting Eq. 16.13a from Eq. 16.14:

$$.50\beta_{01.23} = .25 \qquad (16.15)$$

and

$$\beta_{01.23} = .50 \qquad (16.15a)$$

For the back solution, .50 is substituted for $\beta_{01.23}$ in Eq. 16.13a, yielding

$$.40\beta_{02.13} + (.25 \times .50) = .20 \tag{16.13b}$$

and

$$\beta_{02.13} = .1875 \tag{16.13c}$$

Substitution of .1875 for $\beta_{02.13}$ and .5000 for $\beta_{01.23}$ in Eq. 16.8a yields

$$\beta_{03.12} + (.60 \times .1875) + (.50 \times .5000) = .30 \tag{16.8d}$$

or

$$\beta_{03.12} = -.0625 \tag{16.8e}$$

THE MATRIX SOLUTION

Identical results can be obtained by abandoning the apparatus of the formal equations and working only with coefficients. Since each of the coefficients representing the intercorrelations appears twice in the equations, the procedure can be simplified by using a format in which each such coefficient is written only once. In Example 16.1, all the arithmetical operations used above in solving the equations are exhibited in compact format. In addition, there is a line in each successive matrix in which the variance of the criterion is reduced, as described in Chapter 7.

EXAMPLE 16.1. FINDING BETAS BY REDUCTION ROUTINE AND BACK SOLUTION

		VARIABLES			
VARIABLES	FINAL BETAS	3	2	1	0
3	(−.0625)	1.000	.600	.500	.300
2	(.1875)	.600	1.000	.700	.500
1	(.5000)	.500	.700	1.000	.600
0		.300			1.000
2.3		(.1875)	.640	.400	.320
1.3		(.5000)	.625	.750	.450
0.3			.500		.910
1.23			(.5000)	.500	.250
0.23				.500	.750
0.123					.625

$$R_{0.123.} = \sqrt{1 - .625} = .61$$

$$r_{01.23} = \frac{.250}{\sqrt{.500}\ \sqrt{.750}} = .41$$

The matrix routine in Example 16.1 can be interpreted as:

1. Solving symmetrical simultaneous linear equations with steps identical to those used in Eqs. 16.8a through 16.8e;

2. Forming successive matrices of variances and covariances of residual variables in z form, as described in Chapter 7;
3. Evaluating the determinant of the matrix of r's by condensation, as discussed below; or
4. Beginning a process that would lead to the inverse.

In this case, as in many other cases, one and the same numerical routine has alternate mathematical interpretations. When operations are conceptualized in terms of matrices and determinants, the advantage lies in succinct and clear-cut statements of the operations performed.

DETERMINANTS

Any square matrix of numbers can be regarded as a determinant,[1] thereby acquiring new mathematical properties, including a single, fixed numerical value.

In statistics, the variances and covariances of any set of variables can be arranged in a square matrix, which may then be considered a determinant. The principles of determinants often permit inferences about large groups of data. For example, if the determinant of a variance-covariance matrix is zero, then the multiple correlation of every variable in the matrix with all remaining variables is precisely 1.00.

A special case of a variance-covariance matrix is a matrix of correlation coefficients with unity in each of the diagonal cells. The upper limit of the determinant of such a matrix is 1.00, found only when all intercorrelations are precisely .00.

When a determinant is evaluated, its numerical value is found. Evaluation may be by any one of several routines which superficially appear to be widely different, yet all are precisely equivalent and yield identical results.

In a variance-covariance matrix, the sequence of the variables in the rows is the same as the sequence of the variables in the columns. Changes in this sequence have no effect on the value of the determinant. If rows or columns are interchanged, the determinant changes sign, but in statistical work, pairs of rows and corresponding pairs of columns are ordinarily interchanged simultaneously, an operation that does not change the value of the determinant at all.

TERMINOLOGY AND NOTATION OF DETERMINANTS

When a matrix, **A**, is regarded as a determinant, it is customary to border it on either side with a single line. The border lines may be applied either

---

[1] Mathematicians often define a determinant as a scalar function of a square matrix; that is, a unique numerical value derived from the matrix by a specified operation. Here, for ease in presentation, we have denoted a square matrix that can be so evaluated as a determinant.

to the letter denoting the matrix, as $|A|$, or to the display of the elements, or both. Another general symbol for a determinant is the Greek capital letter Δ. Occasionally D is used. Thus a determinant of the intercorrelations of variables 1 through 4, with the z-score variance of unity in each of the diagonal cells, is

$$\Delta = \begin{vmatrix} 1.00 & r_{12} & r_{13} & r_{14} \\ r_{21} & 1.00 & r_{23} & r_{24} \\ r_{31} & r_{32} & 1.00 & r_{34} \\ r_{41} & r_{42} & r_{43} & 1.00 \end{vmatrix}$$

MINORS OF A DETERMINANT

Determinants formed by eliminating one or more rows and the same number of columns from a determinant are called *minors* of that determinant. A first minor is formed by the elimination of one row and one column; a second minor, by the elimination of two rows and two columns; and so on. A principal minor is formed by eliminating corresponding rows and columns; consequently, the principal diagonal of this type of minor is composed exclusively of elements of the principal diagonal of the original determinant.

A first minor with sign assigned in a special manner is called a *cofactor*. The evaluation of any minor (as of any determinant) may result in zero or in a positive or negative number. Let i be the number of the row that has been eliminated and j the number of the column. Then $(-1)^{i+j}$ is an additional sign that helps to determine the final value of the cofactor. Suppose the value of a minor, found by eliminating the second row and third column is $-.2$; the value of the cofactor would be $(-1)^{2+3}(-.2)$ or $+.2$. If i and j add to an even number, the minor and the cofactor are identical.

Minors may be identified by a superscript indicating the order of the total determinant and by subscripts indicating the row and column or the rows and columns that have been deleted. Thus, $\Delta_{23}{}^n$ would be a first minor formed by deleting the second row and third column from a determinant of order n; and the corresponding cofactor would be $(-1)^{2+3}\Delta_{23}{}^n = -\Delta_{23}{}^n$. Similarly, $\Delta_{22.33}^n$ would be the principal second minor [of order $(n-2)$] formed by deleting the second and third rows and the second and third columns.

EVALUATION OF DETERMINANTS

By definition, a determinant of order n is the sum of factorial n terms, half with attached positive sign and half with attached negative sign, and each the product of n elements. The n elements are assigned to each term in such a manner that no two of them come from the same row or column.

The direct method of evaluation, implicit in the definition, is excellent for evaluating determinants of order two or three, but when the order is greater than two or three, other methods are more convenient.

Direct evaluations are shown below. In finding the value of a determinant of order two, the elements in the main diagonal are multiplied together. From this product is subtracted the product of the other two terms. Thus,

$$\begin{vmatrix} a & b \\ c & d \end{vmatrix} = ad - bc \quad \text{or} \quad \begin{vmatrix} a_{11} & a_{12} \\ a_{21} & a_{22} \end{vmatrix} = a_{11}a_{22} - a_{21}a_{12}$$

In evaluating a determinant of order three, the three products with attached positive sign are formed by multiplying groups of three elements in the diagonals from the upper left to lower right. In the two instances in which there are two elements in a diagonal, the third is the isolated element farthest away. Thus, in Eq. 16.16 below, the three terms that are added to find the determinant are *aei*, *bfg*, and *dhc*. The three negative terms are formed similarly, but by working in the diagonals from lower left to upper right. Accordingly, the terms are $-gec$, $-hfa$, and $-dbi$. Thus,

$$\begin{vmatrix} a & b & c \\ d & e & f \\ g & h & i \end{vmatrix} = aei + bfg + dhc - gec - hfa - dbi \qquad (16.16)$$

or in notation with subscripts indicating rows and columns,

$$\begin{vmatrix} a_{11} & a_{12} & a_{13} \\ a_{21} & a_{22} & a_{23} \\ a_{31} & a_{32} & a_{33} \end{vmatrix} = \begin{aligned} & a_{11}a_{22}a_{33} + a_{21}a_{32}a_{13} + a_{12}a_{23}a_{31} \\ & \quad - a_{31}a_{22}a_{13} - a_{32}a_{23}a_{11} - a_{21}a_{12}a_{33} \end{aligned} \qquad (16.16a)$$

A special case is a symmetrical determinant of order three, with unity in each of the diagonal cells. By the procedure given above, it will be found that

$$\Delta = \begin{vmatrix} 1.00 & r_{12} & r_{13} \\ r_{21} & 1.00 & r_{23} \\ r_{31} & r_{32} & 1.00 \end{vmatrix} = 1 + 2r_{12}r_{13}r_{23} - r_{12}{}^2 - r_{13}{}^2 - r_{23}{}^2 \qquad (16.16b)$$

in which $r_{12} = r_{21}$, $r_{13} = r_{31}$, and $r_{23} = r_{32}$.

While these procedures may seem to be arbitrary, they are actually based on efficient and systematic manipulations of coefficients when linear equations in n unknowns are solved.

A second procedure is based on the following rule, by means of which determinants of order n can be evaluated in terms of determinants of order $(n - 1)$: Any determinant is the sum of the elements of any row or column of that determinant, each weighted by the cofactor formed by eliminating from the determinant the row and column in which the element appears. Thus Eq. 16.16a may be evaluated as follows:

$$\begin{vmatrix} a_{11} & a_{12} & a_{13} \\ a_{21} & a_{22} & a_{23} \\ a_{31} & a_{32} & a_{33} \end{vmatrix} = a_{11}\begin{vmatrix} a_{22} & a_{23} \\ a_{32} & a_{33} \end{vmatrix} - a_{21}\begin{vmatrix} a_{12} & a_{13} \\ a_{32} & a_{33} \end{vmatrix} + a_{31}\begin{vmatrix} a_{12} & a_{13} \\ a_{22} & a_{23} \end{vmatrix}$$

$$= a_{11}a_{22}a_{33} - a_{11}a_{32}a_{23} - a_{21}a_{12}a_{33} + a_{21}a_{32}a_{13}$$

$$+ a_{31}a_{12}a_{23} - a_{31}a_{22}a_{13} \tag{16.16c}$$

It will be noted that although terms appear in different orders and although elements within terms are sometimes differently arranged, the expansion of the determinant in Eq. 16.16a gives exactly the same result as the expansion of the determinant in Eq. 16.16c.

PIVOTAL CONDENSATION

Large determinants are often solved by a third routine, known as *pivotal condensation*. This is based on three principles:

1. If each element of a vector of a determinant is multiplied by any factor, the value of the determinant is multiplied by that factor;
2. When the elements of a vector of a determinant are multiplied by any factor and the products are added to (or subtracted from) corresponding elements of any other vector, the value of the determinant is unchanged; and
3. When all the elements above or below the main diagonal are zeros, the value of the determinant is the product of the diagonal elements.

By means of the second principle, most determinants encountered in practice can be transformed into triangular form, usually with zero elements below the principal diagonal. When a determinant is in triangular form, it is evaluated as the sum of $n!$ terms, each the product of n elements. However, each of the $n!$ terms except one contains at least one zero. Hence, the determinant may be evaluated by multiplying together the final elements in the main diagonal, since this is one of the $n!$ terms of the determinant and it contains no zero elements unless the value of the determinant is zero.

The principle of multiplying all the elements of an array by a constant, thus changing the value of the determinant by multiplication by that constant, sometimes facilitates computation. When used in connection with pivotal condensation, any such multiplier becomes the multiplier of the product of the diagonal elements.

SOME STATISTICAL APPLICATIONS OF DETERMINANTS

MULTIPLE R IN TERMS OF DETERMINANTS

The procedure of finding multiple R by reduction of the variance of the criterion variable, as described in Chapter 7 and illustrated in Example 16.1, can be considered as one application of the theory of determinants to a statistical problem. If the original matrix of r's, with unity in the diagonal cells, is considered as a symmetrical determinant, then multiples of the top row are subtracted from the other rows in such a manner that the first column is modified until it consists of the pivotal element and zero elements. The routine of dividing all other elements in the top row by the pivotal element can be considered to be a method of determining the proper multiplier to apply to the top row so as to subtract the appropriate amounts from the elements in succeeding rows. After the elements in the first column below the pivot are reduced to zero, a second cycle of operations reduces to zero the elements below the diagonal in the second column; and so on, until a triangular matrix results. (The method is also applicable to nonsymmetrical determinants, but the multipliers would have to be obtained directly by dividing the element to be reduced to zero by the pivot.)

The matrix of r's, with unity in the diagonal cells, given in Example 16.1 can be identified as Δ^{n+0}, with n the number of predictor variables and 0 as the criterion. Then

$$\Delta^{n+0} = \begin{vmatrix} 1.000 & .600 & .500 & .300 \\ .600 & 1.000 & .700 & .500 \\ .500 & .700 & 1.000 & .600 \\ .300 & .500 & .600 & 1.000 \end{vmatrix} = \begin{vmatrix} 1.000 & .600 & .500 & .300 \\ .000 & .640 & .400 & .320 \\ .000 & .000 & .500 & .250 \\ .000 & .000 & .000 & .625 \end{vmatrix}$$

$$= (1.000)(.640)(.500)(.625) = .200$$

Statistically, the determinant of a variance-covariance matrix is the product of the pivotal variances. In this instance, with the variables in zero-order or higher-order z scores, and with the order of elimination 3, 2, and 1,

$$\Delta^{n+0} = V_3 V_{2.3} V_{1.23} V_{0.123} \tag{16.17}$$

Since the value of a determinant is not altered when rows are interchanged and when corresponding columns are interchanged simultaneously, the value of the determinant is not affected by the order of elimination. This principle is sometimes useful in finding several multiple R's from the same matrix.

To find the partial variance of the criterion variable, in this case $V_{0.123}$, it is apparent from Eq. 16.17 that it is necessary only to divide the total determinant by the determinant of the first n variables; that is, the minor after the row and the column of the criterion variable have been dropped out. In general,

$$V_{0.12\cdots n} = \frac{\Delta^{n+0}}{\Delta^{n+0}_{00}} \qquad (16.18)$$

in which the two subscripts 00 indicate that row 0 and column 0 are no longer in the determinant.

Since the square of multiple R is unity less the partial variance of the criterion, a formula for R in determinantal notation is

$$R_{0(12\cdots n)} = \sqrt{1 - \frac{\Delta^{n+0}}{\Delta^{n+0}_{00}}} \qquad (16.19)$$

PARTIAL r FROM DETERMINANTS

Formulas for other coefficients used in describing multivariate linear relationships, including higher-order covariances, beta weights, and specialized correlation coefficients, can be expressed in determinantal notation. As a simple example, here is a formula for a partial correlation of the $(n-1)$st order in a matrix of $(n+1)$ variables:

$$r_{01.23\cdots n} = \frac{\Delta^{n+0}_{01}}{\sqrt{\Delta^{n+0}_{00}}\sqrt{\Delta^{n+0}_{11}}} \qquad (16.20)$$

in which the three determinants are first minors of the complete determinant.

In Example 16.2, the principal first minors and an additional first minor of the correlation matrix given in Example 16.1 are evaluated and applied to multiple and partial correlation. In Eq. 16.17, the value of Δ^{n+0}, the total determinant of four variables, was found to be .200.

EXAMPLE 16.2

MULTIPLE AND PARTIAL CORRELATION BY DETERMINANTS

By Eq. 16.17, Δ^{n+0} (comprising the z-score variances and covariances of variables 3, 2, 1, and 0) has a value of .200. Variables in each of the minors below are identified by numbers within parentheses. Evaluation is by the procedure represented in Eqs. 16.16, 16.16a, and 16.16c.

$$\Delta^{n+0}_{33} = \begin{matrix} & (2) & (1) & (0) \\ (2) & 1.0 & .7 & .5 \\ (1) & .7 & 1.0 & .6 \\ (0) & .5 & .6 & 1.0 \end{matrix} \begin{aligned} &= V_2 V_1 V_0 + 2r_{12}r_{02}r_{01} - V_0 r_{12}{}^2 - V_1 r_{02}{}^2 - V_2 r_{01}{}^2 \\ \\ &= 1.00 + .42 - .49 - .25 - .36 = .32 \end{aligned}$$

$$
\begin{array}{c}
\begin{array}{ccc} (3) & (1) & (0) \end{array} \\
\Delta_{22}^{n+0} = \begin{array}{c} (3) \\ (1) \\ (0) \end{array} \left|\begin{array}{ccc} 1.0 & .5 & .3 \\ .5 & 1.0 & .6 \\ .3 & .6 & 1.0 \end{array}\right|
\end{array}
\begin{array}{l}
= V_3 V_1 V_0 + 2 r_{13} r_{03} r_{01} - V_0 r_{13}{}^2 - V_1 r_{03}{}^2 - V_3 r_{01}{}^2 \\
= 1.00 + .18 - .25 - .09 - .36 = .48
\end{array}
$$

$$
\begin{array}{c}
\begin{array}{ccc} (3) & (2) & (0) \end{array} \\
\Delta_{11}^{n+0} = \begin{array}{c} (3) \\ (2) \\ (0) \end{array} \left|\begin{array}{ccc} 1.0 & .6 & .3 \\ .6 & 1.0 & .5 \\ .3 & .5 & 1.0 \end{array}\right|
\end{array}
\begin{array}{l}
= V_3 V_2 V_0 + 2 r_{23} r_{03} r_{02} - V_0 r_{23}{}^2 - V_2 r_{03}{}^2 - V_3 r_{02}{}^2 \\
= 1.00 + .18 - .36 - .09 - .25 = .48
\end{array}
$$

$$
\begin{array}{c}
\begin{array}{ccc} (3) & (2) & (1) \end{array} \\
\Delta_{00}^{n+0} = \begin{array}{c} (3) \\ (2) \\ (1) \end{array} \left|\begin{array}{ccc} 1.0 & .6 & .5 \\ .6 & 1.0 & .7 \\ .5 & .7 & 1.0 \end{array}\right|
\end{array}
\begin{array}{l}
= V_3 V_2 V_1 + 2 r_{23} r_{13} r_{12} - V_1 r_{23}{}^2 - V_2 r_{13}{}^2 - V_3 r_{12}{}^2 \\
= 1.00 + .42 - .36 - .25 - .49 = .32
\end{array}
$$

$$
\begin{array}{c}
\begin{array}{ccc} (3) & (2) & (0) \end{array} \\
\Delta_{01}^{n+0} = \begin{array}{c} (3) \\ (2) \\ (1) \end{array} \left|\begin{array}{ccc} 1.0 & .6 & .3 \\ .6 & 1.0 & .5 \\ .5 & .7 & .6 \end{array}\right|
\end{array}
\begin{array}{l}
= V_3 V_2 r_{01} + r_{23} r_{12} r_{03} + r_{23} r_{02} r_{13} - r_{13} V_2 r_{03} - \\
\quad r_{12} r_{02} V_3 - r_{23}{}^2 r_{01} \\
= .600 + .126 + .150 - .150 - .350 - .216 = .16
\end{array}
$$

$$
R_{0(123)} = \sqrt{1 - \frac{\Delta^{n+0}}{\Delta_{00}^{n+0}}} = \sqrt{1 - \frac{.20}{.32}} = .61
$$

$$
R_{1(023)} = \sqrt{1 - \frac{\Delta^{n+0}}{\Delta_{11}^{n+0}}} = \sqrt{1 - \frac{.20}{.48}} = .76
$$

$$
R_{2(013)} = \sqrt{1 - \frac{\Delta^{n+0}}{\Delta_{22}^{n+0}}} = \sqrt{1 - \frac{.20}{.48}} = .76
$$

$$
R_{3(012)} = \sqrt{1 - \frac{\Delta_{01}^{n+0}}{\Delta_{33}^{n+0}}} = \sqrt{1 - \frac{.20}{.32}} = .61
$$

$$
r_{01.23} = \frac{\Delta_{01}^{n+0}}{\sqrt{\Delta_{00}^{n+0}}\sqrt{\Delta_{11}^{n+0}}} = \frac{.16}{\sqrt{.32}\sqrt{.48}} = .41
$$

By the determinantal routine, $R_{0(123)}$ is .61, exactly the same as by reduction of criterion variance. Similarly, two apparently different routes lead to a value of .41 for $r_{01.23}$. However, while the methods appear to be different, the underlying mathematics is actually much the same.

DETERMINANTS IN SUMMARIZING MATRICES

A complete matrix of data, such as table of intercorrelations, can be sometimes summarized usefully as a determinant. For example, when a multiple correlation is 1.00, the partial variance of the criterion, with variance associated with all other variables removed, is .00. Since this partial variance is one of the factors that are multiplied together in one of the methods of evaluating the determinant, it follows, as stated earlier. that when $R = 1.00$, the determinant is zero.

If the determinant is positive, all multiple correlations throughout the matrix are less than 1.00. If the determinant is negative, one of two conclusions is necessarily true. Either there have been errors in computation in finding the correlations or in evaluating the determinant; or, within the matrix, there are variables with insufficient freedom, as when there are more variables than cases. In the latter instance, the expected determinant is zero, but through rounding error it may be slightly negative. One degree of freedom is lost with each variable entering into a multiple R. When the number of variables increases beyond the number of cases, there are variables without freedom. Multiple R computed on data with markedly limited degrees of freedom are useless.

If the determinant of a matrix is zero (or "vanishes"), the matrix is called *singular*. A singular matrix has no inverse. If the determinant does not vanish, the matrix is nonsingular and has an inverse. A Gramian matrix is symmetric, and all its principal minors are equal to, or greater than, zero. Most variance-covariance matrices are Gramian. Exceptions indicate that at least one of the variables is completely a function of one or more of the other variables in the matrix.

Certain other principles of determinants are sometimes useful. For example, the determinant of a matrix is equal to the determinant of its transpose. If **A** is the matrix, then

$$|\mathbf{A}| = |\mathbf{A}^T|$$

Also, if **A** and **B** are square matrices of the same order, the determinant of their product equals the product of their determinants. That is,

$$|\mathbf{A}| \cdot |\mathbf{B}| = |\mathbf{AB}|$$

Some matrix theorems involve the "adjugate" or "adjoint" matrix, formed by replacing each element of the square matrix, **A**, by its cofactor, and then writing the transpose of the result as adj(**A**). A roundabout way of finding an inverse is by the formula

$$\mathbf{A}^{-1} = \frac{1}{|\mathbf{A}|} \text{adj}(\mathbf{A}) \tag{16.21}$$

Adj(**A**) exists for any square matrix even if the determinant, $|\mathbf{A}|$, is zero. It is apparent from Eq. 16.21, however, that if $|\mathbf{A}|$ is zero, $\mathbf{A}^{-1}$ does not exist.

FINDING THE INVERSE OF A MATRIX

Equation 16.5a, which defines the inverse, also provides a method of finding it. Since $\mathbf{A}$ is a square nonsingular matrix for which $\mathbf{A}^{-1}$ exists, $\mathbf{AA}^{-1} = \mathbf{I}$.

Both $\mathbf{A}$ and $\mathbf{I}$ can be premultiplied by a series of appropriate matrices of the same order, successively modifying $\mathbf{A}$ until it becomes the identity matrix $\mathbf{I}$, while exactly the same operations on $\mathbf{I}$ result in the inverse.

If the premultiplier is the identity matrix except that a_{ii}, the diagonal element in the ith row and ith column, is a instead of 1, then the elements in the ith row of $\mathbf{A}$ and the ith row of $\mathbf{I}$ are multiplied by a. If the premultiplier is the identity matrix except that a_{ij}, the element in the ith row and jth column, is a instead of 0, then the elements in row i of the matrix operated on are multiplied by a and added to the elements in row j. These are, of course, exactly the same operations described earlier for use in evaluating a determinant, and several operations may be accomplished simultaneously.

In Example 16.3 are shown numerical operations required by this method in finding an inverse. In this case it is the inverse of the matrix of the three predictor variables of Example 16.1. In five steps, $\mathbf{A}$ on the left side of the equation is transformed into $\mathbf{I}$, the identity matrix, while on the right-hand side of the equation, $\mathbf{I}$ is in parallel steps transformed into the inverse, $\mathbf{A}^{-1}$.

EXAMPLE 16.3

COMPUTATION OF THE INVERSE: THE USE OF OPERATIONS IN
R_1, R_2, AND R_3, THE ROWS OF A AND I, THUS REDUCING THE EQUATION
$(AA^{-1} = I)$ TO THE IDENTITY $(IA^{-1} = A^{-1})$

Operation in Preceding Matrix	Yield in New Matrix							
		1.000	.600	.500	$\cdot \lvert A^{-1} \rvert =$	1.00000	.00000	.00000
		.600	1.000	.700		.00000	1.00000	.00000
		.500	.700	1.000		.00000	.00000	1.00000
$R_1 \longrightarrow R_1$		1.000	.600	.500	$\cdot \lvert A^{-1} \rvert =$	1.00000	.00000	.00000
$R_2 - .6R_1 \longrightarrow R_2$		.000	.640	.400		−.60000	1.00000	.00000
$R_1 - .5R_1 \longrightarrow R_3$		.000	.400	.750		−.50000	.00000	.00000
$R_1 \longrightarrow R_1$		1.000	.600	.500	$\cdot \lvert A^{-1} \rvert =$	1.00000	.00000	.00000
$R_2 \longrightarrow R_2$		.000	.640	.400		−.60000	1.00000	.00000
$R_3 - .625R_2 \longrightarrow R_3$		.000	.000	.500		−.12500	−.62500	1.00000
$R_1 - R_3 \longrightarrow R_1$		1.000	.600	.000	$\cdot \lvert A^{-1} \rvert =$	1.12500	.62500	−1.00000
$R_2 - .8R_3 \longrightarrow R_2$		.000	.640	.000		−.50000	1.50000	−.80000
$R_3 \longrightarrow R_3$		.000	.000	.500		−.12500	−.62500	1.00000
$R_1 - .9375R_2 \rightarrow R_1$		1.000	.000	.000	$\cdot \lvert A^{-1} \rvert =$	1.59375	−.78135	−.25000
$R_2 \longrightarrow R_2$		.000	.640	.000		−.50000	1.50000	−.80000
$R_3 \longrightarrow R_3$		.000	.000	.500		−.12500	−.62500	1.00000
$R_1 \longrightarrow R_1$		1.000	.000	.000	$\cdot \lvert A^{-1} \rvert =$	1.59375	−.78125	−.25000
$1.5625R_2 \longrightarrow R_2$		.000	1.000	.000		−.78125	2.34375	−1.25000
$2R_3 \longrightarrow R_3$		.000	.000	1.000		−.25000	−1.25000	2.00000

By the usual rules of matrix multiplication it can be determined that the inverse has actually been found.

$$
\begin{matrix} \mathbf{A} \end{matrix}
$$

$$
\left\| \begin{matrix} 1.000 & .600 & .500 \\ .600 & 1.000 & .700 \\ .500 & .700 & 1.000 \end{matrix} \right\|
\left\| \begin{matrix} 1.59375 & -.78125 & -.25000 \\ -.78125 & 2.34375 & -1.25000 \\ -.25000 & -1.25000 & 2.00000 \end{matrix} \right\| =
\left\| \begin{matrix} 1.000 & .000 & .000 \\ .000 & 1.000 & .000 \\ .000 & .000 & 1.000 \end{matrix} \right\|
$$

It is also of interest to apply Eq. 16.11b, $(\boldsymbol{\beta} = \mathbf{R}^{-1}\mathbf{C}_v)$, to finding $\boldsymbol{\beta}$, the vector of betas, from $\mathbf{R}^{-1}$, the inverse of the matrix of predictors and $\mathbf{C}_v$, the vector of validity coefficients as used in Example 16.1. Then

$$
\boldsymbol{\beta} = \left\| \begin{matrix} 1.59375 & -.78125 & -.25000 \\ -.78125 & 2.34375 & -1.25000 \\ -.25000 & -1.25000 & 2.00000 \end{matrix} \right\| \cdot \left\| \begin{matrix} .300 \\ .500 \\ .600 \end{matrix} \right\| = \left\| \begin{matrix} -.0625 \\ .1875 \\ .5000 \end{matrix} \right\| \quad (16.22)
$$

As would be expected, the betas are identical with those obtained in Example 16.1 by pivotal condensation and a back solution.

INVERSE OF THE COMPLETE MATRIX IN CORRELATIONAL ANALYSIS

In Example 16.3 only the inverse of the matrix of three predictors is obtained. By the same method, but with additional steps, the inverse of the complete matrix of the four variables of Example 16.1 can be found. With identification of the variables in parentheses, it is

$$
\mathbf{R}^{-1} = \begin{matrix} & (3) & (2) & (1) & (0) \\ (3) & 1.6000 & -.8000 & -.3000 & .1000 \\ (2) & -.8000 & 2.4000 & -1.1000 & -.3000 \\ (1) & -.3000 & -1.1000 & 2.4000 & -.8000 \\ (0) & .1000 & -.3000 & -.8000 & 1.6000 \end{matrix} \quad (16.23)
$$

Each diagonal element in the inverse of any matrix of correlation coefficients has definite analytic meaning: It is the reciprocal of the partial variance of the variable concerned, after variance predictable from all the other variables has been removed. Thus, in the lower right-hand corner, 1.6000 is $1/V_{0.123}$. Accordingly, $V_{0.123}$ is $1/1.6000$, or .6250, exactly as found in Example 16.1, while $R_{0.123}$ is $\sqrt{1 - .6250}$, or .61, also exactly as found in Example 16.1 and in the determinantal solution.

The off-diagonal elements in rows or columns are functions of the final-order betas, with the variable denoting the row or column as the criterion. They are betas, reversed in algebraic sign, and divided by the final partial variance of the criterion; that is, the criterion variance less the portion predictable from all other variables in the matrix. For example, in Eq. 16.23, the analytic meaning of the elements in the fourth row of the inverse can be taken to be $-\beta_{03.12}/V_{0.123}, - \beta_{02.13}/V_{0.123}, -\beta_{01.23}/V_{0.123}$

and $1/V_{0.123}$. Accordingly, to obtain the betas, each off-diagonal element is reversed in sign and divided by the diagonal element. Thus, $-.1000/1.6000 = -.0625$; $-(-.3000/1.6000) = .1875$ and $-(-.8000/1.6000) = .5000$, exactly the same betas as found in Example 16.1 and again in Eq. 16.22.

FINDING THE INVERSE OF AN ASYMMETRICAL MATRIX

The method demonstrated in Example 16.3 of finding the inverse is applicable to any nonsingular square matrix, whether symmetrical or not. The routine is straightforward. In the first cycle, multipliers of row 1 are chosen so that all off-diagonal elements in column 1 are reduced to zero when multiples of row 1 are subtracted from the other rows. In the second cycle, multipliers of row 2 are chosen so that all elements in column 2 below the diagonal can similarly be reduced to zero, and so on, until the matrix becomes triangular. Then, in a back routine, multiples of the bottom row are found to reduce the off-diagonal elements in the last column to zero, again by subtraction. The routine is continued with successive columns. Finally, multipliers are applied to the rows to make all diagonal elements unity. As operations reduce matrix $\mathbf{A}$ to the identity matrix, corresponding operations in the matrix, which starts as $\mathbf{I}$, result in the inverse, $\mathbf{A}^{-1}$.

There are numerous alternate procedures for finding the inverse, most of them variations of the method illustrated in Example 16.3. Of particular interest in finding the inverse of a correlation matrix is a procedure (1) that preserves the analytic meaning of all elements at every stage. Many of the large electronic computers have routines for finding the inverses of large matrices of various descriptions, especially since matrix inversion is of interest to many fields other than statistics.

AN EXERCISE IN READING MATRIX EQUATIONS

If an inversion method is applicable directly only to symmetric matrices, it nevertheless can be used to find the inverse of a nonsymmetrical, nonsingular matrix. The derivation of this procedure provides an exercise in reading matrix equations.

Let $\mathbf{A}$ be any nonsymmetric matrix of order n for which the inverse, $\mathbf{A}^{-1}$, exists. When a nonsymmetric matrix is multiplied by its transpose, the result is a symmetric matrix. Let $\mathbf{S}$ be the symmetric matrix of order n found by post-multiplying $\mathbf{A}$ by its transpose $\mathbf{A}^T$. Accordingly, $\mathbf{A}\mathbf{A}^T = \mathbf{S}$.

When a matrix is moved from one side of an equation to another, it appears on the other side as an inverse; and when two or more matrices are moved, they appear as inverses in reverse order. Thus,

$$\mathbf{S}^{-1} = (\mathbf{A}^T)^{-1}\mathbf{A}^{-1} \tag{16.24}$$

Both sides of Eq. 16.24 can now be post-multiplied by **A**. It will be remembered that $\mathbf{A}^{-1}\mathbf{A}$ equals the identity matrix and **I** as a multiplier can be dropped out of an equation. Accordingly,

$$\mathbf{S}^{-1}\mathbf{A} = (\mathbf{A}^T)^{-1}\mathbf{A}^{-1}\mathbf{A} = (\mathbf{A}^T)^{-1}\mathbf{I} = (\mathbf{A}^T)^{-1} \qquad (16.25)$$

Since the inverse of a transpose is equal to the transpose of the inverse, Eq. 16.25 can be rewritten as

$$\mathbf{S}^{-1}\mathbf{A} = (\mathbf{A}^{-1})^T \qquad (16.25a)$$

A matrix equation remains an equality if the transpose is taken of both sides. This yields the formula for the inverse of a nonsymmetrical matrix in terms of a symmetrical matrix formed from it:

$$(\mathbf{S}^{-1}\mathbf{A})^T = \mathbf{A}^{-1} \qquad (16.26)$$

This compact formula implies that one way of finding the inverse of a nonsymmetric matrix is by the following four steps:

1. Post-multiply the matrix by its transpose. This yields a symmetric matrix.
2. Find the inverse of this symmetric matrix.
3. Post-multiply this inverse by the original matrix.
4. Transpose the result. This is the inverse of the original nonsymmetric matrix.

SUMMARY

In psychological statistics the concept of a matrix, in which rows and columns have assigned meanings, is applicable to rosters of scores and to complete tables of variances and covariances and of correlation coefficients. Operations that can be described in terms of succinct matrix notation include the computation of variances, covariances, and correlations from the score matrix.

By regarding a square matrix as a determinant, new mathematical properties emerge. For example, a determinant has a unique value, which, for variances and covariances, cannot be negative. Formulas for multiple and partial correlation can be written in terms of total and minor determinants.

A matrix equation may summarize an indefinite number of simultaneous linear equations, such as the "normal" equations in which the beta coefficients are the unknowns. Matrix routines that involve finding the inverse of a matrix of correlations (with unity in each of the diagonal cells) can be used to find final-order betas. In advanced statistical work, equations in terms of matrices have great importance.

EXERCISES

1. Given **X**, the matrix of the deviation scores of ten individuals on three variables, find the product matrix by the operation $X^T X$. Convert the matrix of values of Σx_i^2 and $\Sigma x_i x_j$ into a variance-covariance matrix by multiplying each term by the scalar $1/N$.

   Returning to matrix **X**, divide each column by its standard deviation, thus forming a matrix of z scores, designated as **Z**.

   Post-multiply the transpose of **Z** (that is, Z^T) by **Z**, and divide each element of the product matrix by N, thus forming **R**, the matrix of correlation coefficients with unity in the diagonal. (This is also a variance-covariance matrix of z scores.)

   Compare the **R** matrix so formed with an **R** matrix computed directly from the matrix of values of Σx_i^2 and $\Sigma x_i x_j$, using the conventional formula, $r_{ij} = \Sigma x_i x_j / \sqrt{(\Sigma x_i^2)(\Sigma x_j^2)}$.

$$X = \begin{Vmatrix} -3 & -1 & -8 \\ +4 & +6 & -3 \\ +2 & 0 & +6 \\ -9 & -3 & -9 \\ -6 & -9 & -5 \\ -1 & +4 & +8 \\ +3 & -3 & -6 \\ +4 & +4 & +9 \\ -5 & 0 & +3 \\ +11 & +2 & +5 \end{Vmatrix}$$

2. Given **R** as follows, evaluate the determinant by finding the sum of six terms, and also evaluate the determinant by pivotal condensation.

$$R = \begin{Vmatrix} 1.00 & .48 & .18 \\ .48 & 1.00 & .53 \\ .18 & .53 & 1.00 \end{Vmatrix}$$

3. Find R^{-1}, the inverse of **R** in Exercise 2.

4. The following intercorrelations of two motion picture tests of attention and two stanine scores were reported by Gibson (2):

		2	3	4
1	Flexibility of attention	.40	.35	.23
2	Integration of attention		.36	.25
3	Bombardier stanine			.71
4	Navigator stanine			

Evaluate the total determinant. Then, by evaluating the four principal minors, find $R_{1(234)}$, $R_{2(134)}$, $R_{3(124)}$, and $R_{4(123)}$.

5. Find the inverse of the matrix in Exercise 4 and from the diagonal terms find $R_{1(234)}$, $R_{2(134)}$, $R_{3(124)}$ and $R_{4(123)}$.

6. Stern and Gordon (3) report the following matrix of intercorrelations of three predictor variables and a criterion, recruit final achievement, for 511 naval recruits:

		2	3	4
1	General classification test	.28	.54	.58
2	Clerical test		.36	.18
3	Oral direction test			.36
4	Recruit final achievement			

Find the inverse of the matrix composed of the *z*-score variances and co-variances of variables 1, 2, and 3. From the inverse so formed (R^{-1}) and the vector of the three validities (C_v) find the final-order betas for predicting recruiting final achievement by matrix multiplication (Eq. 16.11b) as follows:

$$R^{-1}C_v = \beta$$

7. Show that the following cannot be considered a correlation matrix:

	1	2	3
1	1.00	.30	.80
2	.30	1.00	.90
3	.80	.90	1.00

8. For each of the following pairs of concepts give an important way in which they are alike and an important way in which they are different.

(a) Matrix and determinant.
(b) Inverse and transpose.
(c) Scalar matrix and identity matrix.
(d) Matrix multiplication and addition of matrices.

REFERENCES

1. DUBOIS, PHILIP H., AND MANNING, WINTON H., "An analytically meaningful approach to matrix inversion," *Educ. Psychol. Measmt.*, 1960, **20**, 705–712.
2. GIBSON, JAMES F. (ED.), *Motion Picture Testing and Research*. Report No. 7, AAF Aviation Psychology Program Research Reports. Washington, D.C., U.S. Government Printing Office, 1947.
3. STERN, FERDINAND, AND GORDON, LEONARD V., "Ability to follow instructions as a predictor of success in recruit training," *J. Appl. Psychol.*, 1961, **45**, 22–24.

Suggested Readings in Matrices and Determinants

AITKEN, A. C., *Determinants and Matrices*. Edinburgh: Oliver and Boyd, Ltd., 1958, 5th Edition.

COHN, P. M., *Linear Equations*. London: Routledge and Kegan Paul, 1958.

HORST, PAUL, *Matrix Algebra for Social Scientists*. New York: Holt, Rinehart and Winston, Inc., 1963.

WRIGHT, E. MURIEL J., MANNING, WINTON H., AND DUBOIS, PHILIP H., "Determinants in multivariate correlation," *J. Exper. Educ.*, 1959, **27**, 195–202.

INTRODUCTION TO FACTOR ANALYSIS

17

Factor analysis is a branch of statistics concerned with the isolation and identification of a limited number of hypothetical variables underlying a group of observed variables. The *factors* so discovered are hypothetical in the sense that, while scores or values for specific cases can sometimes be estimated, they can never be computed precisely. As are the variables entering into coefficients corrected for attenuation, factors are known by their correlations and their variances.

When a correlation coefficient is corrected for attenuation, the variability resulting from random error can be considered to be partialed out from both variables. Somewhat similarly, each variable in a factor analysis is treated as though it included neither random error nor specific variance, the latter being reliable variance not shared with other variables in the matrix being analyzed. In effect, all "unique" variance (that is, variance not common with other variables) is partialed out of each variable before the analysis is begun. This is done by reducing the observed variances, the 1.00's in the diagonal of the matrix of r's, to "communalities."

TWO PHASES OF A FACTOR ANALYSIS

Typically a factor analysis has two phases:

1. The separation of the common variance, or communality, of each of

the variables into a minimum number of uncorrelated portions representing the underlying factors; and

2. The identification of the factors as meaningful.

In the first phase, a small number of theoretical and unobservable factors are inferred, by which the matrix of intercorrelations of a group of observed variables can be reproduced as closely as possible. In the second phase, alternate sets of *loadings*, or correlations of the observed variables with the hypothetical factors, are computed until a set is obtained that appears to be meaningful in understanding the original variables. In this process, alternative solutions are compared as to their scientific acceptability, and sometimes factors are modified so that they become correlated.

Factor analysis starts with a matrix of correlation coefficients, which may be considered as covariances in z form. What can be discovered in a single study is limited by, and must be interpreted in terms of, the observed variables that happen to constitute the matrix. However, factors identified by well-known variables in one matrix may be identified again by the same "marker" variables in other matrices.

CASE OF A SINGLE COMMON FACTOR

Factor analysis originated in the work of Charles Spearman (10), who is chiefly responsible for the basic concepts and formulas useful when a matrix of correlations can be explained as arising from a single general factor.

In z form, let any variable, z_i, be made up of two uncorrelated portions (also in z form with unit variance): g_a, which appears also in other variables; and u_i, which is unique to z_i and which includes both specific and error variance. By definition, u_i is uncorrelated not only with g_a, but also with the unique portion of variables other than variable i. Let a_i be the weight of g_a in variable i and w_i be the weight of u_i. The basic equation is then:

$$z_i = a_i g_a + w_i u_i \qquad (17.1)$$

Squaring both sides of Eq. 17.1, summing the variables while leaving the constants outside the summation signs, and dividing by N yield

$$\frac{\Sigma z_i^2}{N} = a_i^2 \frac{\Sigma g_a^2}{N} + 2a_i w_i \frac{\Sigma g_a u_i}{N} + w_i^2 \frac{\Sigma u_i^2}{N} \qquad (17.2)$$

Since z_i, g_a, and u_i all have variances of 1.00, and since $\Sigma g_a u_i/N$ is .00, Eq. 17.2 becomes

$$a_i^2 + w_i^2 = 1 \qquad (17.3)$$

which shows that the variance of variable i, taken as 1.00, can be divided into two portions: a_i^2, the common variance, and u_i^2, the unique variance.

It is to be noted that a_i^2 is the communality, the more general notation for which is h_i^2, always used when there is more than one common factor.

Multiplying both sides of Eq. 17.1 by g_a, summing, and dividing by N yield

$$\frac{\Sigma z_i g_a}{N} = a_i \frac{\Sigma g_a^2}{N} + w_i \frac{\Sigma u_i g_a}{N} \tag{17.4}$$

Since both z_i and g_a are in z form with unit variances, their covariance on the left side of Eq. 17.4 is their correlation. The expression $\Sigma g_a^2/N$ as a variance of unity can be omitted. Since the unique portion of the variable u_i and the general factor g_a are uncorrelated by definition, their covariance is zero and the final term of Eq. 17.4 drops out. Accordingly, it can be seen that r_{ig_a}, the correlation between any variable, denoted as variable i, and the single factor explaining the intercorrelations of a group of variables, is a_i, which was originally defined as the weight of the variable in factor g_a.

Consider a second variable j, defined in manner parallel to variable i, as follows:

$$z_j = a_j g_a + w_j u_j \tag{17.5}$$

Note that variable j is made up of two uncorrelated portions, g_a and u_j, with weights of a_j and w_j, respectively. The common factor g_a is the same as found in variable i, but u_j is uncorrelated with any other unique factor. Accordingly, when we multiply Eq. 17.1 by Eq. 17.5, sum all terms, and divide by N, expressions involving either u_i or u_j (or both) drop out as covariances of uncorrelated variables and the result is

$$\frac{\Sigma z_i z_j}{N} = a_i a_j \frac{\Sigma g_a^2}{N} \tag{17.6}$$

Since any correlation coefficient is the covariance between two sets of z scores with unit variance, the expression on the left of Eq. 17.6 is equal to r_{ij}. On the right-hand side, $\Sigma g_a^2/N$ is the variance of the general factor g_a and, by definition, is 1.00. Accordingly, Eq. 17.6 becomes

$$r_{ij} = a_i a_j \tag{17.7}$$

a fundamental equation stating that if a single factor is responsible for the intercorrelations of a group of variables, each correlation is precisely equal to the product of a pair of factor weights. The equation provides a basis for finding the unknown factor weights from an observed matrix of correlations.

To find the numerical value of a_i^2, the communality of variable i, three correlations among the three variables z_i, z_j, and z_k are needed, all expressible as the products of factor weights as follows:

$$\frac{r_{ij}r_{ik}}{r_{jk}} = \frac{a_i a_j a_i a_k}{a_j a_k} = a_i^2 = r_{ig_a}^2 \tag{17.8}$$

Taking the square root of both sides of Formula 17.8 yields

$$r_{ig_a} = a_i = \sqrt{\frac{r_{ij}r_{ik}}{r_{jk}}} \tag{17.9}$$

which is the correlation between variable i and the factor central to variables i, j, and k. Accordingly, a_i is the factor loading of variable i in the posited general factor g_a.

Neither Formula 17.8 nor Formula 17.9 is universally true. If Formula 17.8 yields values that are negative or greater than 1.00, then it is impossible to account for the intercorrelations of variables i, j, and k as resulting from a single general factor. Furthermore, even when values from Formula 17.8 are between .00 and 1.00 it may be necessary to posit loadings in more than one factor in order to make the analysis of variables i, j, and k consistent with the analysis of other variables in the matrix.

AN ARTIFICIAL MATRIX

An artificial matrix, generated by a single common factor, is shown as Table 17.1 on page 457. Points about this matrix are:

1. Factor loadings, or correlations between the observed variables and the general factor g_a, are shown in the first column and top row, and are outside the matrix proper. Although these loadings were used to develop the matrix, in the real situation it would be necessary to compute them from the intercorrelations.

2. Communalities, denoted as h_i^2, are in the main diagonal. In the real situation, these, too, would be found from the intercorrelations. In the single factor case, each communality is the square of the corresponding factor loading, so that $h_i^2 = a_i^2$.

3. The matrix proper is symmetrical about the main diagonal. Each correlation (or covariance in z form) appears twice. Above the diagonal in the algebraic representation, the correlations are identified by the factor weights by which they were generated; below the diagonal they are denoted simply as r.

4. In terms of matrix algebra, the matrix is described as of rank one. In factor analysis, this means that it can be generated by a single set of factor loadings, or conversely, when a single factor is partialed out, the "residuals," or resulting partial covariances, are all zero. The communalities in the diagonal are also reduced to zero, but in the real situation they are unknown, except as they are computed so as to be consistent with the r's.

5. Since the variance of the general factor g_a is 1.00, the top row of factor weights can be regarded as a vector of covariances, and the column

of loadings can be regarded as a vector of betas. Accordingly, by the formula for partialing, given in Chapter 8 ($E' = E - \beta C$), each element of a new matrix of coefficients of the six original variables, with the general factor partialed out, would be .00. Thus it can be seen that the objective in factor analysis of reducing observed covariances to zero with the fewest possible posited variables is attained. In this matrix it is sufficient to partial out a single common factor.

6. The general factor could be partialed out just as easily if variances of 1.00 instead of communalities were written in the diagonal. However, the use of observed z-score variances would increase the rank of the matrix to n, the number of variables. Each partial variance remaining in the diagonal of the residual matrix would then represent the unique proportion of the original variable.

7. Whenever any matrix is of rank one, all second-order minors, when evaluated, equal zero. As noted in the preceding chapter, a second-order minor is a determinant of two rows and two columns abstracted from a larger determinant by eliminating the other columns and rows. Format and evaluation follow.

$$\begin{vmatrix} a & b \\ c & d \end{vmatrix} = ad - bc$$

Rows and columns retained to form the minor need not be adjacent, and four different variables may be concerned. Thus, for variables 1, 5, 4, and 6, we have

$$\begin{matrix} & 4 & 6 \\ 1 \\ 5 \end{matrix} \begin{vmatrix} r_{14} & r_{16} \\ r_{45} & r_{56} \end{vmatrix} = \begin{vmatrix} -.24 & .30 \\ -.28 & .35 \end{vmatrix} = (-.24 \times .35) - (-.28 \times .30)$$

$$= -.084 + .084 = .00$$

In terms of products of factor loadings of variables i, j, k, and l, this becomes

$$\begin{matrix} & i & j \\ k \\ l \end{matrix} \begin{vmatrix} r_{ik} & r_{jk} \\ r_{il} & r_{jl} \end{vmatrix} = \begin{vmatrix} a_i a_k & a_j a_k \\ a_i a_l & a_j a_l \end{vmatrix} = a_i a_k a_j a_l - a_j a_k a_i a_l = .00$$

This is Spearman's *tetrad criterion*, which he used in identifying variables with a single common factor.

8. An important application of the evaluation of a second-order minor comes in the case of three variables, when one of the elements is a communality. Thus,

$$\begin{matrix} & i & j \\ i \\ k \end{matrix} \begin{vmatrix} h_i^2 & r_{ij} \\ r_{ik} & r_{jk} \end{vmatrix} = h_i^2 r_{jk} - r_{ij} r_{ik}$$

If the matrix is of rank one, the expression must equal zero. In the real case, the correlations would be known and the communality unknown. Solving for $h_i{}^2$ yields

$$h_i{}^2 = \frac{r_{ij}r_{ik}}{r_{jk}} \tag{17.8a}$$

which is an alternate statement of Formula 17.8. The formula is appropriate when there is evidence that a matrix, or a part of a matrix, is of rank one.

9. By closer examination of Table 17.1, it may be noted that all columns of coefficients correlate perfectly. The coefficients in any vector i are proportional to the coefficients in any other vector j. This is necessarily true if the matrix can be explained on the basis of one general factor. The converse is not necessarily true.

When all columns correlate perfectly and when all tetrad differences of the type $(r_{ik}r_{jl} - r_{jk}r_{il})$ equal zero, it is likely, but not certain, that the matrix, excluding the diagonal terms, is of rank one. In dealing with a matrix of proportional correlations, a value greater than 1.00 may be required to make a communality proportional to the covariances in other columns. Since a communality greater than 1.00 is impossible with correlational data, the rank of the matrix must be greater than one. In that case more than a single factor is required to explain the intercorrelations.

TABLE 17.1. ARTIFICIAL MATRIX GENERATED BY ONE COMMON FACTOR

[Each correlation (below the diagonal) is precisely equal to the factor product (above the diagonal).]

VARIABLE	g_a	1	2	3	4	5	6
g_a	V_{g_a}	a_1	a_2	a_3	a_4	a_5	a_6
1	a_1	$h_1{}^2$	a_1a_2	a_1a_3	a_1a_4	a_1a_5	a_1a_6
2	a_2	r_{12}	$h_2{}^2$	a_2a_3	a_2a_4	a_2a_5	a_2a_6
3	a_3	r_{13}	r_{23}	$h_3{}^2$	a_3a_4	a_3a_5	a_3a_6
4	a_4	r_{14}	r_{24}	r_{34}	$h_4{}^2$	a_4a_5	a_4a_6
5	a_5	r_{15}	r_{25}	r_{35}	r_{45}	$h_5{}^2$	a_5a_6
6	a_6	r_{16}	r_{26}	r_{36}	r_{46}	r_{56}	$h_6{}^2$

Numerical Representation

VARIABLE	g_a	1	2	3	4	5	6
g_a	1.00	.60	.20	−.50	−.40	.70	.50
1	.60	.36	.12	−.30	−.24	.42	.30
2	.20	.12	.04	−.10	−.08	.14	.10
3	−.50	−.30	−.10	.25	.20	−.35	−.25
4	−.40	−.24	−.08	.20	.16	−.28	−.20
5	.70	.42	.14	−.35	−.28	.49	.35
6	.50	.30	.10	−.25	−.20	.35	.25

GRAPHICAL REPRESENTATION OF VARIABLES

In factor analysis it is helpful to represent each variable as a point in space. The projection of such a point on an axis representing a factor can be taken to represent the factor weight or loading. Since a factor loading is the correlation coefficient between the factor and the original variable, it cannot be less than -1.00 nor greater than 1.00. Factors, as extracted, are uncorrelated. To represent uncorrelated factors, orthogonal axes are used, that is, axes at right angles to one another.

In the single factor case, all points fall directly on a single axis, since projections on all other possible axes are zero. In the two-factor case, the points representing the variables are in two-dimensional space, with the projections corresponding to the loadings in the two factors on two co-ordinate axes. As each new factor is added to the solution, an additional axis is required. Although space as we know it has only three orthogonal dimensions, mathematical space has any number of dimensions, with all axes at right angles, one to another. Accordingly, if m factors are required to explain a matrix of correlations, the n points representing the n variables are conceived as plotted in m-dimensional space, and the projections of the points are on m factor axes, all at right angles, one to another.

The variables represented by the points are *common factor* variables; that is, variables consisting exclusively of common variance. Since the unique variance in each observed variable is not shared with other variables in the matrix, it cannot be analyzed and is not represented graphically.

ROTATION OF AXES

When a pair of coordinate axes is rotated, projections on the changed axes differ systematically from the projections on the original axes. It is important to note that rotation has no effect on the sum of the squares of the projections of a single point. Since factor loadings are correlations between a factor and an observed variable, the square of any factor loading gives the proportion of the variable explained by the factor, and the sum of the squares of the factor loadings is h_i^2, the communality of the variable. Accordingly, rotation of axes is a convenient method of redefining factors, without in any way changing the proportions of the original variables explained by the factor analysis. Any matrix of correlations can be reproduced exactly as well by rotated factors as by the factors first extracted or partialed out. The choice among alternate solutions generally depends on subject matter rather than statistical considerations.

To illustrate rotation as a means of redefining factors, results of factoring Table 17.1 are shown in Fig. 17.1. Although the matrix was generated by a single set of factor weights, for illustrative purposes it can be considered as a two-factor matrix. Obtained loadings are plotted directly on axis a, which has uniform projections of zero on axis b. When axes are rotated counterclockwise 36 degrees (an arbitrary figure in this case), points representing variables have projections on the two new axes, a' and b', as shown in the accompanying table.

VARIABLE	LOADING ON AXIS a	ROTATED LOADINGS AXIS a'	ROTATED LOADINGS AXIS b'
1	.60	.48	−.36
2	.20	.16	−.12
3	−.50	−.40	.30
4	−.40	−.32	.24
5	.70	.56	−.42
6	.50	.40	−.30

Of course, with real data, no one would want to convert a single-factor solution to one involving two factors; rather, in factor analysis the objective is to find a matrix of factor loadings, **F**, with a minimum number of vectors such that when post-multiplied by its transpose $\mathbf{F}^T$, the original

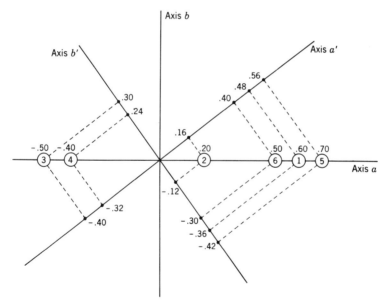

FIG. 17.1.   Rotation of Single Factor Solution to a Two-Factor Solution.
(Points representing variables are identified by the number of the variable in a circle.)

correlation matrix (omitting the diagonal elements) will be reproduced as closely as possible. Occasionally, with real data, a good fit to the observed correlation matrix can be obtained by the use of a single factor. Typically, with psychological data, several factors are required. As the number of factors increases, the fit of $\mathbf{FF}^T$ to the observed matrix becomes closer and closer.

For the data in Table 17.1 it can be seen that by matrix multiplication described in Chapter 16, the unrotated and rotated solutions reproduce the matrix equally well:

$$
\begin{Vmatrix} .60 \\ .20 \\ -.50 \\ -.40 \\ .70 \\ .50 \end{Vmatrix} \cdot \begin{Vmatrix} .60 & .20 & -.50 & -.40 & .70 & .50 \end{Vmatrix}
$$

$$
= \begin{Vmatrix} .48 & -.36 \\ .16 & -.12 \\ -.40 & .30 \\ -.32 & .24 \\ 56 & -.42 \\ .40 & -.30 \end{Vmatrix} \cdot \begin{Vmatrix} .48 & .16 & -.40 & -.32 & .56 & .40 \\ -.36 & -.12 & .30 & .24 & -.42 & -.30 \end{Vmatrix}
$$

$$
= \begin{Vmatrix} .36 & .12 & -.30 & -.24 & .42 & .30 \\ .12 & .04 & -.10 & -.08 & .14 & .10 \\ -.30 & -.10 & .25 & .20 & -.35 & -.25 \\ -.24 & -.08 & .20 & .16 & -.28 & -.20 \\ .42 & .14 & -.35 & -.28 & .49 & .35 \\ .30 & .10 & -.25 & -.20 & .35 & .25 \end{Vmatrix}
$$

SOME LIMITATIONS ON THE FACTOR ANALYTIC METHOD

In most forms of statistical analysis the problem exists of generalizing from the observed sample to the population it represents. This problem appears in factor analysis, but it is compounded by two sources of indeterminacy in the study of the sample itself.

In computing means, standard deviations, differences, correlations, and other descriptive statistics for samples, answers are unequivocal. In factor analysis, however, what is analyzed for each variable is the common variance or communality, generally placed in the diagonal of the correlation matrix. A lower limit is known to be the square of multiple R; that is, the proportion of the variance of the variable predictable from all other variables in the matrix and for which a precise numerical value can be found. The upper limit of the communality is the reliability coefficient, or proportion of nonerror variance, but this coefficient, like the communality itself, is necessarily an estimate rather than a precise descriptive statistic.

Especially with small matrices, results of a factor analysis will vary with how the diagonal cells are filled, and only in special cases are communalities precisely determined.

The second source of indeterminacy is that, when the rank of a matrix is greater than one, there is an unlimited number of **F** matrices, which mathematically are just as adequate in reproducing the original correlations as the **F** matrix first derived. By rotation of the axes of projection, any multiple-factor solution can be modified to any number of equivalent solutions.

Accordingly, factor analysis as applied to psychological data is an art that is somewhat dependent on the skill and intuition of the investigator. It is not a series of precisely defined procedures yielding a rigorously objective result.

BASIC EQUATION OF FACTOR ANALYSIS

Let $\mathbf{R_0}$ be an observed correlation matrix in which, by some method or other, communalities have been inserted in the main diagonal. Let $\mathbf{R}$ be an approximation of $\mathbf{R_0}$ obtained by multiplying the matrix **F** by its transpose. Then the basic equation of factor analysis is

$$\mathbf{F}\mathbf{F}^T = \mathbf{R} \tag{17.10}$$

in which $\mathbf{R} \doteq \mathbf{R_0}$.

Certain characteristics of **R** may be noted:

1. The rank of **R** is the same as the rank of **F**. If **F** has m columns, then m operations of pivotal condensation in **R** will reduce all remaining elements to .00.

2. Since the determinant of **R** is .00, it has no inverse.

3. Each diagonal element, as a communality, must be the variance common with the other variables in the matrix.

4. With real data, the rank of $\mathbf{R_0}$ will, in general, be greater than that of **R**. We have no reason to believe, however, that any set of communalities fitting $\mathbf{R_0}$ are, in truth, unique. Consequently, we are at liberty to alter the factor loadings in **F** in any way that will produce off-diagonal elements of **R** approximating the off-diagonal elements of $\mathbf{R_0}$ as closely as possible. In the interest of parsimony, a low-rank solution is considered better than a high-rank solution. If our factors are designated as $g_a,\ g_b \cdots g_m$ with weights for variable i of $a_i, b_i \cdots m_i$, then by extension of Eqs. 17.1 through 17.7,

$$z_i = a_i g_a + b_i g_b + \cdots + m_i g_m + w_i u_i \tag{17.1a}$$

and

$$a_i^2 + b_i^2 + \cdots + m_i^2 + w_i^2 = 1 \tag{17.3a}$$

in which

$$a_i^2 + b_i^2 + \cdots + m_i^2 = h_i^2$$

and

$$r_{ij} = a_i a_j + b_i b_j + \cdots + m_i m_j \tag{17.7a}$$

That is to say, the communality of any variable is the sum of the squares of the factor weights and any correlation is the sum of products of the factor weights.

These facts are summarized more succinctly in Eq. 17.10.

METHODS OF FACTOR ANALYSIS

Detailed descriptions of the numerical methods that have been used to develop an **F** matrix are beyond the scope of this text. No single method has yet emerged as universally acceptable as the best. The advent of electronic computers has made possible the use of factor extraction and rotation methods that would be prohibitive with desk calculators.

Whatever method of developing **F** is used, there are three bases for evaluating the factor matrix as an analysis of the original matrix of correlations.

1. How closely does **R** approximate $\mathbf{R}_0$? $\mathbf{R}_0 - \mathbf{R}$ is the "residual" matrix consisting, except for the diagonal elements, of partial covariances between the original variables, with the variability associated with the several posited factors partialed out. The aim of factor analysis is to make these residual coefficients so small that they can be taken as chance deviations from zero.

2. The solution should be of low rank; that is, the number of factors, as represented by the number of columns in **F**, should be small. Obviously, this requirement, coupled with the requirement of small residuals, contributes to the indeterminacy of factoring. As the rank of **F** goes up, the approximation of **R** to $\mathbf{R}_0$ becomes better and better. A low-rank solution may require compromises in the size of the residuals, while a good fit of **R** to $\mathbf{R}_0$ may require a goodly number of factors.

3. The final requirement, originally proposed by Thurstone, is for *simple structure*. This means that the **F** matrix, as extracted or as subsequently rotated on *m* axes, must have high loadings in "marker" variables and low positive or zero loadings in other variables. If all elements in **F** are zero or positive, the factor solution is said to have *positive manifold*.

FITTING A SINGLE FACTOR

An observed matrix of correlations can generally be explained as arising from a single, common factor if the elements in different vectors are more or less proportional; that is, if all pairs of vectors have correlations approaching 1.00.[1] A formula developed by Spearman yields the factor weights:

$$r_{ig} \doteq \sqrt{\frac{(\Sigma r_{ij})^2 - \Sigma r_{ij}^2}{2(\Sigma\Sigma r_{jk} - \Sigma r_{ij})}} \qquad i \neq j \neq k \qquad (17.11)$$

---

[1] Mathematically, this is the same as the requirement that the tetrads be .00.

in which $\Sigma\Sigma r_{jk}$ is the sum of all the correlations in the matrix, each counted once, and Σr_{ij} is the sum of the vector of r's involving i. The square of each r_{ig} would be the communality, but in this special case of factor analysis, communalities are not needed.

The procedure is to:

1. Find the vector of factor weights; and
2. Remove the variability of this general factor from the matrix by partialing it out.

If the resultant partial covariances approximate zeroes, then a good fit has been secured. Actually, a decision as to whether or not the residual covariances can be attributed to chance requires that they be converted into partial r's and that their distribution be compared with the standard error of a partial r of .00, for the appropriate number of degrees of freedom. Exercise 2 at the end of this chapter requires a simple analysis of this sort.

DIAGONAL OR SQUARE ROOT METHOD

When the rank of a matrix is m and the communalities of m variables, loaded in m factors, are known precisely, the diagonal or square root method is applicable.

Factor loadings are derived as follows:

1. The loading of the "pivot" variable, the common variance of which is to be partialed out of the matrix, is the square root of its communality. If one or more factors have already been extracted, the loading is the square root of the residual communality.
2. For other variables the loading is the covariance with the pivot, divided by the loading of the pivot. Thus, for variable j, when variable i is being partialed out, the loading is $C_{ij}/\sqrt{h_i^2}$.

A process akin to the pivotal condensation used in multiple and partial correlation reduces all elements in the vector of the pivot variable to zero, and reduces elements in other vectors to partial variances and covariances of higher order. The process is continued until all remaining elements approach zero.

The method works well with artificial matrices in which communalities are known. With real data it is limited by the fact that the communality estimates generally available are not sufficiently precise to make the method useful. Occasionally, however, when good communality estimates are available, the method is feasible. The method can be used with the data of Exercise 3 at the end of this chapter.

COMPUTATIONAL METHODS IN MULTIPLE-FACTOR ANALYSIS

Practical procedures for finding an **F** matrix that can be taken as the roots of an observed matrix of correlations and for rotating the obtained factor solution to a meaningful configuration, either on orthogonal or oblique axes, are beyond the scope of this text. Of the methods available, several will be mentioned briefly. Surveys of existing methods are presented by Harman (5) and Fruchter (4).

The bifactor method was developed by Holzinger to extend Spearman's single-factor formulation to the case in which there is a large general factor, followed by "group" factors in limited clusters of variables. Characteristically, the obtained loadings are as shown in Table 17.2. The use of this method is described by Harman (5).

TABLE 17.2. TYPICAL FACTOR SOLUTIONS

VARIABLE	HOLZINGER BIFACTOR				CENTROID AND PRINCIPAL AXES (UNROTATED)			
	FACTORS				FACTORS			
	I	II	III	$\cdots$ J	I	II	III	$\cdots$ J
1	+	+	0	$\cdots$ 0	+	+	+	$\cdots$ −
2	+	+	0	$\cdots$ 0	+	−	−	$\cdots$ −
3	+	+	0	$\cdots$ 0	+	+	−	$\cdots$ −
4	+	0	+	$\cdots$ 0	+	−	−	$\cdots$ +
5	+	0	+	$\cdots$ 0	+	+	−	$\cdots$ +
6	+	0	+	$\cdots$ 0	+	−	+	$\cdots$ +
7	+	0	0	$\cdots$ +	+	+	+	$\cdots$ −
8	+	0	0	$\cdots$ +	+	+	+	$\cdots$ −
9	+	0	0	$\cdots$ +	+	−	−	$\cdots$ +

+ = Positive loading   − = Negative loading   0 = Zero loading

One of the most popular of the multiple-factor methods has been the centroid solution, developed by Thurstone (11). It involves filling the diagonal cells by making estimates of the communalities; a simple formula for factor weights; extraction of a first factor; "reflection" of vectors until a second factor can be extracted; continuation of the process until the variance of the matrix has been exhausted; iteration of the communalities by repeating the extraction procedure; and rotation of the F matrix until the solution is meaningful. Characteristically, with psychological variables with positive intercorrelations, the first factor as extracted has positive loadings in all variables, and subsequent factors as extracted are "bipolar," with approximately half of the loadings positive and half negative. This characteristic pattern is shown in Table 17.2. Thurstone insists, however, that factors as extracted have little or no meaning, and only by rotation can an alternate solution be obtained that is in any way useful.

A more sophisticated alternate to the centroid method is the principal axes solution, the forerunner of which was envisaged by Pearson (9) and which was developed as a factor method by Hotelling (6) and Kelley (7). In effect, a set of axes is fitted to the swarm of points representing variables in n-dimensional space in such a manner that maximum variance is extracted. The arithmetical work required with any substantial number of variables is such that the method is feasible only with high-speed computers. Characteristically, the original solution is much like that of the centroid and becomes interpretable only through rotation.

A mathematically sophisticated solution to factor analysis is the maximum likelihood method, developed by Lawley (8). This also is difficult computationally. For a given rank of the factor matrix, it develops a matrix of factor loadings such that the sum of the squares of the differences between original correlations and correlations estimated from the **F** matrix is as small as possible.

METHODS OF ROTATING THE **F** MATRIX

In the original development of multiple factor analysis, graphic methods were employed to rotate the several axes of projections until a meaningful factor configuration was obtained. Beginning with the work of Carroll (1) in 1953, several methods, feasible with computers, have been developed by which axes can be rotated analytically, with resultant parsimonious description of the factors. The analytic methods yield either uncorrelated factors (projected on orthogonal axes) or correlated factors (projected on oblique axes).

READING A REPORT OF A FACTOR ANALYSIS

The psychologist is often confronted with a report of a factor analysis, part of which is almost always a table of factor loadings such as the one shown in Example 17.1.

EXAMPLE 17.1

READING THE REPORT OF A FACTOR ANALYSIS

Purposes of a Factor Analysis. A factor analysis such as the one reported by Fleishman and Ellison (3) aims to reduce the number of variables needed to reproduce the off-diagonal elements of a correlation matrix from n, the number of observed variables, to n', the number of factors ($n > n'$). If, by matrix multiplication and with negligible error, the $n(n + 1)/2$ r's can be reproduced from the n' factors, the matrix may be considered factored. Most factor analysts use three other criteria of adequate factorization:

1. n' must be as small as possible and appreciably smaller than n;
2. Each factor must be defined by high correlations with some observed variables, low or zero correlations with others; and
3. To the maximum extent possible, the factor matrix should have *positive manifold*; that is, factor loadings should be positive or zero.

A factor analysis is regarded not only as a means of understanding the composition of observed variables, but also often as a step in making decisions about new variables that need to be developed, sometimes as purer measures of factors appearing in the analysis.

· *Steps in the Factor Analysis.* In the study summarized in Table 17.3, one of a series concerned with the isolation and definition of factors in manipulative and other psychomotor tests, 760 airmen were given a battery yielding 9 printed test scores and 13 scores from apparatus tests. After the computation of the 231 intercorrelations, Thurstone's centroid method was used to extract 7 factors. The largest *residual*[2] was .05, indicating that the fit of FF^T to R_0 is good. As would be anticipated (see Table 17.2), the loadings of the unrotated factors beyond the first were about equally divided into those with positive and those with negative signs, as follows:

FACTOR	I	II	III	IV	V	VI	VII
Positive loadings	22	9	12	13	12	11	9
Negative loadings	0	13	10	9	10	11	13

Results. Rotations of orthogonal axes resulted in the solution presented as Table 17.3, in which factors are identified at the tops of the columns. Important points are:

1. There are only three large negative loadings in **F**, and in each case another score from the same test has a large positive loading in the same factor. Hence **F** has *positive manifold*.
2. Of the 154 factor loadings, 36 have an absolute value of .30 or more, which the authors have taken as the lower limit of significance.
3. The communalities in the last column are the squares of the factor loadings of the variable. They may be taken as the proportion of the variance explained by the common factors. The complement of h^2 is u^2, the proportion of unique variance, including both specific reliable variance and error.
4. The original matrix of *r*'s can be reconstituted, except for discrepancies or residuals and within rounding error, by multiplying **F** by its transpose. Here are a few correlations and residuals as reported in the original article, together with corresponding *r*'s as reconstructed from Table 17.3.

	ORIGINAL *r*	RESIDUAL	RECONSTRUCTED *r*
r_{12}	.83	.04	.80
r_{13}	.57	.00	.58
r_{14}	.57	.00	.57
r_{23}	.57	.00	.58
r_{24}	.57	.00	.57
r_{34}	.74	−.01	.76

---

[2] The term *residual* as used in factor analytical literature refers not to a residual variable nor to a value of such a variable, but rather to the partial covariance between two variables after partialing out the factor(s).

TABLE 17.3. ROTATED FACTOR LOADINGS

	WRIST AND FINGER SPEED I	FINGER DEXTERITY II	SPEED OF ARM MOVEMENT III	MANUAL DEXTERITY IV	AIMING V	RESIDUAL VI	DOUBLET VII	h^2
1. Medium tapping	.77	.10	.28	.22	.14	.10	.21	.79
2. Large tapping	.75	.10	.31	.25	.15	.06	.19	.79
3. Aiming	.52	.30	.20	.01	.57	.13	−.01	.72
4. Pursuit aiming, I	.52	.27	.19	−.01	.63	.11	−.02	.79
5. Pursuit aiming, II	.54	.28	.18	−.01	.63	.05	−.04	.81
6. Square marking	.46	.26	.10	.20	.31	.00	−.11	.44
7. Tracing	.12	.05	.11	.13	.15	.25	.19	.17
8. Steadiness	−.03	.06	.08	.01	.04	.27	.13	.10
9. Discrimination reaction time, printed	.30	.07	.03	.34	.00	.05	−.02	.21
10. Precision steadiness	.05	.17	.00	.10	.13	.34	.09	.18
11. Ten target aiming, errors	.03	.08	−.79	.09	−.04	.27	.08	.59
12. Ten target aiming, corrects	−.04	.14	.72	.13	.31	.07	.06	.65
13. Hand precision aiming, errors	−.02	−.04	−.51	.15	.13	.00	.64	.71
14. Hand precision aiming, corrects	.15	.14	.56	.00	.05	.40	−.50	.75
15. Minnesota rate of manipulation, placing	.10	.37	.24	.53	.34	.14	.09	.62
16. Minnesota rate of manipulation, turning	.09	.34	.23	.52	.30	.23	.08	.60
17. Pin stick	.08	.34	.07	.25	.24	.20	.03	.29
18. Purdue pegboard, right hand	.01	.60	.18	.17	.12	.16	.14	.48
19. Purdue pegboard, left hand	.05	.55	.18	.10	.05	.26	.11	.43
20. Purdue pegboard, both hands	.08	.66	.16	.20	.06	.10	.13	.54
21. Purdue pegboard, assembly	.09	.59	.14	.32	.00	.12	−.01	.50
22. O'Connor finger dexterity	.13	.59	.20	.19	.11	.14	.07	.48

SOURCE: Reproduced by permission from Edwin A. Fleishman and Gaylord D. Ellison, "A Factor Analysis of Manipulative Tests," *J. appl. Psychol.*, 1962, **46**, 96–105.

In reading a factor study, cognizance may be taken of the following points:

1. To what degree does the **F** matrix reproduce the original matrix of correlations? This is never apparent directly from the **F** matrix, but is usually indicated somewhere in the text of the article. Often it is instructive, when axes are orthogonal, to attempt to approximate some of the original r's by matrix multiplication. Obviously, the closeness of fit of $\mathbf{FF}^T$ to $\mathbf{R}_0$ is the first criterion of successful factorization.

2. How many factors have been found? That is to say, what is the rank of **F**? Here, with empirical data, there is always some sort of a compromise. If the rank of $\mathbf{R}_0$ approaches n, the number of variables, then $\mathbf{FF}^T$ can equal $\mathbf{R}_0$ exactly. In general, however, the aim of factor analysis is to reduce the number of dimensions and still permit $\mathbf{FF}^T$ to approximate $\mathbf{R}_0$.

3. As projected on rotated orthogonal or oblique axes, do the loadings of **F** make sense? What observed variables help in the interpretation of **F**, and what loadings in the several factors help in understanding the observed variables? Typically, factor analysis involves the use of *marker* variables to define *factors*, and uses factors to understand variables hitherto less well understood. In Table 17.3, 22 conventional psychological tests have heavy loadings in 7 factors, in terms of which various training criteria can be interpreted.

SUMMARY

Modern factor analysis stems from the work of Spearman, who found evidence for a single factor underlying mental tests. When it was realized that his two-factor theory (that is, one general factor plus specific factors in each variable) was inadequate to explain the matrices of correlations actually obtained in psychological investigations, Thurstone and others developed multiple-factor methods. These yield two or more columns of factor weights by which the original r's can be reproduced more or less exactly.

Since an indefinite number of alternate multiple-factor solutions always exist, the principle of simple structure is generally used as the basis of choosing the most suitable configuration of the rotated factor matrix.

Despite continued development of methods, it must be emphasized that factor analysis is far from being an exact set of procedures for data reduction and for drawing inferences about the parameters of an unknown population. In the hands of skillful research workers, however, it appears useful in the interpretation of a large mass of observations and in suggesting new avenues of exploration.

EXERCISES

1. By matrix multiplication generate a single factor matrix with known communalities from the following **F**-matrix:

VARIABLE	F	F^T
1	.8	‖ .8 .5 .2 .3 .6 ‖
2	.5	
3	.2	
4	.3	
5	.6	

Consider the resultant **R** matrix:

(a) Are the entries in each vector proportional to the entries in any other parallel vector?

(b) Test any off-diagonal 2×2 minor. Does it equal zero?

(c) Test a 2×2 minor that includes one or two communalities. Does it equal zero?

(d) Find an h_i^2 from Formula 17.8a, $h_i^2 = r_{ij}r_{ik}/r_{jk}$. Is the correct value recovered?

2. The following are intercorrelations of five reading skills as reported by Davis (2). Find single-factor loadings by Formula 17.11, partial out the factor, and inspect the residuals to see if they are sufficiently small so that the assumption of a single factor in the original matrix is plausible.

VARIABLE	2	3	4	5
1 Word meanings	.41	.52	.68	.68
2 Following organization		.34	.42	.41
3 Answering questions			.55	.55
4 Drawing inferences				.68
5 Inferring writer's characteristics				

3. The following hypothetical two-factor matrix is from Thurstone (11):

VARIABLE	2	3	4	5
1	.50	.41	.30	.21
2		.58	.44	.34
3			.54	.57
4				.62

The generating **F** matrix, with communalities, is shown below, at the left. At the right is a set of factor weights derived by the square root method.

F MATRIX (FROM THURSTONE)				F MATRIX (SQUARE ROOT METHOD)			
VARIABLE	I	II	h^2	VARIABLE	a	b	h^2
1	.1	.6	.37	1	.60828	.00000	.37
2	.2	.8	.68	2	.82199	.06576	.68
3	.5	.6	.61	3	.67403	.39456	.61
4	.6	.4	.52	4	.49320	.52608	.52
5	.9	.2	.85	5	.34524	.85487	.85

(a) Partial out the two Thurstone factors and note that the final partial covariances are all zero.

(b) Partial out the two square root factors and note that the final partial covariances are all zero.

4. Using cross-section paper, locate each variable in the preceding exercise as a point in two-dimensional space. Let the two orthogonal axes be the "square root" factors. Find the rotated axes that yield the original F matrix.

REFERENCES

1. CARROLL, JOHN B., "An analytical solution for approximating simple structure in factor analysis," *Psychometrika*, 1953, **18**, 23–38.

2. DAVIS, FREDERICK B., "Fundamental factors of comprehension in reading," *Psychometrika*, 1944, **9**, 185–197.

3. FLEISHMAN, EDWIN A., AND ELLISON, GAYLORD D., "A factor analysis of manipulative tests," *J. Appl. Psychol.*, 1962, **46**, 96–105.

4. FRUCHTER, B., *Introduction to Factor Analysis*. New York: D. Van Nostrand Company, Inc., 1954.

5. HARMAN, HARRY H., *Modern Factor Analysis*. Chicago, Illinois: The University of Chicago Press, 1960.

6. HOTELLING, HAROLD, "Analysis of a complex of statistical variables into principal components," *J. Educ. Psychol.*, 1933, **24**, 417–441, 498–520.

7. KELLEY, TRUMAN L., "Essential traits of mental life," *Harvard Studies in Education*. Cambridge, Mass.: Harvard University Press, 1936, **26**, 146.

8. LAWLEY, D. N., "The estimation of factor loadings by the method of maximum likelihood," *Proc. Roy. Soc. Edin.*, 1940, **A 60**, 64–82.

9. PEARSON, KARL, "On lines and planes of closest fit to systems of points in space," *Phil. Mag.*, 1901, **6**, 599–72.

10. SPEARMAN, CHARLES, *The Abilities of Man*. New York: The Macmillan Company, 1927, vi + 416 + xxxiv.

11. THURSTONE, L. L., *Multiple Factor Analysis*. Chicago, Illinois: The University of Chicago Press, 1947.

NOTES ON
DISTRIBUTION-FREE
(OR NONPARAMETRIC)
STATISTICAL TESTS

18

In Chapters 3, 11, and 12 there was consideration of the use of the χ^2 family of distribution curves in testing whether the frequencies within a set of categories may be considered as distributed in accordance with a large variety of hypotheses. In the sense that few assumptions need be made about the parameters of the population represented by the sample, χ^2 is a *nonparametric* statistic. More properly, it may be considered *distribution-free* in that the restriction of an underlying normally distributed variable does not apply to χ^2 as it does to t and F. The application of χ^2 requires the assumption of no particular distribution in the population from which the sample is drawn.

The terms *nonparametric* and *distribution-free* are not completely synonymous, but they are used almost interchangeably with a large group of statistical tests for data in the form of frequencies within categories or in the form of ranks. As with the critical ratio, t and F, the distribution-free statistical tests are used only to make inferences about the population represented by the sample.

Always it is the variable or variables in the population that are free of the assumption of normality. The chance distribution of the statistic must, of course, be known, but it can follow any one of a large number of forms, including the binomial, χ^2 and the normal curve, as well as a form peculiar to the statistic itself.

In general, distribution-free tests require relatively simple arithmetical operations (counting or ranking) and the use of a table based on the distribution of the statistic, which may vary with N, or the N's of subclasses, or with the degrees of freedom.

When original data are in the form of frequencies or ranks, statistical tests necessarily fall in the distribution-free classification. When interval or ratio data are converted to the frequencies or ranks required by the typical distribution-free tests, there are two consequences:

1. Some of the information gathered as original observations is simplified and thus disappears; and
2. When the null hypothesis is in fact false, there is less probability of rejecting it.

For identical data, then, these short-cut and approximate methods of making statistical tests are less powerful than conventional procedures. Even when the assumptions needed for parametric tests are not fully justified, t and F are often preferable to a distribution-free method. However, χ^2 is one of the most versatile devices in the armamentarium of hypothesis testing, while various other distribution-free techniques are finding increasingly numerous applications with psychological data. An attractive feature is that they often permit valid inferences from small numbers of cases. Characteristically, the statistic itself is constructed intuitively, after which its distribution is worked out mathematically by procedures such as those already demonstrated in Chapter 12. When a large number of individual distributions are involved, the published tables generally give only selected significance points, such as those exceeded by .05 and .01 of the chance distribution of the statistic.

RANKING METHODS

SPEARMAN'S ρ AS A DISTRIBUTION-FREE STATISTIC

A statistic that does not assume normal distributions for the two variables in the parent population, but rather forces rectangular distributions on all sets of data, is ρ, Spearman's coefficient of rank correlation, the formula for which was given in Formula 4.5 as

$$\rho = 1 - \frac{6\Sigma D^2}{N(N-1)}$$

Before using ρ to test the null hypothesis of no association between the two variables in the population represented by the sample, its distribution must be known. As implied by the display in Table 18.1, there is a separate distribution of ρ for each value of N, the number of pairs of observations. If two variables, X and Y, each consist of ranks from 1 to N, and X is arranged in a fixed order, there are factorial N (that is, $N!$) ways of arranging the values of Y to match those of X. The $N!$ values of ρ computed from the $N!$ ways of arranging Y constitute the distribution of ρ. Distributions of ρ from $N = 2$ to $N = 5$ are given in Table 18.1.

TABLE 18.1. DISTRIBUTIONS OF ρ FROM $N = 2$ TO $N = 5$

ρ	$N = 2$ f	p	$N = 3$ f	p	$N = 4$ f	p	$N = 5$ f	p
1.00	1	.500	1	.167	1	.042	1	.008
.90							4	.033
.80					3	.125	3	.025
.70							6	.050
.60					1	.042	7	.058
.50			2	.333			6	.050
.40					4	.167	4	.033
.30							10	.083
.20					2	.083	6	.050
.10							10	.083
.00					2	.083	6	.050
−.10							10	.083
−.20					2	.083	6	.050
−.30							10	.083
−.40					4	.167	4	.033
−.50			2	.333			6	.050
−.60					1	.042	7	.058
−.70							6	.050
−.80					3	.125	3	.025
−.90							4	.033
−1.00	1	.500	1	.167	1	.042	1	.008
	$N! = 2$		$N! = 6$		$N! = 24$		$N! = 120$	

Each distribution consists of $N!$ frequencies, and the p for each possible value of ρ is f divided by $N!$. The p are not cumulated, as would be necessary in developing entries for a table of significance points. It can be seen, however, that:

1. If $N = 4$, a ρ of 1.00 is significant at the .05 level (more precisely, the .042 level).
2. If $N = 5$, a ρ of 1.00 is significant at the .01 level (more precisely, the .008 level).
3. If $N = 5$, a ρ of .90 is significant at the .05 level (more precisely, the 5/120, or .042 level).

In testing an observed ρ, one may use the same .05 and .01 levels of significance as are often used with t and F. Table 18.2 gives (for values of N from 4 to 30) values of ρ needed for significance at the .05 and .01 levels (one-tailed tests). A ρ computed for a given N is merely compared with the size of the ρ needed at a predetermined level of significance. It is seen that results of acceptable significance can sometimes be obtained for as few as four or five cases.

TABLE 18.2. CRITICAL VALUES OF ρ AT THE .01 AND .05 LEVELS OF SIGNIFICANCE[a]
(One-Tailed Test)

LEVEL OF SIGNIFICANCE	N								
	4	5	6	7	8	9	10	12	14
.01		1.000	.943	.893	.833	.783	.746	.712	.645
.05	1.000	.900	.829	.714	.643	.600	.564	.506	.456

LEVEL OF SIGNIFICANCE	N							
	16	18	20	22	24	26	28	30
.01	.601	.564	.534	.508	.485	.465	.448	.432
.05	.425	.399	.377	.359	.343	.329	.317	.306

[a] From Olds, E. G., 1938. "Distributions of sums of squares of rank differences for small numbers of individuals," *Ann Math. Statist.*, 9, 133–148; and from Olds, E. G., 1949, "The 5 percent significance levels for sums of squares of rank differences and a correction," *Ann. Math. Statist.*, 20, 117–118, with the kind permission of the publisher.

THE RUN TEST[1]

Occasionally an investigator is interested in whether a sequence of two types of events can be considered random. No parametric test is available for this purpose. The run test can be used to evaluate whether an observed number of unbroken "runs" within a total series is within chance expectancy. It is applicable both to ranks and to sequences in time.

Let the n events in one category be $X_1, X_2 \cdots X_n$ and the m events in the other category be $Y_1, Y_2 \cdots Y_m$. The total number of events is $n + m = N$. The first step is to consolidate the two categories in a single series and to count d (the number of runs), each of which, in the artificial sample below, is enclosed in parentheses:

$$(X_1X_2)(Y_1)(X_3X_4X_5)(Y_2Y_3)(X_6)(Y_4)(X_7X_8X_9X_{10})(Y_5Y_6)$$
$$(+ +)(-)(+ + +)(- -)(+)(-)(+ + + +)(- -)$$

$$(X_{11}X_{12})(Y_7Y_8Y_9Y_{10}Y_{11})(X_{13}X_{14})(Y_{12})$$
$$(+ +)(- - - - -)(+ +)(-)$$

X's and Y's may have numeric values, allowing them to be placed in order, or they may be ranks within the total series, or they may be the presence or absence of a characteristic (as indicated by the $+$ and $-$ signs in the second line).

Here, $d = 12$, $n = 14$, $m = 12$, and $N = 26$.

---

[1] Known also as the Wald-Wolfowitz run test.

Strictly, when n and m are less than 20, deviation from randomness is evaluated by special tables.[2] However, when n and m are 10 or more, the procedure described below and used routinely when n and m are 20 or more is reasonably accurate.

A decision has to be made as to which of the following conditions will be the basis for rejecting the null hypothesis:

1. Fewer runs than anticipated by chance (one-tailed test);
2. More runs than anticipated by chance (one-tailed test); or
3. Either more or fewer runs than anticipated by chance (two-tailed test).

Let us decide to reject the null hypothesis at the 5 percent level of confidence if the runs are fewer in number than would be anticipated by chance. Thus, the strings or runs of like variates would be longer than expected on the basis of the null hypothesis. For large values of n and m, the chance distribution of d is normal, with the following mean and standard deviation:

$$\mu_d = \frac{2mn}{N} - 1$$

$$\sigma_d = \sqrt{\frac{2mn(2mn - N)}{N^2(N - 1)}}$$

To reject the null hypothesis under the conditions chosen, $(d - \mu_d)/\sigma_d$ must be -1.645 or less (that is, farther from the mean, with the same sign and greater absolute value). Here, $\mu_d = 12.92$, $\sigma_d = 2.48$. However, since d is 12, $(d - \mu_d)/\sigma_d$ is only -0.37; therefore there is no reason in this case to reject the null hypothesis.

OTHER TESTS BASED ON RANK ORDER

Some of the distribution-free tests based on ranks parallel in intent conventional parametric tests for differences between means. However, means as such are not computed (but may be reflected in sums of ranks), and information as to variability comes from numbers of cases ranked.

The matched-pairs, signed-ranks test evaluates differences between two correlated variables. It was developed by Wilcoxon (13) who presents a table for use when N, the number of pairs, is 25 or less.

Briefly, differences between the N pairs of values are computed and ranked, retaining the algebraic signs of the differences. The totals of positive and negative ranks are found separately, and the smaller sum of ranks, T, is evaluated either by the table or by computation. When N is

---

[2] Tables for small values of n and m were developed by Swed and Eisenhart (10) and are reproduced by various authors, including Siegel (7) and Tate and Clelland (11).

25 or more, T is considered to be normally distributed with mean of $N(N + 1)/4$ and standard deviation of $\sqrt{N(N + 1)(2N + 1)/24}$. Accordingly, $(T - \mu_T)/\sigma_T$ can be readily evaluated from a table of the area of the normal curve, such as Table A (Appendix).

The U test of Mann and Whitney (5) is applicable to differences between unmatched groups of any size. It is an extension of the T test for the special case of two unmatched groups of identical size, developed by Wilcoxon (13). The procedure involves ranking in a single series from low to high the n observations in one group. Two sums of ranks are then obtained: T_n for the group of n cases and T_m for the group of m cases. Then U is the smaller of the following quantities:

$$nm + \frac{n(n + 1)}{2} - T_n \quad \text{and} \quad nm + \frac{m(m + 1)}{2} - T_m$$

U is evaluated by tables[3] developed by Mann and Whitney. Again, as n and m increase in size (that is, beyond 8), U approaches normality, with mean of $nm/2$ and standard deviation of $\sqrt{nm(N + 1)/12}$, in which $n + m = N$, the total number of observations. The rarity of an obtained U can then be evaluated with the use of a table of the area of the normal curve, and the null hypothesis may be rejected or accepted at a predetermined level of confidence.

In addition to the tests that parallel the critical ratio and t, methods of analysis of variance with ranked data have been developed. Kruskal and Wallis (4) have written on the one-way case; Friedman (2), on the two-way. These methods are useful when original observations must be in the form of ranks.

TESTS BASED ON ALGEBRAIC SIGNS OF DIFFERENCES

THE SIGN TEST

The sign test, one of the most widely used distribution-free techniques, employs the binomial distribution (described in Chapter 12) to test whether the median difference between pairs of observations is zero. If the original observations are in the form of interval data, less information is used in the sign test than in the matched-pairs, signed-ranks test, which also tests differences between paired observations. In the sign test, only information as to the direction of the differences within pairs is used.

Two sets of matched observations are compared, pair by pair, and the sign of each difference is noted as plus or minus. (If both members of a pair are equal, it is the custom to drop that pair from further consideration.)

---

[3] These tables are available in various texts in statistics, as well as in the original reference.

If the median difference in the population were zero, half of the signs, within sampling error, would be expected to be plus and half would be minus.

The chance distribution of plus and minus signs for the null hypothesis of a median difference of zero is given by the binomial expansion $(p + q)^N$, in which N is the total number of pairs yielding differences and in which $p = q = .50$.

There are four ways of evaluating a situation in which X of N pairs yield one sign and $(N - X)$ the other:

1. By Formula 12.1, the exact probabilities of N, $(N - 1) \cdots X$ like signs can be found and summed. If this sum is equal to or less than the proportion corresponding to the predetermined significance level, the null hypothesis may be rejected at that level. Thus, if $X = 2$ and $N = 7$, the sum of the probabilities of $X = 0, 1, 2$ is .013, to which would be added the probabilities of $X = 5, 6, 7$ (also .013) if a two-tailed test is appropriate.

2. The binomial proportions may be read directly from a table such as that published by the National Bureau of Standards (6). Less extensive tables are available in various texts, including Walker and Lev (12).

3. As pointed out in Chapter 12, the binomial becomes a better and better approximation of the normal curve as p and q approach equality and as the exponent applicable to $(p + q)$ increases. Here $p = q = .50$ and the exponent is N. Accordingly, by Formula 12.2, the mean is Np, or $.5N$; and by Formula 12.3, the standard deviation is $\sqrt{Npq}$, or $.5\sqrt{N}$.

If N is large (say, 25), X can be converted to conventional z-score form and evaluated by Table A (Appendix). Thus,

$$z_x = \frac{X - \mu_x}{\sigma_x} = \frac{X - .5N}{.5\sqrt{N}}$$

A simple correction for continuity, discussed by Siegel (7), improves the approximation.

4. When N is 10 or more, the obtained distribution of plus and minus signs can be compared with a theoretical distribution of equal numbers of plus and minus signs, using χ^2 with $1df$, as in the diagram below:

χ^2 APPLIED TO THE SIGN TEST

	OBSERVED FREQUENCIES	THEORETICAL FREQUENCIES
$+$	f_{o+}	$\dfrac{N}{2}$
$-$	f_{o-}	$\dfrac{N}{2}$

Preferably, Yates' correction for continuity (demonstrated in a somewhat different context in Example 3.7) is used. This involves subtracting .5 from the greater f_0 and adding .5 to the lesser f_0.

MEDIAN TEST

The median test resembles the U test in that it compares two groups that may be of unequal size and in which there is no matching of cases. However, only algebraic signs of differences between each case and the median of the combined groups are considered.

The $n + m$ cases of X_1, $X_2 \cdots X_n$ and Y_1, $Y_2 \cdots Y_m$ are ranked in a single series to find their median. Then the frequencies of X and of Y above the median constitute f_{x+} and f_{y+} in the following diagram:

	$-$	$+$	
Group X	f_{x-}	f_{x+}	n
Group Y	f_{y-}	f_{y+}	m
	f_-	f_+	N

For small numbers of cases, Fisher (1) provides an exact test of significance. If n and m are sufficiently large so that each f_e is 5 or more, the 2×2 table can be evaluated for independence by the χ^2 test with $1 df$.

OTHER DISTRIBUTION-FREE STATISTICS

The coefficient of contingency C, considered in Chapter 2, and Kendall's τ and percentiles discussed in Chapter 4 are among the statistics generally classed as distribution-free when used as a basis for significance tests. Methods also exist for finding the confidence limits of percentiles; for testing randomization of values within a set of observations; and for testing the degree to which deviations from some posited value are greater than might be expected by chance.

When data can be collected only in the form of frequencies or ranks, the investigator should consider the use of an appropriate distribution-free method. This discussion of a relatively small number of tests is merely an introduction to the subject. The presentation has been simplified and, in particular, methods of treating ties have been largely omitted. These are given in the references.

SUMMARY

Several of the statistics underlying distribution-free, or nonparametric, tests were presented in Chapters 2 and 4, while some of the logic applicable to them was given in Chapters 3, 10, and 11.

In this chapter, comments on the distribution of ρ illustrate the three stages characterizing an inferential statistic applicable to categorical data or to ranks (or to interval data reduced to categories or ranks).

1. A descriptive statistic is developed, often intuitively;
2. Its distribution on the basis of a null hypothesis is developed; and
3. In dealing with an appropriate sample of cases, the research worker decides on the level of significance that he will use for rejecting the null hypothesis. He then computes the statistic and evaluates its rarity on the basis of the known distribution. This paradigm, of course, follows that of conventional statistical tests.

EXERCISES

1. For the 24 oldest children in a village school, Spearman (8) reports ranks as follows:

SEX	INTELLECTUAL RANK			INTELLECTUAL RANK	
	OUT OF SCHOOL	IN SCHOOL		OUT OF SCHOOL	IN SCHOOL
F	6	2	F	4	8
M	11	22	F	9	14
F	16	7	F	15	10
F	1	1	M	17	17
M	3	3	M	22	5
F	10	9	F	14	15
F	8	12	M	19	24
F	2	6	M	18	16
M	5	11	M	23	20
M	21	19	M	24	23
F	12	4	F	7	13
F	13	18	M	20	21

(a) Test whether the association between the two sets of ranks is significant for the total groups
(b) Rank males and females separately and test whether the association is significant in each of the two subgroups.
2. Drawings by 23 grade school pupils were ranked in order from 1 to 23. when identities were revealed, it was found that drawings with the following ranks were by boys:

$$2, 5, 6, 7, 9, 10, 15, 16, 17, 23$$

By the U test, determine at the 5 percent level of significance whether boys and girls differ in the quality of their drawings.
3. The sequence below represents 57 individuals observed walking past a certain point on a university campus during an 8-minute period. Males are represented as 1, females as 0. Apply the run test to the data to decide at the

5 percent level of confidence whether the number of unbroken sequences differs from what might be expected by chance.

100110011011000001100111110000101010100011001001010101000

4. Sugisaki and Brown (9) report numbers of women's and men's pictures recognized by six Japanese girls and nine Japanese boys as follows:

| | NUMBER OF PICTURES RECOGNIZED | |
| | OWN | OPPOSITE |
GIRLS	SEX	SEX
Fujiwi	172	142
Takagi	134	131
Ishibashi	180	163
Morimoto	161	162
Towata	149	139
Sano	155	130
BOYS		
Fukuzawa	170	159
Tsuchiya	131	125
Towata	114	101
Miyanchi	114	110
Yamagawi	111	122
Joseph	115	124
Nakao	119	128
Kiro	78	89
Takeo	81	114

(a) Considering "Own Sex" and "Opposite Sex" as the two variables, apply Formula 13.13 to test whether the difference between the two means is significant at the .05 level.

(b) Apply a distribution-free technique to determine whether the difference is significant at the .05 level.

REFERENCES

1. FISHER, R. A., *Statistical Methods for Research Workers*. Edinburgh and London: Oliver and Boyd, 1936.
2. FRIEDMAN, MILTON, "Use of ranks to avoid the assumption of normality implicit in the analysis of variance," *J. Amer. Statist. Ass.*, 1937, **32**, 675–701.
3. GAITO, J., "Nonparametric methods in psychological research," *Psychol. Rep.*, 1959, **5**, 115–125.
4. KRUSKAL, WILLIAM H., AND WALLIS, W. A., "Use of ranks in one-criterion variance analysis," *J. Amer. Statist. Ass.*, 1952, **47**, 583–621.
5. MANN, H. B., AND WHITNEY, D. R., "On a test of whether one of two random variables is stochastically larger than the other," *Ann. Math. Statist.*, 1947, **18**, 50–60.

6. National Bureau of Standards, Applied Mathematics Series 6, *Tables of Binomial Probability Distribution*. Washington, D.C.: U.S. Government Printing Office.

7. SIEGEL, S., *Nonparametric Statistics*. New York: McGraw-Hill Book Company, Inc., 1956.

8. SPEARMAN, C., "'General Intelligence,' objectively determined and measured," *Am. J. Psychol.*, 1904, **15**, 201–293.

9. SUGISAKI, YO, AND BROWN, WARNER, "The correlation between the sex of observers and the sex of pictures recognized," *J. Exper. Psychol.*, 1916, **1**, 351–354.

10. SWED, F. S., AND EISENHART, C., "Tables for testing randomness of grouping in a sequence of alternatives," *Ann. Math. Statist.*, 1943, **14**, 66–87.

11. TATE, M. W., AND CLELLAND, R. C., *Nonparametric and Shortcut Statistics*. Danville, Ill.: Interstate, 1957.

12. WALKER, HELEN M., AND LEV, JOSEPH, *Statistical Inference*. New York: Holt, Rinehart and Winston, 1953.

13. WILCOXON, FRANK, *Some Rapid Approximate Statistical Procedures*. New York: American Cyanamid Company, 1949.

APPENDIX

Each entry is the proportion of cases between the mean and a point indicated in standard deviation units (that is, x/σ or the z score). The table may be also used to obtain proportions between two points, neither of which is the mean. If the points are on the same side of the mean, the proportion is obtained by subtraction; if on different sides, by addition.

z or x/σ	.00	.01	.02	.03	.04	.05	.06	.07	.08	.09
0.0	.00000	.00399	.00798	.01197	.01595	.01994	.02392	.02790	.03188	.03586
0.1	.03983	.04380	.04776	.05172	.05567	.05962	.06356	.06749	.07142	.07535
0.2	.07926	.08317	.08706	.09095	.09483	.09871	.10257	.10642	.11026	.11409
0.3	.11791	.12172	.12552	.12930	.13307	.13683	.14058	.14431	.14803	.15173
0.4	.15542	.15910	.16276	.16640	.17003	.17364	.17724	.18082	.18439	.18793
0.5	.19146	.19497	.19847	.20194	.20540	.20884	.21226	.21566	.21904	.22240
0.6	.22575	.22907	.23237	.23565	.23891	.24215	.24537	.24857	.25175	.25490
0.7	.25804	.26115	.26424	.26730	.27035	.27337	.27637	.27935	.28230	.28524
0.8	.28814	.29103	.29389	.29673	.29955	.30234	.30511	.30785	.31057	.31327
0.9	.31594	.31859	.32121	.32381	.32639	.32894	.33147	.33398	.33646	.33891
1.0	.34134	.34375	.34614	.34850	.35083	.35314	.35543	.35769	.35993	.36214
1.1	.36433	.36650	.36864	.37076	.37286	.37493	.37698	.37900	.38100	.38298
1.2	.38493	.38686	.38877	.39065	.39251	.39435	.39617	.39796	.39973	.40147
1.3	.40320	.40490	.40658	.40824	.40988	.41149	.41309	.41466	.41621	.41774
1.4	.41924	.42073	.42220	.42364	.42507	.42647	.42786	.42922	.43056	.43189
1.5	.43319	.43448	.43574	.43699	.43822	.43943	.44062	.44179	.44295	.44408
1.6	.44520	.44630	.44738	.44845	.44950	.45053	.45154	.45254	.45352	.45449
1.7	.45543	.45637	.45728	.45818	.45907	.45994	.46080	.46164	.46246	.46327
1.8	.46407	.46485	.46562	.46638	.46712	.46784	.46856	.46926	.46995	.47062
1.9	.47128	.47193	.47257	.47320	.47381	.47441	.47500	.47558	.47615	.47670

z	.00	.01	.02	.03	.04	.05	.06	.07	.08	.09
2.0	.47725	.47778	.47831	.47882	.47932	.47982	.48030	.48077	.48124	.48169
2.1	.48214	.48257	.48300	.48341	.48382	.48422	.48461	.48500	.48537	.48574
2.2	.48610	.48645	.48679	.48713	.48745	.48778	.48809	.48840	.48870	.48899
2.3	.48928	.48956	.48983	.49010	.49036	.49061	.49086	.49111	.49134	.49158
2.4	.49180	.49202	.49224	.49245	.49266	.49286	.49305	.49324	.49343	.49361
2.5	.49379	.49396	.49413	.49430	.49446	.49461	.49477	.49492	.49506	.49520
2.6	.49534	.49547	.49560	.49573	.49585	.49598	.49609	.49621	.49632	.49643
2.7	.49653	.49664	.49674	.49683	.49693	.49702	.49711	.49720	.49728	.49736
2.8	.49744	.49752	.49760	.49767	.49774	.49781	.49788	.49795	.49801	.49807
2.9	.49813	.49819	.49825	.49831	.49836	.49841	.49846	.49851	.49856	.49861
3.0	.49865	.49869	.49874	.49878	.49882	.49886	.49889	.49893	.49897	.49900
3.1	.49903	.49906	.49910	.49913	.49916	.49918	.49921	.49924	.49926	.49929
3.2	.49931	.49934	.49936	.49938	.49940	.49942	.49944	.49946	.49948	.49950
3.3	.49952	.49953	.49955	.49957	.49958	.49960	.49961	.49962	.49964	.49965
3.4	.49966	.49968	.49969	.49970	.49971	.49972	.49973	.49974	.49975	.49976
3.5	.49977	.49978	.49978	.49979	.49980	.49981	.49981	.49982	.49983	.49983
3.6	.49984	.49985	.49985	.49986	.49986	.49987	.49987	.49988	.49988	.49989
3.7	.49989	.49990	.49990	.49990	.49991	.49991	.49992	.49992	.49992	.49992
3.8	.49993	.49993	.49993	.49994	.49994	.49994	.49994	.49995	.49995	.49995
3.9	.49995	.49995	.49996	.49996	.49996	.49996	.49996	.49996	.49997	.49997
4.0	.4999683									
4.1	.4999793									
4.2	.4999867									
4.3	.4999915									
4.4	.4999946									
4.5	.4999966									

a Adapted from Sheppard, W. F., " New Tables of the Probability Integral," *Biometrika*, 1902–3, **2**, 174–190, by permission of the editor.

TABLE C. DISTRIBUTION OF χ^2

df	.50	.20	.10	.05	.02	.01	.001
	P						
1	.455	1.642	2.706	3.841	5.412	6.635	10.827
2	1.386	3.219	4.605	5.991	7.824	9.210	13.815
3	2.366	4.642	6.251	7.815	9.837	11.345	16.266
4	3.357	5.989	7.779	9.488	11.668	13.277	18.467
5	4.351	7.289	9.236	11.070	13.388	15.086	20.515
6	5.348	8.558	10.645	12.592	15.033	16.812	22.457
7	6.346	9.803	12.017	14.067	16.622	18.475	24.322
8	7.344	11.030	13.362	15.507	18.168	20.090	26.125
9	8.343	12.242	14.684	16.919	19.679	21.666	27.877
10	9.342	13.442	15.987	18.307	21.161	23.209	29.588
11	10.341	14.631	17.275	19.675	22.618	24.725	31.264
12	11.340	15.812	18.549	21.026	24.054	26.217	32.909
13	12.340	16.985	19.812	22.362	25.472	27.688	34.528
14	13.339	18.151	21.064	23.685	26.873	29.141	36.123
15	14.339	19.311	22.307	24.996	28.259	30.578	37.697
16	15.338	20.465	23.542	26.296	29.633	32.000	39.252
17	16.338	21.615	24.769	27.587	30.995	33.409	40.790
18	17.338	22.760	25.989	28.869	32.346	34.805	42.312
19	18.338	23.900	27.204	30.144	33.687	36.191	43.820
20	19.337	25.038	28.412	31.410	35.020	37.566	45.315
21	20.337	26.171	29.615	32.671	36.343	38.932	46.797
22	21.337	27.301	30.813	33.924	37.659	40.289	48.268
23	22.337	28.429	32.007	35.172	38.968	41.638	49.728
24	23.337	29.553	33.196	36.415	40.270	42.980	51.179
25	24.337	30.675	34.382	37.652	41.566	44.314	52.620
26	25.336	31.795	35.563	38.885	42.856	45.642	54.052
27	26.336	32.912	36.741	40.113	44.140	46.963	55.476
28	27.336	34.027	37.916	41.337	45.419	48.278	56.893
29	28.336	35.139	39.087	42.557	46.693	49.588	58.302
30	29.336	36.250	40.256	43.773	47.692	50.892	59.703

Note: For larger values of ν, the expression $\sqrt{2\chi^2} - \sqrt{2\nu-1}$ (in which ν is the number of degrees of freedom) may be used as a normal deviate with unit variance remembering that the probability of χ^2 corresponds with that of a single tail of the normal curve.

Source: Table C is abridged from Table IV of Fisher and Yates: "Statistical Tables for Biological, Agricultural and Medical Research," published by Oliver and Boyd Ltd., Edinburgh, and by permission of the authors and publishers.

TABLE E. VALUES OF THE EXPONENTIAL e^{-M} FROM $M = .01$ TO $M = .99$

In a Poisson distribution, $M = \sigma^2$. The probability of any value X, as given by Formula 12.7, is

$$p_x = e^{-M} \frac{M^X}{X!} \qquad (X = 0, 1, 2 \cdots)$$

The following table gives values of e^{-M} from $M = .01$ to $M = .99$, in which e is $2.718 \cdots$, the base of the natural system of logarithms.

M	e^{-M}	M	e^{-M}	M	e^{-M}
.01	.990	.34	.712	.67	.512
.02	.980	.35	.705	.68	.507
.03	.970	.36	.698	.69	.502
.04	.961	.37	.691	.70	.497
.05	.951	.38	.684	.71	.492
.06	.942	.39	.677	.72	.487
.07	.932	.40	.670	.73	.482
.08	.923	.41	.664	.74	.477
.09	.914	.42	.657	.75	.472
.10	.905	.43	.651	.76	.468
.11	.896	.44	.644	.77	.463
.12	.887	.45	.638	.78	.458
.13	.878	.46	.631	.79	.454
.14	.869	.47	.625	.80	.449
.15	.861	.48	.619	.81	.445
.16	.852	.49	.613	.82	.440
.17	.844	.50	.607	.83	.436
.18	.835	.51	.600	.84	.432
.19	.827	.52	.595	.85	.427
.20	.819	.53	.589	.86	.423
.21	.811	.54	.583	.87	.419
.22	.803	.55	.577	.88	.415
.23	.795	.56	.571	.89	.411
.24	.787	.57	.566	.90	.407
.25	.779	.58	.560	.91	.403
.26	.771	.59	.554	.92	.399
.27	.763	.60	.549	.93	.395
.28	.756	.61	.543	.94	.391
.29	.748	.62	.538	.95	.387
.30	.741	.63	.533	.96	.383
.31	.733	.64	.527	.97	.379
.32	.726	.65	.522	.98	.375
.33	.719	.66	.517	.99	.372

TABLE F_1. THE 1 PERCENT POINTS FOR THE DISTRIBUTION OF F

NUMERATOR df

DENO-MINATOR df	1	2	3	4	5	6	8	12	24	∞
1	4052	4999	5403	5625	5764	5859	5982	6106	6234	6366
2	98.50	99.00	99.17	99.25	99.30	99.33	99.37	99.42	99.46	99.50
3	34.12	30.82	29.46	28.71	28.24	27.91	27.49	27.05	26.60	26.12
4	21.20	18.00	16.69	15.98	15.52	15.21	14.80	14.37	13.93	13.46
5	16.26	13.27	12.06	11.39	10.97	10.67	10.29	9.89	9.47	9.02
6	13.74	10.92	9.78	9.15	8.75	8.47	8.10	7.72	7.31	6.88
7	12.25	9.55	8.45	7.85	7.46	7.19	6.84	6.47	6.07	5.65
8	11.26	8.65	7.59	7.01	6.63	6.37	6.03	5.67	5.28	4.86
9	10.56	8.02	6.99	6.42	6.06	5.80	5.47	5.11	4.73	4.31
10	10.04	7.56	6.55	5.99	5.64	5.39	5.06	4.71	4.33	3.91
11	9.65	7.20	6.22	5.67	5.32	5.07	4.74	4.40	4.02	3.60
12	9.33	6.93	5.95	5.41	5.06	4.82	4.50	4.16	3.78	3.36
13	9.07	6.70	5.74	5.20	4.86	4.62	4.30	3.96	3.59	3.16
14	8.86	6.51	5.56	5.03	4.69	4.46	4.14	3.80	3.43	3.00
15	8.68	6.36	5.42	4.89	4.56	4.32	4.00	3.67	3.29	2.87
16	8.53	6.23	5.29	4.77	4.44	4.20	3.89	3.55	3.18	2.75
17	8.40	6.11	5.18	4.67	4.34	4.10	3.79	3.45	3.08	2.65
18	8.28	6.01	5.09	4.58	4.25	4.01	3.71	3.37	3.00	2.57
19	8.18	5.93	5.01	4.50	4.17	3.94	3.63	3.30	2.92	2.49
20	8.10	5.85	4.94	4.43	4.10	3.87	3.56	3.23	2.86	2.42
21	8.02	5.78	4.87	4.37	4.04	3.81	3.51	3.17	2.80	2.36
22	7.94	5.72	4.82	4.31	3.99	3.76	3.45	3.12	2.75	2.31
23	7.88	5.66	4.76	4.26	3.94	3.71	3.41	3.07	2.70	2.26
24	7.82	5.61	4.72	4.22	3.90	3.67	3.36	3.03	2.66	2.21
25	7.77	5.57	4.68	4.18	3.86	3.63	3.32	2.99	2.62	2.17
26	7.72	5.53	4.64	4.14	3.82	3.59	3.29	2.96	2.58	2.13
27	7.68	5.49	4.60	4.11	3.78	3.56	3.26	2.93	2.55	2.10
28	7.64	5.45	4.57	4.07	3.75	3.53	3.23	2.90	2.52	2.06
29	7.60	5.42	4.54	4.04	3.73	3.50	3.20	2.87	2.49	2.03
30	7.56	5.39	4.51	4.02	3.70	3.47	3.17	2.84	2.47	2.01
40	7.31	5.18	4.31	3.83	3.51	3.29	2.99	2.66	2.29	1.80
60	7.08	4.98	4.13	3.65	3.34	3.12	2.82	2.50	2.12	1.60
120	6.85	4.79	3.95	3.48	3.17	2.96	2.66	2.34	1.95	1.38
∞	6.64	4.60	3.78	3.32	3.02	2.80	2.51	2.18	1.79	1.00

Note: In using this table, the greater mean square must be the numerator of F. (The 5 percent points for the distribution of F are on page 489.)

Source: Table F_1 is abridged from Table V of Fisher and Yates: "Statistical Tables for Biological, Agricultural and Medical Research," published by Oliver and Boyd Ltd., Edinburgh, and by permission of the authors and publishers.

TABLE F₅. THE 5 PERCENT POINTS FOR THE DISTRIBUTION OF *F*

NUMERATOR *df*

DENO-MINATOR *df*	1	2	3	4	5	6	8	12	24	∞
1	161.4	199.5	215.7	224.6	230.2	234.0	238.9	243.9	249.0	254.3
2	18.51	19.00	19.16	19.25	19.30	19.33	19.37	19.41	19.45	19.50
3	10.13	9.55	9.28	9.12	9.01	8.94	8.84	8.74	8.64	8.53
4	7.71	6.94	6.59	6.39	6.26	6.16	6.04	5.91	5.77	5.63
5	6.61	5.79	5.41	5.19	5.05	4.95	4.82	4.68	4.53	4.36
6	5.99	5.14	4.76	4.53	4.39	4.28	4.15	4.00	3.84	3.67
7	5.59	4.74	4.35	4.12	3.97	3.87	3.73	3.57	3.41	3.23
8	5.32	4.46	4.07	3.84	3.69	3.58	3.44	3.28	3.12	2.93
9	5.12	4.26	3.86	3.63	3.48	3.37	3.23	3.07	2.90	2.71
10	4.96	4.10	3.71	3.48	3.33	3.22	3.07	2.91	2.74	2.54
11	4.84	3.98	3.59	3.36	3.20	3.09	2.95	2.79	2.61	2.40
12	4.75	3.88	3.49	3.26	3.11	3.00	2.85	2.69	2.50	2.30
13	4.67	3.80	3.41	3.18	3.02	2.92	2.77	2.60	2.42	2.21
14	4.60	3.74	3.34	3.11	2.96	2.85	2.70	2.53	2.35	2.13
15	4.54	3.68	3.29	3.06	2.90	2.79	2.64	2.48	2.29	2.07
16	4.49	3.63	3.24	3.01	2.85	2.74	2.59	2.42	2.24	2.01
17	4.45	3.59	3.20	2.96	2.81	2.70	2.55	2.38	2.19	1.96
18	4.41	3.55	3.16	2.93	2.77	2.66	2.51	2.34	2.15	1.92
19	4.38	3.52	3.13	2.90	2.74	2.63	2.48	2.31	2.11	1.88
20	4.35	3.49	3.10	2.87	2.71	2.60	2.45	2.28	2.08	1.84
21	4.32	3.47	3.07	2.84	2.68	2.57	2.42	2.25	2.05	1.81
22	4.30	3.44	3.05	2.82	2.66	2.55	2.40	2.23	2.03	1.78
23	4.28	3.42	3.03	2.80	2.64	2.53	2.38	2.20	2.00	1.76
24	4.26	3.40	3.01	2.78	2.62	2.51	2.36	2.18	1.98	1.73
25	4.24	3.38	2.99	2.76	2.60	2.49	2.34	2.16	1.96	1.71
26	4.22	3.37	2.98	2.74	2.59	2.47	2.32	2.15	1.95	1.69
27	4.21	3.35	2.96	2.73	2.57	2.46	2.30	2.13	1.93	1.67
28	4.20	3.34	2.95	2.71	2.56	2.44	2.29	2.12	1.91	1.65
29	4.18	3.33	2.93	2.70	2.54	2.43	2.28	2.10	1.90	1.64
30	4.17	3.32	2.92	2.69	2.53	2.42	2.27	2.09	1.89	1.62
40	4.08	3.23	2.84	2.61	2.45	2.34	2.18	2.00	1.79	1.51
60	4.00	3.15	2.76	2.52	2.37	2.25	2.10	1.92	1.70	1.39
120	3.92	3.07	2.68	2.45	2.29	2.17	2.02	1.83	1.61	1.25
∞	3.84	2.99	2.60	2.37	2.21	2.10	1.94	1.75	1.52	1.00

Note: In using this table, the greater mean square must be the numerator of *F*. (The 1 percent points for the distribution of *F* are on page 488.)

Source: Table F₅ is abridged from Table V of Fisher and Yates: "Statistical Tables for Biological, Agricultural and Medical Research," published by Oliver and Boyd Ltd., Edinburgh, and by permission of the authors and publishers.

TABLE O. ORDINATES OF THE NORMAL PROBABILITY CURVE[a]

This table gives values of y, the ordinate of the normal curve, corresponding to values of z, the distance in standard deviation units above or below the mean, in accordance with Formulas 11.5 and 11.5a.
The normal curve (Formula 11.5a) is

$$y = \frac{.39894}{e^{Z^2/2}}$$

z or x/σ	.00	.01	.02	.03	.04	.05	.06	.07	.08	.09
0.0	.39894	.39892	.39886	.39876	.39862	.39844	.39822	.39797	.39767	.39733
0.1	.39695	.39654	.39608	.39559	.39505	.39448	.39387	.39322	.39253	.39181
0.2	.39104	.39024	.38940	.38853	.38762	.38667	.38568	.38466	.38361	.38251
0.3	.38139	.38023	.37903	.37780	.37654	.37524	.37391	.37255	.37115	.36973
0.4	.36827	.36678	.36526	.36371	.36213	.36053	.35889	.35723	.35553	.35381
0.5	.35207	.35029	.34849	.34667	.34482	.34294	.34105	.33912	.33718	.33521
0.6	.33322	.33121	.32918	.32713	.32506	.32297	.32086	.31874	.31659	.31443
0.7	.31225	.31006	.30785	.30563	.30339	.30114	.29887	.29659	.29431	.29200
0.8	.28969	.28737	.28504	.28269	.28034	.27798	.27562	.27324	.27086	.26848
0.9	.26609	.26369	.26129	.25888	.25647	.25406	.25164	.24923	.24681	.24439
1.0	.24197	.23955	.23713	.23471	.23230	.22988	.22747	.22506	.22265	.22025
1.1	.21785	.21546	.21307	.21069	.20831	.20594	.20357	.20121	.19886	.19652
1.2	.19419	.19186	.18954	.18724	.18494	.18265	.18037	.17810	.17585	.17360
1.3	.17137	.16915	.16694	.16474	.16256	.16038	.15822	.15608	.15395	.15183
1.4	.14973	.14764	.14556	.14350	.14146	.13943	.13742	.13542	.13344	.13147
1.5	.12952	.12758	.12566	.12376	.12188	.12001	.11816	.11632	.11450	.11270
1.6	.11092	.10915	.10741	.10567	.10396	.10226	.10059	.09893	.09728	.09566
1.7	.09405	.09246	.09089	.08933	.08780	.08628	.08478	.08329	.08183	.08038
1.8	.07895	.07754	.07614	.07477	.07341	.07206	.07074	.06943	.06814	.06687
1.9	.06562	.06438	.06316	.06195	.06077	.05959	.05844	.05730	.05618	.05508

x	.00	.01	.02	.03	.04	.05	.06	.07	.08	.09
2.0	.05399	.05292	.05186	.05082	.04980	.04879	.04780	.04682	.04586	.04491
2.1	.04398	.04307	.04217	.04128	.04041	.03955	.03871	.03788	.03706	.03626
2.2	.03547	.03470	.03394	.03319	.03246	.03174	.03103	.03034	.02965	.02898
2.3	.02833	.02768	.02705	.02643	.02582	.02522	.02463	.02406	.02349	.02294
2.4	.02239	.02186	.02134	.02083	.02033	.01984	.01936	.01889	.01842	.01797
2.5	.01753	.01709	.01667	.01625	.01585	.01545	.01506	.01468	.01431	.01394
2.6	.01358	.01323	.01289	.01256	.01223	.01191	.01160	.01130	.01100	.01071
2.7	.01042	.01014	.00987	.00961	.00935	.00909	.00885	.00861	.00837	.00814
2.8	.00792	.00770	.00748	.00727	.00707	.00687	.00668	.00649	.00631	.00613
2.9	.00595	.00578	.00562	.00545	.00530	.00514	.00499	.00485	.00471	.00457
3.0	.00443	.00430	.00417	.00405	.00393	.00381	.00370	.00358	.00348	.00337
3.1	.00327	.00317	.00307	.00298	.00288	.00279	.00271	.00262	.00254	.00246
3.2	.00238	.00231	.00224	.00216	.00210	.00203	.00196	.00190	.00184	.00178
3.3	.00172	.00167	.00161	.00156	.00151	.00146	.00141	.00136	.00132	.00127
3.4	.00123	.00119	.00115	.00111	.00107	.00104	.00100	.00097	.00094	.00090
3.5	.00087	.00084	.00081	.00079	.00076	.00073	.00071	.00068	.00066	.00063
3.6	.00061	.00059	.00057	.00055	.00053	.00051	.00049	.00047	.00046	.00044
3.7	.00042	.00041	.00039	.00038	.00037	.00035	.00034	.00033	.00031	.00030
3.8	.00029	.00028	.00027	.00026	.00025	.00024	.00023	.00022	.00021	.00021
3.9	.00020	.00019	.00018	.00018	.00017	.00016	.00016	.00015	.00014	.00014
4.0	.00013									
4.1	.00009									
4.2	.00006									
4.3	.00004									
4.4	.00002									
4.5	.00002									

a Adapted from Sheppard, W. F., "New Tables of the Probability Integral," *Biometrika*, 1902–1903, **2**, 174–190, by permission of the editor.

TABLE P. VALUES OF $\sqrt{p/q}$ AND $\sqrt{q/p}$ AND OF y, THE ORDINATE OF THE NORMAL CURVE

$$(p+q)=1$$

p	q	$\sqrt{p/q}$	$\sqrt{q/p}$	y	p	q	$\sqrt{p/q}$	$\sqrt{q/p}$	y
.01	.99	.1005	9.9499	.0267	.51	.49	1.0202	.9802	.3988
.02	.98	.1429	7.0000	.0484	.52	.48	1.0408	.9608	.3984
.03	.97	.1759	5.6862	.0680	.53	.47	1.0619	.9417	.3978
.04	.96	.2041	4.8990	.0862	.54	.46	1.0835	.9230	.3969
.05	.95	.2294	4.3589	.1031	.55	.45	1.1055	.9045	.3958
.06	.94	.2526	3.9581	.1191	.56	.44	1.1282	.8864	.3944
.07	.93	.2744	3.6450	.1343	.57	.43	1.1513	.8686	.3928
.08	.92	.2949	3.3912	.1487	.58	.42	1.1751	.8510	.3909
.09	.91	.3145	3.1798	.1624	.59	.41	1.1996	.8336	.3887
.10	.90	.3333	3.0000	.1755	.60	.40	1.2247	.8165	.3863
.11	.89	.3516	2.8445	.1880	.61	.39	1.2506	.7996	.3837
.12	.88	.3693	2.7080	.2000	.62	.38	1.2773	.7829	.3808
.13	.87	.3866	2.5870	.2115	.63	.37	1.3049	.7664	.3776
.14	.86	.4035	2.4785	.2226	.64	.36	1.3333	.7500	.3741
.15	.85	.4201	2.3805	.2332	.65	.35	1.3628	.7338	.3704
.16	.84	.4364	2.2913	.2433	.66	.34	1.3933	.7177	.3664
.17	.83	.4526	2.2096	.2531	.67	.33	1.4249	.7018	.3621
.18	.82	.4685	2.1344	.2624	.68	.32	1.4577	.6860	.3576
.19	.81	.4843	2.0647	.2714	.69	.31	1.4919	.6703	.3528
.20	.80	.5000	2.0000	.2800	.70	.30	1.5275	.6547	.3477
.21	.79	.5156	1.9396	.2882	.71	.29	1.5647	.6391	.3423
.22	.78	.5311	1.8829	.2961	.72	.28	1.6036	.6236	.3366
.23	.77	.5465	1.8297	.3036	.73	.27	1.6443	.6082	.3306
.24	.76	.5620	1.7795	.3109	.74	.26	1.6871	.5927	.3244
.25	.75	.5774	1.7321	.3178	.75	.25	1.7321	.5774	.3178
.26	.74	.5927	1.6871	.3244	.76	.24	1.7795	.5620	.3109
.27	.73	.6082	1.6443	.3306	.77	.23	1.8297	.5465	.3036
.28	.72	.6236	1.6036	.3366	.78	.22	1.8829	.5311	.2961
.29	.71	.6391	1.5647	.3423	.79	.21	1.9396	.5156	.2882
.30	.70	.6547	1.5275	.3477	.80	.20	2.0000	.5000	.2800
.31	.69	.6703	1.4919	.3528	.81	.19	2.0647	.4843	.2714
.32	.68	.6860	1.4577	.3576	.82	.18	2.1344	.4685	.2624
.33	.67	.7018	1.4249	.3621	.83	.17	2.2096	.4526	.2531
.34	.66	.7177	1.3933	.3664	.84	.16	2.2913	.4364	.2433
.35	.65	.7338	1.3628	.3704	.85	.15	2.3805	.4201	.2332
.36	.64	.7500	1.3333	.3741	.86	.14	2.4785	.4035	.2226
.37	.63	.7664	1.3049	.3776	.87	.13	2.5870	.3866	.2115
.38	.62	.7829	1.2773	.3808	.88	.12	2.7080	.3693	.2000
.39	.61	.7996	1.2506	.3837	.89	.11	2.8445	.3516	.1880
.40	.60	.8165	1.2247	.3863	.90	.10	3.0000	.3333	.1755
.41	.59	.8336	1.1996	.3887	.91	.09	3.1798	.3145	.1624
.42	.58	.8510	1.1751	.3909	.92	.08	3.3912	.2949	.1487
.43	.57	.8686	1.1513	.3928	.93	.07	3.6450	.2744	.1343
.44	.56	.8864	1.1282	.3944	.94	.06	3.9581	.2526	.1191
.45	.55	.9045	1.1055	.3958	.95	.05	4.3589	.2294	.1031
.46	.54	.9230	1.0835	.3969	.96	.04	4.8990	.2041	.0862
.47	.53	.9417	1.0619	.3978	.97	.03	5.6862	.1759	.0680
.48	.52	.9608	1.0408	.3984	.98	.02	7.0000	.1429	.0484
.49	.51	.9802	1.0202	.3988	.99	.01	9.9499	.1005	.0267
.50	.50	1.0000	1.0000	.3989					

TABLE R. CRITICAL VALUES OF THE CORRELATION COEFFICIENT

	LEVEL OF SIGNIFICANCE FOR ONE-TAILED TEST			
	.05	.025	.01	.005
	LEVEL OF SIGNIFICANCE FOR TWO-TAILED TEST			
df	.10	.05	.02	.01
1	.9877	.9969	.9995	.9999
2	.9000	.9500	.9800	.9900
3	.8054	.8783	.9343	.9587
4	.7293	.8114	.8822	.9172
5	.6694	.7545	.8329	.8745
6	.6215	.7067	.7887	.8343
7	.5822	.6664	.7498	.7977
8	.5494	.6319	.7155	.7646
9	.5214	.6021	.6851	.7348
10	4973	.5760	.6581	.7079
11	.4762	.5529	.6339	.6835
12	.4575	.5324	.6120	.6614
13	.4409	.5139	.5923	.6411
14	.4259	.4973	.5742	.6226
15	.4124	.4821	.5577	.6055
16	.4000	.4683	.5425	.5897
17	.3887	.4555	.5285	.5751
18	.3783	.4438	.5155	.5614
19	.3687	.4329	.5034	.5487
20	.3598	.4227	.4921	.5368
25	.3233	.3809	.4451	.4869
30	.2960	.3494	.4093	.4487
35	.2746	.3246	.3810	.4182
40	.2573	.3044	.3578	.3932
45	.2428	.2875	.3384	.3721
50	.2306	.2732	.3218	.3541
60	.2108	.2500	.2948	.3248
70	.1954	.2319	.2737	.3017
80	.1829	.2172	.2565	.2830
90	.1726	.2050	.2422	.2673
100	.1638	.1946	.2301	.2540

Source: Table R is abridged from Table VI of Fisher and Yates: "Statistical Tables for Biological, Agricultural and Medical Research," published by Oliver and Boyd Ltd., Edinburgh, and by permission of the authors and publishers.

TABLE SQ. SQUARES OF NUMBERS FROM 1. TO 99.9

For numbers from 1 to 999, move decimal point of square two places to the right; for numbers from .01 to 9.99, move decimal point two places to the left.

	.0	.1	.2	.3	.4	.5	.6	.7	.8	.9
00.	...	.01	.04	.09	.16	.25	.36	.49	.64	.81
01.	1.00	1.21	1.44	1.69	1.96	2.25	2.56	2.89	3.24	3.61
02.	4.00	4.41	4.84	5.29	5.76	6.25	6.76	7.29	7.84	8.41
03.	9.00	9.61	10.24	10.89	11.56	12.25	12.96	13.69	14.44	15.21
04.	16.00	16.81	17.64	18.49	19.36	20.25	21.16	22.09	23.04	24.01
05.	25.00	26.01	27.04	28.09	29.16	30.25	31.36	32.49	33.64	34.81
06.	36.00	37.21	38.44	39.69	40.96	42.25	43.56	44.89	46.24	47.61
07.	49.00	50.41	51.84	53.29	54.76	56.25	57.76	59.29	60.84	62.41
08.	64.00	65.61	67.24	68.89	70.56	72.25	73.96	75.69	77.44	79.21
09.	81.00	82.81	84.64	86.49	88.36	90.25	92.16	94.09	96.04	98.01
10.	100.00	102.01	104.04	106.09	108.16	110.25	112.36	114.49	116.64	118.81
11.	121.00	123.21	125.44	127.69	129.96	132.25	134.56	136.89	139.24	141.61
12.	144.00	146.41	148.84	151.29	153.76	156.25	158.76	161.29	163.84	166.41
13.	169.00	171.61	174.24	176.89	179.56	182.25	184.96	187.69	190.44	193.21
14.	196.00	198.81	201.64	204.49	207.36	210.25	213.16	216.09	219.04	222.01
15.	225.00	228.01	231.04	234.09	237.16	240.25	243.36	246.49	249.64	252.81
16.	256.00	259.21	262.44	265.69	268.96	272.25	275.56	278.89	282.24	285.61
17.	289.00	292.41	295.84	299.29	302.76	306.25	309.76	313.29	316.84	320.41
18.	324.00	327.61	331.24	334.89	338.56	342.25	345.96	349.69	353.44	357.21
19.	361.00	364.81	368.64	372.49	376.36	380.25	384.16	388.09	392.04	396.01
20.	400.00	404.01	408.04	412.09	416.16	420.25	424.36	428.49	432.64	436.81
21.	441.00	445.21	449.44	453.69	457.96	462.25	466.56	470.89	475.24	479.61
22.	484.00	488.41	492.84	497.29	501.76	506.25	510.76	515.29	519.84	524.41
23.	529.00	533.61	538.24	542.89	547.56	552.25	556.96	561.69	566.44	571.21
24.	576.00	580.81	585.64	590.49	595.36	600.25	605.16	610.09	615.04	620.01

	0	1	2	3	4	5	6	7	8	9
25.	625.00	630.01	635.04	640.09	645.16	650.25	655.36	660.49	665.64	670.81
26.	676.00	681.21	686.44	691.69	696.96	702.25	707.56	712.89	718.24	723.61
27.	729.00	734.41	739.84	745.29	750.76	756.25	761.76	767.29	772.84	778.41
28.	784.00	789.61	795.24	800.89	806.56	812.25	817.96	823.69	829.44	835.21
29.	841.00	846.81	852.64	858.49	864.36	870.25	876.16	882.09	888.04	894.01
30.	900.00	906.01	912.04	918.09	924.16	930.25	936.36	942.49	948.64	954.81
31.	961.00	967.21	973.44	979.69	985.96	992.25	998.56	1004.89	1011.24	1017.61
32.	1024.00	1030.41	1036.84	1043.29	1049.76	1056.25	1062.76	1069.29	1075.84	1082.41
33.	1089.00	1095.61	1102.24	1108.89	1115.56	1122.25	1128.96	1135.69	1142.44	1149.21
34.	1156.00	1162.81	1169.64	1176.49	1183.36	1190.25	1197.16	1204.09	1211.04	1218.01
35.	1225.00	1232.01	1239.04	1246.09	1253.16	1260.25	1267.36	1274.49	1281.64	1288.81
36.	1296.00	1303.21	1310.44	1317.69	1324.96	1332.25	1339.56	1346.89	1354.24	1361.61
37.	1369.00	1376.41	1383.84	1391.29	1398.76	1406.25	1413.76	1421.29	1428.84	1436.41
38.	1444.00	1451.61	1459.24	1466.89	1474.56	1482.25	1489.96	1497.69	1505.44	1513.21
39.	1521.00	1528.81	1536.64	1544.49	1552.36	1560.25	1568.16	1576.09	1584.04	1592.01
40.	1600.00	1608.01	1616.04	1624.09	1632.16	1640.25	1648.36	1656.49	1664.64	1672.81
41.	1681.00	1689.21	1697.44	1705.69	1713.96	1722.25	1730.56	1738.89	1747.24	1755.61
42.	1764.00	1772.41	1780.84	1789.29	1797.76	1806.25	1814.76	1823.29	1831.84	1840.41
43.	1849.00	1857.61	1866.24	1874.89	1883.56	1892.25	1900.96	1909.69	1918.44	1927.21
44.	1936.00	1944.81	1953.64	1962.49	1971.36	1980.25	1989.16	1998.09	2007.04	2016.01
45.	2025.00	2034.01	2043.04	2052.09	2061.16	2070.25	2079.36	2088.49	2097.64	2106.81
46.	2116.00	2125.21	2134.44	2143.69	2152.96	2162.25	2171.56	2180.89	2190.24	2199.61
47.	2209.00	2218.41	2227.84	2237.29	2246.76	2256.25	2265.76	2275.29	2284.84	2294.41
48.	2304.00	2313.61	2323.24	2332.89	2342.56	2352.25	2361.96	2371.69	2381.44	2391.21
49.	2401.00	2410.81	2420.64	2430.49	2440.36	2450.25	2460.16	2470.89	2480.04	2490.01

TABLE SQ (continued)

	.0	.1	.2	.3	.4	.5	.6	.7	.8	.9
50.	2500.00	2510.01	2520.04	2530.09	2540.16	2550.25	2560.36	2570.49	2580.64	2590.81
51.	2601.00	2611.21	2621.44	2631.69	2641.96	2652.25	2662.56	2672.89	2683.24	2693.61
52.	2704.00	2714.41	2724.84	2735.29	2745.76	2756.25	2766.76	2777.29	2787.84	2798.41
53.	2809.00	2819.61	2830.24	2840.89	2851.56	2862.25	2872.96	2883.69	2894.44	2905.21
54.	2916.00	2926.81	2937.64	2948.49	2959.36	2970.25	2981.16	2992.09	3003.04	3014.01
55.	3025.00	3036.01	3047.04	3058.09	3069.16	3080.25	3091.36	3102.49	3113.64	3124.81
56.	3136.00	3147.21	3158.44	3169.69	3180.96	3192.25	3203.56.	3214.89	3226.24	3237.61
57.	3249.00	3260.41	3271.84	3283.29	3294.76	3306.25	3317.76	3329.29	3340.84	3352.41
58.	3364.00	3375.61	3387.24	3398.89	3410.56	3422.25	3433.96	3445.69	3457.44	3469.21
59.	3481.00	3492.81	3504.64	3516.49	3528.36	3540.25	3552.16	3564.09	3576.04	3588.01
60.	3600.00	3612.01	3624.04	3636.09	3648.16	3660.25	3672.36	3684.49	3696.64	3708.81
61.	3721.00	3733.21	3745.44	3757.69	3769.96	3782.25	3794.56	3806.89	3819.24	3831.61
62.	3844.00	3856.41	3868.84	3881.29	3893.76	3906.25	3918.76	3931.29	3943.84	3956.41
63.	3969.00	3981.61	3994.24	4006.89	4019.56	4032.25	4044.96	4057.69	4070.44	4083.21
64.	4096.00	4108.81	4121.64	4134.49	4147.36	4160.25	4173.16	4186.09	4199.04	4212.01
65.	4225.00	4238.01	4251.04	4264.09	4277.16	4290.25	4303.36	4316.49	4329.64	4342.81
66.	4356.00	4369.21	4382.44	4395.69	4408.96	4422.25	4435.56	4448.89	4462.24	4475.61
67.	4489.00	4502.41	4515.84	4529.29	4542.76	4556.25	4569.76	4583.29	4596.84	4610.41
68.	4624.00	4637.61	4651.24	4664.89	4678.56	4692.25	4705.96	4719.69	4733.44	4747.21
69.	4761.00	4774.81	4788.64	4802.49	4816.36	4830.25	4844.16	4858.09	4872.04	4886.01
70.	4900.00	4914.01	4928.04	4942.09	4956.16	4970.25	4984.36	4998.49	5012.64	5026.81
71.	5041.00	5055.21	5069.44	5083.69	5097.96	5112.25	5126.56	5140.89	5155.24	5169.61
72.	5184.00	5198.41	5212.84	5227.29	5241.76	5256.25	5270.76	5285.29	5299.84	5314.41
73.	5329.00	5343.61	5358.24	5372.89	5387.56	5402.25	5416.96	5431.69	5446.44	5461.21
74.	5476.00	5490.81	5505.64	5520.49	5535.36	5550.25	5565.16	5580.09	5595.04	5610.01

	0	1	2	3	4	5	6	7	8	9
75.	5625.00	5640.01	5655.04	5670.09	5685.16	5700.25	5715.36	5730.49	5745.64	5760.81
76.	5776.00	5791.21	5806.44	5821.69	5836.96	5852.25	5867.56	5882.89	5898.24	5913.61
77.	5929.00	5944.41	5959.84	5975.29	5990.76	6006.25	6021.76	6037.29	6052.84	6068.41
78.	6084.00	6099.61	6115.24	6130.89	6146.56	6162.25	6177.96	6193.69	6209.44	6225.21
79.	6241.00	6256.81	6272.64	6288.49	6304.36	6320.25	6336.16	6352.09	6368.04	6384.01
80.	6400.00	6416.01	6432.04	6448.09	6464.16	6480.25	6496.36	6512.49	6528.64	6544.81
81.	6561.00	6577.21	6593.44	6609.69	6625.96	6642.25	6658.56	6674.89	6691.24	6707.61
82.	6724.00	6740.41	6756.84	6773.29	6789.76	6806.25	6822.76	6839.29	6855.84	6872.41
83.	6889.00	6905.61	6922.24	6938.89	6955.56	6972.25	6988.96	7005.69	7022.44	7039.21
84.	7056.00	7072.81	7089.64	7106.49	7123.36	7140.25	7157.16	7174.09	7191.04	7208.01
85.	7225.00	7242.01	7259.04	7276.09	7293.16	7310.25	7327.36	7344.49	7361.64	7378.81
86.	7396.00	7413.21	7430.44	7447.69	7464.96	7482.25	7499.56	7516.89	7534.24	7551.61
87.	7569.00	7586.41	7603.84	7621.29	7638.76	7656.25	7673.76	7691.29	7708.84	7726.41
88.	7744.00	7761.61	7779.24	7796.89	7814.56	7832.25	7849.96	7867.69	7885.44	7903.21
89.	7921.00	7938.81	7956.64	7974.49	7992.36	8010.25	8028.16	8046.09	8064.04	8082.01
90.	8100.00	8118.01	8136.04	8154.09	8172.16	8190.25	8208.36	8226.49	8244.64	8262.81
91.	8281.00	8299.21	8317.44	8335.69	8353.96	8372.25	8390.56	8408.89	8427.24	8445.61
92.	8464.00	8482.41	8500.84	8519.29	8537.76	8556.25	8574.76	8593.29	8611.84	8630.41
93.	8649.00	8667.61	8686.24	8704.89	8723.56	8742.25	8760.96	8779.69	8798.44	8817.21
94.	8836.00	8854.81	8873.64	8892.49	8911.36	8930.25	8949.16	8968.09	8987.04	9006.01
95.	9025.00	9044.01	9063.04	9082.09	9101.16	9120.25	9139.36	9158.49	9177.64	9196.81
96.	9216.00	9235.21	9254.44	9273.69	9292.96	9312.25	9331.56	9350.89	9370.24	9389.61
97.	9409.00	9428.41	9447.84	9467.29	9486.76	9506.25	9525.76	9545.29	9564.84	9584.41
98.	9604.00	9623.61	9643.24	9662.89	9682.56	9702.25	9721.96	9741.69	9761.44	9781.21
99.	9801.00	9820.81	9840.64	9860.49	9880.36	9900.25	9920.16	9940.09	9960.04	9980.01

TABLE SR. SQUARE ROOTS OF INTEGERS FROM 1 TO 999

The first two digits (including zeroes) of each three-digit number are indicated at the left; the units digit is shown at the top of the column.

	**0	**1	**2	**3	**4	**5	**6	**7	**8	**9
00*	...	1.0000	1.4142	1.7321	2.0000	2.2361	2.4495	2.6458	2.8284	3.0000
01*	3.1623	3.3166	3.4641	3.6056	3.7417	3.8730	4.0000	4.1231	4.2426	4.3589
02*	4.4721	4.5826	4.6904	4.7958	4.8990	5.0000	5.0990	5.1962	5.2915	5.3852
03*	5.4772	5.5678	5.6569	5.7446	5.8310	5.9161	6.0000	6.0828	6.1644	6.2450
04*	6.3246	6.4031	6.4807	6.5574	6.6332	6.7082	6.7823	6.8557	6.9282	7.0000
05*	7.0711	7.1414	7.2111	7.2801	7.3485	7.4162	7.4833	7.5498	7.6158	7.6811
06*	7.7460	7.8102	7.8740	7.9373	8.0000	8.0623	8.1240	8.1854	8.2462	8.3066
07*	8.3666	8.4261	8.4853	8.5440	8.6023	8.6603	8.7178	8.7750	8.8318	8.8882
08*	8.9443	9.0000	9.0554	9.1104	9.1652	9.2195	9.2736	9.3274	9.3808	9.4340
09*	9.4868	9.5394	9.5917	9.6437	9.6954	9.7468	9.7980	9.8489	9.8995	9.9499
10*	10.0000	10.0499	10.0995	10.1489	10.1980	10.2470	10.2956	10.3441	10.3923	10.4403
11*	10.4881	10.5357	10.5830	10.6301	10.6771	10.7238	10.7703	10.8167	10.8628	10.9087
12*	10.9545	11.0000	11.0454	11.0905	11.1355	11.1803	11.2250	11.2694	11.3137	11.3578
13*	11.4018	11.4455	11.4891	11.5326	11.5758	11.6190	11.6619	11.7047	11.7473	11.7898
14*	11.8322	11.8743	11.9164	11.9583	12.0000	12.0416	12.0830	12.1244	12.1655	12.2066
15*	12.2474	12.2882	12.3288	12.3693	12.4097	12.4499	12.4900	12.5300	12.5698	12.6095
16*	12.6491	12.6886	12.7279	12.7671	12.8062	12.8452	12.8841	12.9228	12.9615	13.0000
17*	13.0384	13.0767	13.1149	13.1529	13.1909	13.2288	13.2665	13.3041	13.3417	13.3791
18*	13.4164	13.4536	13.4907	13.5277	13.5647	13.6015	13.6382	13.6748	13.7113	13.7477
19*	13.7840	13.8203	13.8564	13.8924	13.9284	13.9642	14.0000	14.0357	14.0712	14.1067
20*	14.1421	14.1774	14.2127	14.2478	14.2829	14.3178	14.3527	14.3875	14.4222	14.4568
21*	14.4914	14.5258	14.5602	14.5945	14.6287	14.6629	14.6969	14.7309	14.7648	14.7986
22*	14.8324	14.8661	14.8997	14.9332	14.9666	15.0000	15.0333	15.0665	15.0997	15.1327
23*	15.1658	15.1987	15.2315	15.2643	15.2971	15.3297	15.3623	15.3948	15.4272	15.4596
24*	15.4919	15.5242	15.5563	15.5885	15.6205	15.6525	15.6844	15.7162	15.7480	15.7797

25*	15.8114	15.8430	15.8745	15.9060	15.9374	15.9687	16.0000	16.0312	16.0624	16.0935
26*	16.1245	16.1555	16.1864	16.2173	16.2481	16.2788	16.3095	16.3401	16.3707	16.4012
27*	16.4317	16.4621	16.4924	16.5227	16.5529	16.5831	16.6132	16.6433	16.6733	16.7033
28*	16.7332	16.7631	16.7929	16.8226	16.8523	16.8819	16.9115	16.9411	16.9706	17.0000
29*	17.0294	17.0587	17.0880	17.1172	17.1464	17.1756	17.2047	17.2337	17.2627	17.2916
30*	17.3205	17.3494	17.3781	17.4069	17.4356	17.4642	17.4929	17.5214	17.5499	17.5784
31*	17.6068	17.6352	17.6635	17.6918	17.7200	17.7482	17.7764	17.8045	17.8326	17.8606
32*	17.8885	17.9165	17.9444	17.9722	18.0000	18.0278	18.0555	18.0831	18.1108	18.1384
33*	18.1659	18.1934	18.2209	18.2483	18.2757	18.3030	18.3303	18.3576	18.3848	18.4120
34*	18.4391	18.4662	18.4932	18.5203	18.5472	18.5742	18.6011	18.6279	18.6548	18.6815
35*	18.7083	18.7350	18.7617	18.7883	18.8149	18.8414	18.8680	18.8944	18.9209	18.9473
36*	18.9737	19.0000	19.0263	19.0526	19.0788	19.1050	19.1311	19.1572	19.1833	19.2094
37*	19.2354	19.2614	19.2873	19.3132	19.3391	19.3649	19.3907	19.4165	19.4422	19.4679
38*	19.4936	19.5192	19.5448	19.5704	19.5959	19.6214	19.6469	19.6723	19.6977	19.7231
39*	19.7484	19.7737	19.7990	19.8242	19.8494	19.8746	19.8997	19.9249	19.9499	19.9750
40*	20.0000	20.0250	20.0499	20.0749	20.0998	20.1246	20.1494	20.1742	20.1990	20.2237
41*	20.2485	20.2731	20.2978	20.3224	20.3470	20.3715	20.3961	20.4206	20.4450	20.4695
42*	20.4939	20.5183	20.5426	20.5670	20.5913	20.6155	20.6398	20.6640	20.6882	20.7123
43*	20.7364	20.7605	20.7846	20.8087	20.8327	20.8567	20.8806	20.9045	20.9284	20.9523
44*	20.9762	21.0000	21.0238	21.0476	21.0713	21.0950	21.1187	21.1424	21.1660	21.1896
45*	21.2132	21.2368	21.2603	21.2838	21.3073	21.3307	21.3542	21.3776	21.4009	21.4243
46*	21.4476	21.4709	21.4942	21.5174	21.5407	21.5639	21.5870	21.6102	21.6333	21.6564
47*	21.6795	21.7025	21.7256	21.7486	21.7715	21.7945	21.8174	21.8403	21.8632	21.8861
48*	21.9089	21.9317	21.9545	21.9773	22.0000	22.0227	22.0454	22.0681	22.0907	22.1133
49*	22.1359	22.1585	22.1811	22.2036	22.2261	22.2486	22.2711	22.2935	22.3159	22.3383

The first two digits (including zeroes) of each three-digit number are indicated at the left; the units digit is shown at the top of the column.

	**0	**1	**2	**3	**4	**5	**6	**7	**8	**9
50*	22.3607	22.3830	22.4054	22.4277	22.4499	22.4722	22.4944	22.5167	22.5389	22.5610
51*	22.5832	22.6053	22.6274	22.6495	22.6716	22.6936	22.7156	22.7376	22.7596	22.7816
52*	22.8035	22.8254	22.8473	22.8692	22.8910	22.9129	22.9347	22.9565	22.9783	23.0000
53*	23.0217	23.0434	23.0651	23.0868	23.1084	23.1301	23.1517	23.1733	23.1948	23.2164
54*	23.2379	23.2594	23.2809	23.3024	23.3238	23.3452	23.3666	23.3880	23.4094	23.4307
55*	23.4521	23.4734	23.4947	23.5160	23.5372	23.5584	23.5797	23.6008	23.6220	23.6432
56*	23.6643	23.6854	23.7065	23.7276	23.7487	23.7697	23.7908	23.8118	23.8328	23.8537
57*	23.8747	23.8956	23.9165	23.9374	23.9583	23.9792	24.0000	24.0208	24.0416	24.0624
58*	24.0832	24.1039	24.1247	24.1454	24.1661	24.1868	24.2074	24.2281	24.2487	24.2693
59*	24.2899	24.3105	24.3311	24.3516	24.3721	24.3926	24.4131	24.4336	24.4540	24.4745
60*	24.4949	24.5153	24.5357	24.5561	24.5764	24.5967	24.6171	24.6374	24.6577	24.6779
61*	24.6982	24.7184	24.7386	24.7588	24.7790	24.7992	24.8193	24.8395	24.8596	24.8797
62*	24.8998	24.9199	24.9399	24.9600	24.9800	25.0000	25.0200	25.0400	25.0599	25.0799
63*	25.0998	25.1197	25.1396	25.1595	25.1794	25.1992	25.2190	25.2389	25.2587	25.2784
64*	25.2982	25.3180	25.3377	25.3574	25.3772	25.3969	25.4165	25.4362	25.4558	25.4755
65*	25.4951	25.5147	25.5343	25.5539	25.5734	25.5930	25.6125	25.6320	25.6515	25.6710
66*	25.6905	25.7099	25.7294	25.7488	25.7682	25.7876	25.8070	25.8263	25.8457	25.8650
67*	25.8844	25.9037	25.9230	25.9422	25.9615	25.9808	26.0000	26.0192	26.0384	26.0576
68*	26.0768	26.0960	26.1151	26.1343	26.1534	26.1725	26.1916	26.2107	26.2298	26.2488
69*	26.2679	26.2869	26.3059	26.3249	26.3439	26.3629	26.3818	26.4008	26.4197	26.4386
70*	26.4575	26.4764	26.4953	26.5141	26.5330	26.5518	26.5707	26.5895	26.6083	26.6271
71*	26.6458	26.6646	26.6833	26.7021	26.7208	26.7395	26.7582	26.7769	26.7955	26.8142
72*	26.8328	26.8514	26.8701	26.8887	26.9072	26.9258	26.9444	26.9629	26.9815	27.0000
73*	27.0185	27.0370	27.0555	27.0740	27.0924	27.1109	27.1293	27.1477	27.1662	27.1846
74*	27.2029	27.2213	27.2397	27.2580	27.2764	27.2947	27.3130	27.3313	27.3496	27.3679

75*	27.3861	27.4044	27.4226	27.4408	27.4591	27.4773	27.4955	27.5136	27.5318	27.5500
76*	27.5681	27.5862	27.6043	27.6225	27.6405	27.6586	27.6767	27.6948	27.7128	27.7308
77*	27.7489	27.7669	27.7849	27.8029	27.8209	27.8388	27.8568	27.8747	27.8927	27.9106
78*	27.9285	27.9464	27.9643	27.9821	28.0000	28.0179	28.0357	28.0535	28.0713	28.0891
79*	28.1069	28.1247	28.1425	28.1603	28.1780	28.1957	28.2135	28.2312	28.2489	28.2666
80*	28.2843	28.3019	28.3196	28.3373	28.3549	28.3725	28.3901	28.4077	28.4253	28.4429
81*	28.4605	28.4781	28.4956	28.5132	28.5307	28.5482	28.5657	28.5832	28.6007	28.6182
82*	28.6356	28.6531	28.6705	28.6880	28.7054	28.7228	28.7402	28.7576	28.7750	28.7924
83*	28.8097	28.8271	28.8444	28.8617	28.8791	28.8964	28.9137	28.9310	28.9482	28.9655
84*	28.9828	29.0000	29.0172	29.0345	29.0517	29.0689	29.0861	29.1033	29.1204	29.1376
85*	29.1548	29.1719	29.1890	29.2062	29.2233	29.2404	29.2575	29.2746	29.2916	29.3087
86*	29.3258	29.3428	29.3598	29.3769	29.3939	29.4109	29.4279	29.4449	29.4618	29.4788
87*	29.4958	29.5127	29.5296	29.5466	29.5635	29.5804	29.5973	29.6142	29.6311	29.6479
88*	29.6648	29.6816	29.6985	29.7153	29.7321	29.7489	29.7658	29.7825	29.7993	29.8161
89*	29.8329	29.8496	29.8664	29.8831	29.8998	29.9166	29.9333	29.9500	29.9666	29.9833
90*	30.0000	30.0167	30.0333	30.0500	30.0666	30.0832	30.0998	30.1164	30.1330	30.1496
91*	30.1662	30.1828	30.1993	30.2159	30.2324	30.2490	30.2655	30.2820	30.2985	30.3150
92*	30.3315	30.3480	30.3645	30.3809	30.3974	30.4138	30.4302	30.4467	30.4631	30.4795
93*	30.4959	30.5123	30.5287	30.5450	30.5614	30.5778	30.5941	30.6105	30.6268	30.6431
94*	30.6594	30.6757	30.6920	30.7083	30.7246	30.7409	30.7571	30.7734	30.7896	30.8058
95*	30.8221	30.8383	30.8545	30.8707	30.8869	30.9031	30.9192	30.9354	30.9516	30.9677
96*	30.9839	31.0000	31.0161	31.0322	31.0483	31.0644	31.0805	31.0966	31.1127	31.1288
97*	31.1448	31.1609	31.1769	31.1929	31.2090	31.2250	31.2410	31.2570	31.2730	31.2890
98*	31.3050	31.3209	31.3369	31.3528	31.3688	31.3847	31.4006	31.4166	31.4325	31.4484
99*	31.4643	31.4802	31.4960	31.5119	31.5278	31.5436	31.5595	31.5753	31.5911	31.6070

TABLE T. ABSOLUTE VALUES OF STUDENT'S t

df	P^a .10	.05	.02	.01
	P^b .05	.025	.01	.005
1	6.314	12.706	31.821	63.657
2	2.920	4.303	6.965	9.925
3	2.353	3.182	4.541	5.841
4	2.132	2.776	3.747	4.604
5	2.015	2.571	3.365	4.032
6	1.943	2.447	3.143	3.707
7	1.895	2.365	2.998	3.499
8	1.860	2.306	2.896	3.355
9	1.833	2.262	2.821	3.250
10	1.812	2.228	2.764	3.169
11	1.796	2.201	2.718	3.106
12	1.782	2.179	2.681	3.055
13	1.771	2.160	2.650	3.012
14	1.761	2.145	2.624	2.977
15	1.753	2.131	2.602	2.947
16	1.746	2.120	2.583	2.921
17	1.740	2.110	2.567	2.898
18	1.734	2.101	2.552	2.878
19	1.729	2.093	2.539	2.861
20	1.725	2.086	2.528	2.845
21	1.721	2.080	2.518	2.831
22	1.717	2.074	2.508	2.819
23	1.714	2.069	2.500	2.807
24	1.711	2.064	2.492	2.797
25	1.708	2.060	2.485	2.787
26	1.706	2.056	2.479	2.779
27	1.703	2.052	2.473	2.771
28	1.701	2.048	2.467	2.763
29	1.699	2.045	2.462	2.756
30	1.697	2.042	2.457	2.750
40	1.684	2.021	2.423	2.704
60	6.671	2.000	2.390	2.660
∞	1.645	1.960	2.326	2.576

[a] Probability of a deviation numerically greater than t; for use in two-sided tests.
[b] Probability of a deviation greater than t; for use in one-sided tests.

Source: Table T is abridged from Table III of Fisher and Yates: "Statistical Tables for Biological, Agricultural and Medical Research," published by Oliver and Boyd Ltd., Edinburgh, and by permission of the authors and publishers.

TABLE V. VALUES OF THE PARTIAL VARIANCE IN RELATION TO MULTIPLE *R*

PARTIAL VARIANCE	*R*	PARTIAL VARIANCE	*R*	PARTIAL VARIANCE	*R*
.0000–.0099	1.00	.5710–.5839	.65	.9070–.9129	.30
.0100–.0297	.99	.5840–.5967	.64	.9130–.9187	.29
.0298–.0493	.98	.5968–.6093	.63	.9188–.9243	.28
.0494–.0687	.97	.6094–.6217	.62	.9244–.9297	.27
.0688–.0879	.96	.6218–.6339	.61	.9298–.9349	.26
.0880–.1069	.95	.6340–.6459	.60	.9350–.9399	.25
.1070–.1257	.94	.6460–.6577	.59	.9400–.9447	.24
.1258–.1443	.93	.6578–.6693	.58	.9448–.9493	.23
.1444–.1627	.92	.6694–.6807	.57	.9494–.9537	.22
.1628–.1809	.91	.6808–.6919	.56	.9538–.9579	.21
.1810–.1989	.90	.6920–.7029	.55	.9580–.9619	.20
.1990–.2167	.89	.7030–.7137	.54	.9620–.9657	.19
.2168–.2343	.88	.7138–.7243	.53	.9658–.9693	.18
.2344–.2517	.87	.7244–.7347	.52	.9694–.9727	.17
.2518–.2689	.86	.7348–.7449	.51	.9728–.9759	.16
.2690–.2859	.85	.7450–.7549	.50	.9760–.9789	.15
.2860–.3027	.84	.7550–.7647	.49	.9790–.9817	.14
.3028–.3193	.83	.7648–.7743	.48	.9818–.9843	.13
.3194–.3357	.82	.7744–.7837	.47	.9844–.9867	.12
.3358–.3519	.81	.7838–.7929	.46	.9868–.9889	.11
.3520–.3679	.80	.7930–.8019	.45	.9890–.9909	.10
.3680–.3837	.79	.8020–.8107	.44	.9910–.9927	.09
.3838–.3993	.78	.8108–.8193	.43	.9928–.9943	.08
.3994–.4147	.77	.8194–.8277	.42	.9944–.9957	.07
.4148–.4299	.76	.8278–.8359	.41	.9958–.9969	.06
.4300–.4449	.75	.8360–.8439	.40	.9970–.9979	.05
.4450–.4597	.74	.8440–.8517	.39	.9980–.9987	.04
.4598–.4743	.73	.8518–.8593	.38	.9988–.9993	.03
.4744–.4887	.72	.8594–.8667	.37	.9994–.9997	.02
.4888–.5029	.71	.8668–.8739	.36	.9998–.9999	.01
.5030–.5169	.70	.8740–.8809	.35		
.5170–.5307	.69	.8810–.8877	.34		
.5308–.5443	.68	.8878–.8943	.33		
.5444–.5577	.67	.8944–.9007	.32		
.5578–.5709	.66	.9008–.9069	.31		

Source: From DuBois, Philip H., *Multivariate Correlational Analysis.* New York: Harper & Row, 1957.

TABLE Z. VALUES OF Z, CORRESPONDING TO VALUES OF r FROM .000 TO .999

r	.000	.001	.002	.003	.004	.005	.006	.007	.008	.009
.00	.0000	.0010	.0020	.0030	.0040	.0050	.0060	.0070	.0080	.0090
.01	.0100	.0110	.0120	.0130	.0140	.0150	.0160	.0170	.0180	.0190
.02	.0200	.0210	.0220	.0230	.0240	.0250	.0260	.0270	.0280	.0290
.03	.0300	.0310	.0320	.0330	.0340	.0350	.0360	.0370	.0380	.0390
.04	.0400	.0410	.0420	.0430	.0440	.0450	.0460	.0470	.0480	.0490
.05	.0500	.0510	.0520	.0530	.0541	.0551	.0561	.0571	.0581	.0591
.06	.0601	.0611	.0621	.0631	.0641	.0651	.0661	.0671	.0681	.0691
.07	.0701	.0711	.0721	.0731	.0741	.0751	.0761	.0772	.0782	.0792
.08	.0802	.0812	.0822	.0832	.0842	.0852	.0862	.0872	.0882	.0892
.09	.0902	.0913	.0923	.0933	.0943	.0953	.0963	.0973	.0983	.0993
.10	.1003	.1013	.1024	.1034	.1044	.1054	.1064	.1074	.1084	.1094
.11	.1104	.1115	.1125	.1135	.1145	.1155	.1165	.1175	.1186	.1196
.12	.1206	.1216	.1226	.1236	.1246	.1257	.1267	.1277	.1287	.1297
.13	.1307	.1318	.1328	.1338	.1348	.1358	.1368	.1379	.1389	.1399
.14	.1409	.1419	.1430	.1440	.1450	.1460	.1471	.1481	.1491	.1501
.15	.1511	.1522	.1532	.1542	.1552	.1563	.1573	.1583	.1593	.1604
.16	.1614	.1624	.1634	.1645	.1655	.1665	.1676	.1686	.1696	.1706
.17	.1717	.1727	.1737	.1748	.1758	.1768	.1779	.1789	.1799	.1809
.18	.1820	.1830	.1841	.1851	.1861	.1872	.1882	.1892	.1903	.1913
.19	.1923	.1934	.1944	.1955	.1965	.1975	.1986	.1996	.2007	.2017
.20	.2027	.2038	.2048	.2059	.2069	.2079	.2090	.2100	.2111	.2121
.21	.2132	.2142	.2153	.2163	.2174	.2184	.2195	.2205	.2216	.2226
.22	.2237	.2247	.2258	.2268	.2279	.2289	.2300	.2310	.2321	.2331
.23	.2342	.2352	.2363	.2374	.2384	.2395	.2405	.2416	.2427	.2437
.24	.2448	.2458	.2469	.2480	.2490	.2501	.2512	.2522	.2533	.2543

	0	1	2	3	4	5	6	7	8	9
.25	.2554	.2565	.2575	.2586	.2597	.2608	.2618	.2629	.2640	.2650
.26	.2661	.2672	.2683	.2693	.2704	.2715	.2726	.2736	.2747	.2758
.27	.2769	.2779	.2790	.2801	.2812	.2823	.2833	.2844	.2855	.2866
.28	.2877	.2888	.2899	.2909	.2920	.2931	.2942	.2953	.2964	.2975
.29	.2986	.2997	.3008	.3018	.3029	.3040	.3051	.3062	.3073	.3084
.30	.3095	.3106	.3117	.3128	.3139	.3150	.3161	.3172	.3183	.3194
.31	.3205	.3217	.3228	.3239	.3250	.3261	.3272	.3283	.3294	.3305
.32	.3316	.3328	.3339	.3350	.3361	.3372	.3383	.3395	.3406	.3417
.33	.3428	.3440	.3451	.3462	.3473	.3484	.3496	.3507	.3518	.3530
.34	.3541	.3552	.3564	.3575	.3586	.3598	.3609	.3620	.3632	.3643
.35	.3654	.3666	.3677	.3689	.3700	.3712	.3723	.3734	.3746	.3757
.36	.3769	.3780	.3792	.3803	.3815	.3826	.3838	.3850	.3861	.3873
.37	.3884	.3896	.3907	.3919	.3931	.3942	.3954	.3966	.3977	.3989
.38	.4001	.4012	.4024	.4036	.4047	.4059	.4071	.4083	.4094	.4106
.39	.4118	.4130	.4142	.4153	.4165	.4177	.4189	.4201	.4213	.4225
.40	.4236	.4248	.4260	.4272	.4284	.4296	.4308	.4320	.4332	.4344
.41	.4356	.4368	.4380	.4392	.4404	.4416	.4428	.4441	.4453	.4465
.42	.4477	.4489	.4501	.4513	.4526	.4538	.4550	.4562	.4574	.4587
.43	.4599	.4611	.4624	.4636	.4648	.4660	.4673	.4685	.4698	.4710
.44	.4722	.4735	.4747	.4760	.4772	.4784	.4797	.4809	.4822	.4834
.45	.4847	.4860	.4872	.4885	.4897	.4910	.4922	.4935	.4948	.4960
.46	.4973	.4986	.4999	.5011	.5024	.5037	.5049	.5062	.5075	.5088
.47	.5101	.5114	.5126	.5139	.5152	.5165	.5178	.5191	.5204	.5217
.48	.5230	.5243	.5256	.5269	.5282	.5295	.5308	.5321	.5334	.5347
.49	.5361	.5374	.5387	.5400	.5413	.5427	.5440	.5453	.5466	.5480

TABLE Z (continued)

r	.000	.001	.002	.003	.004	.005	.006	.007	.008	.009
.50	.5493	.5506	.5520	.5533	.5547	.5560	.5573	.5587	.5600	.5614
.51	.5627	.5641	.5654	.5668	.5682	.5695	.5709	.5722	.5736	.5750
.52	.5763	.5777	.5791	.5805	.5818	.5832	.5846	.5860	.5874	.5888
.53	.5901	.5915	.5929	.5943	.5957	.5971	.5985	.5999	.6013	.6027
.54	.6042	.6056	.6070	.6084	.6098	.6112	.6127	.6141	.6155	.6169
.55	.6184	.6198	.6213	.6227	.6241	.6256	.6270	.6285	.6299	.6314
.56	.6328	.6343	.6358	.6372	.6387	.6401	.6416	.6431	.6446	.6460
.57	.6475	.6490	.6505	.6520	.6535	.6550	.6565	.6580	.6595	.6610
.58	.6625	.6640	.6655	.6670	.6685	.6700	.6716	.6731	.6746	.6761
.59	.6777	.6792	.6807	.6823	.6838	.6854	.6869	.6885	.6900	.6916
.60	.6931	.6947	.6963	.6978	.6994	.7010	.7026	.7042	.7057	.7073
.61	.7089	.7105	.7121	.7137	.7153	.7169	.7185	.7201	.7218	.7234
.62	.7250	.7266	.7283	.7299	.7315	.7332	.7348	.7365	.7381	.7398
.63	.7414	.7431	.7447	.7464	.7481	.7498	.7514	.7531	.7548	.7565
.64	.7582	.7599	.7616	.7633	.7650	.7667	.7684	.7701	.7718	.7736
.65	.7753	.7770	.7788	.7805	.7823	.7840	.7858	.7875	.7893	.7910
.66	.7928	.7946	.7964	.7981	.7999	.8017	.8035	.8053	.8071	.8089
.67	.8107	.8126	.8144	.8162	.8180	.8199	.8217	.8236	.8254	.8273
.68	.8291	.8310	.8328	.8347	.8366	.8385	.8404	.8423	.8441	.8460
.69	.8480	.8499	.8518	.8537	.8556	.8576	.8595	.8614	.8634	.8653
.70	.8673	.8693	.8712	.8732	.8752	.8772	.8792	.8812	.8832	.8852
.71	.8872	.8892	.8912	.8933	.8953	.8973	.8994	.9014	.9035	.9056
.72	.9076	.9097	.9118	.9139	.9160	.9181	.9202	.9223	.9245	.9266
.73	.9287	.9309	.9330	.9352	.9373	.9395	.9417	.9439	.9461	.9483
.74	.9505	.9527	.9549	.9571	.9594	.9616	.9639	.9661	.9684	.9707

	.9730	.9752	.9775	.9798	.9822	.9845	.9868	.9892	.9915	.9939
.75	.9730	.9752	.9775	.9798	.9822	.9845	.9868	.9892	.9915	.9939
.76	.9962	.9986	1.0010	1.0034	1.0058	1.0082	1.0106	1.0130	1.0154	1.0179
.77	1.0203	1.0228	1.0253	1.0277	1.0302	1.0327	1.0352	1.0378	1.0403	1.0428
.78	1.0454	1.0479	1.0505	1.0531	1.0557	1.0583	1.0609	1.0635	1.0661	1.0688
.79	1.0714	1.0741	1.0768	1.0795	1.0822	1.0849	1.0876	1.0903	1.0931	1.0958
.80	1.0986	1.1014	1.1042	1.1070	1.1098	1.1127	1.1155	1.1184	1.1212	1.1241
.81	1.1270	1.1299	1.1329	1.1358	1.1388	1.1417	1.1447	1.1477	1.1507	1.1538
.82	1.1568	1.1599	1.1630	1.1660	1.1692	1.1723	1.1754	1.1786	1.1817	1.1849
.83	1.1881	1.1914	1.1946	1.1979	1.2011	1.2044	1.2077	1.2111	1.2144	1.2178
.84	1.2212	1.2246	1.2280	1.2315	1.2349	1.2384	1.2419	1.2454	1.2490	1.2526
.85	1.2562	1.2598	1.2634	1.2671	1.2707	1.2745	1.2782	1.2819	1.2857	1.2895
.86	1.2933	1.2972	1.3011	1.3050	1.3089	1.3129	1.3169	1.3209	1.3249	1.3290
.87	1.3331	1.3372	1.3414	1.3456	1.3498	1.3540	1.3583	1.3626	1.3670	1.3714
.88	1.3758	1.3802	1.3847	1.3892	1.3938	1.3984	1.4030	1.4077	1.4124	1.4171
.89	1.4219	1.4268	1.4316	1.4365	1.4415	1.4465	1.4516	1.4567	1.4618	1.4670
.90	1.4722	1.4775	1.4828	1.4882	1.4937	1.4992	1.5047	1.5103	1.5160	1.5217
.91	1.5275	1.5334	1.5393	1.5453	1.5513	1.5574	1.5636	1.5698	1.5762	1.5826
.92	1.5890	1.5956	1.6022	1.6089	1.6157	1.6226	1.6296	1.6366	1.6438	1.6510
.93	1.6584	1.6658	1.6734	1.6811	1.6888	1.6967	1.7047	1.7129	1.7211	1.7295
.94	1.7380	1.7467	1.7555	1.7645	1.7736	1.7828	1.7923	1.8019	1.8117	1.8216
.95	1.8318	1.8421	1.8527	1.8635	1.8745	1.8857	1.8972	1.9090	1.9210	1.9333
.96	1.9459	1.9588	1.9721	1.9857	1.9996	2.0140	2.0287	2.0439	2.0595	2.0756
.97	2.0923	2.1095	2.1273	2.1457	2.1649	2.1847	2.2054	2.2269	2.2494	2.2729
.98	2.2976	2.3235	2.3507	2.3796	2.4101	2.4427	2.4774	2.5147	2.5550	2.5987
.99	2.6467	2.6996	2.7587	2.8257	2.9031	2.9945	3.1063	3.2504	3.4534	3.8002

GLOSSARY
OF SYMBOLS

Symbols used in statistical writings vary widely. The following list comprises most of the symbols used in this text. Here the prime ($'$) is used to indicate a statistic or variable that has been altered in some way. A tilde ($\sim$) indicates a predicted value, either of a statistic or of a variable. A sample mean is indicated as $\bar{X}$ or M and a sample standard deviation as s, with μ and σ as corresponding parameters. Other parameters are denoted by a circumflex accent ($\wedge$) over the symbol for the statistic.

a	(1) Element in matrix $\mathbf{A}$. The element in the ith row and jth column is denoted as a_{ij}; (2) weight to be applied to the wrongs in a scoring formula; (3) in deviation form, the true or reliable portion of an observed score or value. If the error is e, then $x = a + e$.
$\mathbf{A}$	Matrices, consisting of rows and columns with assigned meaning, are generally denoted by boldface capitals. Examples are $\mathbf{A}$, $\mathbf{X}$, $\mathbf{Z}$. The transpose of $\mathbf{A}$ is $\mathbf{A}'$ or $\mathbf{A}^{\tau}$, while the inverse is $\mathbf{A}^{-1}$.
$b_{ij.q}$	Regression weight to be used with scores with original standard deviations. Here i is the criterion, j the variable to which the weight is applied and q refers to all other variables taken into consideration.
c	Number of columns.
C	(1) Coefficient of contingency expressing the relationship between two categorical variables; (2) covariance or mean product of pairs of deviations of two variables. Any covariance divided by the standard

deviations of the variables becomes a product moment r; (3) a transformation of scores having approximately normal distribution; (4) a term in Bartlett's test of homogeneity of variance.

Cf Cumulative frequency.

$C_{ij.q}$ The covariance between two residual variables, q representing the variable or variables partialed out from the two primary variables i and j.

$Conf.$ Confidence coefficient designating limits within which, at a stated level of certainty, a parameter is likely to be found.

d Deviation in terms of step intervals from an arbitrary origin.

df Degrees of freedom, the number of values free to vary after one or more independent restrictions have been imposed on the total number of values.

D (1) Difference, as between two means, or the two members of a pair of scores, or between pairs of ranks; (2) a modified range, $(P_{90} - P_{10})$.

e (1) In deviation form, the random error component of a variable. $(e = x - a)$; (2) the base of the natural system of logarithms, approximately 2.7183.

E An arbitrary symbol used to indicate an element, either variance or covariance, in matrix computations leading to multivariate correlation.

f Frequency of a subgroup. Frequencies in rows may be denoted as f_r, frequencies in columns as f_c. In a scatter diagram the marginal frequencies are f_x and f_y, with f_{xy} indicating cell frequencies. When distinction is needed between observed and theoretical or expected frequencies, they may be denoted as f_o and f_e respectively.

F Ratio of two independent estimates of the population variance, which may be tested for significance by comparison with the appropriate F distribution.

$\mathbf{F}$ A factor matrix consisting of the correlations of each variable in $\mathbf{R}$ with each of the extracted factors.

g_i A hypothetical variable or factor posited to explain the intercorrelations of observed variables. In multiple factor analysis, the general factors may be denoted as $g_a, g_b \ldots$.

g_1 A statistic reflecting skewness in a distribution.

g_2 A statistic reflecting kurtosis in a distribution.

h_i^2 The common variance of an observed variable. The object of factor analysis is to divide the observed variance into two portions: h_i^2, the communality; and u_i^2, the unique variance. The communality is further subdivided into portions identical with each of the posited factors.

i (1) Value of the step interval; (2) as a subscript, i refers to any variable or any value. When other subscripts are needed, $j, k, l \ldots$ may be used.

$\mathbf{I}$ Identity matrix. It has unity in the diagonal cells, zeroes elsewhere. Used in matrix equations.

k In simple analysis of variance, number of treatments or categories in the independent variable.

L Lower confidence limit.

m	(1) Moment about the mean. The value of the nth moment is $\Sigma x^n/N$; (2) a number different from N and from n; (3) multiplying factor, used in computations from a cumulative distribution.
M	Arithmetic mean.
M'	Assigned or arbitrary mean or the value of an arbitrary origin used in computations with a frequency distribution.
M_o	Mode.
n	Number different from N, such as number of variables or categories; number of items in a test; number of cases within a category; or the number of times a test is lengthened.
N	Total number of cases in a sample.
N_p	Number of cases in one of two categories. The number in the other category is N_q.
p	Proportion of cases within a category. When there are only two categories, $p = N_p/N$, $q = N_q/N$ and $p + q = 1$.
P	(1) Percentile. P_j is defined as the point in the distribution below which j percent of the cases are found; (2) probability.
$P.E.$	Probable error.
q	(1) The proportion of cases in a second category, with p being the proportion of cases in the first category; (2) an arbitrary symbol designating one or more variables that have been partialed out of the primary variable or variables.
Q	Semi-interquartile range, defined as $(P_{75} - P_{25})/2$.
r	(1) Product moment correlation, the covariance of two variables in z form; (2) number of rows.
$r_{bis.}$	Correlation between a continuous and a dichotomous variable that would be expected if the dichotomous variable were normally and continuously distributed.
$r_{ij.q}$	Partial r, that is, the product moment correlation between two residual variables, used to estimate the correlation between variables i and j in samples with no variability in q, the variable or variables partialed out.
$r_{p(o.q)}$	Part correlation, that is, the product moment r between an observed and a residual variable.
$r_{pt.bis.}$	Point biserial correlation, that is, the product moment r between a dichotomous variable and a continuous variable.
$r_{tet.}$	Tetrachoric correlation, that is, an estimate of the correlation that would be found if two observed dichotomous variables were continuously and normally distributed and if full information were available.
$r_{xx'}$	Reliability or self-correlation of a variable, available only as an estimate.
R	(1) Multiple correlation, that is, product moment r between an unmodified variable on the one hand and the weighted sum of two or more variables on the other, the weights being developed so that, in the sample, the correlation is at a maximum; (2) rank; (3) in a scoring formula, number of right answers.
R	A matrix of correlations.

s	Standard deviation in the sample, defined as $\sqrt{\Sigma x^2/N}$.
$S_{est\ 0}$	Standard error of estimate, defined as the standard deviation of the errors around the regression line used in estimating variable 0.
$S_{i.q}$	Partial standard deviation, or s of variable i after the variable or variables denoted as q have been partialed out.
$S_{meas.}$	Standard error of measurement or the expected standard deviation of the differences between observed scores and true scores.
$s_{\dot{X}}$	With $\dot{X}$ indicating any statistic, $s_{\dot{X}}$ refers to the standard error of the statistic as estimated from a sample. Examples are s_M and $s_{M_1-M_2}$.
Sk	Skewness.
$S.S.$	Standard score. A linear transformation of obtained scores, with assigned mean and standard deviation.
t	Theoretical distribution of a normally distributed variable divided by $\sqrt{\chi^2/\nu}$; also an observed statistic tested by this distribution.
T	(1) Standard score with arbitrary mean of 50 and arbitrary standard deviation of 10; (2) the smaller sum of ranks in the matched pairs, signed-ranks test; (3) total score.
u_i	The unique component of any observed variable, consisting of error and specific variability.
U	(1) Upper confidence limit; (2) a statistic involving ranks that may be tested for significance by a procedure developed by Mann and Whitney.
V	The variance, or mean of the squares of the deviations from the arithmetic mean.
V_b	In analysis of variance, the between groups variance or the between groups sum of squares divided by the appropriate number of degrees of freedom. The ratio, V_b/V_w, yields F.
V_w	Within groups variance, or within groups mean square.
$V_{i.q}$	Partial variance. The variance of variable i after the variable or variables denoted as q have been partialed out.
w_i	Weight applied to variable i.
W	In a scoring formula, number of wrong answers.
x	Deviation from the sample mean.
x'	Deviation in coded scores from an arbitrary mean.
X	Any measured variable in original units.
$\dot{X}$	Any statistic.
y	Height of the ordinate of the normal curve.
Y	Symbol alternate to X, indicating any measured variable in original units.
z	A standard score with mean of zero and standard deviation of unity. Also, the number of standard deviation units above or below the mean.
$z_{i.q}$	A residual variable in z form, q referring to the variable or variables partialed out and which are uncorrelated with $z_{i.q}$. In such "higher order z scores" the variance is less than 1.00.
z_r	Fisher's transformation of the correlation coefficient, a transformation which varies without limit and is distributed approximately normally.

α	(Alpha) (1) Selected level of significance; (2) constant of a Poisson distribution, in which $\mu = \sigma^2 = \alpha$.
β	(Beta) Regression weight applicable to z scores.
Δ	(Delta) Determinant.
η	(Eta) The correlation ratio, measuring the fit of the observations to the means of the vertical or horizontal arrays.
μ	(Mu) Parameter mean.
ν	(Nu) Number of degrees of freedom.
ρ	(Rho) Coefficient of rank correlation developed by Spearman. It is a variant of product moment r.
σ	(Sigma) Parameter standard deviation.
Σ	(Sigma) Summation sign.
τ	(Tau) Coefficient of rank correlation developed by Kendall.
ϕ	(Phi) Product moment r between two dichotomous variables.
χ^2	(Chi) Chi square, used to determine the probability that a distribution of frequencies within categories is in accordance with a stated hypothesis.
$\binom{n}{r}$	Combinations of n things r at a time.
$\doteq$	Equals approximately.
$\neq$	Does not equal.
$> <$	Greater than; less than.
$\geqslant \leqslant$	Greater than or equal to; less than or equal to.
$\cdot$	Factorial. Factorial N is the product of N terms: $N(N - 1)(N - 2) \ldots 1$.

INDEX

INDEX